D1214105

Pfleger/Maurer/Weber

Mass Spectral and GC Data of Drugs, Poisons and Their Metabolites

Part I

Introduction, Tables, GC Data

© VCH Verlagsgesellschaft mbH, D-6940 Weinheim (Federal Republic of Germany), 1985

Distribution:
VCH Verlagsgesellschaft, P.O. Box 1260/1280, D-6940 Weinheim (Federal Republic of Germany)
USA and Canada: VCH Publishers, 303 N.W. 12th Avenue, Deerfield Beach FL 33442-1705 (USA)

ISBN 3-527-26303-9 (VCH Verlagsgesellschaft)
ISBN 0-89573-430-3 (VCH Publishers)

Karl Pfleger/Hans Maurer/Armin Weber

Mass Spectral and GC Data of Drugs, Poisons and Their Metabolites

Part I

Introduction, Tables, GC Data

Prof. Dr. med. Karl Pfleger
Dr. rer. nat. Hans Maurer
Armin Weber
Institut für Pharmakologie und Toxikologie
- Klinische Toxikologie -
Universität des Saarlandes
D-6650 Homburg (Saar)
Federal Republic of Germany

First Edition 1985

Editorial Director: Dr. Hans F. Ebel

Library of Congress Card No. 85-11282

Deutsche Bibliothek Cataloguing-in-Publication Data

Pfleger, Karl: Mass spectral and GC data of drugs, poisons and their metabolites / Karl Pfleger; Hans Maurer; Armin Weber. - Weinheim; Deerfield Beach, Fl.: VCH
ISBN 3-527-26303-9 (Weinheim)
ISBN 0-89573-430-3 (Deerfield Beach, Fl.)

NE: Maurer, Hans:; Weber, Armin:

Pt. 1. Introduction, tables, GC data. - 1985.

© VCH Verlagsgesellschaft mbH, D-6940 Weinheim (Federal Republic of Germany), 1985

All rights reserved (including those of translation into other languages). No part of this book may be reproduced in any form - by photoprint, microfilm, or any other means - nor transmitted or translated into a machine language without written permission from the publishers. Registered names, trademarks, etc. used in this book, even when not specifically marked as such, are not to be considered unprotected by law.

Composition and Printing: Zechnersche Buchdruckerei, D-6720 Speyer
Bookbinding: Wilhelm Osswald + Co., D-6730 Neustadt/Weinstraße

Printed in the Federal Republic of Germany

Foreword

Clinical and forensic toxicologists have long awaited a book of this nature.

More than 1500 mass spectra and retention indices of 1000 compounds relevant to toxicology have been recorded under standardized conditions by the authors. Further, data are given for important metabolites - an addition that will be greatly appreciated by all workers in the field.

The tables are well-organized and easy to work with; for example, the user can quickly determine whether a compound can be detected directly or through a suitable derivative.

The molecular mass, chemical formula, occurrence and application of more than 6000 potentially poisonous substances, including pesticides, can be found at a glance. In each case, it is clearly indicated whether a mass spectrum has been included or not.

With this book, Pfleger, Maurer and Weber have provided a reference work that will prove invaluable in daily laboratory practice. The detailed instructions for the isolation, enrichment and derivatization required for a successful GC-MC search make profitable reading, even for experts in mass spectrometry. The same is true of the computer-monitoring programs, which have been included in order to assist users to rapidly identify unknown compounds.

Professor Pfleger has pioneered the application of GC-MC to clinical toxicological analysis. Together with his associates, he has developed this technique to a fast and reliable routine method. The authors have successfully met the challenge of presenting their experiences succinctly and understandably: these volumes are the admirable result.

Prof. Dr. Dr. M. Geldmacher-von Mallinckrodt
Head of the Senate Commission
"Clinical-Toxicological Analysis"
of the German Science Foundation (DFG)

Preface

About 10% of admissions to the medical departments of hospitals are because of medicaments or poisons. The consumption of poisons from the environment is increasingly being regarded as a cause of illness. The student is told in medical lectures that whenever there is any suspicion of intoxication samples should be collected. The same is to be found in any text book on the treatment of intoxication. Nevertheless in only a few places throughout the world are laboratories available which are willing and able to detect these poisons at short notice and with sufficient certainty.

One reason for this situation is the lack of one analytical method which can fulfil the necessary demands. Poison analysis is like looking for a needle in a haystack, a search which is made more difficult by the fact that the analyst usually has no idea what he is looking for. In addition the analyses—at least in the clinical field—have to be carried out around the clock and the analytical results should be available within 30 to 100 minutes, so that the necessary treatment can be instigated in time.

One of the authors of this book has personally lived with the development of poison analysis since 1950. At that time the barbiturates were recognized as the cause of poisoning—perhaps because it was not possible to detect other substances. Barbiturates were extracted from the body fluids by the Stas-Otto method and attempts were then made to identify them after microsublimation, with a melting point microscope according to Kofler. There was no question of a quantitative evaluation or an exact correlation of the analysis result and the clinical symptoms or the behaviour of the accused in a forensic investigation. The replacement of the Pulfrich photometer involving visual comparison of two coloured liquids, in the 1950s, by the spectrophotometer made possible measurements in the UV range and, thus, for the first time, the determination of medicaments in the blood. However, it was the chromatographic techniques which first brought about the vital step forward (paper chromatography ca. 1952; thin layer chromatography ca. 1960) with new highly sensitive and qualitatively evaluable demonstration possibilities on the chromatographic stationary phase. With the advent of less polar phases and carrier materials, gas chromatography (from 1965) and later high pressure liquid chromatography could also be employed for analysis of poisons. These made possible a reduction in the analysis time, particularly for quantitative determinations. As a result of the improvement in analysis techniques more and more drugs, pesticides and chemical substances came to be recognized as the cause of clinical symptoms.

All these techniques have an important disadvantage. They can usually rule out the presence of a postulated poison, but they cannot identify substances with the certainty which is required if the application of a treatment or the instigation of criminal proceedings is to be based on the analysis. In addition, they give no information which can lead to the identification of unknown substances. The psychological pressure on the analyst was often very great when he was faced with a mountain of signals in the gas chromatogram or a chain of spots on the TLC plate and was obliged to make rapid decisions which could have far-reaching consequences. For this reason security was increased by checking the results using a second, independent method; however, this increased the time of analysis and even then could not rule out errors.

Poison analysis first became satisfactory with the application of mass spectrometry in the toxicological laboratory following the development in the mid-1970s of easier-to-use mass spectrometers and of higher performance pumping systems. A mass spectrum can be recorded of every substance that can enter the ionization chamber of the mass spectrometer. It can also be quantitatively determined, using the same method, providing a reference substance is available. The admission of the substance via gas chromatography is favoured since with this method the analysed substance is presented as a gas and can therefore be directly admitted into the ion source. Identification with the "probability bordering on certainty" demanded by law is possible by comparison with reference spectra. In most cases, even compounds for which there are no reference spectra available can be identified by exploiting further analytical possibilities of mass spectrometry.

The introduction of mass spectrometry into the Clinical Toxicological Department of the University of Saarland has enormously increased the number of substances recognized as the cause of poisoning, particularly in the field of psychopharmaceuticals. A change in the prescription regulations, brought about largely by the analytical results obtained in this department, led to the removal of dangerous bromourea derivatives, available off prescription, and diethylpentenamides from the medicaments market. Nowadays, these substances are rarely found in intoxications. They have been replaced by a larger number of other less toxic substances which can scarcely be identified without mass spectrometry.

The spectrum file presented in part 2 comprises 1550 mass spectra of relevant drugs and poisons and their metabolites insofar as they were recorded in samples by the analysis method.

In toxicological analysis every substance foreign to the body, i. e. every peak on a gas chromatogram or zone on a TLC plate, has to be viewed as a potential poison, until proved otherwise by identification and, hence, the identification of metabolites occurring in the samples is of great importance. Up to the present time most of the intoxications are covered by the spectrum file. The file should place the novice in mass spectrometry in the position of beeing able to identify the substance by visual comparison. The standard method employed to obtain the mass spectra in part 2 is described in part 1. Additional informations in part 2, such as the pharmacological effect or the employment of the substance as an pesticide or household chemical, is intended to facilitate correlation with clinically observed symptoms for the analyst. The alphabetical list of the substances with a statement of the most important fragment masses and the list of retention indices in part 1 is intended to facilitate the search for particular substances, particulary in trace analysis. Knowledge of these data is necessary in order to exploit the possibilities offered by mass spectrometers with data systems. Furthermore, part 1 contains a table with a list in order of increasing molecular masses of about 6000 substances, which people can come into contact with in the normal course of events, together with informations about their application. This allows the analyst to identify substances whose spectra have not yet been recorded using high resolution mass spectrometry and considering further criteria.

The entire mass spectra are shown in part 2. They were generated from measured data recorded on a magnetic data carrier with a computer plotter. The question arises as to why magnetic data carriers are not on offer. The authors are of the opinion that toxicological analysis is made immeasurably easier by computers and that GC-MS analysis in particular cannot forego the use of computers. However, there are several reasons for publication in book from at the present time: A book is the securest "data carrier" as the experience of computer users has repeatedly demonstrated. Until now the manufacturers of mass spectrometers have not agreed upon a uniform and interchangeable data structure. Even if this were the case the users of older apparatus could not employ data published on magnetic carriers. Many mass spectrometers are not equipped with a data processing system. Then again limited resolution of the video screens available today limits the simultaneous display of more than 2 spectra. In the spectrum atlas of this book 10 spectra can be viewed at a glance, on one double page. Therefore the access time is competitive with that of any computer. It is our experience that large computers from which data may be called up and which may be reached via a terminal are often not available when they are required. All the information necessary for toxicological analysis should be available and accessible at any time and, if possible, be present in the laboratory.

Until now one the major reasons for the limited use of mass spectrometry in clinical and forensic toxicological analysis has been the very high capital cost of the apparatus. Just recently highly sensitive mass filters, which in our experience are sufficient for most problems of toxicological analysis, have been offered at reasonable prices. We are delighted to be able to publish our data compilation at just this point in time and believe that the prerequisites are thus available for the satisfactory performance of toxicological analyses which are of relevance to patients and to society.

Acknowledgement

The authors are indebted to the Universität des Saarlandes and to Prof. Dr. med. W. Rummel, Head of Department of Pharmacology and Toxicology, for generously supporting the development of a problem-oriented clinical toxicology, which allowed to acquire the data collection presented here.

Further, the authors wish to thank their families for forbearance, sacrifice of personal interests, and active help in accomplishing this book.

Contents of Part 1 (Introduction, Tables, GC Data)

Contents of Part 2 (Mass Spectra and Indexes)

1 Introduction

Recently analytical methods have been gaining more significance in clinical and forensic toxicology. They allow diagnosis of an intoxication and control of the efficiency of detoxification. It is our experience that in many cases the information supplied by the patient or his relatives does not agree with the toxicological analysis. A large proportion of suspected intoxications are not intoxication at all. This is corroborated by the studies of Widdop (1974). Therefore the diagnosis of intoxication should always be confirmed by a suitable toxicological analysis. Furthermore toxicological analysis allows the monitoring of addicted patients and a check on patient compliance during medication. Finally it also enables therapeutic drug monitoring.

Clinical toxicological analysis are usually single-analysis and the service must be available round the clock. The method should be as rapid and precise as is necessary for clinical diagnosis and therapy. Ideally one procedure should allow the detection of nearly all relevant intoxicants. Similar problems arise in forensic toxicology; because of the grave legal consequences forensic toxicological analysis also has to be of high precision.

The most important problem in analytical toxicology is the identification of unknown drugs and poisons in body fluids. Several problems result from the so called "general unknown analysis". There are thousands of drugs and poisons, which could have been taken. Each compound may form several metabolites, which complicate the identification. Some substances are completely metabolized and so they can only be identified in plasma or urine by their metabolites. On the other hand all metabolites must be differentiated from other potential poisons. Often low substance concentrations must be detected. Furthermore all exogenous substances must be separated and differentiated from endogenous biological substances. Finally the results must be available as rapidly as possible so that a specific therapy can be initiated. Numerous chromatographic and immunological methods have been published for detection of drugs, including: paper chromatography (PC) (Moffat and Smalldon, 1974), thin layer chromatography (TLC) (Daldrup et al., 1981; Interschick et al., 1978; Moffat and Smalldon, 1974; Oellerich et al., 1977), gas chromatography (GC) (Cailleux et al., 1981; Daldrup et al., 1981; Deutsche Forschungsgemeinschaft, 1982a; Moffat et al., 1974; Pentz et al., 1978), high performance liquid chromatography (HPLC) (Daldrup et al., 1981), enzyme immunoassay (EMIT) (Oellerich et al., 1977) and radioimmunoassay (RIA) (Cleeland et al., 1976). A combination of several of these methods enables the diagnosis of some intoxications. However, TLC is insensitive and unspecific for many substances. GC with the normal detectors and HPLC are relatively sensitive but unspecific. Finally all chromatographic zones or peaks have to be identified because any of them may represent a potential poison. Radio or enzyme immunoassays are very sensitive but they are too unspecific for the identification of unknown drugs. Furthermore kits are only available for determination of a few drugs.

At present the computerized gas chromatographic-mass spectrometric technique (GC-MS) is the only method that is sensitive, highly specific and relatively quick. It is therefore the ideal method for the identification of unknown drugs, poisons and their metabolites (Arnold and Grützmacher, 1969; Costello et al., 1974; Ehrenthal et al., 1979; Finkle et al., 1972; 1974; Foltz et al., 1974; Maurer et al., 1984; Skinner et al., 1972). A further advantage is that the GC-MS technique allows sensitive and precise quantitation of the identified compounds using single or multi-ion monitoring particularly with isotopically labelled analogous as internal standards (Millard, 1978).

In addition to the instrument itself suitable procedures are necessary for sample preparation as is a collection of reference spectra of drugs, poisons and their metabolites. Several collections of mass spectra have been published (Ardry et al., 1983; Stenhagen et al., 1974; Sunshine and Caplis, 1981; The Royal Society of Chemistry, 1983). Two of these collections contain several ten thousands of spectra but most of them come from the chemical industry. Only a few spectra of drugs and pesticides are included. The other collections include many drug spectra but only report the eight predominant peaks or mass list. One of the last collections includes a few bar graph spectra. In many cases the fingerprint of the bar graph spectrum is necessary and sufficient for the identification of unknown compounds particularly if the spectrum contains only a few peaks (e.g. Carbamazepine-M/Artifact and Disopyramide on p. 282 and 283 in Part 2). Comparing mass spectra with mass lists is very troublesome, whereas they can be compared at a glance with entire bar graph spectra.

Data concerning metabolites are only reported sporadically, even though they are necessary for the reasons described above.

None of these collections includes structures which are necessary for the identification of unknown metabolites. Generally there are no hints concerning the sample preparation necessary for the detection of the compound. The chromatographic characteristics of the compounds are not reported even though they are important when using a GC-MS system. All this information is necessary for routine use in a toxicological laboratory.

Therefore, in the last few years we have collected mass spectral, gas chromatographic and toxicological data of drugs and poisons in our laboratory. All investigations were carried out using samples from man or, in the absence of human samples, in samples from rats (2.1).

Not only a collection of data but a complete method is presented. A simple and rapid sample preparation has been developed. The extraction procedures with recoveries of 60–90% (Maurer, 1983; Maurer et al., 1982) are adequate for most problems (2.2.2). Simple derivatization procedures have been investigated to improve the gas chromatographic characteristics of polar compounds (2.2.3).

A gas chromatographic procedure with flame-ionization detection (FID) and nitrogen-sensitive FID was set up to select the extract which should be analyzed by GC-MS. This involved determination of retention indices (2.3.1). In our experience although they are not essential using GC-MS, they provide preliminary indications and are useful to gas chromatographers without this facility. In addition they enable the differentiation of isomeric metabolites which yield the same spectra.

A computerized GC-MS technique was employed for the identification of unknown compounds (2.4.2). In order to evaluate recorded spectra rapidly fragment ions typical for special groups of drugs were collected and summarized as computer monitoring programs (CMP) for mass chromatography (2.4.3).

One thousand five hundred and fifty EI mass spectra recorded in our laboratory have been collected and included in Part 2. Only EI spectra are included because they are more useful for the identification of unknown compounds than CI spectra. Even spectra containing no molecular ion can be identified in almost all cases by comparison with the EI reference spectra with the aid of their typical fragment ions. The collection is specifically designed for analytical toxicology and includes the most important drugs, poisons and their metabolites. It has proved adequate for carrying out about 10,000 analyses submitted in recent years by about 50 different clinics and institutes of forensic medicine. It is the first collection which also contains data covering the metabolites which were normally present when using the described analytical procedures. Some of the metabolites have not been described in the literature. However, it cannot be excluded that some of the compounds described as metabolites are artifacts of the analytical procedures. The spectra are depicted as bar graphs, for easier visualization, making rapid fingerprint comparisons possible. The structures of the compounds are also reproduced to facilitate the identification of unknown metabolites by correlating the fragmentation pattern with the probable structure (3). Further data are also included as explained on p. VII in Part 2.

At present the spectra are only published in bookform and not as a computer tape. In our experience the combination of computer monitoring programs with visual comparison of the spectra is the most rapid and reliable procedure for the evaluation of GC-MS data. Many impurities may be present in biological materials. If the spectra of small amounts of poison are hidden in large amounts of an impurity the commonly employed library search programs do not detect them. Further the spectra selected by a library search then have to be compared visually anyway. The time expended in the visual comparison of spectra is competitive with that required for the computer comparison of spectra.

Several artifacts have been detected which are formed during sample preparation and the GC procedure (4); since their formation is reproducible and they are mass spectrometrically identifiable, such artifacts can be employed as markers for the presence of the parent compounds. Metabolites or decomposition products which could not be identified but whose origin is known are also included in Part 2.

All the compounds included are listed alphabetically in Table I (9) in order to assist the search for data concerning specific compounds.

The compounds are listed in order of ascending retention index in Table II (10); this facilitates the identification of gas chromatographic peaks.

In order to assist the identification of compounds whose spectra have not yet been recorded the molecular masses of about 6000 drugs, pesticides and common chemicals are listed in Table III (11). These compounds were selected from a list of drugs (ABDA, 1984) and a list of pesticides (Perkow, 1983), which together encompass most of the drugs and pesticides used throughout the world. In order to avoid complications in selection, chemicals were only included if they were likely to be available e.g. in the household. The accurate mass of unknown compounds can be measured by high resolution mass spectrometry (2.4.5). In most cases the drug or poison can then be identified by the consideration of further criteria (Fig. 11-1), (11.2).

CAS cross indexes are listed in Part 2 for the use of the CHEMICAL ABSTRACT SERVICE (CAS).

The amount of data presented makes it likely that some errors will be present in this handbook. The authors cannot be responsible for such errors or for any consequences arising from the employment of the published data.

Users are requested to report any errors that are found and to suggest other data and other groups of compounds which are of interest. If possible they will be included in a future edition along with corrections of any errors.

2 Experimental Section

All mass spectral and gas chromatographic data were collected in our laboratory, according to the methods outlined below.

2.1 Origin of Samples

The investigations were made on samples (plasma, gastric contents or urine) from patients suspected of intoxications and admitted to several anti-poison centers, from inpatients of several clinics particularly the University Hospital at Homburg, or from students or the authors treated with therapeutic dosages of drugs. If suitable samples from man were not available, samples from rats were used. They were administered 20–40 mg/kg body weight of drugs in aqueous suspension by gastric tube. (See "Notes" in the legends of the mass spectra in Part 2.)

2.2 Sample Preparation

2.2.1 Apparatus

Function of the STED:

The organic extract was transferred from the tube into the pear-shaped flask by suction through the capillary and then evaporated to dryness by drawing air or, if necessary, nitrogen through the same capillary. Whereby the residue is collected in the tip of the pear-shaped flask (Maurer et al., 1982).

2.2.2 Extraction and Hydrolysis Procedures

2.2.2.1 Standard extraction (P, G, U)

Two to ten milliliters of sample (plasma, gastric contents, urine) were extracted with 10 mL diethyl ether (redistilled to remove antioxidant) after addition of 10 mL saturated sodium sulphate solution. After phase separation by centrifugation the organic extract was transferred into a pear-shaped flask and evaporated to dryness using the STED described in 2.2.1. The aqueous residue was then basified with 1 mL 1 N sodium hydroxide and extracted a second time with 10 mL diethyl ether. This organic extract was transferred to the same pear-shaped flask and evaporated too. The combined residues were dissolved in 0.1 mL methanol (Maurer et al., 1982).

2.2.2.2 Extraction of amphetamines (UA)

Amphetamines are highly volatile, in order to avoid evaporation they were converted into their hydrochlorides.

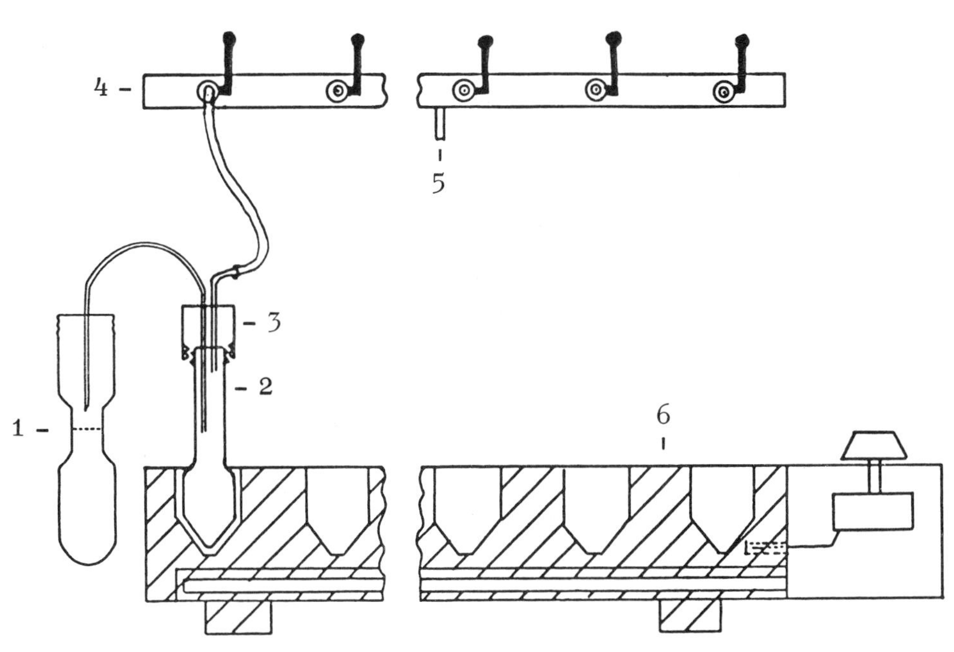

Fig. 2-1: Solvent transfer and evaporation device (STED)
1 Threaded centrifuge tubes, 30 mL, with screw caps
2 Threaded pear-shaped flasks, 30 mL
3 Screw caps, in which two nickel capillaries have been fixed with an epoxide adhesive
4; 5 Manifold with several valves, each of which is connected to one of the above mentioned capillaries by flexible tubing (4). The manifold is also connected to a water pump (5).
6 Variable temperature aluminium heating block with several holes for the accomodation of the pear-shaped flasks. A temperature of 60 °C was normally used for evaporation.
Additional apparatus:
Microvials, 2 mL
Reflux condenser with adaptor for threaded tubes
Infra red heater
Centrifuge

Two to ten milliliters of sample were extracted twice with 10 mL portions of diethyl ether after addition of 10 mL saturated sodium sulphate solution and 1 mL 1 N sodium hydroxide. After phase separation by centrifugation the organic extracts were transferred into a pear-shaped flask, containing a small drop of hydrochloric acid (37%) and evaporated to dryness using the STED as described in 2.2.1. The residue was dissolved in 0.1 mL methanol (Maurer et al., in prep.).

2.2.2.3 Acid hydrolysis and extraction of urine (UHY)

Many drugs and poisons are excreted in urine in a completely metabolized and conjugated form. Since conjugates can only be detected by relatively complicated procedures (Böttcher et al., 1982; Ehrenthal and Pfleger, 1979), they were cleaved before extraction by acid hydrolysis, a procedure which only required a short time.

Ten milliliters of urine were refluxed with 3 mL hydrochloric acid (37%) for 15 min, then basified with about 3 g potassium hydroxide pellets and mixed with 10 mL 30% aqueous ammonium sulphate to obtain a pH between 8 and 9. These solutions were extracted twice with 10 mL portions each of a mixture of two parts of dichloromethane, two parts of isopropylalcohol and six parts of ethyl acetate. After phase separation by centrifugation the combined organic extracts were transferred into a pear-shaped flask and evaporated to dryness using the STED described in 2.2.1. The residue was dissolved in 0.1 mL methanol (Maurer et al., 1982).

2.2.2.4 Enzymatic hydrolysis and extraction of urine (UGLUC)

Conjugated compounds destroyed during acid hydrolysis could be detected in urine after enzymatic hydrolysis.

Ten milliliters of urine were hydrolyzed with 0.1 mL of an aqueous solution of beta-glucuronidase (12 units/mL) and aryl sulphatase (60 units/mL) for 12–24 hours at 36 °C. Then solid sodium hydrogen carbonate was added to obtain a pH between 8 and 9. The samples were extracted, transferred, evaporated and redissolved as described in 2.2.2.3.

2.2.3 Derivatization Procedures

Derivatization procedures were used to improve the gas chromatographic characteristics of polar compounds, by increasing their volatility or their thermal stability. Furthermore mass spectra of several compounds are altered on derivatization so that they contain more typical ions e.g. the molecular ion (cf. the mass spectra of Norpseudoephedrine on p. 125 in Part 2 and of acetylated Norspeudoephedrine on p. 385).

Acetylation was routinely employed, because the primary and secondary amino groups and alcoholic and phenolic hydroxy groups usually formed on metabolism are derivatized. Carboxylic acids were methylated or ethylated. In a few instances amino and hydroxy groups were trimethylsilylated.

2.2.3.1 Acetylation (AC)

A 40 µL aliquot of extract was evaporated to dryness and then acetylated for 30 min at 60 °C with 40 µL of a mixture of three parts of acetic anhydride and two parts pyridine. After evaporation of the acetylation mixture the residue was dissolved in 40 µL ethyl acetate or methanol (Maurer et al., 1982).

2.2.3.2 Methylation (ME)

A 40 µL aliquot of extract in methanol was methylated for 10 min (carboxylic acids) or for several hours (phenols) at room temperature with 200 µL of a ethanol-free solution of diazomethane in diethyl ether (Eistert et al., 1968). This solution was stable for several months, if it was stored in sealed 10 mL flasks in the freezer at −20 °C. After evaporation of the methylation mixture the residue was dissolved in 40 µL methanol.

2.2.3.3 Ethylation (ET)

The procedure was as for methylation but using diazoethane synthesized from p-toluenesulfonic acid N-nitrosoethylamide (Eistert et al., 1968).

2.2.3.4 Trimethylsilylation (TMS)

A 40 µL aliquot of extract was evaporated and then silylated for 30 min at 60 °C with 40 µL bistrimethylsilylacetamide. This mixture was injected into the gas chromatograph with a methanol-free syringe.

2.3 Gas Chromatography (GC)

2.3.1 Apparatus for Measurement of Retention Indices

In our experience retention indices provide preliminary indications and may be useful to gas chromatographers without a GC-MS facility and hence we have included them in this book. Furthermore, they allow a distinction to be made between isomeric metabolites which give the same mass spectra (e.g. the hydroxy metabolites of doxepin, cf. 10.2). A Varian gas chromatograph series 3700 was used for the exact determination of the retention indices (Kovats, 1958).

The column effluent was directed to a flame-ionization detector (FID) and a nitrogen-sensitive flame-ionization detector (N-FID) after splitting 1:1 in a splitter constructed from nickel tubing (Maurer and Pfleger, 1981a).

Column: nickel tube, 60 cm × 2 mm I.D. packed with Chromosorb G HP 100–120 mesh coated with 5% OV-101.

Column temperature: programmed from 100 to 310 °C at 20 °C/min, 3 min at max. temp.
Injector port temp.: 270 °C
Carrier gas: nitrogen, flow rate 30 mL/min
Detector temp.: 270 °C

2.3.2 Apparatus for the GC-MS System

A Varian Aerograph gas chromatograph series 1400 was coupled to the MS.

Column: nickel capillary, 60 cm × 1 mm I. D. packed with Chromosorb G HP 100–120 mesh coated with 5% OV-101
Column temperature: programmed from 100 to 310 °C in 20 °C/min, 3 min at max. temp.
Injector port temp.: 270 °C
Carrier gas: helium, flow rate 7 mL/min

2.4 Mass Spectrometry (MS)

2.4.1 Apparatus

A Varian mass spectrometer type 311 A was employed fitted with two 200-L-turbo molecular pumps (Balzers AG, Balzers, Liechtenstein), a Varian data system 111 MS and a Tektronix storage display unit type 611. The technique of open coupling allowed the introduction of about 2 mL/min of gas dosed via a SGE micro-needle valve and a SGE shut-off valve (Scientific Glass Engineering, Ringwood, Australia) into the ion source through a nickel capillary, 0.15 mm I. D., heated to 270 °C (Maurer and Pfleger, 1981a).

Ionization energy: 90 eV
Ion source temperature: 200 °C
Acceleration voltage: 2900 V
Emission current: 0.5–3.0 mA
Resolution: 1000–2000 (10% valley) (low resolution) 10,000 (10% valley) (high resolution)
Scan rate: 6 sec/decade

For the daily check of apparatus performance a standard solution of typical drugs was injected into the GC-MS. The separation and detection limit for each drug had to be at least 100 ng (Deutsche Forschungsgemeinschaft, 1982b).

2.4.2 Computerized Gas Chromatographic-Mass Spectrometric Analysis (GC-MS-DS)

The computerized GC-MS technique (Fig. 2-2) is approved in analytical toxicology to identify unknown drugs, poisons and their metabolites (Ehrenthal and Pfleger, 1975; 1977; Ehrenthal et al., 1979; Maurer, 1983; Maurer and Pfleger, 1981a; 1982; 1983a,b; 1984a–c; Maurer et al., 1984). During the temperature-programmed GC analysis whole mass spectra are recorded at a speed of 6 sec/decade and stored on computer tape. Scanning at this relatively slow rate ensures the recording of at least two mass spectra for each GC peak and avoids excessive data accumulation. An on-line computer rapidly evaluates the stored spectra by searching simultaneously for fragment ions typical for particular groups of drugs, poisons and metabolites (see computer monitoring programs (CMP) in 2.4.3). The identity of positive signals in the reconstructed mass chromatograms is confirmed by a comparison of the entire mass spectra with the reference spectra published in Part 2 of this book.

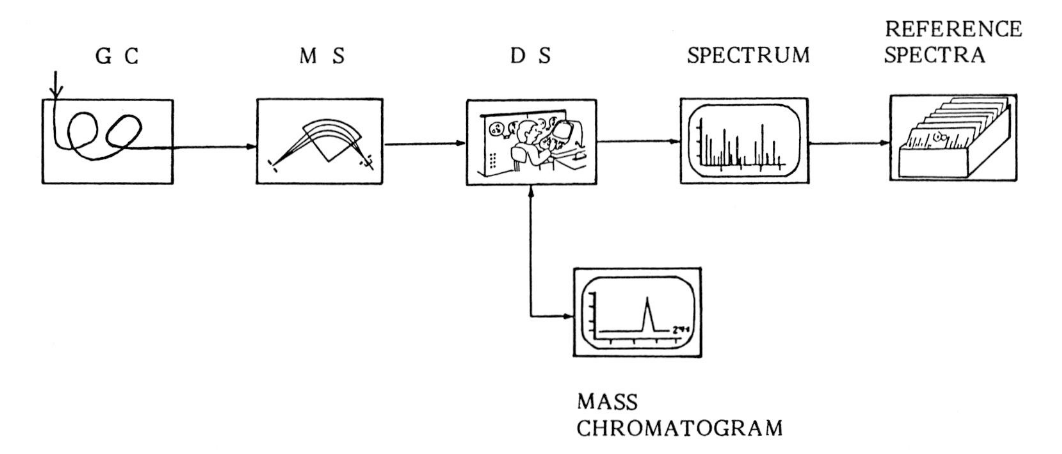

Fig. 2-2: GC-MS-DS procedure

2.4.3 Computer Monitoring Programs (CMP)

Many structurally related drugs and their metabolites have the same fundamental structure and/or the same side chains. But structurally related drugs may have very different pharmacological potencies and, hence, must be unambiguously differentiated in analytical toxicology. Chromatographic methods with the normal detection procedures are insufficient for differentiation because of chemical analogy of such compounds. But this chemical analogy possesses the advantage that, in computerized gas chromatography-mass spectrometry, fragment ions appear which are specific to the particular fundamental structures or side chains. These fragment ions can therefore be employed for the rapid evaluation of stored mass spectra (2.4.2). The compounds revealed by these mass chromatograms can then be identified unambiguously by comparison of their entire mass spectra with the reference spectra. Mass chromatograms typical for several categories of drugs have been collected and published as computer monitoring programs (CMP). They accelerate general unknown analysis by detecting or excluding entire groups of drugs. The CMPs are listed in Table 2-1, together with the samples to which they are applicable and the original literature references. Similar data for other compounds of toxicological interest are being collected (Maurer et al., in prep.) so that it will then be possible to detect all relevant drugs, poisons and metabolites in less than one hour.

Some fragment ions included in CMPs 6–9 are typical of several groups of drugs and so are included several times. When searching for several of these groups in an UHYAC these fragment ions only have to be included once. In this reason the reduced CMPs are listed in Table 2-2.

Tab. 2-1: Computer monitoring programs (CMP) searching for several categories of drug in a standard extract of plasma (P), gastric contents (G) or urine (U) or in an acetylated extract of urine after acid hydrolysis (UHYAC).

CMP	Category	Typical fragment ions	Sample
1a	Hypnotics	141.156.165.167.204.207.221.250	P, G, U
1b		112.124.139.140.144.154.189.218	P, G, U
2	Anti-inflammatory analgesics	137.151.188.217.230.231.299.308	P, G
3	Benzodiazepines	236.239.269.270.281.282.283.315	P, G
4	Antidepressants, Neuroleptics	42. 44. 58. 72. 84. 86.284.318	P, G
5	Benzodiazepines	211.230.241.244.249.262.276.285	UHYAC
6a	Butyrophenones	112.123.134.148.169.257.259.321	UHYAC
6b		189.191.223.233.235.245.287.297	UHYAC
7	Antidepressants	58. 84. 86.100.191.193.194.205	UHYAC
8a	Neuroleptics	58. 72. 86. 98.100.113.114.141	UHYAC
8b		132.148.154.191.198.199.243.267	UHYAC
9a	Opioids, potent analgesics	58. 72. 87.299.327.341.343.371	UHYAC
9b		69. 71.100.125.187.220.242.261	UHYAC
10	Anti-inflammatory analgesics	109.123.137.188.245.259.288.308	UHYAC

References: CMP 1–4: Ehrenthal et al., 1979
CMP 5: Maurer and Pfleger, 1981a
CMP 6: Maurer and Pfleger, 1983a
CMP 7: Maurer and Pfleger, 1984a
CMP 8: Maurer and Pfleger, 1984b
CMP 9: Maurer and Pfleger, 1984c
CMP 10: Maurer and Pfleger, 1983b

Tab. 2-2: Reduced computer monitoring programs (CMP) for the detection of psychotropic and analgesic drugs in an acetylated extract of urine after acid hydrolysis (UHYAC).

CMP	Category	Typical fragment ions	Sample
5	Benzodiazepines	211.230.241.244.249.262.276.285	UHYAC
6	Butyrophenones	112.134.169.189.223.233.287.321	UHYAC
7	Antidepressants, Neuroleptics	58. 72. 86.100.114.141.193.194	UHYAC
8	Antidepressants, Neuroleptics	98.132.154.191.198.205.243.267	UHYAC
9	Opioids, potent analgesics	69. 71. 87.187.242.327.341.343	UHYAC
10	Anti-inflammatory analgesics	109.123.137.188.245.259.288.308	UHYAC

Reference: Maurer, 1983

2.4.4 Example Illustrating the Described GC-MS-DS Procedure

Case report:
A patient with a suspected polytoxicomania was committed to a psychiatric clinic. He declared that he had not taken any drugs at all. His urine was monitored to check on the suspected polytoxicomania.

Procedure:
Since there was no evidence of which drugs might have been taken a general unknown analysis had to be carried out. Hence all the CMPs applicable to UHYAC were employed for the evaluation of the stored mass spectra. Fig. 2-3 illustrates six mass chromatograms indicating psychotropic and analgesic drugs. Peaks 1 and 2 in mass chromatogram 10 indicate large amounts of anti-inflammatory analgesics, peak 4 in 5 a benzodiazepine and peaks 5–8 in 9 opioids. Peaks in 6–8 indicate the probable presence of butyrophenones, antidepressants or neuroleptics. The mass spectra of these peaks are shown in Fig. 2-4. The reference spectra of those (column 1 in Tab. 2-3) can be found in Part 2 under their molecular ions (M^+) or their base peaks (BP) (column 2) on the pages given in column 3. The compounds thus identified are listed in column 4.

The peaks in 6–8 indicate group-extraneous drugs. Therefore the entire mass spectrum underlying the peaks must always be compared with the reference spectra in Part 2, because the specifity increases with the number of fragment ions compared. The CMPs only constitute the wide-meshed "screen" while the matching the entire mass spectrum is the finest meshed "screen" of this procedure for detection of drugs (Maurer, 1983).

Tab. 2-3: Identity of the compounds indicated by the peaks in Fig. 2-3.

Peak No.	Fragment ion	page in Part 2	Identified compound
1	179 (M^+)	255	Salicylamide AC
	120 (BP)	150	
2	193 (M^+)	283	Paracetamol AC
	109 (BP)	133	
3	223 (M^+)	358	Methoxyparacetamol AC
	139 (BP)	184	
4	273 (M^+)	463	Oxazepam HYAC
	230 (BP)	371	
5	341 (M^+/BP)	597	Codeine AC
6	369 (M^+)	623	Morphine 2AC
	327 (BP)	574	
7	369 (M^+)	624	N-desmethylcodeine 2AC
	87 (BP)	99	
8	397 (M^+)	645	N-desmethylmorphine 3AC
	87 (BP)	99	

2.4.5 Measurement of the Accurate Mass and Calculation of the Elemental Composition of Fragment Ions

With the exception of that of carbon atomic masses are not integral numbers. Therefore different elemental compositions have different masses. If the mass is measured with sufficient precision the elemental composition can be calculated. This means that compounds having different elemental composition can be differentiated (cf. the example given in 11.2).

High resolution mass spectrometry was employed for accurate mass measurement. For high resolution the entrance and exit slits are made very narrow, and a reference substance (Perfluorokerosine (PFK)), which gives rise to positive fragment ions covering the entire range of interest, is introduced into the ion source through a separate inlet. The sample containing the unknown compound is introduced via the GC-MS interface or the direct insert system. The mass spectrum of the unknown compound which results is superimposed on that of PFK. The data system performs the mass scale adjustment for each and every mass spectrum in the whole run by comparison with the known masses of the ions produced by the reference substance. Further it undertakes the accurate measurement of the masses of the ions produced by the unknown compound and then calculates the elemental composition which corresponds best to this accurate mass. The number of possible elemental compositions is greatly reduced, because only those combinations need be considered which obey the valence rules. (Ehrenthal et al., 1976).

2.5 Quantitative Determination

Gas chromatography with nitrogen-sensitive flame ionization detection or gas chromatography-mass spectrometry with single or multi-ion monitoring (Millard, 1978) can be employed for quantitative determination of identified compounds. The optimal method is single or multi-ion monitoring using isotopically labelled analogues as internal standards since it is highly sensitive and specific and isotopically-labelled analogues have identical chemical and physical properties as the parent compounds. Unfortunately isotopically labelled analogues are still very expensive and rarely available.

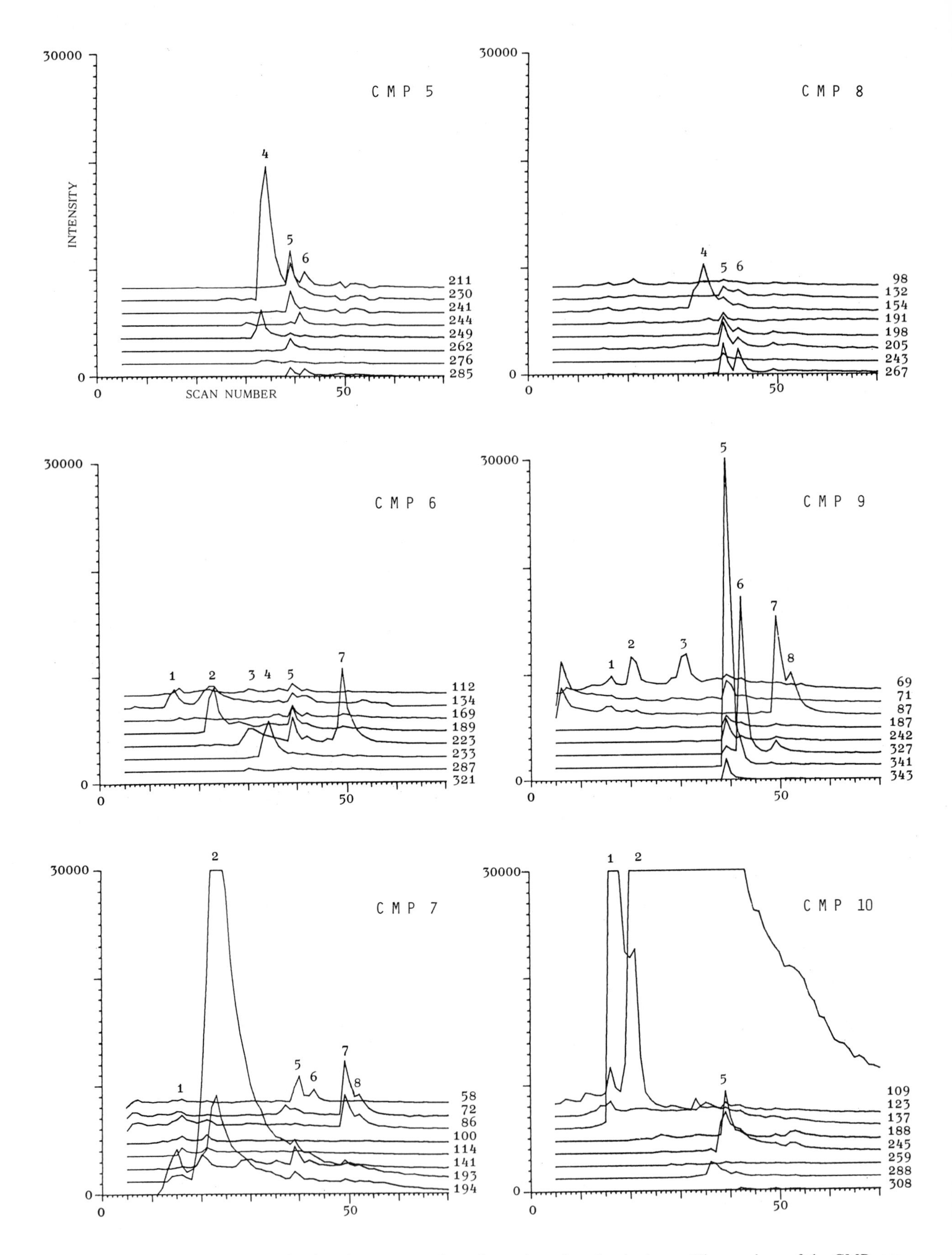

Fig. 2-3: Mass chromatograms indicating the presence of psychotropic and analgesic drugs. (The numbers of the CMPs are those given in Tab. 2-2)

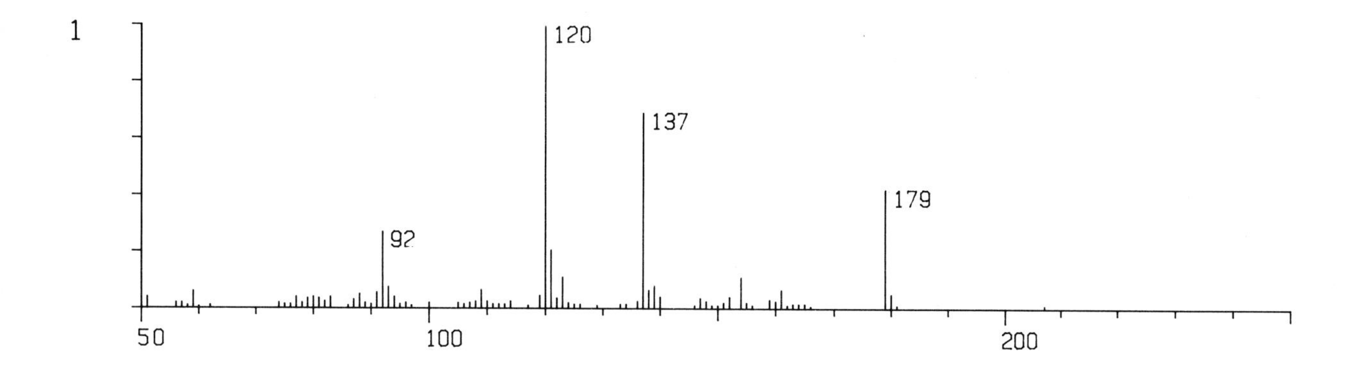
1
120
137
179
92
50
100
200

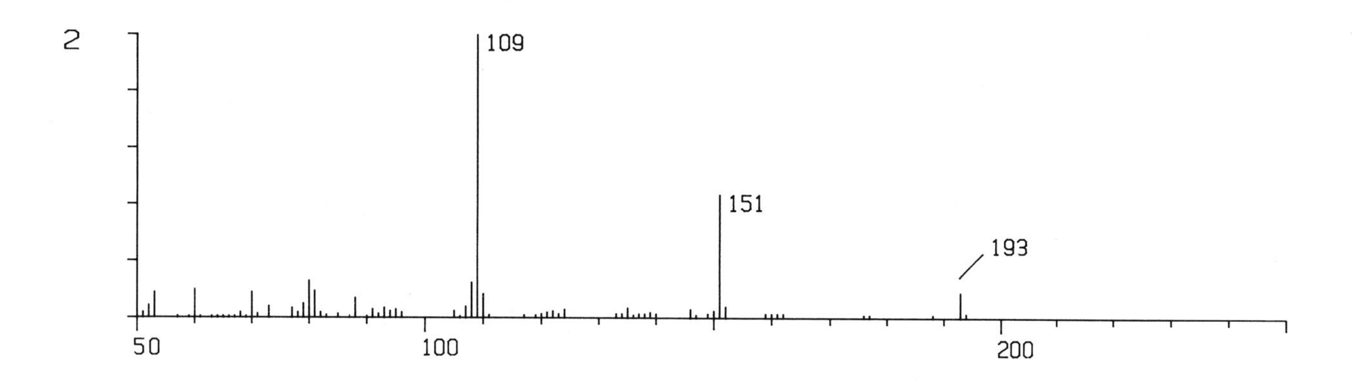
2
109
151
193
50
100
200

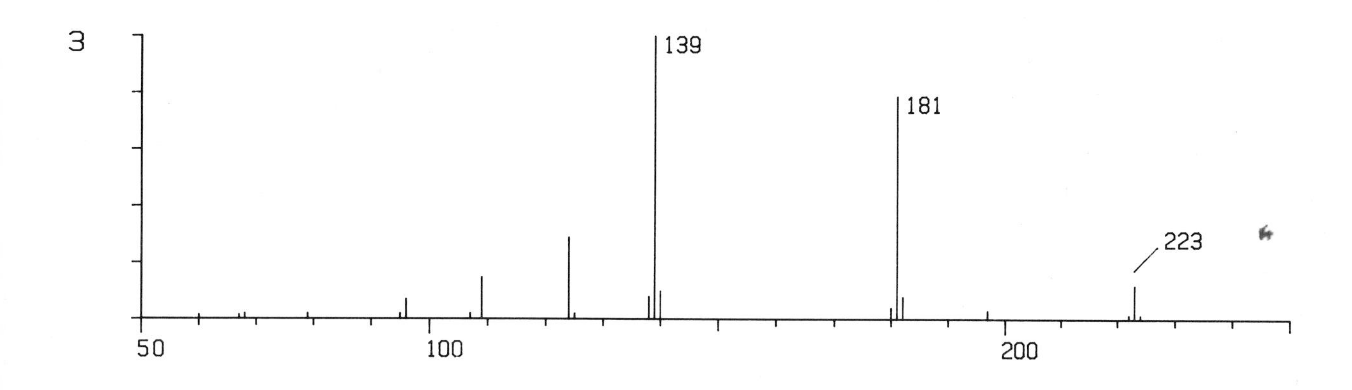
3
139
181
223
50
100
200

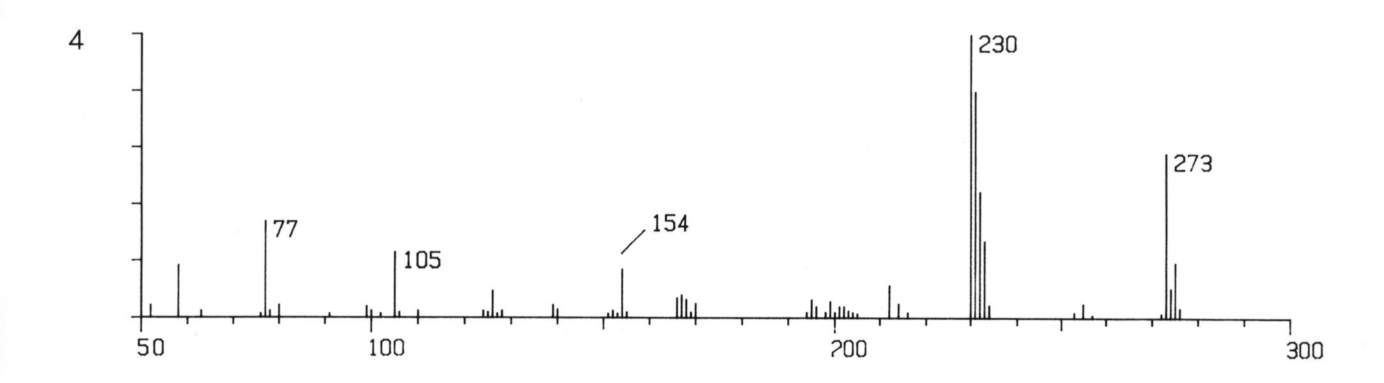
4
230
273
77
154
105
50
100
200
300

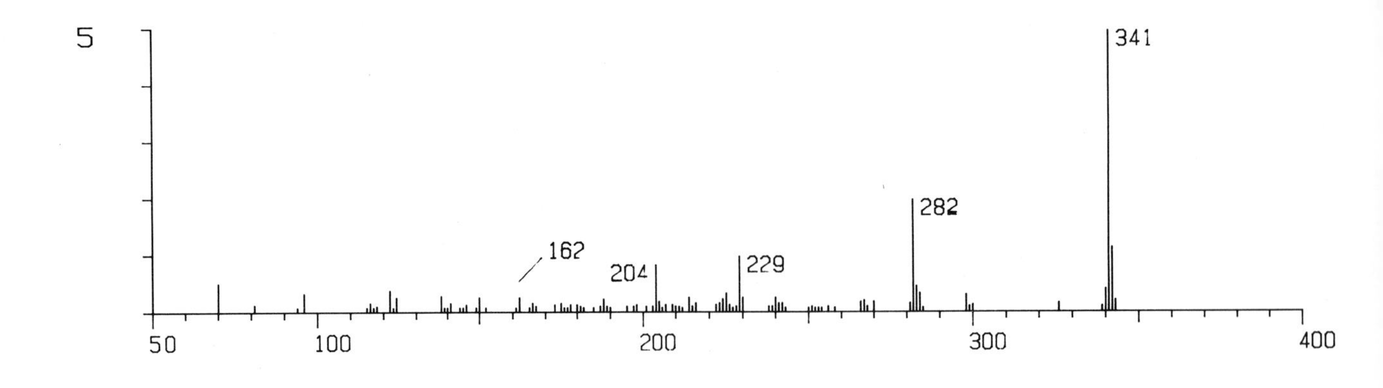

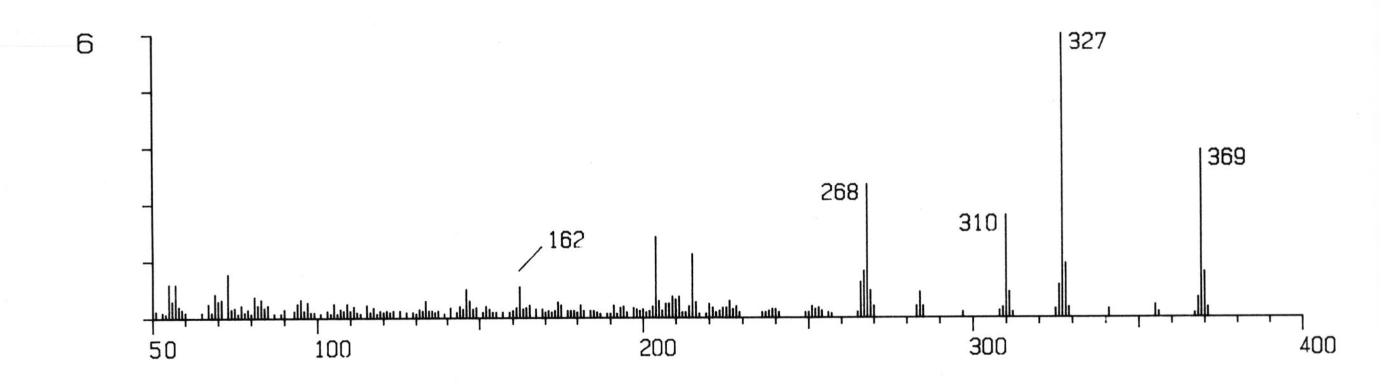

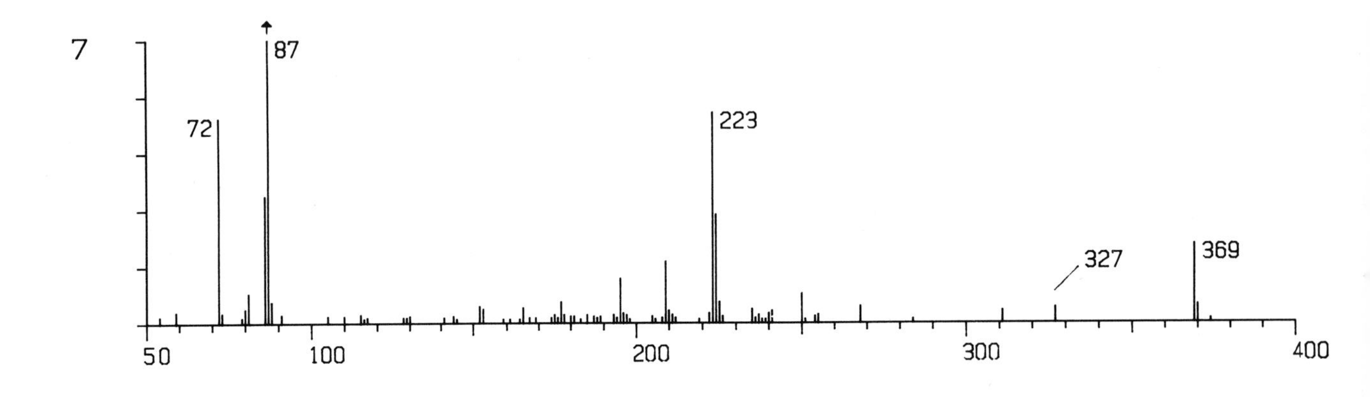

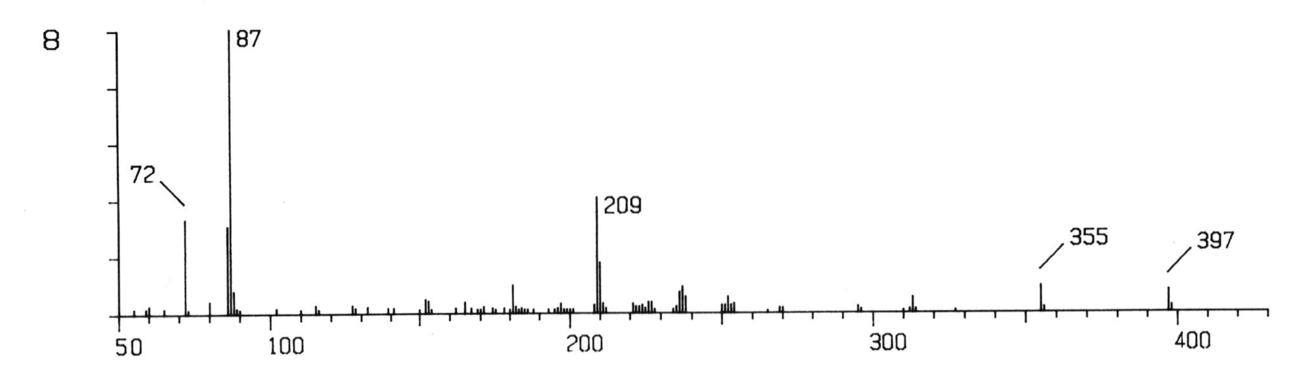

Fig. 2-4: Mass spectra indicated by peaks 1–8 in Fig. 2-3

3 Correlation between Structure and Fragmentation Pattern

This chapter deals with the correlation between chemical structure and mass fragmentation pattern. Only descriptive explanations are included for the purpose of illustrating the identification of metabolites using electron-impact mass spectrometry. Detailed mechanistic explanations for the interpretation of mass spectra are included in specialists texts (e.g. McLafferty, 1973).

3.1 Principle of Electron-Impact Mass Spectrometry (EI-MS)

The substance, dispersed in the helium carrier gas, is introduced into the ion source of the mass spectrometer through a GC-MS interface (on-line). Compounds of low volatility can be introduced through a direct insert system (DIS) (off-line). A small fraction of the evaporated substance is ionized by electron bombardment in the high vacuum of the ion source. In the main positive ions are formed according to the following equation:

$$M + e^- \rightarrow M^+ + 2e^-$$

The resulting ions (M^+) decompose to defined fragment ions. All the positive ions are accelerated, focused and than separated according to their mass to charge ratio (*m/z*) in the magnetic field. The current of each separated ion is measured. The mass spectrum represents the relation between the mass to charge ratio of the several fragment ions and the relative intensity of their ion currents. The mass spectrum is usually represented as a bar graph, in which the abscissa represents the mass to charge ratio (*m/z*) in atomic mass units (AMU) and the ordinate represents the relative intensity of the ion currents of the several fragment ions in %.

The fragmentation pattern is reproducible and characteristic for each organic compound. For this reason mass spectrometry is the most specific method for the identification of organic compounds.

3.2 The Correlation between Fundamental Structures or Side Chains and Fragment Ions

Fundamental structures or side chains of organic compounds can be correlated to fragment ions by observing the fragmentation pattern of analogous compounds or drugs. The elemental composition of fragment ions can be calculated from accurate mass measurement (2.4.5). This allows confirmation of suspected correlations. These empirical observations are useful for the identification of metabolites of known drugs or poisons (3.3). They are even useful for identifying unknown drugs or poisons with the aid of the molecular mass listing (11.2).

Metabolites usually have the same fundamental structure and/or the same side chains as their parent compounds and therefore their mass spectra contain similar or identical fragment ions. Chemical changes to fundamental structures and side chains by metabolism and/or derivatization procedures lead to typical shifts in the mass spectrum. Consideration of these correlations and of the fundamental principles of the metabolism of foreign compounds (La Du et al., 1971; Jakoby et al., 1982; Pfeifer, 1977–1983) allow the identification of metabolites (Ehrenthal, 1980; Ehrenthal and Pfleger, 1976; 1978; Ehrenthal et al., 1975; 1976; Maurer, 1983; Maurer and Pfleger, 1981a,b; 1983a,b; 1984a–c; Maurer et al., 1983). It does not constitute a precise chemical identification but it enables the detection of the presence of particular drugs or poisons in biological materials, or the exclusion of the spectrum as that of another poison.

3.3 Example of Mass Spectrum Interpretation and of the Identification of Metabolites

This chapter includes an example of the interpretation of mass spectra and identification of metabolites. The interpretation is limited to descriptive illustration.

The mass spectrum of the azaphenothiazine neuroleptic Prothipendyl (Fig. 3-1) contains the molecular ion (M^+) at 285 AMU, a fragment ion at 200 ($C_{11}H_8N_2S$) for the azaphenothiazine ring and an ion at 86 ($C_5H_{12}N$) typical for the dimethylaminopropyl side chain. The propyl chain is split into the corresponding ions 214/72 ($C_{12}H_{10}N_2S/C_4H_{10}N$) and 227/58 ($C_{13}H_{11}N_2S/C_3H_8N$). The azaphenothiazine ring eliminates sulphur forming the ion 168 ($C_{11}H_8N_2$).

Table 3-1 sets out the shifts of the fragment ions of the mass spectra of the acetylated metabolites (Fig. 3-2) compared with those of the mass spectrum of the parent compound (Fig. 3-1). Acetylation leads to a shift of +42 AMU.

The fragment ions of the metabolites reported in Table 3-2 result from the shifts given in Table 3-1.

Tab. 3-1: Shifts of the fragment ions of the metabolites of Prothipendyl (Fig. 3-2) compared with those of Prothipendyl (Fig. 3-1).

Metabolite	Elemental Difference	Shift in AMU	Shift after AC (+42)
Azaphenothiazine	$-C_5H_{11}N$	−85	−85
Hydroxy-	+O	+16	+58
Nor-Hydroxy-	$-CH_2+O$	+ 2	+86 (2 AC)
Nor-	$-CH_2$	−14	+28
Bis-Nor-	$-C_2H_4$	−28	+14

Tab. 3-2: Predominant fragment ions of Prothipendyl and its acetylated metabolites

M^+	Fragment ions of aromatic residue			HO-	Metabolite	Nor-	Fragment ions of aliphatic residue		
285	**227**	**214**	**200**	—	**Prothipendyl**	—	**86**	**72**	**58**
200	—	—	200	—	Azaphenothiazine	—	—	—	—
343	—	—	258	+58	Hydroxy-	—	86	72	58
	243	230	216	+16[a]					
371	—	—	258	+58	Nor-Hydroxy-	+28	114	100	86
	243	230	216	+16[a]					
313	227	214	200	—	Nor-	+28	114	100	86
299	227	214	200	—	Bis-Nor-	+14	100	86	72

[a] The acetyl group has split.

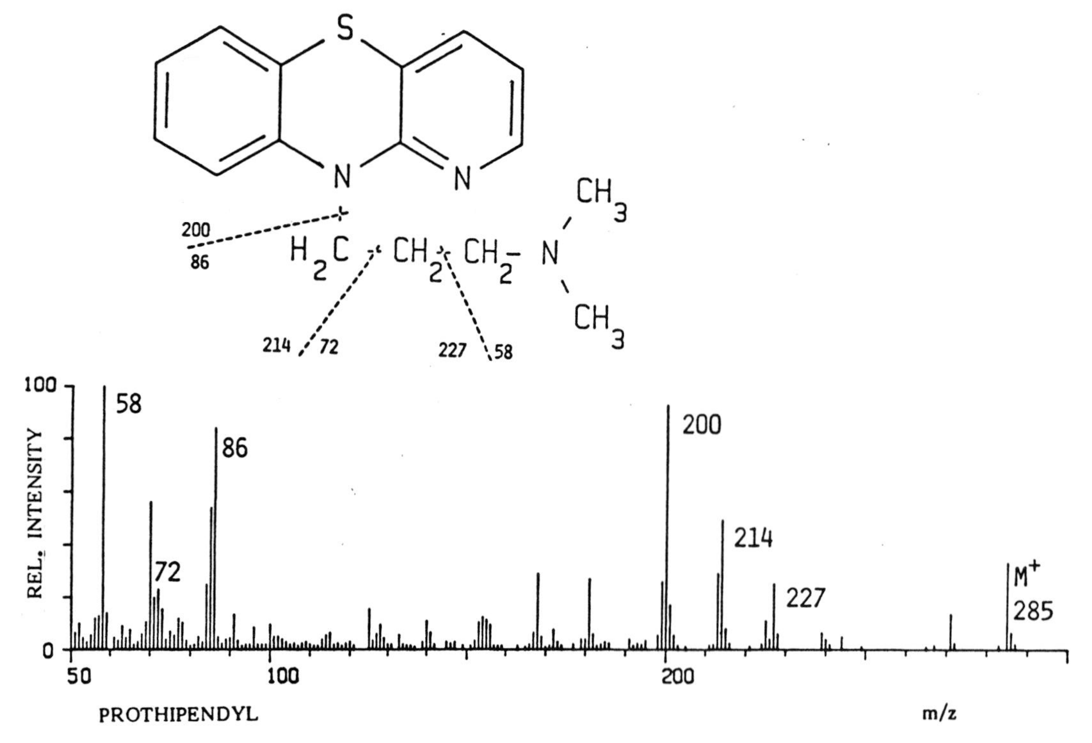

Fig. 3-1: Mass spectrum and fragmentation of Prothipendyl

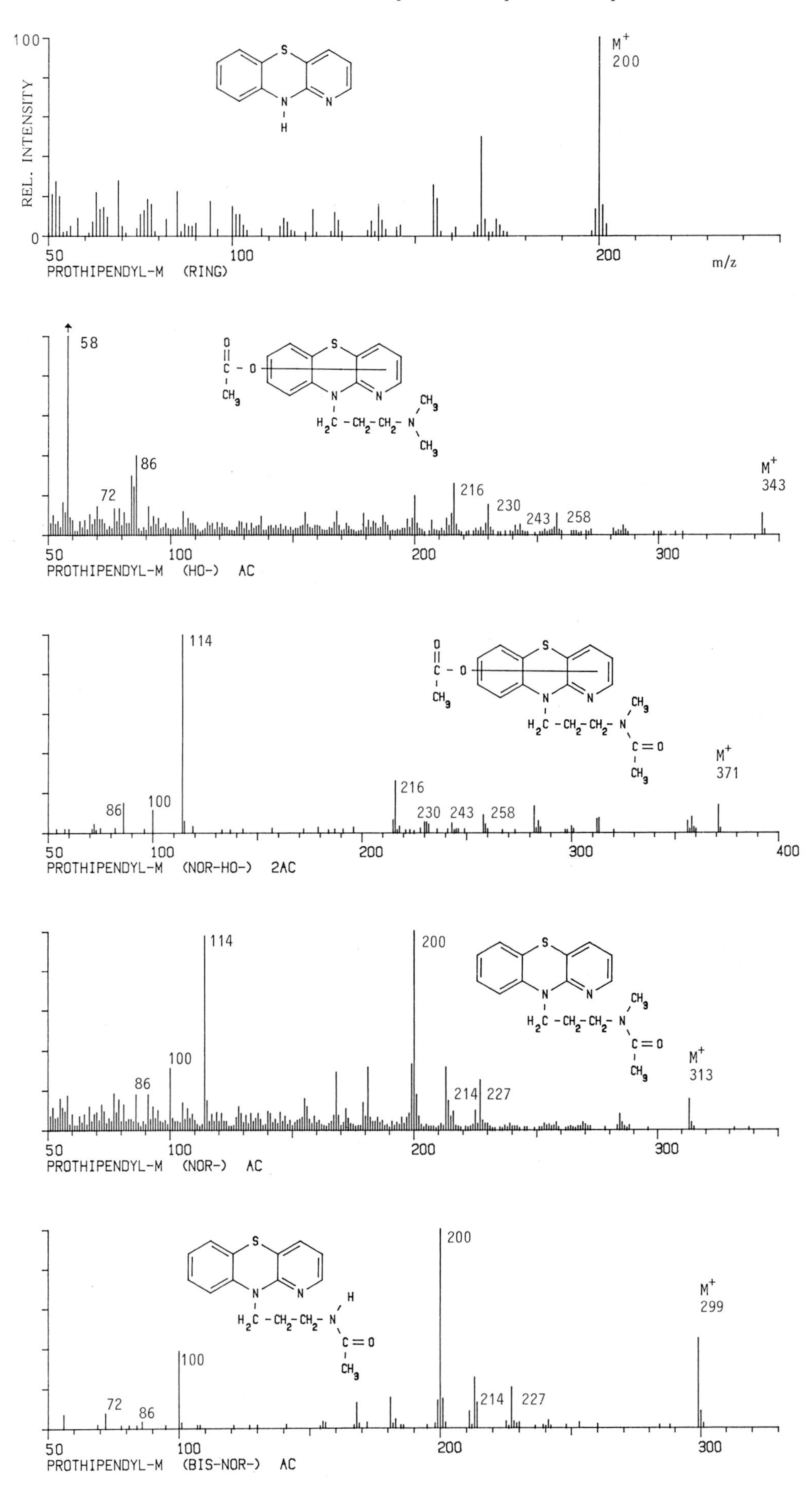

Fig. 3-2: Mass spectra of the acetylated metabolites of Prothipendyl

4 The Formation of Artifacts

Several of the compounds studied were modified during the analytical procedure employed. Sometimes this occurred thermally during the GC and sometimes during acid hydrolysis. Since the artifacts were formed reproducibly and they have been identified by mass spectrometry, they can be used for detection of the parent compounds. The artifacts are indicated in Table I and II (9, 10) and in the legends of the mass spectra in Part 2 ($-CO_2$, $-H_2O$, HY etc.; cf. abbreviation in 6). It cannot be excluded that further compounds were modified. (It should be noted at this point that compounds can be acetylated by simultaneously consumed acetylsalicylic acid in the gastric contents.)

4.1 Artifacts Formed by Thermolysis During GC (GC ARTIFACT)

4.1.1 Decarboxylation of Carboxylic Acids ($-CO_2$)

$$\text{R-COOH} \xrightarrow[-\,CO_2]{\Delta T} \text{R-H}$$

Reference: Sykes, 1982

4.1.2 Methylation of Carboxylic Acids in Methanol ((ME), ME IN METHANOL)

Some carboxylic acids are methylated when their methanolic solutions are subjected to GC.

$$\text{R-COOH} \xrightarrow[-\,H_2O]{+\,CH_3OH/\Delta T} \text{R-COOCH}_3$$

Reference: Sykes, 1982

4.1.3 Cope Elimination of N-oxides ($-(CH_3)_2NOH$, $-C_6H_{14}N_2O_2$)

$$R^4\text{-CH}(R^3)\text{-CH}_2\text{-CH}_2\text{-N}(R^1)(R^2)\rightarrow O \xrightarrow[-\,(R^1R^2)NOH]{\Delta T} R^4\text{-CH}(R^3)\text{-CH=CH}_2$$

Reference: Sykes, 1982

4.1.4 Methyl Substitution of Beta-adrenergic Blocking Agents (GC ARTIFACT IN METHANOL)

Beta-adrenergic blocking agents are methylated when their methanolic solutions are subjected to GC, the artifacts were identified by high resolution mass spectrometry. The empirical formulas and the fragmentation patterns of these artifacts suggest that they are formed by methylation of the hydroxy and the secondary amino groups. Further spectroscopic studies are in progress.

$$\text{AR-O-CH}_2\text{-CH(OH)-CH}_2\text{-NH-CH(CH}_3\text{)-CH}_3 \xrightarrow[-\,3\,H_2O]{+\,2\,CH_3OH/\Delta T} \text{AR-O-CH}_2\text{-CH(CH}_3\text{)-CH}_2\text{-N(CH}_3\text{)-CH(CH}_3\text{)-CH}_3$$

Reference: Maurer et al., in prep.

4.1.5 Rearrangement of Bis-desethyl Flurazepam ($-H_2O$)

NH2 O N Cl N F $\xrightarrow[-\,H_2O]{\Delta T}$ N N Cl N F

Reference: Clatworthy et al., 1977

4.2 Artifacts Formed by Thermolysis During GC and During Acid Hydrolysis (GC ARTIFACT, HY ARTIFACT)

4.2.1 Dehydration of Alcohols ($-H_2O$)

$$R^3\text{-CH(OH)-CH}(R^2)\text{-}R^1 \xrightarrow[-\,H_2O]{\Delta T/[H^+]} R^3\text{-CH=C}(R^2)\text{-}R^1$$

Reference: Sykes, 1982

4.2.2 Cleavage of Morazone to Phenmetrazine

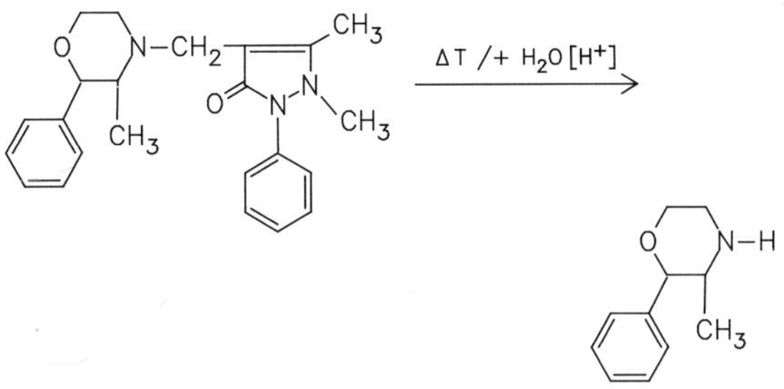

O N–CH_2 CH_3 O N N CH_3 CH_3

ΔT /+ H_2O [H^+]

O N–H CH_3

References: Cartoni et al., 1973 (GC)
Bohn et al., 1976 (HY)

4.3 Artifacts Formed During Acid Hydrolysis

4.3.1 Cleavage of Diarylmethyl Alkyl Ethers (HY)

cf. benzatropine, chlorphenoxamine, clemastine, diphenhydramine, diphenylpyraline, doxylamine, mecloxamine and orphenadrine

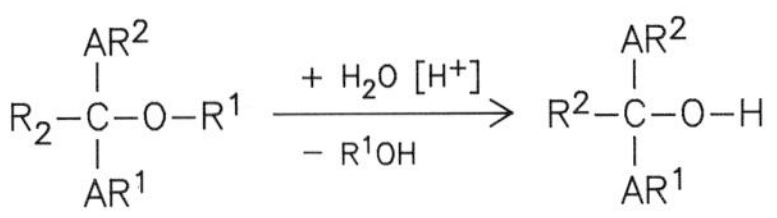

$$R_2-\underset{AR^1}{\overset{AR^2}{C}}-O-R^1 \xrightarrow[-\,R^1OH]{+\,H_2O\,[H^+]} R^2-\underset{AR^1}{\overset{AR^2}{C}}-O-H$$

Reference: Gielsdorf, 1981

4.3.2 Cleavage of 1,4-Benzodiazepines to Aminobenzoyl Derivatives (HY)

cf. bromazepam, camazepam, chlordiazepoxide, clonazepam, clorazepate, diazepam, flunitrazepam, flurazepam, ketazolam, lorazepam, lormetazepam, medazepam-M, nitrazepam, oxazepam, oxazolam, prazepam, temazepam, tetrazepam and their metabolites

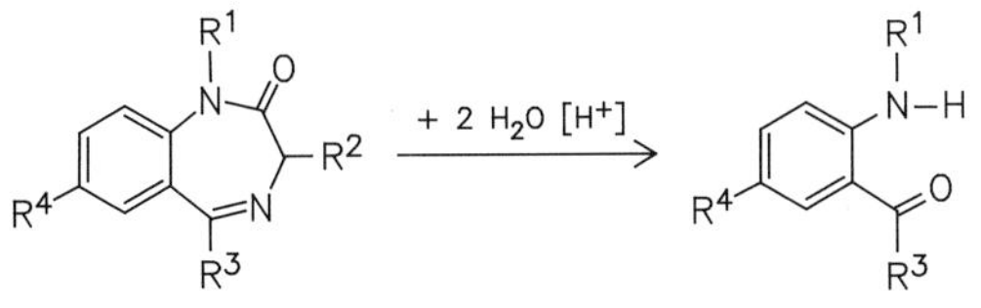

R^1 N O R^2 R^4 N R^3

+ 2 H_2O [H^+]

R^1 N–H R^4 O R^3

Reference: Bäumler and Rippstein, 1961

4.3.3 Cleavage and Rearrangement of the N-Desmethyl Metabolites of Clobazam to Benzimidazole Derivatives (HY)

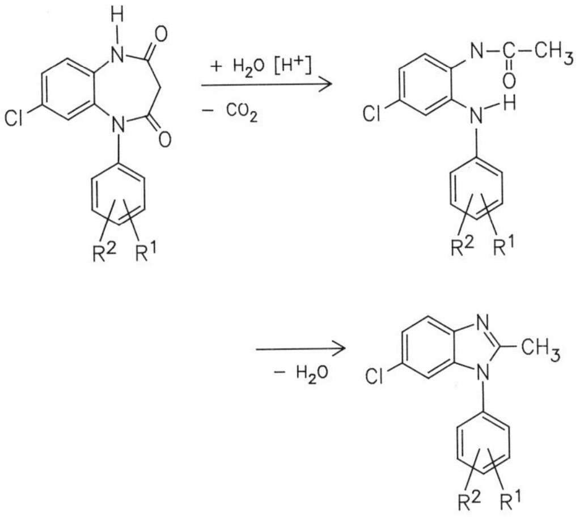

H N O Cl N O R^2 R^1

+ H_2O [H^+]
– CO_2

N–C–CH_3 O Cl N–H R^2 R^1

– H_2O

N –CH_3 Cl N R^2 R^1

References: Eiden and Schmiz, 1980
Maurer and Pfleger, 1981a

4.3.4 Cleavage and Rearrangement of Bis-desethyl Flurazepam (HY $-H_2O$)

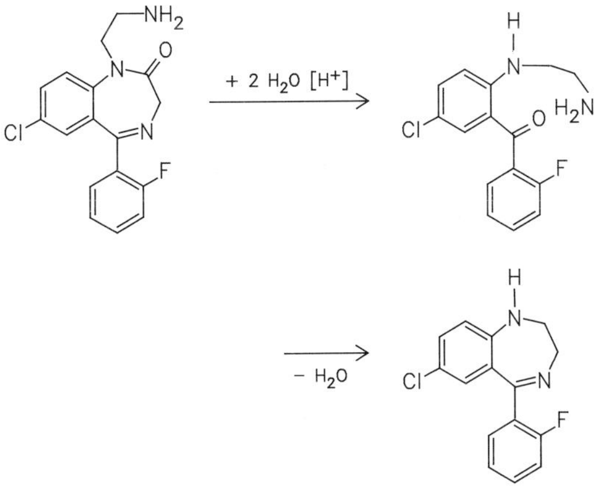

NH_2 N O Cl N F

+ 2 H_2O [H^+]

H N Cl O H_2N F

– H_2O

H N Cl N F

Reference: Maurer and Pfleger, 1981a

4.3.5 Hydration of the Double Bond of Pentazocine ($+H_2O$)

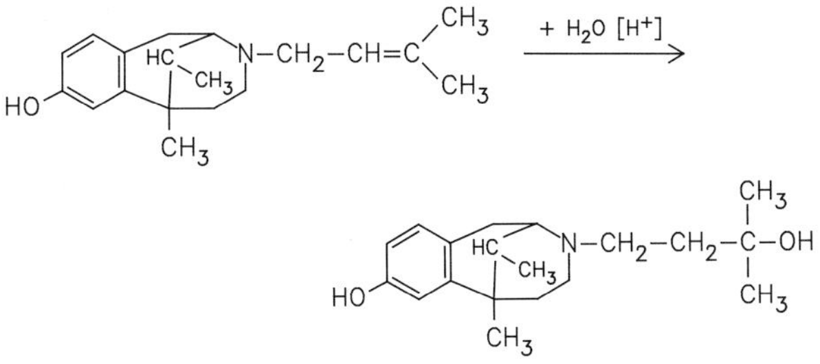

HO HC CH_3 N–CH_2–CH=C(CH_3)–CH_3 CH_3

+ H_2O [H^+]

HO HC CH_3 N–CH_2–CH_2–C(CH_3)(CH_3)–OH CH_3

Reference: Gielsdorf and Tümmers, 1983

5 Table of Atomic Masses

The accurate atomic masses of the most abundant isotops of the elements which were employed for the calculations in 11 and in Part 2 are listed in Table 5-1.

Tab. 5-1: Atomic masses of elements

Symbol	Element	Atomic mass
As	Arsenic	74.921595
Br	Bromine	78.918336
C	Carbon	12.000000
Cl	Chlorine	34.968853
F	Fluorine	18.998403
Fe	Iron	55.934939
H	Hydrogen	1.007825
Hg	Mercury	201.970632
I	Iodine	126.904477
N	Nitrogen	14.003074
O	Oxygen	15.994915
P	Phosphorus	30.973763
Pb	Lead	207.976641
S	Sulfur	31.970272
Si	Silicon	27.976928

Reference: Wapstra and Bos, 1977

6 Abbreviations

The abbreviations used in this book are listed in Table 6-1.

Tab. 6-1: Abbreviations

Abbreviation	Meaning	see
AC	Acetylated	2.2.3.1
(AC)	Possibly acetylated	
ALTERED DURING HY	The altered compound can be detected in UHY	4.3
AMU	Atomic mass unit = 1/12 of the mass of the ^{12}C isotope	
ARTIFACT ( )	( ) artifact	4
BP	Base peak = The most intense fragment ion in a mass spectrum	
CAS	Chemical Abstract Service	
CI	Chemical ionization	
CMP	Computer monitoring program	2.4.3
$-C_6H_{14}N_2O$	Artifact formed by Cope elimination of the N-oxide	4.1.3
$-(CH_3)_2NOH$	Artifact formed by Cope elimination of the N-oxide	4.1.3
$-CO_2$	Artifact formed by decarboxylation	4.1.1
D:	Detectable in	
DIS	Direct insert system = This mass spectrum was recorded using the DIS	
DS	Data system	2.4.1
EI	Electron impact ionization	3.1
EMIT	Enzyme multiplied immunoassay technique	
ET	Ethylated	2.2.3.3
FID	Flame-ionisation detector	2.3.1

Abbreviation	Meaning	see
G	Standard extract of gastric contents	2.2.2.1
GC	Gas chromatographic, -graph, -graphy	2.3
GC ARTIFACT	Artifact formed during GC	4.1
GC ARTIFACT IN METHANOL	Artifact of beta-adrenergic blocking agents by reaction with methanol during GC	4.1.4
$+H_2O$	Artifact formed by hydration of an alkene	4.3.5
$-H_2O$	Artifact formed by dehydration of an alcohol or by rearrangement of an amino oxo compound	4.2.1 4.1.5
HPLC	High performance liquid chromatographic, -graph, -graphy	
HY	Acid hydrolyzed or acid hydrolysis	2.2.2.3
HY ARTIFACT	Artifact formed during acid hydrolysis	4.3
−I	Intoxication = This compound is detectable after a toxic dosage	
I. D.	Internal diameter	
INN	International non proprietary name (WHO)	
LM	Low resolution mass spectrum	
LS	Background substracted low resolution mass spectrum	
M^+	Molecular ion	
−M	Metabolite	
−M ( )	( ) metabolite	
−M (HO-)	Hydroxy metabolite	
−M (HOOC-)	Carboxylated metabolite	
−M (NOR-)	N-desmethyl metabolite	
−M (RING)	Ring compound as metabolite e.g. of phenothiazines	
−M ARTIFACT	Artifact of a metabolite	
−M/ARTIFACT	Metabolite or artifact	
m/z	Mass to charge ratio	3.1
ME	Methylated	2.2.3.2
(ME)	Methylated by methanol during GC	4.1.2
ME IN METHANOL	Methylated by methanol during GC	4.1.2
MS	Mass spectrometric, -meter, -metry, mass spectrum	2.4
N:	Notes	
N-FID	Nitrogen-sensitive flame-ionisation detector	2.3.1
NOT DETECTABLE AFTER HY	This compound is destroyed during acid hydrolysis	
P	Standard extract of plasma	2.2.2.1
PC	Paper chromatography	
PS	Pure substance	
RAT	This compound was found in the urine of rats	2.1
RI	Retention index (Kovats, 1958) on OV-101	2.3.1
RIA	Radio immunoassay	
STED	Solvent transfer and evaporation device	2.2.1
TLC	Thin layer chromatography	
TMS	Trimethylsilylated	2.2.3.4
U	Standard extract of urine	2.2.2.1
UA	Extract of urine for detection of amphetamines	2.2.2.2
UGLUC	Extract of urine after cleavage of conjugates using glucuronidase and arylsulfatase	2.2.2.4
UHY	Extract of urine after acid hydrolysis	2.2.2.3
*	This compound contains no nitrogen. Therefore it cannot be detected by a N-FID but by a FID	
----	This RI was not determined	
OOOO	This compound was not volatile and could not be detected by GC	

7 User's Guide

This chapter is a guide to the use of this book, which can be employed to solve various problems in analytical toxicology. The instructions are laid out according to the problem addressed.

7.1 General Unknown Analysis – Screening for Special Groups of Drugs (CMP)

Screening for special groups of drugs is very useful, if general unknown analysis must be carried out. It enables the detection or exclusion of entire groups of drugs within about one hour. First a suitable sample preparation is selected (2.2). The extract is analyzed by computerized gas chromatography-mass spectrometry using suitable computer monitoring programs (CMP) for mass chromatography (2.4.2–4). The mass spectra selected in the screening process are then identified by comparison with the reference spectra in Part 2.

The procedure is illustrated by an example in 2.4.4.

7.2 Identification of a Particular Drug or Poison (Table I: Alphabetical List)

Suspected drugs or poisons can be identified after suitable sample preparation (2.2) by computerized mass spectrometry using mass chromatography on the basis of fragment ions typical for specific compounds. This procedure has the advantage that the suspected compound can be detected even if it is overlapped by large amounts of other substances. The typical ions are given in the alphabetical list (9) of all the compounds included. If a characteristic peak appears in the mass chromatogram the underlying mass spectrum is then identified by comparison with the reference spectrum in Part 2.

The parent compound of some drugs and poisons cannot itself be detected if urine is analyzed. Therefore its metabolites are listed under the heading of the parent compound.

7.3 Identification of a Gas Chromatographic Peak (Table II: List of Retention Indices)

Retention indices (OV-101) are listed for the benefit of gas chromatographers, who are temporarily without GC-MS facilities (10). The problems arising from identification of compounds using retention indices are generally known and therefore they are not discussed here. An identification using retention indices is more certain, if the presence or absence of GC peaks of metabolites or derivatives of a suspected compound is also considered. But this identification should always be confirmed by a GC-MS procedure.

7.4 Identification of a Recorded Mass Spectrum (Part 2)

A recorded mass spectrum can be identified by comparing with the reference spectra in Part 2. Various criteria were selected to aid the selection of the reference spectrum. Because the molecular ion (M^+) normally contains the most important information the reference spectrum can be found under it. But in many cases the M^+ is too low or hidden by the background so that it cannot be detected. Therefore in many cases the spectrum can also be found under the next highest predominant ion. In order to avoid accumulation of data these ions were chosen sparingly. Finally the reference spectrum can be found under the base peak. If there are two or more large fragment ions (>80%), the spectrum can be found under both, because it is possible that their relationship could vary.

The search for reference spectra is illustrated in the example in 2.4.4.

7.5 Identification of Unknown Drugs or Poisons in the Absence of Reference Spectra (Table III: Molecular Mass List)

Identification of unknown drugs or poisons can also be attempted from a list of the molecular masses of drugs, pesticides and common chemicals such as are used in the household (11). If the condition is fulfilled that the electron-impact mass spectrum includes the molecular ion a search can be made for the probable compound. In most cases several compounds are listed under the same rounded off mass. Knowledge of whether the unknown compound contains nitrogen (nitrogen-sensitive detection on GC) and/or chlorine, bromine or sulfur (typical isotopic abundances (Fig. 11-1, B) in the mass spectrum) facilitates the selection. If the mass of the molecular ion is odd-numbered, the compound contains an odd number of nitrogens. The correlation between the mass fragmentation pattern and the structure of the suspected compound (3) is a further criterion. Even so in many cases there are still several potential compounds. Accurate determination of the mass of the molecular ion (2.4.5) allows calculation of the elemental composition. Now it is only necessary to distinguish between isomers, this can often be accomplished from the fragmentation pattern and the case history. However, the identification should always be confirmed by comparison of the mass spectrum with that of the pure reference substance. An example of this procedure is given in 11.2.

If plasma or urine is analyzed the unknown compound may be a metabolite. (In our experience parenterally administered drugs and their metabolites can also be detected in the gastric contents, if they diffuse into the stomach and are dissociated there by hydrochloric acid.) Metabolites can be identified as described above, if their molecular ion is decreased by 15.994915 AMU ($-O$) for hydroxylated metabolites or increased by 14.01565 ($+CH_2$) or 28.03130 AMU ($+C_2H_4$) for desmethyl or desethyl metabolites.

Since carboxylic acids are usually decarboxylated during gas chromatography (4.1.1) they are to be found in the list after addition of 43.98983 AMU ($+CO_2$) to the mass of the highest ion in the mass spectrum.

8 References

Ardrey, R.E., Brown, C., Allan, A.R., Bal, T.S., and Moffat, A.C. (eds.) (1982): An Eight Peak Index of Mass Spectra of Compounds of Forensic Interest. Scottish Academy Press, Edinburgh.

Arzneibüro der Bundesvereinigung Deutscher Apothekerverbände (ABDA) (ed.) (1984): Pharmazeutische Stoffliste, 6th Ed. Werbe- und Vertriebsgesellschaft Deutscher Apotheker, Frankfurt.

Arnold, W., and Grützmacher, H.F. (1969), Z. Anal. Chem. 247, 179-188.

Bäumler, J., and Rippstein, S. (1961), Helv. Chim. Acta 44, 2208-2210.

Böttcher, J., Bässmann, H., Schüppel, R., and Lehmann, W.D. (1982), Naunyn-Schmiedeberg's Arch. Pharmacol. 321, 226-233.

Bohn, G., Rücker, G., and Kröger, H. (1976), Arch. Toxicol. 35, 213-220.

Cailleux, A., Turcant, A., Premel-Cabic, A., and Allain, P. (1981), J. Chrom. Sci. 19, 163-176.

Cartoni, G.P., Cavalli, A., Giarusso, A., and Rosati, F. (1973), J. Chromatogr. 84, 419-422.

Clatworthy, A.J., Jones, L.V., and Whitehouse, M.J. (1977), Biomed. Mass Spectr. 4, 248-254.

Cleeland, R., Christenson, J., Usageti-Gomez, M., Heveran, J., Davis, R., and Grunberg, E. (1976), Clin. Chem. 22, 712-725.

Costello, C.E., Hertz, H.S., Sakai, T., and Biemann, K. (1974), Clin. Chem. 20, 255-265.

Daldrup, T., Susanto, F., and Michalke, P. (1981), Fresenius Z. Anal. Chem. 308, 413-427.

Deutsche Forschungsgemeinschaft (ed.) (1982a): Mitteilung I der Kommission für Klinisch-toxikologische Analytik: Gaschromatographische Retentionindices toxikologisch relevanter Verbindungen. Verlag Chemie, Weinheim.

Deutsche Forschungsgemeinschaft, Senatskommission für Klinisch-toxikologische Analytik (1982b), J. Clin. Chem. Clin. Biochem. 20, 699-701.

Ehrenthal, W. (1980), Dissertation, Universität des Saarlandes, Homburg, FRG.

Ehrenthal, W., and Pfleger, K. (1975), Varian MAT Publication No. 19, 1-17.

Ehrenthal, W., and Pfleger, K. (1976), Analyt. Chem. 279, 135-136.

Ehrenthal, W., and Pfleger, K. (1977), in Eggstein, M., and Liebich, H.M. (eds.), Proceedings of the symposium of the University Tübingen "Massenspektrometrie und kombinierte Techniken in Medizin, Klinischer Chemie und Klinischer Biochemie" in Tübingen, FRG, p. 330-345.

Ehrenthal, W., and Pfleger, K. (1978), Naunyn-Schmiedeberg's Arch. Pharmacol. Suppl. to 302, R 13.

Ehrenthal, W., and Pfleger, K. (1979), Naunyn-Schmiedeberg's Arch. Pharmacol. Suppl. to 308, R 91.

Ehrenthal, W., Pfleger, K., and Möller, M. (1975), Varian MAT Publication No. 22, 23.

Ehrenthal, W., Pfleger, K., and Stübing, G. (1976), Acta Pharmacol. Toxicol. Suppl. 2 to 41, 199-211.

Ehrenthal, W., Doenecke, P., Traut, G., and Pfleger, K. (1979), in Okonek, S., Fülgraff, G., and Frey, R. (eds.): Humantoxikologie, Akute Vergiftungen - Giftinformation, p. 1-15. Fischer, Stuttgart.

Eiden, F., and Schmiz, E. (1980), Dtsch. Apoth. Ztg. 120, 933-937.

Eistert, B., Regitz, M., Heck, G., and Schwall, H. (1968) in Houben-Weyl: Methoden der organischen Chemie, Vol. 10, 4th Ed., p. 552-553. Thieme, Stuttgart.

Finkle, B.S., Taylor, D.M., and Bonelli, E.J. (1972), J. Chrom. Sci. 10, 312-333.

Finkle, B.S., Foltz, R.L., and Taylor, D.M. (1974), J. Chrom. Sci. 12, 304-328.

Foltz, R.L., Clarke, P.A., Knowlton, D.A., and Hoyland, J.R. (1974): Research Report "The Rapid Identification of Drugs from Mass Spectra". Batelle Columbus Lab., Columbus, Ohio.

Gielsdorf, W. (1981), J. Clin. Chem. Clin. Biochem. 19, 485-490.

Gielsdorf, W., and Tümmers M.H. (1983), Intern. J. Mass Spectr. Ion Phys. 48, 133-136.

Interschick, E., Wüst, H., and Wimmer, H. (1978), GIT Fachzeitschrift für das Laboratorium 22, 555-572.

Jakoby, W.B., Bend, J.R., and Caldwell, J. (eds.) (1982): Metabolic Basis of Detoxication. Academic Press, New York.

Kovats, E. (1958), Helv. Chim. Acta 41, 1915-1932.

La Du, B.N., Mandel, H.G., and Way, E.L. (eds.) (1971): Fundamentals of Drug Metabolism and Disposition. Williams & Wilkins Company, Baltimore.

Maurer, H. (1983), Dissertation, Universität des Saarlandes, Saarbrücken, FRG.

Maurer, H., and Pfleger, K. (1981a), J. Chromatogr. 222, 409-419.

Maurer, H., and Pfleger, K. (1981b), in Bäumler, J., and Müller, G. (eds.), Proceedings of the Symposium of the Gesellschaft für Toxikologische und Forensische Chemie (GTFCH) "Pestizide und Brände" in Mosbach, FRG, p. 82-97.

Maurer, H., and Pfleger, K. (1982), J. Clin. Chem. Clin. Biochem. 20, 667-668.

Maurer, H., and Pfleger, K. (1983a), J. Chromatogr. 272, 75-85.
Maurer, H., and Pfleger, K. (1983b), Fresenius Z. Anal. Chem. 314, 586-594.
Maurer, H., and Pfleger, K. (1984a), Fresenius Z. Anal. Chem. 317, 42-52.
Maurer, H., and Pfleger, K. (1984b), J. Chromatogr. 305, 309-323.
Maurer, H., and Pfleger, K. (1984c), J. Chromatogr. 306, 125-145.
Maurer, H., Weber, A., and Pfleger, K. (1982), Fresenius Z. Anal. Chem. 311, 414-415.
Maurer, H., Kleff, I., and Pfleger, K. (1983), Naunyn-Schmiedeberg's Arch. Pharmacol. Suppl. to 322, R 450.
Maurer, H., Weber, A., and Pfleger, K. (1984), in Maes, R. A. A. (ed.), Topics in Forensic and Analytical Toxicology, p. 127-130. Elsevier, Amsterdam.
Maurer, H., Weber, A., and Pfleger, K., in preparation.
McLafferty, F. W. (1973): Interpretation of Mass Spectra, 2nd Ed. W. A. Benjamin, Inc., Reading, Massachusetts.
Midgley, I., Hawkins, D. R., and Chasseaud, L. F. (1978), Drug Res. 28, 1911-1916.
Millard, B. J. (1978): Quantitative mass spectrometry. Heyden, London.
Moffat, A. C., and Smalldon, K. W. (1974), J. Chromatogr. 90, 9-17.
Moffat, A. C., Stead, A. H., and Smalldon, K. W. (1974), J. Chromatogr. 90, 19-33.
Negwer, M. (1978): Organisch-chemische Arzneimittel und ihre Synonyma, Vol. 1-3, Akademie Verlag, Berlin, GDR.
Oellerich, M., Külpmann, W. R., and Haeckel, R. (1977), J. Clin. Chem. Clin. Biochem. 15, 275-283.
Pentz, R., and Schütt, A. (1978), Arch. Toxicol. 39, 225-233.
Perkow, P. (1983): Wirksubstanzen der Pflanzenschutz- und Schädlingsbekämpfungsmittel, 2nd Ed. Verlag Paul Parey, Berlin.
Pfeifer, S. (1977-1983): Biotransformation von Arzneimitteln, Vol. 1-5. Verlag Chemie, Weinheim.
Skinner, R. F., Gallaher, E. J., Kneight, J. B., and Bonelli, E. J. (1972), J. Forensic Sci. 17, 189-198.
Stenhagen, E., Abrahamsson, S., and McLafferty, F. W. (1974): Registry of Mass Spectral Data. J. Wiley & Sons, New York.
Sunshine, I., and Caplis, M. (eds.) (1981): CRC Handbook of Mass Spectra of Drugs. CRC Press, Boca Raton (F).
Sykes, P. (1982): Reaktionsmechanismen der organischen Chemie, 8th Ed. Verlag Chemie, Weinheim.
The Royal Society of Chemistry (ed.) (1983): The Eight Peak Index of Mass Spectra, 3rd Ed. Mass Spectrometry Data Center, Nottingham.
Wapstra, A. H., and Bos, K. (1977), Atomic Data and Nuclear Data Tables 19, 177-214.
Widdop, B. (1974), in CIBA Foundation Symposium 26: The Poisoned Patient: The Role of the Laboratory. Elsevier, Amsterdam.
Windholz, M., Budavari, S., Stroumtsos, L. Y., and Fertig, M. N. (1983): The Merck Index, 10th Ed., Merck & Co., Rahway (N. J.).

9 Table I: Alphabetical List of Measured Compounds

9.1 Explanatory Notes

This section consists of an alphabetical list of the measured compounds in order to facilitate the search for the data of specific compounds (7.2). Derivatives, metabolites and derivatized metabolites are listed in order of ascending retention index under and after their parent compounds. Metabolites or derivatives common to several substances are listed under all their parent compounds.

The title of the list is printed at the top of each page together with the first or last substance, the page number is printed at the bottom.

The first column contains the retention indices, the second column the compound name (INN for drugs, common names for pesticides, chemical name for chemicals) and the third column contains the derivatives. If necessary, a synonym index (e. g. ABDA, 1984; Negwer, 1978; Perkow, 1983; Windholz et al., 1983) should be employed in conjunction with this list. Additional information from the CAS is accessible through the list of common names (Part 2, 5.1). The fourth column lists fragment ions typical for the compound. The ions under which the mass spectrum is listed in Part 2 are printed boldface. The fifth column indicates the page in Part 2 on which the mass spectrum is reproduced under its most massive ion, in order to facilitate finding it.

9.2 Table I: Alphabetical List

RI	NAME	DERIVATIVE	TYPICAL IONS	PAGE
2850	ACEBUTOLOL -H2O		**318** 303 140 **98**	560
2450	ACEBUTOLOL ARTIFACT (PHENOL)		**221** **151** 136	353
3100	ACEBUTOLOL -H20	AC	**360** 259 230 **151** 98	616
1720	ACECARBROMAL		**191** **149** 113 **69**	279
1210	ACECARBROMAL ARTIFACT 1		**180** 129 **69**	256
1510	ACECARBROMAL ARTIFACT 2		**165** **113** 98 69	227
2875	ACEMETACIN	ME	**429** **371** 312 **139** 111	659
2130	ACEMETACIN ARTIFACT 1	ME	**233** **174**	381
2390	ACEMETACIN ARTIFACT 2	ME	**291** 233 **174** 159 131	507
3210	ACENOCOUMAROL	ME	**367** 310 193 121 72	622
2755	ACEPROMAZINE		**326** 241 86 **58**	572
2720	ACEPROMAZINE-M (DIHYDRO-) -H2O		**310** 225 86 **58**	544
2765	ACEPROMAZINE-M (DIHYDRO-)	AC	**370** 310 225 86 **58**	625
3000	ACEPROMAZINE-M (HO-DIHYDRO-)	2AC	**428** **343** 154 86 **58**	659
3040	ACEPROMAZINE-M (HO-)	AC	**384** 256 86 **58**	638
3145	ACEPROMAZINE-M (NOR-)	AC	**354** 241 **114** 100	610
3150	ACEPROMAZINE-M (NOR-DIHYDRO-) -H2O	AC	**338** **114** 100	593
2625	ACEPROMETHAZINE		**326** 255 222 **72**	572
2920	ACEPROMETHAZINE-M (METHOXY-DIHYDRO-) -H2O		**340** 271 238 **72**	595
2690	ACEPROMETHAZINE-M (DIHYDRO-)	AC	**370** **299** 224 **72**	625
2940	ACEPROMETHAZINE-M (NOR-)	AC	**354** **254** 114 72 **58**	610
3025	ACEPROMETHAZINE-M (HO-)	AC	**384** **313** 256 **72**	638
3165	ACEPROMETHAZINE-M (METHOXY-DIHYDRO-)	AC	**400** **329** 270 **72**	647
3205	ACEPROMETHAZINE-M (NOR-HO-)	2AC	**412** **254** 114 100 **58**	653
1380	ACETANILIDE		**135** **93**	174
<1000*	ACETIC ACID		**60** **43**	47
<1000*	ACETONE		**58** **43**	19
1545*	ACETYLSALICYLIC ACID		**180** 138 **120** 92	256
1295*	ACETYLSALICYLIC ACID-M (DESACETYL-)		**138** 120 **92** 64	182
----	ACETYLSALICYLIC ACID-M		**195** 177 149 **120** 92 65	288
1350*	ACETYLSALICYLIC ACID-M (DESACETYL-)	ET	**166** **120** 92 65	231
1200*	ACETYLSALICYLIC ACID-M (DESACETYL-)	ME	**152** 120 **92** 65	210
1810	ACETYLSALICYLIC ACID-M	ME	**209** **121** 92 65	323
----	ACETYLSALICYLIC ACID-M	2ME	**223** **135** 90 77	360
2690	ACETYLSULFANILAMIDE		**214** **172** 156 92	336
2375	ADEPTOLON (TM) INGREDIENT		**347** 275 **169** 86 **72**	604
2215	ADIPHENINE		**311** 239 **167** 99 **86**	546
1715*	ADIPHENINE-M/ARTIFACT (HOOC-)	(ME)	**226** **167** 152	364
1945*	ALDRIN		**362** 327 291 263 **261**	617

RI	NAME	DERIVATIVE	TYPICAL IONS	PAGE
2315	ALIMEMAZINE		**298 198** 100 84 **58**	521
2010	ALIMEMAZINE-M (RING)		**199** 167	296
2650	ALIMEMAZINE-M (HO-)		**314** 228 214 **100 58**	552
2665	ALIMEMAZINE-M (SULFOXIDE)		**314** 298 **212** 199 **58**	552
2550	ALIMEMAZINE-M (HO-RING)	AC	**257 215** 183	431
2600	ALIMEMAZINE-M (HO-)	AC	**356** 228 214 **100 58**	612
2710	ALIMEMAZINE-M (NOR-)	AC	**326 212** 180 **128** 86	573
2765	ALIMEMAZINE-M (BIS-NOR-)	AC	**312 212** 114	548
2930	ALIMEMAZINE-M (NOR-HO-)	2AC	**384** 228 214 196 **128**	638
1595	ALLOBARBITAL		**208** 193 **167** 141 **124** 80	317
1505	ALLOBARBITAL	2ME	**236 195 138** 80	388
2370*	ALLYLESTRENOL		**300** 259 **241** 201 91	524
1825	ALPRENOLOL		**249** 234 205 100 **72**	414
2280	ALPRENOLOL -H2O	AC	**273 200** 126 98 **72**	464
1240	AMANTADINE		**151 94**	206
1640	AMANTADINE	AC	**193 136** 94	283
2665	AMBROXOL		**376** 279 **262 114 70**	631
2030	AMBROXOL-M/ARTIFACT	AC	**317** 304 **275**	559
3015	AMBROXOL	2AC	**460 417** 279 **262 81** 70	665
1505	AMFEPRAMONE		**205 203** 188 105 **100**	311
2800*	AMIADARONE ARTIFACT		**420 294** 265 **142** 121	656
1820	P-AMINOBENZOIC ACID	ET	**165** 137 **120** 92 65	227
1985	P-AMINOBENZOIC ACID	MEAC	**193** 151 **120** 92 65	284
1990	P-AMINOBENZOIC ACID	ETAC	**207** 165 137 **120** 92	316
1550	P-AMINOBENZOIC ACID	ME	**151 120** 92 65	208
1895	AMINOPHENAZONE		**231** 123 97 **56**	373
1855	AMINOPHENAZONE-M (DESAMINO-HO-)		**204** 120 **85** 56	309
1945	AMINOPHENAZONE-M (BIS-NOR-) ARTIFACT		**180 119** 91	257
1955	AMINOPHENAZONE-M (BIS-NOR-)		**203** 93 **84 56**	306
1980	AMINOPHENAZONE-M (NOR-)		**217** 123 98 **83 56**	341
2095	AMINOPHENAZONE-M (DESAMINO-HO-)	AC	**246** 204 119 **57**	408
2270	AMINOPHENAZONE-M (BIS-NOR-)	AC	**245** 203 84 **56**	405
2395	AMINOPHENAZONE-M (NOR-)	AC	**259** 217 123 **56**	434
1290	M-AMINOPHENOL		**109 80**	132
1860	M-AMINOPHENOL	AC	**151 109** 80	207
1240	P-AMINOPHENOL		**109** 80 52	131
1765	P-AMINOPHENOL	2AC	193 151 **109**	283
1290	P-AMINOSALICYLIC ACID-M (M-AMINOPHENOL)		**109 80**	132
1860	P-AMINOSALICYLIC ACID-M ACETYL CONJUGATE		**151 109** 80	207

RI	NAME	DERIVATIVE	TYPICAL IONS	PAGE
1600	P-AMINOSALICYLIC ACID	ME	**167** **135** 107 79	235
1735	P-AMINOSALICYLIC ACID	2ME	**181** 149 121	262
1995	P-AMINOSALICYLIC ACID ACETYL CONJUGATE	ME	**209** 167 **135**	323
2170	AMIPHENAZOLE		**191** 149 121 104 77	279
2575	AMIPHENAZOLE	2AC	**275** 233 **191** 121	469
1925	AMIPHENAZOLE	2ME	**219** **191** 147 121 77	349
2205	AMITRIPTYLINE		**277** 215 **202** **58**	471
1975*	AMITRIPTYLINE-M (N-OXIDE) -(CH3)2NOH		**232** 217 202	376
2000*	AMITRIPTYLINE-M (HO-N-OXIDE) -H2O -(CH3)2NOH		**230** 215	370
2235	AMITRIPTYLINE-M (HO-) -H2O		**275** **215** 202 **58**	467
2255	AMITRIPTYLINE-M (NOR-)		**263** **202** 58 **44**	445
2380	AMITRIPTYLINE-M (HO-)		**293** 275 215 **202** **58**	510
2390	AMITRIPTYLINE-M (NOR-HO-)		**279** 261 **218** 203 58 **44**	477
2660	AMITRIPTYLINE-M (NOR-)	AC	**305** **232** 219 202 86	535
2670	AMITRIPTYLINE-M (NOR-HO-) -H2O	AC	**303** **230** 215 202 86	533
2800	AMITRIPTYLINE-M (NOR-DI-HO-) -H2O	2AC	**361** 319 **277**	616
----	AMITRIPTYLINE-M (HO-)	AC	**335** 273 215 **202** **58**	589
1975*	AMITRIPTYLINOXIDE -(CH3)2NOH		**232** 217 202	376
2000*	AMITRIPTYLINOXIDE-M (HO-) -H2O -(CH3)2NOH		**230** 215	370
2235	AMITRIPTYLINOXIDE-M (DESOXO-HO-) -H2O		**275** **215** 202 **58**	467
2380	AMITRIPTYLINOXIDE-M (DESOXO-HO-)		**293** 275 215 **202** **58**	510
2670	AMITRIPTYLINOXIDE-M (DESOXO-NOR-HO-) -H2O	AC	**303** **230** 215 202 86	533
----	AMITRIPTYLINOXIDE-M (DESOXO-HO-)	AC	**335** 273 215 **202** **58**	589
1710	AMOBARBITAL		**211** 198 **197** **156** **141**	326
1830	AMOBARBITAL-M (HO-) -H2O		**224** 195 156 **141** **69**	361
1915	AMOBARBITAL-M (HO-)		**227** 195 157 **156** **141**	365
----	AMOBARBITAL-M (HOOC-)		**256** **212** 183 156 **141**	428
1595	AMOBARBITAL	2ME	**239** 225 **184** **169**	393
1750	AMOBARBITAL-M (HO-)	2ME	**270** 255 **184** 169 **137**	460
----	AMOBARBITAL-M (HOOC-)	3ME	**240** **184** **169** 137	395
1160	AMPHETAMINE		**135** 120 **91** 65 **44**	174
1505	AMPHETAMINE	AC	**177** 118 **86**	252
1755	AMPHETAMINIL		**132** 105	170
1160	AMPHETAMINIL-M/ARTIFACT (AMPHETAMINE)		**135** 120 **91** 65 **44**	174
1505	AMPHETAMINIL	AC	**177** 118 **86**	252
----	AMPICILLIN -M/ARTIFACT		**187** **172** 143	275
<1000	AMYLNITRITE		**85** 70 57 **41**	84
2475*	ANDROSTERONE		**290** 272 257 244	504
2580*	ANDROSTERONE	AC	**332** **272** 257	584
1160	ANILINE		**93** 66	105
2350	ANTAZOLINE		**182** 91 **84**	263

RI	NAME	DERIVATIVE	TYPICAL IONS	PAGE
2460	APRINDINE		**322** 249 209 113 **86**	565
1610	APROBARBITAL		**210** 195 **167** 124	324
1540	APROBARBITAL	2ME	**238** **195** 138 111	391
2120*	ASCORBIC ACID		**176** **116** 85	250
2390	ATENOLOL ARTIFACT		**278** **263** 127 86 **72** 56	475
2975	ATENOLOL -H2O	AC	**290** 205 188 **140** 98	505
1720	ATRAZINE		**215** **200** 173 **58**	337
1670	ATRAZINE-M (DESETHYL-DESCHLORO-METHOXY-)		**183** **168** 141 70 **58**	266
1680	ATRAZINE-M (DESETHYL-)		**187** **172** 70 **58**	274
2215	ATROPINE		**289** 140 **124** 94 83	502
2085	ATROPINE -H2O		**271** 140 **124** 96 82	460
2275	ATROPINE	AC	**331** 140 **124** 94 83	583
2375	AZATADINE		**290** 246 232 96 **70**	504
2570	AZINPHOS-ETHYL		**345** **186** 160 **132** 77	602
2460	AZINPHOS-METHYL		**317** **160** 132 93 **77**	559
2310	BAMETHAN -H2O	2AC	**275** **233** 191 148 98	468
2330	BAMETHAN	3AC	**335** **275** **233** 191 148	587
2250	BAMIPINE		**280** **180** **97**	480
1500	BARBITAL		**167** **156** **141**	231
1420	BARBITAL	2ME	**184** **169** 126 112	271
1455	BARBITAL	ME	**170** **155** 126 112	243
1645	BARBITURIC ACID	3ME	**170** 113 98 82	244
1720	BECLAMIDE		**197** 162 148 106 **91**	293
1680	BECLAMIDE ARTIFACT		**161** 117 106 91 **55**	223
1350	BEMEGRIDE		**155** 127 113 83 **55**	212
2270	BENACTYZINE		**327** **239** 182 105 **86**	574
1840*	BENACTYZINE-M (HOOC-)	ME	**242** **183** 105 77	400
2120	BENCYCLANE		**289** **198** 102 86 **58**	502
2370	BENCYCLANE-M (HO-)		**214** 185 102 86 **58**	336
1750*	BENCYCLANE-M (OXO-)	HYAC	**260** 218 200 127 **91**	436
1380*	BENCYCLANE-M (OXO-) ISOMER 1	HY	**218** 190 **127** **99**	347
1415*	BENCYCLANE-M (OXO-) ISOMER 2	HY	**218** 200 128 **109** 81	347
0000	BENOXAPROFEN		**301** **256** 119 **91** 65	528
2485	BENOXAPROFEN	ME	**315** **256** 119 91	556
3440	BENPERIDOL		**381** **363** **230** 134 109 82	635

RI	NAME	DERIVATIVE	TYPICAL IONS	PAGE
1490*	BENPERIDOL-M 1		**180** 125 123 95 **56**	256
2290	BENPERIDOL-M 2		**231** **134** 106 79	373
2415	BENPERIDOL-M 3		**217** **134** 106 79	342
2750	BENPERIDOL-M 3	2AC	**301** **259** 216 134 82	529
2770	BENPERIDOL-M 3	AC	**259** 216 134 125 **82**	435
1400	BENZAMIDE		**121** **105** 77	152
2315	BENZATROPINE		**307** 201 **167** 140 124 **83**	537
1700*	BENZATROPINE	HYAC	**226** 184 **165** 105 **77**	364
1645*	BENZATROPINE	HY	**184** **105** 77	270
2750*	BENZBROMARONE		**422** **344** 279 264 173	656
< 1000*	BENZENE		**78**	73
1820	BENZOCAINE		**165** 137 **120** 92 65	227
1985	BENZOCAINE-M (PABA)	MEAC	**193** 151 **120** 92 65	284
1990	BENZOCAINE	AC	**207** 165 137 **120** 92	316
1550	BENZOCAINE-M (PABA)	ME	**151** **120** 92 65	208
2070	BENZOCTAMINE		**249** **218** 191 178	415
2145*	BENZOCTAMINE-M (HO-METHYL-)	AC	**278** **250** 191	476
2420	BENZOCTAMINE-M (NOR-)	AC	**277** **249** 191 178	473
2470*	BENZOCTAMINE-M (DI-HO-)	2AC	**336** 266 **249** 191	590
2540	BENZOCTAMINE	AC	**291** **263** **218** 191	506
2685*	BENZOCTAMINE-M (DI-HO-METHOXY-)	2AC	**366** 324 **296**	620
2725	BENZOCTAMINE-M (NOR-HO-) ISOMER 1	2AC	**335** 293 **265**	588
2790	BENZOCTAMINE-M (NOR-HO-) ISOMER 2	2AC	**335** 307 **265** 207	588
2875	BENZOCTAMINE-M (NOR-HO-METHOXY-)	2AC	**365** 323 **295**	619
2890	BENZOCTAMINE-M (HO-)	2AC	**349** 321 **279** 207	606
1235*	BENZOIC ACID		**122** **105** 77	155
1180*	BENZOIC ACID METHYLESTER		**136** **105** 77	176
1225*	BENZOIC ACID ETHYLESTER		**150** 122 **105** 77	204
1275*	BENZOIC ACID BUTYLESTER		**178** **163** 135 105 91 77	252
1745	BENZOIC ACID GLYCINE CONJUGATE		**161** 117 **105** 77	223
1660	BENZOIC ACID GLYCINE CONJUGATE	ME	**193** 134 **105** 77	284
2400	BENZYDAMINE		**309** **224** 91 85 **58**	542
< 1000	BENZYLAMINE		**107** 91 77	129
1800	BENZYLNICOTINATE		**213** 168 106 **91**	332
1680*	BENZYLPHENOL ISOMER 1		**184** 165 106 78	269
1720*	BENZYLPHENOL ISOMER 2		**184** 165 106 91 77	269
2280	BIPERIDEN		**311** **218** **98**	546
2645	BIPERIDEN-M (HO-)		**327** **218** 114 **98**	574
2620	BIPERIDEN-M (HO-)	AC	**369** 327 269 112 **98** 84	623

RI	NAME	DERIVATIVE	TYPICAL IONS	PAGE
1460	2.2'-BIPYRIDYL		**156** 128 78	213
2835	BISACODYL		**361** 319 **277** 199	616
2655	BISACODYL-M (BIS-DESACETYL-)		**277** 199	474
2680	BISACODYL-M (METHOXY-BIS-DESACETYL-)		**307** 276 229 199	537
2750	BISACODYL-M (METHOXY-DESACETYL-)	AC	**349** 307 **277** 199	606
2655	BISACODYL	HY	**277** 199	474
----*	BISPHENOL A		**228 213**	367
2260	BORNAPRINE		**329** 314 257 171 **86**	579
2385	BORNAPRINE-M (HO-) ISOMER 1	AC	**387 372** 214 142 **86**	639
2465	BORNAPRINE-M (HO-) ISOMER 2	AC	**387 372** 214 142 **86**	640
2565	BORNAPRINE-M (HO-) ISOMER 3	AC	**387 372** 214 142 **86**	640
2790	BORNAPRINE-M (DESETHYL-HO-) ISOMER 1	2AC	**401 358** 142 112 84 **58**	648
2875	BORNAPRINE-M (DESETHYL-HO-) ISOMER 2	2AC	**401 358** 169 128 84 **58**	648
2890	BORNAPRINE-M (DESETHYL-HO-) ISOMER 3	2AC	**401 358** 169 128 84 **58**	649
1870*	BORNYL SALICYLATE		**274 137** 121 **81**	465
2110*	BORNYL SALICYLATE	ME	**288 135** 81	501
0000	BRAKE FLUID		**133** 119 89 **59 45**	171
1850	BRALLOBARBITAL		**207** 165 124	315
1795	BRALLOBARBITAL-M (DESBROMO-OXO-)		**224** 181 **167** 141 124	360
1835	BRALLOBARBITAL-M (DESBROMO-HO-DIHYDRO-)		**183 139** 95 67	266
2040	BRALLOBARBITAL-M (OXO-)		**223**	358
2135	BRALLOBARBITAL-M (HO-DIHYDRO-)		**182** 138	263
----	BRALLOBARBITAL-M (DESBROMO-DI-OXO-)		**222** 197 155 **109** 82	356
----	BRALLOBARBITAL-M (DESBROMO-HOOC-)		**209** 179 167 141 120	322
----	BRALLOBARBITAL-M (DESBROMO-OXO-HO-DIHYDRO-)		**181 137** 122 109 94	261
----	BRALLOBARBITAL-M (HOOC-)		**180** 137 123 **97** 57	258
1725	BRALLOBARBITAL	2ME	**235** 193	386
1900	BROMACIL		**260** 231 **205** 188 162	435
2670	BROMAZEPAM		**315** 286 259 **236** 208 179	555
2255	BROMAZEPAM-M (HO-) ARTIFACT		**285 206** 179	491
2470	BROMAZEPAM-M (HO-)		**313** 284 206 179	549
2490	BROMAZEPAM	HYAC	**318** 289 275 **247 121**	561
2250	BROMAZEPAM	HY	**276 247** 198 168	470
2385	BROMAZEPAM ISOMER 1	ME	**329 250** 208 179	580
2540	BROMAZEPAM ISOMER 2	ME	**329** 300 250	580
2375	BROMHEXINE		**374** 305 293 **262** 112 **70**	629
2660	BROMHEXINE-M (HO-)		**390** 293 **262 128** 86	641
2665	BROMHEXINE-M (NOR-HO-)		**376** 279 **262 114 70**	631
2930	BROMHEXINE-M (HO-)	2AC	**474** 417 **335** 304 264	666
2935	BROMHEXINE-M (NOR-HO-) ISOMER 1	2AC	**460** 417 279 **262 81**	665
3015	BROMHEXINE-M (NOR-HO-) ISOMER 2	2AC	**460 417** 279 **262 81** 70	665

RI	NAME	DERIVATIVE	TYPICAL IONS	PAGE
3165	BROMHEXINE-M (NOR-HO-) ISOMER 3	2AC	**460** **417** 279 262 **81**	666
1540	BROMISOVAL		**222** **163** 70 **55**	356
1510	BROMISOVAL ARTIFACT		**137** 120 100	179
----	BROMISOVAL-M		**102** **59**	124
1995*	BROMOPHOS		**364** **329** 211 **125**	618
2850	BROMOPRIDE		**343** **293** 195 178 **58**	599
1490*	BROMPERIDOL-M 1		**180** 125 123 95 **56**	256
1850	BROMPERIDOL-M 2		**233** 154 127	377
1890	BROMPERIDOL-M 3		**267** **233** 127 94 **56**	452
2260	BROMPERIDOL-M 4	AC	**293** 279 **251** 222	511
2335	BROMPERIDOL-M 5	AC	**297** 279 254 183 99 **57**	520
2105	BROMPHENIRAMINE		**247** 167 72 **58**	411
2195	BROMPHENIRAMINE-M (NOR-)	AC	**346** 260 **247** 180 169	603
3100	BROTIZOLAM		**392** 363 316 291 245	642
3275	BRUCINE		**394** 379 355	643
2020	BUCETIN		**223** 205 **179** 137 109 **108**	358
1240	BUCETIN-M (AMINOPHENOL)		**109** 80 52	131
1280	BUCETIN-M (P-PHENETIDINE)		**137** **108** 80 65	178
1680	BUCETIN-M (P-PHENETIDINE)	AC	**179** 137 109 **108**	254
1755	BUCETIN-M (HO-P-PHENETIDINE)	2AC	**237** 195 **153** 124	390
1765	BUCETIN-M (P-AMINOPHENOL)	2AC	**193** 151 **109**	283
2095	BUCETIN	AC	**265** 205 **137** 109 108	448
2110	BUCETIN-M (O-DESETHYL-)	2AC	**279** 237 177 **109**	478
1980	BUNITROLOL ARTIFACT		**260** **245** 86 70 57	435
2070	BUNITROLOL	AC	**275** 119 98 **86** 56	468
2420	BUPHENINE		**176** 121 91 71	250
2260	BUPIVACAINE		**286** **243** **140** 96 84	494
1915	BUPRANOLOL ARTIFACT		**283** **268** 142 86 70	487
2370	BUPRANOLOL	AC	**298** 142 112 **86**	521
3360	BUPRENORPHINE ARTIFACT		**435** 410 **378** 84 **55**	661
3410	BUPRENORPHINE	AC	**509** 453 **421** 84 55	668
1655	BUTABARBITAL		**183** **156** **141**	266
1925	BUTABARBITAL-M (HO-)		**213** 199 181 **156** **141**	333
1565	BUTABARBITAL	2ME	**211** 184 **169**	328
1690	BUTALBITAL		**209** 181 **168** 167 **141**	320
1940	BUTALBITAL-M (OXO-)		**240** **168** 167 141	394
1630	BUTALBITAL	(ME)	**223** 195 **182** 181 155	360

RI	NAME	DERIVATIVE	TYPICAL IONS	PAGE
1655	BUTALBITAL	2ME	**237** 209 **196** 195 169	390
2030	BUTANILICAINE		**223** 141 **98** 86 **57**	358
3190	BUTAPERAZINE		**409** 269 141 **113** **70**	651
3800	BUTAPERAZINE-M (NOR-)	AC	**437** **269** **141** 99	661
1760	BUTETAMATE		**263** 248 191 99 **86**	443
1665	BUTOBARBITAL		**184** 167 **156** **141**	269
1880	BUTOBARBITAL-M (OXO-)		**226** 198 **156** **141**	364
1920	BUTOBARBITAL-M (HO-)		**213** 199 **156** **141**	333
1585	BUTOBARBITAL	2ME	**212** 184 **169** 112	332
----	BUTOCARBOXIM		**133** 102 **87** 75	171
----*	BUTYLHEXADECANOATE		**312** **257** 239 185 129	548
2380*	BUTYLOCTADECANOATE		**340** 285 267 **57**	595
1700*	BUTYLPARABEN		**194** **138** **121**	285
2960	CAFEDRINE		**339** **249** 105 **70**	594
1360	CAFEDRINE-M (NORPSEUDOEPHEDRINE)		**105** 77 **44**	125
1740	CAFEDRINE-M (NORPSEUDOEPHEDRINE)	2AC	**235** 176 **129** 107 **86**	385
1820	CAFFEINE		**194** **109** 82 67 55	285
2960	CAMAZEPAM		**371** 283 **271** 256 227 **72**	626
2320	CAMAZEPAM-M		**268** 239 233 205 **77**	454
2625	CAMAZEPAM-M (METHYLOXAZEPAM)		**300** **271** 256 239	525
2245	CAMAZEPAM-M	HYAC	**273** **230** 154 105 77	463
2050	CAMAZEPAM-M	HY	**231** **230** 154 105 77	375
2100	CAMAZEPAM	HY	**245** 228 193 105 **77**	405
2600	CAMAZEPAM-M (METHYLOXAZEPAM)	ME	**314** **271** 255	554
2085	CAMYLOFINE		**320** 235 204 135 **86**	563
2400*	CANNABIDIOL		**314** 246 **231** 174	551
2450*	CANNABIDIOL	2AC	**398** 355 297 **231** 121	645
2555*	CANNABINOL		**310** **295** 238 223	543
2540*	CANNABINOL	AC	**352** **337** 295 238	608
2820	CARAZOLOL ARTIFACT		**310** **183** 154 127 86	544
3130	CARAZOLOL -H2O	AC	**322** **220** **140** 98	566
2285	CARBAMAZEPINE		**236** **193** 165	388
1800	CARBAMAZEPINE-M (ACRIDINE)		**179** 151	254
1985	CARBAMAZEPINE-M/ARTIFACT		**193** 165	282
2025	CARBAMAZEPINE-M (ACRIDINE-CHO)		**207** **179** 151	315
3220	CARBAMAZEPINE-M	(AC)	**361** 232 218 207 **193**	616

RI	NAME	DERIVATIVE	TYPICAL IONS	PAGE
----	CARBAMAZEPINE-M		**239** 224 209 180	393
2580	CARBAMAZEPINE-M	AC	**251 209** 180	423
3195	CARBAMAZEPINE-M	AC	**340 297** 205 **179**	596
2715	CARBAMAZEPINE-M CYSTEINE-CONJUGATE	(ME)	**326** 283 **180** 152	573
1515	CARBROMAL		**208** 191 **165 69**	317
1115	CARBROMAL ARTIFACT		**157 129 57**	217
1215	CARBROMAL-M/ARTIFACT (CARBROMIDE)		**165** 150 114 **69**	226
1340	CARBROMAL-M (HO-CARBROMIDE)		**194** 181 **165 150** 69	284
1380	CARBROMAL-M (DESBROMO-)		**143 130 113** 87 71	197
----	CARBROMAL ARTIFACT		**171 143 57**	245
----	CARBROMAL-M		**113 98** 69 55	142
----	CARBROMAL-M (CYAMURIC-ACID)		**129 114** 98 85 **57**	167
----	CARBROMAL-M (DESBROMO-HO-) -H2O		**156** 139 **113** 98 **69**	216
<1000*	CARBROMAL-M (ETHYL-HO-BUTYRIC ACID)	ME	**117 87** 69 57	147
2690	CARTEOLOL ARTIFACT		**304 289** 163 84 **57**	534
2700	CARTEOLOL	AC	**334** 319 163 **86 57**	587
2075	CETOBEMIDONE		**247** 218 190 **70**	411
2095	CETOBEMIDONE	AC	**289** 247 190 **70**	503
2265	CETOBEMIDONE-M (METHOXY-)	AC	**319** 220 **70**	562
2545	CETOBEMIDONE-M (NOR-)	2AC	**317 261** 218 70 **58**	559
1950	CETOBEMIDONE	ME	**261 204 70**	440
2900	CHAVICINE		**285** 201 173 **115** 84	493
0000	CHLORAL HYDRATE		**146 111 82**	200
<1000*	CHLORAL HYDRATE-M (TRICHLOROETHANOL)		**148** 119 **113** 82 **77**	201
2420	CHLORAMBUCIL		**303 268** 118	532
2630	CHLORAMPHENICOL	2AC	**273 212** 170 **153** 118	464
2220	CHLORCYCLIZINE		**300** 165 **99** 56	524
2820	CHLORDIAZEPOXIDE		**299 282**	523
2535	CHLORDIAZEPOXIDE ARTIFACT (DESOXO-)		**283 282**	487
2245	CHLORDIAZEPOXIDE	HYAC	**273 230** 154 105 77	463
2050	CHLORDIAZEPOXIDE	HY	**231 230** 154 105 77	375
2210	CHLORMEZANONE		**209 152** 98	321
1235	CHLORMEZANONE ARTIFACT		**152**	208
1555	CHLORMEZANONE-M/ARTIFACT		**169 139** 111	237
1400*	CHLOROCRESOL		**142 107** 77	194
<1000*	CHLOROFORM		**118 83**	147
1390*	P-CHLOROPHENOL		**128** 100 65	163
1520*	O-CHLOROPHENOL-M (HO-)	2AC	**228** 186 **144**	367

RI	NAME	DERIVATIVE	TYPICAL IONS	PAGE
1510*	P-CHLOROPHENOXYACETIC ACID	ME	**200** 141	302
2190	CHLOROPYRAMINE		**289** 231 **125** 72 **58**	502
2595	CHLOROQUINE		**319** 290 245 **86** 58	561
1420*	CHLOROXYLENOL		**156** **121** 91 77	213
1450*	CHLOROXYLENOL	AC	**198** **156** 121 91	295
2020	CHLORPHENAMINE		**203** 167 72 **58**	307
2095	CHLORPHENOXAMINE		**303** 214 **178** 165 **58**	531
1650*	CHLORPHENOXAMINE	HY	**232** **217** 139 **77**	377
1710*	CHLORPHENOXAMINE ARTIFACT -H2O	HY	**214** **179** 139	336
1355	CHLORPHENTERMINE		**168** 125 107 **58**	236
1730	CHLORPHENTERMINE	AC	**225** **166** 100 86 **58**	363
2500	CHLORPROMAZINE		**318** 272 232 86 **58**	560
2100	CHLORPROMAZINE-M (RING)		**233** 198	378
----	CHLORPROMAZINE-M (SULFOXIDE)		**334** 318 **246** **58**	587
2990	CHLORPROMAZINE-M (BIS-NOR-)	AC	**332** 233 **100**	585
3070	CHLORPROMAZINE-M (NOR-)	AC	**346** 232 **114** 86	604
----	CHLORPROMAZINE-M (HO-)	ME	**348** 302 262 86 **58**	605
2510	CHLORPROTHIXENE		**315** 255 **221** 58	554
2280	CHLORPROTHIXENE-M (NOR-HO-)		**317** 247 **44**	558
2410*	CHLORPROTHIXENE-M (N-OXIDE) -(CH3)2NOH		**270** 255 **234** 202 117	458
2480*	CHLORPROTHIXENE-M (N-OXIDE-SULFOX.) -(CH3)2NOH		**286** 271 234 **203**	494
2750	CHLORPROTHIXENE-M (HO-DIHYDRO-)		**333** 247 **58**	585
2800	CHLORPROTHIXENE-M (HO-DIHYDRO-)	AC	**375** 247 **58**	631
2930	CHLORPROTHIXENE-M (NOR-DIHYDRO-)	AC	**345** 270 **231** 114 58	603
2945	CHLORPROTHIXENE-M (NOR-)	AC	**343** **270** 235 **221** 86	600
3195	CHLORPROTHIXENE-M (NOR-HO-DIHYDRO-)	2AC	**403** 289 **247** 114 86	650
1980	CHLORPYRIFOS		**349** 314 286 **197** **97**	606
2075	8-CHLOROTHEOPHYLLINE		**214** 157 129 68	335
3085*	CHOLESTEROL		**386** 368 353 301 275	639
3000*	CHOLESTEROL -H2O		**368** 353 260 147	622
2600	CINCHONIDINE		**294** **136**	513
2600	CINCHONINE		**294** **136**	513
2445	CLEMASTINE		**217** **214** 179 128 **84**	342
1650*	CLEMASTINE	HY	**232** **217** 139 **77**	377
1710*	CLEMASTINE ARTIFACT -H2O	HY	**214** **179** 139	336
2610	CLOBAZAM		**300** 283 255 231 181 77	525
2740	CLOBAZAM-M (NOR-)		**286** 244 215 77	495

RI	NAME	DERIVATIVE	TYPICAL IONS	PAGE
3000	CLOBAZAM-M (HO-)		**316** 299 271	557
3255	CLOBAZAM-M (HO-METHOXY-)		**346** 316 301 271 245	603
2615	CLOBAZAM-M (NOR-HO-METHOXY-)	HYAC	**330** **288**	582
2900	CLOBAZAM-M (HO-)	AC	**358** **316** 299 271	615
3000	CLOBAZAM-M (NOR-HO-)	HYAC	**300** **258**	526
2210	CLOBAZAM-M (NOR-)	HY	**242** 206 166 77	399
2225	CLOBAZAM	HY	**274** **257** 231 215 77	466
2405	CLOBAZAM-M (NOR-HO-METHOXY-)	HY	**288**	501
2650	CLOBAZAM-M (NOR-HO-)	HY	**258**	432
2905	CLOBAZAM-M (HO-METHOXY-)	HY	**320** 240 206	564
1540*	CLOFIBRATE		**242** 169 **128**	397
1390*	CLOFIBRATE-M (P-CHLOROPHENOL)		**128** 100 65	163
1580*	CLOFIBRATE-M (CLOFIBRIC ACID) ARTIFACT		**168** **128**	236
1640*	CLOFIBRATE-M (CLOFIBRIC ACID)		**214** 168 **128** 86 65	335
1500*	CLOFIBRATE-M (CLOFIBRIC ACID)	ME	**228** 169 **128**	368
1640*	CLOFIBRIC ACID		**214** 168 **128** 86 65	335
1390*	CLOFIBRIC ACID-M (P-CHLOROPHENOL)		**128** 100 65	163
1580*	CLOFIBRIC ACID ARTIFACT		**168** **128**	236
1500*	CLOFIBRIC ACID	ME	**228** 169 **128**	368
1230	CLOMETHIAZOLE		**161** **112** 85	223
1235	CLOMETHIAZOLE-M (DESCHLORO-HOOC-)		**157** 128 **112** 85	218
1260	CLOMETHIAZOLE-M (DESCHLORO-2-HO-)		**143** **128** 100	196
1375	CLOMETHIAZOLE-M (HO-)		**177** **128** 100	251
1380	CLOMETHIAZOLE-M (DESCHLORO-1-HO-)		**143** **113** 85	197
1315	CLOMETHIAZOLE-M (DESCHLORO-2-HO-)	AC	**185** 143 128 **125**	272
1480	CLOMETHIAZOLE-M (DESCHLORO-DI-HO-) -H2O	AC	**183** 170 141 **128**	267
1500	CLOMETHIAZOLE-M (HO-)	AC	**219** 183 **141** **128**	349
2455	CLOMIPRAMINE		**314** **269** 85 **58**	551
2540	CLOMIPRAMINE-M (HO-) ISOMER 1		**330** **285** 245 85 **58**	581
2800	CLOMIPRAMINE-M (HO-) ISOMER 2		**330** **285** 245 85 **58**	582
----	CLOMIPRAMINE-M (RING)		**229** 214 194 165	368
2805	CLOMIPRAMINE-M (HO-) ISOMER 1	AC	**372** 327 **285** 245 85 **58**	628
2905	CLOMIPRAMINE-M (HO-) ISOMER 2	AC	**372** 327 **285** 245 85 **58**	628
2995	CLOMIPRAMINE-M (NOR-)	AC	**342** 240 **114**	599
3205	CLOMIPRAMINE-M (NOR-HO-)	2AC	**400** 358 **300** 258 244 **114**	648
----	CLOMIPRAMINE-M (BIS-NOR-)	AC	**328** **242** 227 100	579
2840	CLONAZEPAM		**315** 286 280 240 234 205	555
2325	CLONAZEPAM-M (AMINO-HO-) ARTIFACT		**255** **220**	427
2880	CLONAZEPAM-M (AMINO-)		**285** 256 250 222 111	492
2935	CLONAZEPAM-M (AMINO-HO-)		**283** 255 220	488
2845	CLONAZEPAM-M (AMINO-)	HY2AC	**330** 288 **246** 211	582
3190	CLONAZEPAM-M (AMINO-)	AC	**327** 299 292 256 220	577
2285	CLONAZEPAM-M (AMINO-)	HY	**246** 211 139 111 107	409
2470	CLONAZEPAM	HY	**276** **241** 195 165 139 111	470
2555	CLONAZEPAM ISOMER 1	ME	**329** 294 248	581
2760	CLONAZEPAM ISOMER 2	ME	**329** 302 294 248	581
2315	CLONIDINE	2AC	**313** 278 236 **194** **58**	550

RI	NAME	DERIVATIVE	TYPICAL IONS	PAGE
3400	CLOPENTHIXOL		**400** **221** **143** 100 70	647
2410*	CLOPENTHIXOL-M (N-OXIDE) -C6H14N2O2		**270** 255 **234** 202 117	458
3450	CLOPENTHIXOL-M (DESALKYL-DIHYDRO-)	AC	**400** **268** **141** 99	648
3460	CLOPENTHIXOL	AC	**442** 221 **185** 98 87	663
3490	CLOPENTHIXOL-M (DESALKYL-)	AC	**398** **268** **141** 99	646
2520	CLORAZEPATE GC ARTIFACT		**270** **242** 77	459
2320	CLORAZEPATE-M		**268** 239 233 205 **77**	454
2245	CLORAZEPATE	HYAC	**273** **230** 154 105 77	463
2050	CLORAZEPATE	HY	**231** **230** 154 105 77	375
2225	CLORAZEPATE ISOMER 1	ME	**284** **283**	490
2430	CLORAZEPATE ISOMER 2	ME	**284** **256** 221	489
1950*	CLOROFENE		**218** 183 140	344
1885*	CLOROFENE	AC	**260** **218** 183 140	437
2540	CLOTIAZEPAM		**318** **289**	560
2660	CLOTIAZEPAM-M (OXO-)		**332** **303**	584
2705	CLOTIAZEPAM-M (HO-)		**316** **287**	557
2870	CLOTIAZEPAM-M (HO-)	AC	**376** 316 **271** 256	632
2995	CLOTIAZEPAM-M (DI-HO-)	2AC	**434** **374** **332** 319 291	660
2895	CLOZAPINE		**326** 256 **243** 227 192 70	572
3105	CLOZAPINE-M (NOR-)		**312** 269 256 **243** 192 85	548
3490	CLOZAPINE-M (NOR-)	2AC	**396** 310 298 227 192	645
3650	CLOZAPINE-M (NOR-)	AC	**354** 243 192 112	610
2200	COCAINE		**303** 198 **182** **82**	531
1465	COCAINE-M (METHYLECGONINE)		**199** 168 96 **82**	296
----	COCAINE-M (HO-)		**319** **182** 121 **82**	562
----	COCAINE-M (HO-METHOXY-)		**349** 198 **182** 82	606
1595	COCAINE-M (METHYLECGONINE)	AC	**241** **182** 96 **82**	396
2250	COCAINE-M (BENZOYLECGONINE)	ET	**317** 272 **196** 82	560
----	COCAINE-M (HO-)	ME	**333** **182** 135 **82**	586
----	COCAINE-M (HO-METHOXY-)	ME	**363** 198 **182** 82	618
2375	CODEINE		**299** 229 162 124	522
2455	CODEINE-M (O-DESMETHYL-)		**285** 268 162 124	492
2500	CODEINE	AC	**341** 282 229 204 162	597
2620	CODEINE-M (O-DESMETHYL-)	2AC	**369** **327** 310 268 162	623
2945	CODEINE-M (NOR-)	2AC	**369** 327 223 **87** 72	624
2955	CODEINE-M (N-O-BIS-DESMETHYL-)	3AC	**397** 355 209 **87** 72	645
1715	COTININE		**176** 118 **98**	250
1560	CRIMIDINE		**171** 156 **142** 93	244
1725	CROPROPAMIDE		**240** 195 **168** **100** 69	394
1600	CROTAMITON		**203** 188 120 **69**	306
----	CROTAMITON-M (HO-)		**219** 188 **118** 69	348
----	CROTAMITON-M (HOOC-)		**233** 188 **134** 120	379

RI	NAME	DERIVATIVE	TYPICAL IONS	PAGE
1675	CROTETHAMIDE		**226** 181 **154** **86** 69	363
1620	CROTYLBARBITAL		**210** 181 **156** **141** **55**	324
----	CROTYLBARBITAL-M (HO-) -H2O		**208** 179 **157** **141**	319
2610*	CUMATETRALYL		**292** 188 130 121 91	508
1290	CYCLAMATE-M	AC	**141** 98 **57**	193
1970	CYCLOBARBITAL		**236** **207** 141	387
2170	CYCLOBARBITAL-M (HO-)		**234** **205** 156 141	382
2190	CYCLOBARBITAL-M (OXO-)		**250** **221** 193 179 150	418
1845	CYCLOBARBITAL	2ME	**264** **235** 169	446
----	CYCLOBARBITAL-M (OXO-)	2ME	**278** **249** 221	477
<1000*	CYCLOHEXANOL		**100** **82** **57**	116
1865	CYCLOPENTOBARBITAL		**193** 169 **67**	282
1775	CYCLOPENTOBARBITAL	2ME	**221** 196 **67**	356
2065	CYCLOPHOSPHAMIDE		**260** **211** **175** 147 69	436
1975	CYCLOPHOSPHAMIDE ARTIFACT		**224** **175** 147 69	361
2340	CYPROHEPTADINE		**287** 215 96	496
3310*	CYPROTERONE -H2O		**356** 246 **175**	612
3320*	CYPROTERONE-M/ARTIFACT 1	AC	**374** 356 **339** 175	630
3330*	CYPROTERONE-M/ARTIFACT 2	AC	**372** 354 **339**	628
3340*	CYPROTERONE	AC	**416** 356 **313** 246 175	655
2225	DESIPRAMINE		**266** 235 **195** 71 **44**	450
1930	DESIPRAMINE-M (RING)		**195** 180	287
2535	DESIPRAMINE-M (HO-RING)	AC	**253** **211**	425
2670	DESIPRAMINE	AC	**308** **208** 193 114	541
3065	DESIPRAMINE-M (HO-)	2AC	**366** 266 **114**	622
2920	DEXTROMORAMIDE		**392** **265** 128 **100**	642
3270	DEXTROMORAMIDE-M (METHOXY-)		**422** **323** 194 128 **100**	657
3210	DEXTROMORAMIDE-M (HO-)	AC	**450** 407 **323** 194 128 **100**	664
2255	DEXTRORPHAN		**257** 200 150 **59**	430
2280	DEXTRORPHAN	AC	**299** 231 150 **59**	524
2430	DIAZEPAM		**284** **256** 221	489
2320	DIAZEPAM-M		**268** 239 233 205 **77**	454
2520	DIAZEPAM-M		**270** **242** 77	459
2245	DIAZEPAM-M	HYAC	**273** **230** 154 105 77	463
2050	DIAZEPAM-M	HY	**231** **230** 154 105 77	375
2100	DIAZEPAM	HY	**245** 228 193 105 **77**	405
2465	DIBENZEPIN		**224** 180 71 **58**	362
2460	DIBENZEPIN-M (NOR-)		**281** **210** 72 **58**	484

RI	NAME	DERIVATIVE	TYPICAL IONS	PAGE
2800	DIBENZEPIN-M (NOR-)	AC	**323** 250 237 **209** 100	568
2825	DIBENZEPIN-M (TER-NOR-)	AC	**295** 236 **223** 195	516
2870	DIBENZEPIN-M (BIS-NOR-)	AC	**309** 236 **223** 195 100	543
1915*	DIBUTYLPHTHALATE		**278** 222 205 **149**	474
<1000*	DICHLOROMETHANE		**84** **49**	81
1320*	DICHLOROPHENOL		**162** 126 98	224
1820*	2.4-DICHLOROPHENOXYACETIC ACID (2.4-D)		**220** 175 **162** 133 111	350
1320*	2.4-DICHLOROPHENOXYACETIC ACID-M		**162** 126 98	224
1600*	DICHLORPROP		**234** **199** 175 145 111	381
1320*	DICHLORPROP-M (DICHLOROPHENOL)		**162** 126 98	224
1850	DICHLORQUINOLINOL		**213** 185 150	333
1275*	DICHLORVOS		**220** 185 145 **109** 79	350
2175	DICLOBENIL		**171** 136 100	244
2135	DICLOFENAC		**277** 242 **214** 179 89	471
2540	DICLOFENAC-M (HO-)	AC	**335** **293** 258 230	588
3225	DICLOFENAC-M	AC	**413** 371 **336** 60	653
2195	DICLOFENAC	ME	**309** 277 242 **214**	543
2120	DICYCLOVERINE		**309** 294 99 **86**	541
1285	DIETHYLALLYLACETAMIDE		**155** **140** 126 **69** **55**	212
----*	DIETHYLALLYLACETAMIDE-M		**144** 113 95 **69** **55**	199
1495*	DIETHYLPHTHALATE		**222** 177 **149**	356
2295*	DIETHYLSTILBESTROL		**268** 239 159 145 107	454
2450*	DIETHYLSTILBESTROL	2AC	**352** 310 **268** 239 107	608
2190*	DIETHYLSTILBESTROL	2ME	**296** 267 159 121	519
2095*	DIFLUNISAL		**250** 232 **206** 175	417
1990*	DIFLUNISAL	2ME	**278** 247 204 188 175	476
2410	DIHYDROCODEINE		**301** 164	527
2400	DIHYDROCODEINE-M (O-DESMETHYL-)		**287**	496
2435	DIHYDROCODEINE	AC	**343** 300 226 70	600
2545	DIHYDROCODEINE-M (O-DESMETHYL-)	2AC	**371** **329** 288 164 70	626
2750	DIHYDROCODEINE-M (NOR-)	2AC	**371** **87** 72	626
2400	DIHYDROMORPHINE		**287**	496
2545	DIHYDROMORPHINE	2AC	**371** **329** 288 164 70	626
2385*	DIISOBUTYLADIPATE		**258** **185** **129** 111	432
2700*	DIISONONYLPHTHALATE		**418** 362 **293** **149**	655

RI	NAME	DERIVATIVE	TYPICAL IONS	PAGE
2540*	DIISOOCTYLPHTHALATE		**390** **279** 167 **149**	641
1250	DIMEPHENOPANE		**163** **148** 117 91 **72**	225
2315	DIMETACRINE		**294** 279 **86** 58	513
1905	DIMETACRINE-M (RING)		**209** **194**	321
2020	DIMETACRINE-M (N-OXIDE) -(CH3)2NOH		**249** **234** 194	415
1725	DIMETHOATE		**229** 125 93 **87**	368
1180	DIMETHYLANILINE		**121** 106	152
1470*	DIMETHYLBROMOPHENOL		**200** **121** 91 77	299
1155*	DIMETHYLPHENOL		**122** 107	154
1760	DIMETHYLPHENYLTHIAZOLANIMIN		**206** 132 118 83 **58**	313
<1000*	DIMETHYLSULFOXIDE		**78** **63** 45	73
2290	DIMETINDENE		**292** **218** **58**	507
2775	DIMETINDENE-M (NOR-)	AC	**320** 218 **100** 86 58	564
3090	DIMETINDENE-M (NOR-HO-)	2AC	**378** 276 234 **100** 86	633
1140	DIMPYLATE ARTIFACT 1		**166** **151** 138	229
1400*	DIMPYLATE ARTIFACT 2		**198** 170 **138** 111	294
1685	DIMPYLATE ARTIFACT 3		**152** **137** 109 84	208
1520	2.4-DINITROPHENOL		**184** 154 107 91	268
----*	DIOXACARB-M (PHENOL)		**166** **121** 73	230
<1000*	DIOXANE		**88** 58	100
1870	DIPHENHYDRAMINE		**255** **165** 152 73 **58**	427
1890	DIPHENHYDRAMINE-M (HO-)		**213** **183** 167 **58**	333
1895*	DIPHENHYDRAMINE-M (DI-HO-)		**244** **213** **167**	401
1700*	DIPHENHYDRAMINE	HYAC	**226** 184 **165** 105 **77**	364
2265	DIPHENHYDRAMINE-M (NOR-)	AC	**283** 241 **167** **101** 86	488
1645*	DIPHENHYDRAMINE	HY	**184** **105** 77	270
1335*	DIPHENHYDRAMINE-M	HY(ME)	**198** **167** **121**	296
3415	DIPHENOXYLATE		**452** **377** **246** 165	664
2115	DIPHENYLPYRALINE		**281** **167** 114 **99**	483
1700*	DIPHENYLPYRALINE	HYAC	**226** 184 **165** 105 **77**	364
1645*	DIPHENYLPYRALINE	HY	**184** **105** 77	270
2455	DIPROPHYLLINE	2AC	**338** 236 194 **180** 159	592
1650	DIPROPYLBARBITAL		**170** **141** 98	242
2490	DISOPYRAMIDE		**193** 165	283

RI	NAME	DERIVATIVE	TYPICAL IONS	PAGE
0000	DISULFIRAM		**296** **148** 116 88 **60**	517
1780*	DISULFOTON		**274** 186 125 97 **88**	465
2900	DITAZOL		**324** 293 249 165 77	570
1825*	DITAZOL-M (BENZIL)		**210** **105** 77	324
2560	DITAZOL-M (BIS-DESALKYL-)	AC	**278** **236** 105	476
2845	DITAZOL-M (BIS-DESALKYL-HO-)	2AC	**336** 294 **252** 121	590
2960	DITAZOL-M (BIS-DESALKYL-HO-)	MEAC	**308** 266 **135**	541
2970	DITAZOL-M (DESALKYL-HO-)	ME2AC	**394** **352** 266 135	644
2985	DITAZOL	2AC	**408** 322 262 **87**	651
3020	DITAZOL-M (DESALKYL-HO-)	3AC	**422** 380 338 **252** 87	657
3200	DITAZOL-M (HO-)	ME2AC	**438** 352 266 135 87	662
3250	DITAZOL-M (HO-)	2AC	**424** 338 252 **87**	658
1850	DIURON		**219** **187** 174 124 59	347
3220	DIXYRAZINE		**427** 352 **212** 187	658
2010	DIXYRAZINE-M (RING)		**199** 167	296
2550	DIXYRAZINE-M (HO-RING)	AC	**257** **215** 183	431
2765	DIXYRAZINE-M (AMINO-)	AC	**312** **212** 114	548
3350	DIXYRAZINE-M (O-DESALKYL-)	AC	**425** 365 199 **185** 98	658
3355	DIXYRAZINE-M (N-DESALKYL-)	AC	**381** 339 199 **141** 99	635
3530	DIXYRAZINE	AC	**469** 229 212 **199**	666
2240	DOXEPIN		**279** 165 **58**	477
1970*	DOXEPIN-M (N-OXIDE) -(CH3)2NOH		**234** 219 165	382
2270	DOXEPIN-M (NOR-)		**265** **204** 178 44	447
2500*	DOXEPIN-M (HO-N-OXIDE) -(CH3)2NOH		**250** 231 203	418
2530	DOXEPIN-M (HO-DIHYDRO-)		**297** 71 **58**	519
2535	DOXEPIN-M (HO-) ISOMER 1		**295** 178 165 **58**	515
2540	DOXEPIN-M (NOR-HO-)		**281** 238 165 **44**	484
2560	DOXEPIN-M (HO-) ISOMER 2		**295** 178 165 **58**	516
2340	DOXEPIN-M (HO-DIHYDRO-)	AC	**339** **211** 165 **58**	594
2360*	DOXEPIN-M (HO-N-OXIDE) -(CH3)2NOH	AC	**292** **250** **233** 165	508
2540	DOXEPIN-M (HO-) ISOMER 1	AC	**337** **257** **58**	591
2585	DOXEPIN-M (HO-) ISOMER 2	AC	**337** **257** **58**	591
2700	DOXEPIN-M (NOR-)	AC	**307** **234** 219 86	539
2995	DOXEPIN-M (NOR-HO-) ISOMER 1	2AC	**365** **292** 250 233 **86**	619
3035	DOXEPIN-M (NOR-HO-) ISOMER 2	2AC	**365** **292** 250 233 **86**	620
1920	DOXYLAMINE		**270** **200** 183 167 71 **58**	458
2055	DOXYLAMINE-M (HO-)	AC	**239** **196** 71 **58**	393
2100	DOXYLAMINE-M (DI-HO-)	AC	**257** 180 71 **58**	431
2300	DOXYLAMINE-M (NOR-)	AC	**298** **183** 167	521
1520	DOXYLAMINE-M	HY	**183** **182** 167	268
1560	DOXYLAMINE-M ARTIFACT -H2O	HY	**181** **180** 152	262
1630	DOXYLAMINE	HY	**199** 184	298
2180	DROFENINE		**317** 173 99 **86**	558
0000	DROPERIDOL		**379** **246** 165 134 **123**	634

RI	NAME	DERIVATIVE	TYPICAL IONS	PAGE
1490*	DROPERIDOL-M 1		**180** 125 123 95 **56**	256
1950	DROPERIDOL-M 2		**134** 106 79 67	172
2000	DROPERIDOL-M 3 -H2O		**241** **112**	395
1730	DROPERIDOL-M 2	2AC	**218** 176 **134** 106	346
2060	DROPERIDOL-M 4	3AC	**276** 234 192 **150**	470
3370	DROPERIDOL	ME	**393** **246** 165 **123**	643
1375	EPHEDRINE		**146** 105 77 **58**	200
1795	EPHEDRINE	2AC	**249** **189** **100** **58**	415
2145	EPHEDRINE-M (HO-)	3AC	**307** **247** 163 86 **58**	538
----	ERGOMETRINE		**325** 307 **221** 196	571
2550*	ESTRADIOL		**272** 213 172 160 146	462
2780*	ESTRADIOL	2AC	**356** **314** 172 146	612
2940*	ESTRIOL		**288** 213 172 160 146	500
3010*	ESTRIOL	3AC	**414** **372** 330 270 160	654
2210	ETAMIPHYLLINE		**279** 99 **86** 58	477
1900	ETAMIVAN		**223** **151** 72	358
1970	ETAMIVAN	AC	**265** 223 195 **151** 72	447
1120	ETHADIONE		**157** 70 **58**	218
<1000*	ETHANOL		**46** **45** **31**	5
2950	ETHAVERINE		**395** **366** 73	644
1575	ETHENZAMIDE		**165** 150 **120** 92	227
1460	ETHENZAMIDE-M (DESETHYL-)		**137** **120** 92 65	178
1660	ETHENZAMIDE-M (DESETHYL-)	AC	**179** 137 **120** 92	255
1395*	ETHINAMATE		**167** **124** **95** 81	231
1225	ETHOSUXIMIDE		**141** **113** 70 **55**	188
1325	ETHOSUXIMIDE-M (3-HO-)		**157** **129** 86 **71**	218
1370	ETHOSUXIMIDE-M (HO-ETHYL-)		**157** 142 **113** 69	218
----	ETHOSUXIMIDE-M (3-HO-)	AC	**199** **171** 129 86	298
----	ETHOSUXIMIDE-M (HO-ETHYL-)	AC	**171** 155 139 **113**	245
----*	7-ETHOXYCOUMARIN		**190** 162 134	278
2230	ETHOXYPHENYLDIETHYLPHENYL BUTYRAMINE		**325** **252** 237 115	571
<1000*	ETHYLACETATE		**88** 73 70 **61** **43**	100
<1000*	ETHYLENEGLYCOL		**62** 43 **33**	48
<1000*	ETHYLENEGLYCOL	2AC	**116** **86** **43**	146
2420	ETHYLMORPHINE		**313** 284 162 124	549

RI	NAME	DERIVATIVE	TYPICAL IONS	PAGE
2455	ETHYLMORPHINE-M (O-DESETHYL-)		**285** 268 162 124	492
2530	ETHYLMORPHINE	AC	**355** 327 204 162 124	611
2620	ETHYLMORPHINE-M (O-DESETHYL-)	2AC	**369** **327** 310 268 162	623
2930	ETHYLMORPHINE-M (NOR-)	2AC	**383** 341 237 209 **87** 72	636
2955	ETHYLMORPHINE-M (N-O-BIS-DESALKYL-)	3AC	**397** 355 209 **87** 72	645
1580*	ETHYLPARABEN		**166** 138 **121**	229
----	ETHYLPARABEN-M (P-HYDROXYHIPPURIC ACID)	ME	**209** 177 149 121	324
2040	ETIDOCAINE		**276** **259** 245 **128** 86	469
2220	ETIFELMIN	AC	**279** 220 205 191 **112**	479
1230	ETILAMFETAMINE		**163** 148 **91** **72**	225
1675	ETILAMFETAMINE	AC	**205** **114** 91 **72**	312
2150	ETILEFRINE	3AC	**307** **247** 205 163 100 **58**	538
3155	ETODROXIZINE		**418** **299** **201** 165	655
2210	ETODROXIZINE-M 1		**280** 201 165	480
2220	ETODROXIZINE-M 2		**300** 165 **99** 56	524
1890*	ETODROXIZINE	HYAC	**260** 200 **165** 105	437
2700	ETODROXIZINE-M (N-DESALKYL-)	AC	**328** 242 **201** 165 **85**	578
2935	ETODROXIZINE M/ARTIFACT	HYAC	**280** **201** 165	483
1850*	ETODROXIZINE ARTIFACT	HY	**216** 139 **105** 77	341
1900*	ETODROXIZINE	HY(ME)	**232** 201 165 **105** 77	377
2125	ETOFYLLINE		**224** 194 **180** 109	361
2200	ETOFYLLINE	AC	**266** 180 151 **87**	451
2680	FENBUTRAZATE		**367** 261 **190** 91 **69**	622
1685	FENCAMFAMINE		**215** 186 98 84 **58**	337
2005	FENCAMFAMINE-M (DESETHYL-)	AC	**229** **170** **142**	369
2085	FENCAMFAMINE	AC	**257** **170** **142** 58	430
2305	FENCAMFAMINE-M (DESETHYL-HO-)	2AC	**287** 228 168 **142**	497
2470	FENCARBAMIDE		**326** 196 **169** 99 **86**	572
2450	FENDILINE		**315** 181 167 132 **105**	554
2825	FENDILINE	AC	**357** 162 120 **105** 72	613
2830	FENETHYLLINE		**341** **250** 207 91	596
1160	FENETHYLLINE-M (AMPHETAMINE)		**135** 120 **91** 65 **44**	174
1505	FENETHYLLINE-M (AMPHETAMINE)	AC	**177** 118 **86**	252
3110	FENETHYLLINE	AC	**383** 292 **250** 207	636
1250	FENFLURAMINE		**230** 216 **159** **72**	369
1510	FENFLURAMINE-M (DESETHYL-)	AC	**245** 226 159 **86**	404
1580	FENFLURAMINE	AC	**254** 216 **159** 114 **72**	426
1760*	FENOPROP		**268** **233** 209 181	454

RI	NAME	DERIVATIVE	TYPICAL IONS	PAGE
1440*	FENOPROP-M (TRICHLOROPHENOL)		**196** 132 97	291
2690	FENPIPRAMIDE		**322 211** 112 **98**	565
1585	FENPROPOREX		**97** 57	108
1900	FENPROPOREX	AC	**139 97**	184
2250*	FENSULFOTHION		**308 293** 141 125 97	539
1910*	FENSULFOTHION IMPURITY		**292** 156 140 125 97	507
2720	FENTANYL		**336 245** 189 146	589
2500	FLECAINIDE		**301** 218 **125** 97	527
2515	FLECAINIDE	AC	**456 301** 218 126 **84**	665
2795	FLUANISONE		**356** 218 205 **162** 123	612
1490*	FLUANISONE-M 1		**180** 125 123 95 **56**	256
2715	FLUANISONE-M (O-DESMETHYL-)		**342 194** 165 123	598
2140	FLUANISONE-M (HO-PHENYL-PIPERAZINE)	2AC	**262** 220 **148**	442
2445	FLUANISONE-M/ARTIFACT	AC	**292** 250 178 **154** 123	508
2830	FLUANISONE-M (O-DESMETHYL-)	AC	**384** 246 **233 123**	637
3135	FLUNARIZINE		**404 287 203** 201	650
2610	FLUNITRAZEPAM		**313** 285 266 238	550
2615	FLUNITRAZEPAM-M (AMINO-)		**283** 255	487
2690	FLUNITRAZEPAM-M (NOR-AMINO-)		**269** 241	457
2705	FLUNITRAZEPAM-M (NOR-)		**299** 272 252 **224**	523
2715	FLUNITRAZEPAM-M (NOR-AMINO-)	HY2AC	**314** 272 **230**	553
2870	FLUNITRAZEPAM-M (AMINO-)	HY2AC	**328** 286 244 **205**	578
2950	FLUNITRAZEPAM-M (AMINO-)	AC	**325** 297 255	571
3035	FLUNITRAZEPAM-M (NOR-AMINO-)	AC	**311** 283 241	547
2165	FLUNITRAZEPAM-M (NOR-AMINO-)	HY	**230** 211	372
2335	FLUNITRAZEPAM-M (NOR-)	HY	**260** 241 123	437
2370	FLUNITRAZEPAM	HY	**274** 257 211	466
2795	FLUNITRAZEPAM-M (AMINO-)	HY	**244** 227	402
3055	FLUPENTIXOL		**302** 265 234 80	529
3005	FLUPENTIXOL-M (DIHYDRO-)	AC	**478** 418 **265** 185 125 98	667
3045	FLUPENTIXOL	AC	**302** 265 234 **185**	531
3055	FLUPENTIXOL-M (DESALKYL-DIHYDRO-)	AC	**434** 265 **185 141** 99	660
3050	FLUPHENAZINE		**437 280** 143 113 **70**	661
2190	FLUPHENAZINE-M (RING)		**267** 235	453
2765	FLUPHENAZINE-M (AMINO-)	AC	**366** 267 **100**	621
3145	FLUPHENAZINE-M (DESALKYL-)	AC	**435 267 141** 99	661
3170	FLUPHENAZINE	AC	**479 419 280** 185 125 70	667
2780	FLURAZEPAM		**387** 315 99 **86**	639
2265	FLURAZEPAM-M (DESALKYL-HO-)		**286** 258 223 75	494
2470	FLURAZEPAM-M (DESALKYL-)		**288** 260	499
2650	FLURAZEPAM-M (BIS-DESETHYL-) -H2O		**313**	550

RI	NAME	DERIVATIVE	TYPICAL IONS	PAGE
2660	FLURAZEPAM-M (HO-ETHYL-)		**332** **288** 273 211	584
2195	FLURAZEPAM-M (DESALKYL-)	HYAC	**291** **249** 123 95	506
2460	FLURAZEPAM-M (BIS-DESETHYL-) -H2O	HYAC	**316** 273 **246** 211	557
2465	FLURAZEPAM-M (HO-ETHYL-)	HYAC	**335** 275 **262** 166 109	588
2725	FLURAZEPAM-M (HO-ETHYL-)	AC	**374** 346 **314** 287	630
3025	FLURAZEPAM-M (BIS-DESETHYL-)	AC	**373** 314 286 **273** 246	629
2030	FLURAZEPAM-M (DESALKYL-)	HY	**249** 154 122 95	416
2295	FLURAZEPAM-M (BIS-DESETHYL-) -H2O	HY	**274** 246 **211**	466
2385	FLURAZEPAM-M (HO-ETHYL-)	HY	**293** **262** 166 109	512
2555	FLURAZEPAM	HY	**348** **86**	605
1900*	FLURBIPROFEN		**244** **199** 183 170	401
1880*	FLURBIPROFEN	ME	**258** **199** 183 170	433
2180*	FLURBIPROFEN-M (HO-)	2ME	**288** **229**	501
2310*	FLURBIPROFEN-M (HO-METHOXY-)	2ME	**318** 259 215	561
0000	FLUSPIRILENE		**475** 418 **244** 187 72	666
2120*	FLUSPIRILENE-M 1		**262** **203** 183	440
2230*	FLUSPIRILENE-M 2		**276** **203** 183	469
2350	FLUSPIRILENE-M 3		**259** **71**	434
2405	FLUSPIRILENE-M 4		**245** **57**	403
2500	FLUSPIRILENE-M 5		**245** **71** **57**	404
2150*	FLUSPIRILENE-M 1	AC	**304** 244 216 **203** 183	534
2730	FLUSPIRILENE-M 4	AC	**287** **245** **57**	497
3340	FLUSPIRILENE	AC	**517** **475** **286** **72**	668
2130*	GLUCOSE	5AC	**331** **157** 115 **97**	583
1830	GLUTETHIMIDE		**217** **189** 160 132 117	341
1865	GLUTETHIMIDE-M (HO-ETHYL-)		**233** 205 189 **146** 104	378
1875	GLUTETHIMIDE-M (HO-PHENYL-)		**233** **204** 176 148 133	378
2060	GLUTETHIMIDE-M (HO-ETHYL-)	AC	**275** 247 233 **189** **187**	467
2250	GLUTETHIMIDE-M (HO-PHENYL-)	AC	**275** **233** 204 189 176	468
1610*	GUAIFENESIN		**198** **124** 109	294
----*	GUAIFENESIN-M		**268** **124** 109 **59**	455
----*	GUAIFENESIN-M		**268** 221 **126** 99	455
1865*	GUAIFENESIN	2AC	**282** **159**	487
1920*	GUAIFENESIN-M (O-DESMETHYL-)	3AC	**310** 268 204 **159**	545
2560*	GUAIFENESIN-M	AC	**328** 245 170 **159**	578
----*	GUAIFENESIN-M	AC	**390** 348 **306** 227 159	641
2940	HALOPERIDOL		**375** **237** **224** 189 123	631
1490*	HALOPERIDOL-M 1		**180** 125 123 95 **56**	256
1650	HALOPERIDOL-M 2		**189** 154 127	276
1750	HALOPERIDOL-M 3		**223** 189 **84** **56**	357
1800	HALOPERIDOL-M 4		**211** 139 **84** **56**	326
2250	HALOPERIDOL-M 5		**239** 189 139 **100** **56**	392
2155	HALOPERIDOL-M 4 -H2O	AC	**235** 193 189	386
2235	HALOPERIDOL-M 4	AC	**253** **189** 139 **57**	425
2965	HALOPERIDOL	AC	**357** 206 **192** 123	613
2070	HEPTABARBITAL		**221** **141**	352

RI	NAME	DERIVATIVE	TYPICAL IONS	PAGE
2275	HEPTABARBITAL-M (HO-)		**266** 237 **219** **141** 93	450
2300	HEPTABARBITAL-M (HO-) -H2O		**248** **219** 157 141 **93**	413
1915	HEPTABARBITAL	2ME	**249** 169 133	417
2240*	HEPTACHLOROBIPHENYL		**392** **322** 252	642
1125	HEPTAMINOL		**130** 127 **59** 56 **44**	168
1530	HEPTAMINOL	2AC	**172** **169** 114 95 **86**	247
2620	HEROIN		**369** **327** 310 268 162	623
2455	HEROIN-M (MORPHINE)		**285** 268 162 124	492
2535	HEROIN-M (6-ACETYL-MORPHINE)		**327** 268 162 124	574
2955	HEROIN-M (NOR-MORPHINE)	3AC	**397** 355 209 **87** 72	645
1690*	HEXACHLOROBENZENE		**282** 247 212 177 142	486
2220*	HEXACHLOROBIPHENYL		**358** **288** 218	614
1835	HEXETHAL		**211** **156** **141** 55	326
1745	HEXETHAL	2ME	**210** 184 **169** 112 55	325
1855	HEXOBARBITAL		**236** **221** **157** 155 81	387
2055	HEXOBARBITAL-M (OXO-)		**250** **235** 193 156 **95**	417
1805	HEXOBARBITAL	ME	**250** **235** 169 81	419
1745	HIPPURIC ACID		**161** 117 **105** 77	223
1660	HIPPURIC ACID	ME	**193** 134 **105** 77	284
3165	HOMOFENAZINE		**451** **433** **280** 248 167 **58**	664
2190	HOMOFENAZINE-M (RING)		**267** 235	453
2765	HOMOFENAZINE-M (AMINO-)	AC	**366** 267 **100**	621
3240	HOMOFENAZINE-M (DESALKYL-)	AC	**449** **267** 112	664
3260	HOMOFENAZINE	AC	**493** **433** 280 **167** 87	667
1750*	HOMOVANILLIC ACID	ME	**196** **137** 107	292
0000	HYDROCHLOROTHIAZIDE		**297** **269** 221	520
2440	HYDROCODONE		**299** 242 185 96 59	523
2400	HYDROCODONE-M (O-DESMETHYL-DIHYDRO-)		**287**	496
2545	HYDROCODONE-M (O-DESMETHYL-DIHYDRO-)	2AC	**371** **329** 288 164 70	626
2620	HYDROCODONE-M (O-DESMETHYL-) ENOL	2AC	**369** **327** 284 228 162	624
2750	HYDROCODONE-M (NOR-DIHYDRO-)	2AC	**371** **87** 72	626
2760	HYDROCODONE-M (NOR-)	AC	**327** 241 **87** 72	576
2445	HYDROMORPHONE		**285** 228	492
2400	HYDROMORPHONE-M (DIHYDRO-)		**287**	496
2545	HYDROMORPHONE-M (DIHYDRO-)	2AC	**371** **329** 288 164 70	626
2595	HYDROMORPHONE	AC	**327** 285 228 162	575
2620	HYDROMORPHONE ENOL	2AC	**369** **327** 284 228 162	624
< 1000*	HYDROQUINONE		**110** 81	135

RI	NAME	DERIVATIVE	TYPICAL IONS	PAGE
1395*	HYDROQUINONE	2AC	**194** 152 **110**	286
----*	HYDROXYANDROSTANEDIONE		**304** 286 **232** 191	534
----*	3-HYDROXYBENZOIC ACID	2ME	**166** **135** 107	230
2145	HYDROXYEPHEDRINE	3AC	**307** **247** 163 86 **58**	538
----	P-HYDROXYHIPPURIC ACID	ME	**209** 177 149 121	324
2205	HYDROXYPETHIDINE	AC	**305** 230 188 **71**	535
1565*	P-HYDROXYPHENYLACETIC ACID		**152** **107**	208
1270	HYDROXYSCATOL		**147** **146**	201
2900	HYDROXYZINE		**374** 299 **201** 165	630
1890*	HYDROXYZINE	HYAC	**260** 200 **165** 105	437
2380	HYDROXYZINE-M	AC	**285** **226** 191 84	493
2700	HYDROXYZINE-M (N-DESALKYL-)	AC	**328** 242 **201** 165 **85**	578
2935	HYDROXYZINE-M/ARTIFACT	HYAC	**280** **201** 165	483
3000	HYDROXYZINE	AC	**416** 355 299 **201** 165	654
1850*	HYDROXYZINE ARTIFACT	HY	**216** 139 **105** 77	341
1900*	HYDROXYZINE	HY(ME)	**232** 201 165 **105** 77	377
2215	HYOSCYAMINE		**289** 140 **124** 94 83	502
2085	HYOSCYAMINE -H2O		**271** 140 **124** 96 82	460
2275	HYOSCYAMINE	AC	**331** 140 **124** 94 83	583
1700	IDOBUTAL		**181** **167** 124	261
1610	IDOBUTAL	2ME	**223** **195** 181 169 138	359
2215	IMIPRAMINE		**280** **235** 193 85 **58**	480
1930	IMIPRAMINE-M (RING)		**195** 180	287
1985	IMIPRAMINE-M (HO-RING) -H2O		**193** 165	282
2225	IMIPRAMINE-M (NOR-)		**266** 235 **195** 71 **44**	450
2565	IMIPRAMINE-M (HO-)		**296** 251 85 **58**	517
2535	IMIPRAMINE-M (HO-RING)	AC	**253** **211**	425
2610	IMIPRAMINE-M (HO-)	AC	**338** 251 **211** 85 **58**	592
2670	IMIPRAMINE-M (NOR-)	AC	**308** **208** 193 114	541
3065	IMIPRAMINE-M (NOR-HO-)	2AC	**366** 266 **114**	622
2480	IMIPRAMINE-M (HO-)	ME	**310** 265 85 **58**	546
1350	INDOLE		**117** 90 63	147
----	INDOLE ACETIC ACID	ME	**189** **130**	278
2550	INDOMETACIN		**313** **139** 111	549
2130	INDOMETACIN ARTIFACT	ME	**233** **174**	381
2835	INDOMETACIN	ME	**371** 312 **139** 111	627
1830	INSTILLAGEL (TM) INGREDIENT		**232** **218** 132 85 **71**	375
1515*	IONOL		**220** **205** 57	350

RI	NAME	DERIVATIVE	TYPICAL IONS	PAGE
<1000*	ISOBUTANOL		**74** 55 **43**	70
1650	ISONIAZID		**137** 106 **78**	179
1840	ISONIAZID ACETONE DERIVATE		**177** 162 106 **78**	251
----	ISONIAZID-M GLYCINE CONJUGATE		**180** 137 106 78	259
1825	ISONIAZID	2AC	**221** 179 **161** 137 106	355
1950	ISONIAZID	AC	**179** 137 **106** 78	255
----	ISONICOTINIC ACID GLYCINE CONJUGATE		**180** 137 106 78	259
2460	ISOPRENALINE	4AC	**365** **319** 277 193 **84**	619
<1000*	ISOPROPANOL		**60** **45**	47
2045	ISOPYRIN		**245** 230 137 83 **56**	403
2160	ISOPYRIN-M (NOR-HO-) -H2O	2AC	**313** 271 **229** **57**	550
2365	ISOPYRIN-M (NOR-)	2AC	**315** **273** 231 **123** 70	556
2400	ISOPYRIN	AC	**287** 244 137 **56**	497
2245	ISOTHIPENDYL		**285** **214** 200 181 **72**	491
2235*	KAVAIN		**230** **186** 128 98 91	370
1705*	KAVAIN -CO2		**186** 128 95	273
1835	KETAMINE		**237** 209 **180** 152	388
1700*	KETAMINE-M (DESAMINO-HO-) -H2O		**204** **169** 139	308
1760*	KETAMINE-M (DESAMINO-HO-)		**222** 187 **113**	356
----	KETAMINE-M (NOR-HO-) -H2O		**221** 194 **153**	354
----	KETAMINE-M/ARTIFACT		**137** 102	180
----	KETAMINE-M/ARTIFACT		**195** **166**	288
2170	KETAMINE	AC	**279** **216** 208 180 152	478
----*	KETAMINE-M (DESAMINO-HO-) -H2O	AC	**246** **204** 169	409
2430	KETAZOLAM ARTIFACT		**284** **256** 221	489
2060	KETAZOLAM-M ARTIFACT 1		**240** **239** 205	394
2070	KETAZOLAM-M ARTIFACT 2		**254** **253** 219	425
2320	KETAZOLAM-M		**268** 239 233 205 **77**	454
2430	KETAZOLAM-M		**284** **256** 221	489
2520	KETAZOLAM-M		**270** **242** 77	459
2245	KETAZOLAM-M	HYAC	**273** **230** 154 105 77	463
2050	KETAZOLAM-M	HY	**231** **230** 154 105 77	375
2100	KETAZOLAM	HY	**245** 228 193 105 **77**	405
2245*	KETOPROFEN		**254** **208** 131 **105** 77	426
2090*	KETOPROFEN	ME	**268** **209** 191 105 77	456
2580	KETOTIFEN		**309** 237 208 96 70	542
3400	LABETALOL	3AC	**409** 376 **335** 160 133	652
1320	LABETALOL ARTIFACT		**149** 132 117 **91** 57	203
1885	LACTYLPHENETIDINE		**209** 137 109 **108**	321

RI	NAME	DERIVATIVE	TYPICAL IONS	PAGE
1240	LACTYLPHENETIDINE-M (AMINOPHENOL)		**109** 80 52	131
1280	LACTYLPHENETIDINE-M (P-PHENETIDINE)		**137** **108** 80 65	178
1680	LACTYLPHENETIDINE-M (P-PHENETIDINE)	AC	**179** 137 109 **108**	254
1755	LACTYLPHENETIDINE-M (HO-P-PHENETIDINE)	2AC	**237** 195 **153** 124	390
1765	LACTYLPHENETIDINE-M (P-AMINOPHENOL)	2AC	**193** 151 **109**	283
1960	LACTYLPHENETIDINE	AC	**251** **137** 109 108	421
1975	LACTYLPHENETIDINE-M (O-DESETHYL-)	2AC	**265** **223** 151 **109**	448
1515	LAUDAMONIUM AMINE 1		**213** 91 71 **58**	332
1710	LAUDAMONIUM AMINE 2		**241** 91 **58**	395
2115	LAUDAMONIUM AMINE 3		**289** **134** **91**	501
2295	LAUDAMONIUM AMINE 4		**317** **134** **91**	558
2355	LEVALLORPHAN		**283** 256 176 157 85	487
2390	LEVALLORPHAN	AC	**325** 298 257 176 **85**	571
2450	LEVOBUNOLOL ARTIFACT		**303** **288** 162 **86** 57	532
2460	LEVOBUNOLOL	AC	**333** **318** 259 200 **86**	586
2570	LEVOBUNOLOL -H2O	AC	**315** **259** 200 160 **57**	556
1750*	LEVODOPA-M (HOMOVANILLIC ACID)	ME	**196** **137** 107	292
2070	LEVODOPA-M	2AC	251 209 **150** 137	421
2540	LEVOMEPROMAZINE		**328** 228 185 100 **58**	577
2600	LEVOMEPROMAZINE-M (NOR-)		**314** 229 **213** **72**	552
2735	LEVOMEPROMAZINE-M (HO-)		**344** **100** **58**	601
2750	LEVOMEPROMAZINE-M (NOR-HO-)		**330** 258 **245** 86 **72**	581
2940	LEVOMEPROMAZINE-M (SULFOXIDE)		**344** 328 **242** 229 100 **58**	602
2745	LEVOMEPROMAZINE-M (HO-)	AC	**386** 312 **212** 114 100 **58**	639
2970	LEVOMEPROMAZINE-M (NOR-)	AC	**356** 242 228 **128**	613
3220	LEVOMEPROMAZINE-M (NOR-HO-)	2AC	**414** 372 300 258 244 **128**	654
2255	LEVORPHANOL		**257** 200 150 **59**	430
2280	LEVORPHANOL	AC	**299** 231 150 **59**	524
2555	LEVORPHANOL-M (HO-)	2AC	**357** 315 298 231 **57**	613
2710	LEVORPHANOL-M (NOR-)	2AC	**327** 285 **87** 72	576
1875	LIDOCAINE		**234** **86** 72 58	381
1180	LIDOCAINE-M (DIMETHYLANILINE)		**121** 106	152
1460	LIDOCAINE-M (DIMETHYLHYDROXYANILINE)		**137** 122 107	179
1790	LIDOCAINE-M (DESETHYL-)		**206** 149 **58**	313
1885	LIDOCAINE-M (DIMETHYLHYDROXYANILINE)	2AC	**221** 179 **137**	355
1900	LIDOCAINE-M (DIMETHYLHYDROXYANILINE)	3AC	**263** 221 **179** 137	445
2115	LIDOCAINE-M (DESETHYL-)	AC	**248** 128 **100** **58**	413
1740*	LINDANE		**288** 252 217 **181** 109	498
2110*	LINOLEIC ACID	ME	**294** 95 **81** 67	514
1820	LOBELINE		**120** **105** 77	150
2225	LOFEPRAMINE-M (DESALKYL-)		**266** 235 **195** 71 **44**	450

RI	NAME	DERIVATIVE	TYPICAL IONS	PAGE
1930	LOFEPRAMINE-M (RING)		**195** 180	287
2535	LOFEPRAMINE-M (HO-RING)	AC	**253** **211**	425
2670	LOFEPRAMINE-M (DESALKYL-)	AC	**308** **208** 193 114	541
3065	LOFEPRAMINE-M (DESALKYL-HO-)	2AC	**366** 266 **114**	622
2685	LONAZOLAC	ME	**326** **267** 232 164 77	573
1800	LOPERAMIDE-M		**211** 139 **84** **56**	326
2235	LOPERAMIDE-M	AC	**253** **189** 139 **57**	425
2440	LORAZEPAM		302 274 **239** **75**	529
2170	LORAZEPAM ARTIFACT		**274** **239**	465
2325	LORAZEPAM-M (HO-) ARTIFACT		**290** **255**	504
2300	LORAZEPAM	HYAC	**307** 265 **230**	538
2730	LORAZEPAM	2AC	**345** 307 265 **230**	603
2180	LORAZEPAM	HY	**265** **230** 139 111	449
2360	LORAZEPAM-M (HO-)	HY	**281** **246**	485
2780	LORAZEPAM-M (HO-METHOXY-)	HY	**311** 281 **246**	547
2485	LORAZEPAM ISOMER 1	2ME	**348** 305 **75**	605
2525	LORAZEPAM ISOMER 2	2ME	**330** 316 274 239 **75**	582
2815	LORCAINIDE		**370** **355** 245 127 **91**	624
2735	LORMETAZEPAM		**334** **305**	586
2170	LORMETAZEPAM ARTIFACT		**274** **239**	465
2300	LORMETAZEPAM-M (NOR-)	HYAC	**307** 265 **230**	538
2180	LORMETAZEPAM-M (NOR-)	HY	**265** **230** 139 111	449
2220	LORMETAZEPAM	HY	**279** **244** 229	479
2470	LORMETAZEPAM-M (HO-)	HY	**295** **260** 245	516
2555	LOXAPINE		**327** **257** 83 **70**	574
2935	LOXAPINE-M (HO-)	AC	**385** 315 **83** **70**	638
3450	LOXAPINE-M (NOR-HO-)	2AC	**413** **207** 112	654
3445	LYSERGIDE (LSD)		**323** **221** 181	567
----	LYSERGIDE (LSD)	TMS	**395** 293 253 73	644
1940*	MALATHION		**330** 285 **173** **127** 93	581
1485*	MANDELIC ACID		**166** **107** 79	229
2390	MAPROTILINE		**277** 70 59 **44**	472
2570*	MAPROTILINE-M (DI-HO-)		**280** **252** 207	481
2425*	MAPROTILINE-M (HO-PROPYL-)	AC	**306** **278** 191	536
2760	MAPROTILINE-M (NOR-)	AC	**305** **277** 218 191	535
2800	MAPROTILINE	AC	**319** **291** 218 100	563
2820*	MAPROTILINE-M (DI-HO-)	2AC	**364** 336 **294** 207	618
2995	MAPROTILINE-M (HO-ETHANEDIYL-)	2AC	**377** **291** 218 191 100	632
3095	MAPROTILINE-M (HO-ANTHRYL-)	2AC	**377** **349** 307 234	633
3150	MAPROTILINE-M (NOR-HO-)	2AC	**363** **335** 293 **207** **100**	617
3200*	MAPROTILINE-M (TRI-HO-)	3AC	**422** **394** 352 **310** 223	657
2345	MAZINDOL		**266** 231	450

RI	NAME	DERIVATIVE	TYPICAL IONS	PAGE
2705	MAZINDOL	AC	326 284 256 220	573
1460*	MCPA		200 165 141 111	298
1510*	MCPB		228 169 142 107	366
1790	MECLOFENOXATE		257 111 58	429
1510*	MECLOFENOXATE-M	ME	200 141	302
2180	MECLOXAMINE		317 215 179 72	558
1650*	MECLOXAMINE	HY	232 217 139 77	377
1710*	MECLOXAMINE ARTIFACT -H2O	HY	214 179 139	336
3040	MECLOZINE		390 285 189 105	641
1890*	MECLOZINE	HYAC	260 200 165 105	437
2380	MECLOZINE-M	AC	285 226 191 84	493
2700	MECLOZINE-M (N-DESALKYL-)	AC	328 242 201 165 85	578
1850*	MECLOZINE ARTIFACT	HY	216 139 105 77	341
1900*	MECLOZINE	HY(ME)	232 201 165 105 77	377
1540*	MECOPROP		214 155 141 125	335
2235	MEDAZEPAM		270 242 207 165	458
2280	MEDAZEPAM-M (NOR-)		256 228 193 165	428
2520	MEDAZEPAM-M		270 242 77	459
2245	MEDAZEPAM-M	HYAC	273 230 154 105 77	463
2470	MEDAZEPAM-M (NOR-)	AC	298 297 256 228 193	522
2050	MEDAZEPAM-M	HY	231 230 154 105 77	375
1575	MEFENOREX		91 84 56	102
1935	MEFENOREX	AC	253 162 120	425
2185	MEFEXAMIDE		280 263 155 99 86	480
2285	MELITRACENE		291 217 202 58	505
1900*	MELITRACENE-M (RING)		208 193 178	318
2760	MELITRACENE-M (NOR-)	AC	319 246 231 86	563
3030	MELITRACENE-M (NOR-HO-DIHYDRO-)	2AC	379 265 223 114	634
1890	MELPERONE		263 125 112	444
1490*	MELPERONE-M 1		180 125 123 95 56	256
1835	MELPERONE-M 2		112	137
1900	MELPERONE-M 3 -H2O		261 125 123 112	438
2165	MELPERONE-M 4		307 246 123 112	536
1270	MEMANTINE		179 163 122 107 91	253
1600	MEMANTINE	AC	221 164 150 122 107	354
1780	MEPHENYTOIN		218 189 104	343
2390	MEPINDOLOL		262 147 114 100 72	441
2750	MEPINDOLOL	2AC	346 286 184 140 98	604

RI	NAME	DERIVATIVE	TYPICAL IONS	PAGE
2075	MEPIVACAINE		**246** **98** 70	406
2410	MEPIVACAINE-M (HO-)		**262** **98** 96 70	441
2450	MEPIVACAINE-M (HO-)	AC	**304** **98** 96 70	534
1785*	MEPROBAMATE		**144** 114 96 **83** **55**	198
1535*	MEPROBAMATE ARTIFACT 1		**84**	81
1720*	MEPROBAMATE ARTIFACT 2		**101** **84** 56	123
2765	MEQUITAZINE		**322** 212 198 180 **124**	566
1690	MESCALINE		**211** **181**	325
2160	MESCALINE	AC	**253** **194** 181	425
2545*	MESTEROLONE		**304** 218 200	533
1020*	METALDEHYDE		**131** 117 **89**	169
1355	METAMFEPRAMONE		**177** **175** 152 120 **72**	251
1995	METAMIZOL		**215** **123** 56	337
1945	METAMIZOL-M (BIS-DESALKYL-) ARTIFACT		**180** **119** 91	257
1955	METAMIZOL-M (BIS-DESALKYL-)		**203** 93 **84** **56**	306
1980	METAMIZOL-M (DESALKYL-)		**217** 123 98 **83** **56**	341
2270	METAMIZOL-M (BIS-DESALKYL-)	AC	**245** 203 84 **56**	405
2395	METAMIZOL-M (DESALKYL-)	AC	**259** 217 123 **56**	434
1745	METARAMINOL -H2O	2AC	**233** 93 **69**	379
2065	METARAMINOL	3AC	**293** **233** 191 86 **69**	511
2160	METHADONE		**309** 294 165 **72**	542
2040	METHADONE-M		**277** 262 248 165	471
1195	METHAMPHETAMINE		**134** **91** **58**	172
1575	METHAMPHETAMINE	AC	**191** **100** **58**	280
2155	METHAQUALONE		**250** **235** 132 91	418
2165	METHAQUALONE-M (2-CARBOXY-) -CO2		**236** **219** 132 91	387
2240	METHAQUALONE-M (2-FORMYL-)		**264** **235** 132 91	446
2360	METHAQUALONE-M (2-HO-METHYL-)		**266** **235** 132 91	450
2400	METHAQUALONE-M (2-CARBOXY-)		**280** **235** 146 132	480
2410	METHAQUALONE-M (2'CARBOXY-)		**280** **235** 146 132	480
2490	METHAQUALONE-M (3'CARBOXY-)		**280** **235** 146 132	480
2500	METHAQUALONE-M (4'CARBOXY-)		**280** **235** 146 132	480
2525	METHAQUALONE-M (6-HO-)		**266** **251** 249 132 91	451
2560	METHAQUALONE-M (4'HO-)		**266** **251** 249 132 91	451
2440	METHAQUALONE-M (2-HO-METHYL-)	AC	**308** **265** 235	541
2530	METHAQUALONE-M (4'HO-METHYL-)	AC	**308** **265** 235	541
1455	METHARBITAL		**170** **155** 126 112	243
1420	METHARBITAL	ME	**184** **169** 126 112	271
1210	METHENAMINE		**140** 112	185

RI	NAME	DERIVATIVE	TYPICAL IONS	PAGE
2240	METHITURAL		**288** 214 171 155 **74**	499
1780	METHOHEXITAL		**262** 246 233 **221** **79**	440
1735	METHOHEXITAL	ME	**261** **235** 195 178 **81**	440
2145	METHORPHAN		**271** 150 70 **58**	460
2255	METHORPHAN -M (O-DESMETHYL-)		**257** 200 150 **59**	430
2280	METHORPHAN -M (O-DESMETHYL-)	AC	**299** 231 150 **59**	524
2710	METHORPHAN -M (BIS-DESMETHYL-)	2AC	**327** 285 **87** 72	576
----*	3-METHOXYBENZOIC ACID METHYLESTER		**166** **135** 107	230
2450*	METHOXYCHLOR		**344** **308** 274 238 **227**	601
2030*	METHOXYHYDROXYPHENYLGLYCOL (MHPG)	3AC	**310** 268 208 **166** 153	545
<1000*	METHYLATED BENZENES 106/N=2 120/N=3 134/N=4		**134** **120** **106** 105 91 **57**	172
0000	METHYLDEMETON		**230** 131 **100** **81**	371
0000	METHYLDEMETON SULFOXIDE		**246** **218** **169** 125 109	408
1430	METHYLEPHEDRINE		**151** **119** 106 **72**	206
1375	METHYLEPHEDRINE-M (NOR-)		**146** 105 77 **58**	200
1495	METHYLEPHEDRINE	AC	**221** **162** 117 **72**	354
1795	METHYLEPHEDRINE-M (NOR-)	2AC	**249** **189** **100** **58**	415
1510*	METHYLPARABEN		**152** **121** 93 65	208
1495*	METHYLPARABEN	ME	**166** **135** 107	231
----	METHYLPARABEN-M (P-HYDROXYHIPPURIC ACID)	ME	**209** 177 149 121	324
<1000*	METHYLPENTYNOL		**83** **69**	78
1740	METHYLPHENIDATE		**150** 91 **84**	205
2085	METHYLPHENIDATE	AC	**275** 126 **84**	468
1895	METHYLPHENOBARBITAL		**246** **218** 146 117	406
----	METHYLPHENOBARBITAL-M (HO-)		**262** 233 218 162 134	442
1860	METHYLPHENOBARBITAL	ME	**260** **232** 175 146 118	438
1200*	METHYLSALICYLATE		**152** 120 **92** 65	210
2130*	METHYLSTEARATE		**298** 255 **143** 87 **74**	522
1525	METHYPRYLONE		**183** 155 **140** 98 **83**	266
1540	METHYPRYLONE-M (HO-)		**181** 166 **153** 98 **83**	260
2240	METIPRANOLOL ARTIFACT		**321** 306 194 **152** **72**	564
2660	METIPRANOLOL -H2O	AC	**333** 248 152 **140** 98	586
2670	METIPRANOLOL	2AC	**393** 333 **200** 140 98	642
2500	METIXENE		**309** 197 165 **99**	542
2960	METIXENE-M (NOR-)	AC	**337** **197**	592

RI	NAME	DERIVATIVE	TYPICAL IONS	PAGE
2610	METOCLOPRAMIDE		**299** **184** **99** **86**	523
2095	METOCLOPRAMIDE-M		**71** **58**	58
2735	METOCLOPRAMIDE	AC	**341** 269 226 **184** **99** **86**	597
3350	METONITAZENE		**382** 352 121 **86**	635
2130	METOPROLOL		**267** 252 223 **100** **72**	453
2140	METOPROLOL ARTIFACT		**279** 264 127 **72**	477
2240	METOPROLOL-M (HO-ETHYL-) ARTIFACT		**277** 262 114 **72**	472
2290	METOPROLOL-M (HO-PHENYL-) ARTIFACT		**295** 280 250 127 86 **72**	515
2330	METOPROLOL -H2O	AC	**291** 140 98 **72**	506
2480	METOPROLOL	2AC	**351** 291 **200** 98 **72**	607
2640	METOPROLOL-M (O-DESMETHYL-)	3AC	**379** **319** **200** 140 **72**	634
2730	METOPROLOL-M (HO-ETHYL-)	3AC	**409** 349 **200** 140 **72**	652
1625	METRONIDAZOLE		**171** 124 **81** 54	244
1665	METRONIDAZOLE	AC	**213** 171 **87**	335
1425	MEXILETINE		**179** 122 105 91 **58**	253
1780	MEXILETINE	AC	**221** **122** **100** 77 58	355
2210	MIANSERIN		**264** **193** 178 72	446
2485	MIANSERIN-M (HO-)		**280** 236 **209** 72	481
2580	MIANSERIN-M (HO-)	AC	**322** 278 **209** 72	566
2595	MIANSERIN-M (NOR-)	AC	**292** 248 193 **100**	508
3005	MIANSERIN-M (NOR-HO-)	2AC	**350** 265 209 **100**	607
2955	MICONAZOLE		**414** **333** **159** 121 81	654
2580	MIDAZOLAM		**325** **310**	571
2830	MIDAZOLAM-M (HO-)		**339** **310**	594
2820	MIDAZOLAM-M (HO-)	AC	**383** 340 **310**	636
3020	MIDAZOLAM-M (DI-HO-)	2AC	**441** **399** 383 340 326 **310**	662
2800	MOPERONE		**355** 217 **204** **123**	610
1490*	MOPERONE-M 1		**180** 125 123 95 **56**	256
1600	MOPERONE-M 2		**169** 91	238
1875	MOPERONE-M 3		**185** 156	272
2710	MOPERONE -H2O		**337** 214 188 **123**	590
3110	MOPERONE-M 4		**329** 234 185 **123**	580
2055	MOPERONE-M 3	AC	**227** **185**	365
2105	MOPERONE-M 5	AC	**215** 173	338
	MORAZONE		**377** **201** 176 56	632
1440	MORAZONE-M/ARTIFACT (PHENMETRAZINE)		**177** **71** 57	251
1800	MORAZONE-M		**204** **92**	308
1815	MORAZONE-M/ARTIFACT		**188** 105 **77**	275
1830	MORAZONE-M		**193** 107 **71** 56	282
1845	MORAZONE-M/ARTIFACT (PHENAZONE)		**188** 96 77	276
1810	MORAZONE-M/ARTIFACT (PHENMETRAZINE)	AC	**219** 176 **113** 86 **71**	349
2455	MORPHINE		**285** 268 162 124	492

RI	NAME	DERIVATIVE	TYPICAL IONS	PAGE
2620	MORPHINE	2AC	**369** **327** 310 268 162	623
2955	MORPHINE-M (NOR-)	3AC	**397** 355 209 **87** 72	645
2375	MORPHINE	ME	**299** 229 162 124	522
2515	MOXAVERINE		**307** **292** 248 91	537
1760*	MYRISTIC ACID		**228** 185 **129** 73 **56**	366
1710*	MYRISTIC ACID	ME	**242** 185 87 **74**	399
2560	NADOLOL ARTIFACT		**321** 277 236 120 **86**	565
2650	NADOLOL	3AC	**435** **420** 301 **86** 56	661
2715	NALOXONE		**327** 286 242	575
2810	NALOXONE-M (DIHYDRO-)	2AC	**413** 371 242 **82**	653
2840	NALOXONE	AC	**369** **327** 286 242	624
2890	NALOXONE	MEAC	**383** 340 324 242	636
2830	NALOXONE	2ET	**383** **270**	637
2825	NALOXONE	ME	**341** 300 256	598
2885	NALOXONE	2ME	**355** 256 82	611
2100	NAPHAZOLINE		**210** **209** 141	324
1545*	NAPHTHOL		**144** 115	198
1555*	NAPHTHOL	AC	**186** **144** 115	274
1805	NARCOBARBITAL		**223** 181 138 124	357
1560	NARCONUMAL		**209** **181** 167 124 97	320
1520	NARCONUMAL	2ME	**238** 220 **195** 138 111	391
1720	NEALBARBITAL		**223** 181 167 **141** **57**	357
1620	NEALBARBITAL	2ME	**250** 209 195 **169** 57	419
2035	NEFOPAM		**253** 225 **179** 165 **58**	424
2080	NEFOPAM-M (NOR-)	AC	**281** **208** 194 179 87	485
2250	NEFOPAM-M (HO-) ISOMER 1	AC	**311** 238 **195** 165 87	547
2285	NEFOPAM-M (HO-) ISOMER 2	AC	**311** 268 208 195 **178**	547
2610	NEFOPAM-M (NOR-DI-HO-) -H2O ISOMER 1	2AC	**337** 295 266 **87**	591
2640	NEFOPAM-M (NOR-DI-HO-) -H2O ISOMER 2	2AC	337 295 195 **87**	592
1535	NICETHAMIDE		**178** **177** 149 **106** 78	252
1605	NICOTINAMIDE		**122** 106 78	155
1380	NICOTINE		**162** 133 **84**	224
1715	NICOTINE-M (COTININE)		**176** 118 **98**	250
1390	NICOTINIC ACID	ME	**137** **106** 78	181
1900	NIFENALOL ARTIFACT		**236** 221 191 **151** 77	387
2305	NIFENALOL	2AC	308 **248** 206 114 **72**	540
3080	NIFENAZONE		**308** 202 **56**	540

RI	NAME	DERIVATIVE	TYPICAL IONS	PAGE
1945	NIFENAZONE-M (DESACYL-) ARTIFACT		**180** **119** 91	257
1955	NIFENAZONE-M (DESACYL-)		**203** 93 **84** **56**	306
2270	NIFENAZONE-M (DESACYL-)	AC	**245** 203 84 **56**	405
2085	NIFLUMIC ACID		**282** 263 **237** 168 145	486
2055	NIFLUMIC ACID -CO2		**238** **237** 217 168 145	390
1960	NIFLUMIC ACID	ME	**296** 263 236 168 145	519
2760	NITRAZEPAM		**281** 253 234 222 206	484
2785	NITRAZEPAM-M (AMINO-)		**251** 223 222	421
2985	NITRAZEPAM-M (AMINO-)	HY2AC	**296** 254 **212** 211	518
3150	NITRAZEPAM-M (AMINO-)	AC	**293** 265 223 222	512
2225	NITRAZEPAM-M (AMINO-)	HY	**212** **211** 195 107 77	331
2365	NITRAZEPAM	HY	**242** 241 195 165 105 77	399
2485	NITRAZEPAM ISOMER 1	ME	**295** **294** 248 91	516
2690	NITRAZEPAM ISOMER 2	ME	**276** **275** **249** 231	470
1530	P-NITROPHENOL		**139** 109 93 65	183
1500	P-NITROPHENOL	AC	**181** 139 109 **65**	262
1455	P-NITROPHENOL	ME	**153** 123 92 77	211
2150	NOMIFENSINE		**238** **194** 178 165	391
2450	NOMIFENSINE-M (HO-)		**254** 210 194 **86**	426
2505	NOMIFENSINE-M (HO-METHOXY-) ISOMER 1		**284** 241 **210** 86	489
2590	NOMIFENSINE-M (HO-METHOXY-) ISOMER 2		**284** 241 210 **86**	490
2470	NOMIFENSINE	AC	**280** **222** 194 178	482
2850	NOMIFENSINE-M (HO-) ISOMER 1	2AC	**338** 310 **280** 268 238 226	593
2880	NOMIFENSINE-M (HO-) ISOMER 2	2AC	**338** 308 **280** 268 194	593
2970	NOMIFENSINE-M (HO-METHOXY-)	2AC	**368** 310 **268** 224	623
2945	NORCODEINE	2AC	**369** 327 223 **87** 72	624
2520	NORDAZEPAM		**270** **242** 77	459
2720*	NORETHISTERONE	AC	**340** **298** 283 91 **56**	596
2085	NORFENEFRINE	3AC	**279** **220** 165 73 **55**	478
1790*	NORFENEFRINE-M (DESAMINO-HO-)	3AC	**280** **220** 178 **136** 123	482
2105	NORMETHADONE		**295** 263 224 165 72 **58**	514
2030	NORMETHADONE-M (NOR-)		**263** 220	444
2505	NORMETHADONE-M (HO-)	AC	**353** **294** 72 **58**	609
2665	NORMETHADONE-M (NOR-)	2AC	**365** 323 **267** 193 **86**	619
2850	NORMETHADONE-M (NOR-DIHYDRO-) -H2O	AC	**307** **266** 193 **86**	539
1360	D-NORPSEUDOEPHEDRINE		**105** 77 **44**	125
1740	D-NORPSEUDOEPHEDRINE	2AC	**235** 176 **129** 107 **86**	385
2255	NORTRIPTYLINE		**263** **202** 58 **44**	445
2390	NORTRIPTYLINE-M (HO-)		**279** 261 **218** 203 58 **44**	477
2660	NORTRIPTYLINE	AC	**305** **232** 219 202 86	535
2670	NORTRIPTYLINE-M (HO-) -H2O	AC	**303** **230** 215 202 86	533

RI	NAME	DERIVATIVE	TYPICAL IONS	PAGE
2800	NORTRIPTYLINE-M (DI-HO-) -H2O	2AC	**361** 319 **277** **87**	616
0000	NOSCAPINE		**413** **342** 191 151 **58**	653
2270	NOXIPTYLINE		**224** **208** 71 **58**	361
1850*	NOXIPTYLINE-M		**208** 180 165	317
2000*	NOXIPTYLINE-M -H2O		**206** **178** 152	314
2750	NOXIPTYLINE-M (NOR-HO-) -H2O	AC	**320** **205** **178** 100	564
3020	NOXIPTYLINE-M (NOR-DI-HO-) -H2O	2AC	**378** **336** 220 **178** 100	633
1585	OMETHOATE		**213** **156** **110** 79 58	332
3055	OPIPRAMOL		**363** **218** 193 70	617
1985	OPIPRAMOL-M (RING)		**193** 165	282
3170	OPIPRAMOL	AC	**405** 345 218 **193**	650
2370	ORCIPRENALINE	4AC	**379** **319** **277** 235 72	634
1935	ORPHENADRINE		**181** **165** 73 **58**	261
1560*	ORPHENADRINE-M		**182** **167** 108 107	263
1900	ORPHENADRINE-M (NOR-)		**255** **180** 165 86	427
1750*	ORPHENADRINE	HYAC	**240** **180** 165	395
2005	ORPHENADRINE-M	HYAC	**239** **180** 165	393
1700*	ORPHENADRINE ARTIFACT	HY	**196** **195** 165 91 77	292
1760*	ORPHENADRINE	HY	**198** 180 165 119 **77**	295
2625	OXAPADOL		**278** 248 219 105 77	475
2320	OXAZEPAM		**268** 239 233 205 **77**	454
2060	OXAZEPAM ARTIFACT 1		**240** **239** 205	394
2070	OXAZEPAM ARTIFACT 2		**254** **253** 219	425
2500	OXAZEPAM ARTIFACT 3		**298** **240** 203	521
2245	OXAZEPAM	HYAC	**273** **230** 154 105 77	463
2050	OXAZEPAM	HY	**231** **230** 154 105 77	375
2425	OXAZEPAM ISOMER 1	2ME	**314** **271** 239 205	554
2575	OXAZEPAM ISOMER 2 -H2O	2ME	**296** **295** 267 239 205	519
2540	OXAZOLAM		**328** 283 **251** 70	577
2320	OXAZOLAM-M		**268** 239 233 205 **77**	454
2520	OXAZOLAM-M		**270** **242** 77	459
2245	OXAZOLAM	HYAC	**273** **230** 154 105 77	463
2050	OXAZOLAM-M	HY	**231** **230** 154 105 77	375
2180	OXELADIN		**335** 320 219 **144** **86**	587
1985	OXPRENOLOL ARTIFACT		**277** 262 248 148 **56**	471
1900*	OXPRENOLOL-M (DESAMINO-HO-)	2AC	**308** 249 **159** 99	540
1920*	OXPRENOLOL-M (DESAMINO-HO-DESALKYL-)	3AC	**310** 268 204 **159**	545
2260	OXPRENOLOL -H2O	AC	**289** 188 **72**	503
2390	OXPRENOLOL	2AC	**349** **289** **200** 98 **72**	606
2520	OXPRENOLOL-M (HO-) -H2O ISOMER 1	2AC	**347** 305 200 **72**	604
2570	OXPRENOLOL-M (HO-) -H2O ISOMER 2	2AC	**347** 305 204 **72**	605

RI	NAME	DERIVATIVE	TYPICAL IONS	PAGE
3050	OXPRENOLOL-M (HO-) ISOMER 1	3AC	**407** **347** 305 204 **72**	650
3100	OXPRENOLOL-M (HO-) ISOMER 2	3AC	**407** 347 200 140 **72**	651
2540	OXYCODONE		**315** 258 230 140 70	555
2555	OXYCODONE	AC	**357** 314 298 240	613
2560	OXYCODONE ENOL	2AC	**399** 357 314 240	646
2570	OXYCODONE-M (DIHYDRO-)	2AC	**401** **359** 242 70	648
2680	OXYCODONE-M (NOR-) ENOL	3AC	**427** **385** 343 87	658
2900	OXYCODONE-M (NOR-DIHYDRO-)	2AC	**387** **343** 258 87 72	640
2935	OXYCODONE-M (NOR-DIHYDRO-)	3AC	**429** **387** **242** 87 72	659
2195	OXYMETAZOLINE		**260** **245** 217 81	436
2760	OXYMETAZOLINE	2AC	**344** **302** 287 230 203	602
3445	OXYPERTINE		**379** 217 **175** 132 70	633
1870	OXYPERTINE-M (PHENYLPIPERAZINE)	AC	**204** 161 **132** 56	310
2355	OXYPERTINE-M (HO-PHENYLPIPERAZINE)	2AC	**262** 220 **148**	442
0000	OXYPHENBUTAZONE		**324** **205** 149 119 **93**	570
2700	OXYPHENBUTAZONE	AC	**366** **324** 211 119 **93**	621
2545	OXYPHENBUTAZONE ISOMER 1	2ME	**352** 272 213 149 119	609
2720	OXYPHENBUTAZONE ISOMER 2	2ME	**352** 309 190 160 77	609
1965*	PALMITIC ACID		**256** 129 73 **56**	428
1920	PANTHENOL		**205** **175** 157 **133** 102	311
1920	PANTHENOL ARTIFACT		**189** 159 145 **71**	276
2055	PANTHENOL	3AC	**331** 211 **169** 115 109	583
2820	PAPAVERINE		**339** **324** 154	594
1780	PARACETAMOL		**151** **109** 80	206
1240	PARACETAMOL-M (AMINOPHENOL)		**109** 80 52	131
1765	PARACETAMOL	AC	**193** 151 **109**	283
1940	PARACETAMOL-M (METHOXY-)	AC	**223** 181 **139**	358
2085	PARACETAMOL	3AC	**277** **235** 193 151 **109**	473
3060	PARACETAMOL-M CONJUGATE	AC	**438** 396 **246** 204 **162**	662
1110	PARAMETHADIONE		**157** **129** 57	217
1890	PARAOXON		**275** **149** **109** 99 81	467
1970	PARATHION-ETHYL		**291** 137 **109** 97	505
1530	PARATHION-ETHYL-M (P-NITROPHENOL)		**139** 109 93 65	183
1890	PARATHION-ETHYL-M (PARAOXON)		**275** **149** **109** 99 81	467
1900	PARATHION-ETHYL-M (AMINO-)		**261** **125** **109** 80	439
1500	PARATHION-ETHYL-M (P-NITROPHENOL)	AC	**181** 139 109 **65**	262
1455	PARATHION-ETHYL-M (P-NITROPHENOL)	ME	**153** 123 92 77	211
1855	PARATHION METHYL		**263** 233 125 **109** 79	444
2545	PECAZINE		**310** 199 112 96 **58**	543
2010	PECAZINE-M (RING)		**199** 167	296

RI	NAME	DERIVATIVE	TYPICAL IONS	PAGE
2550	PECAZINE-M (HO-RING)	AC	**257 215** 183	431
2750	PECAZINE-M (HO-)	AC	**368** 326 215 **112 58**	623
2985	PECAZINE-M (NOR-)	AC	**338 212** 198 98	593
3415	PECAZINE-M (NOR-HO-)	2AC	**396** 354 **228** 214 98	644
1590	PEMOLINE	2ME	**204** 190 **118** 90	310
2205	PENBUTOLOL	2AC	**375 315** 158 98 **56**	631
2150	PENBUTOLOL ARTIFACT		**303 288** 160 **86** 57	531
2425	PENBUTOLOL-M (HO-) ARTIFACT		**319 304** 178 **86** 57	561
2520	PENBUTOLOL-M (HO-)	2AC	**391 376** 158 86 **56**	642
3350	PENFLURIDOL		**523 292** 201 109	668
1920	PENFLURIDOL-M 1		**257** 222 167	429
2120*	PENFLURIDOL-M 2		**262 203** 183	440
2230*	PENFLURIDOL-M 3		**276 203** 183	469
----	PENFLURIDOL-M 4		**291** 274 154 84 **56**	505
----	PENFLURIDOL-M 5		**279** 261 82 **56**	478
2150*	PENFLURIDOL-M 2	AC	**304** 244 216 **203** 183	534
2240	PENFLURIDOL-M 5	AC	**321** 303 278 99 **57**	565
2020	PENOXALIN		**281 252**	483
2155*	PENTACHLOROBIPHENYL		**324 290** 254 220 184	568
1760*	PENTACHLOROPHENOL		**264** 228 200 165	446
1815*	PENTACHLOROPHENOL	ME	**278** 263 235	476
2280	PENTAZOCINE		**285 217** 110 **70**	491
2375	PENTAZOCINE ARTIFACT (+H2O)		**303** 288 **230** 58	532
2545	PENTAZOCINE-M (HO-)		**301** 268 **217** 110 70	527
2330	PENTAZOCINE	AC	**327** 312 **259** 110 70	575
2350	PENTAZOCINE-M	AC	**323 109** 94	568
2380	PENTAZOCINE-M (DESALKYL-)	2AC	**301 87** 72	528
2435	PENTAZOCINE ARTIFACT (+H2O)	AC	**345** 330 **272** 87	602
1540	PENTETRAZOL		**138** 109 82 **55**	182
2240	PENTIFYLLINE		**264** 193 **180** 137 109	446
1740	PENTOBARBITAL		**197 156 141**	293
1890	PENTOBARBITAL-M (HO-) -H2O		**224** 195 **156 141 69**	361
1955	PENTOBARBITAL-M (HO-)		**227** 197 195 **156 141**	365
1630	PENTOBARBITAL	2ME	**225 184** 169	363
1250	PENTOREX		**148 58**	201
1580	PENTOREX	AC	**148** 131 **100 58**	202
2435	PENTOXIFYLLINE		**278 221** 193 180 109	475
2505	PENTOXIFYLLINE-M (HO-)		**280** 236 193 **180** 109	481
2560	PENTOXIFYLLINE-M (HO-)	AC	**322** 262 193 **180**	566
2680	PENTOXIFYLLINE-M (DI-HO-)	2AC	**380** 251 **181** 180	634

RI	NAME	DERIVATIVE	TYPICAL IONS	PAGE
2790	PERAZINE		**339** 199 141 113 **70**	594
2010	PERAZINE-M (RING)		**199** 167	296
3175	PERAZINE-M (HO-)		**355** 215 155 141 113 **70**	611
2550	PERAZINE-M (HO-RING)	AC	**257** **215** 183	431
3190	PERAZINE-M (HO-)	AC	**397** 214 141 113 **70** **58**	645
3210	PERAZINE-M (NOR-)	AC	**367** 238 **199** 141 99	622
3400	PERAZINE-M	AC	**397** 355 199 **100**	645
3265	PERICIAZINE		**365** 264 223 142 **114**	618
2555	PERICIAZINE-M (RING)		**224** 192	362
3390	PERICIAZINE	AC	**407** 263 224 184 **156** 114	651
3360	PERPHENAZINE		**403** 372 **246** 143	649
2100	PERPHENAZINE-M (RING)		**233** 198	378
2990	PERPHENAZINE-M (AMINO-)	AC	**332** 233 **100**	585
3470	PERPHENAZINE	AC	**445** 246 185 **98** **70**	663
3500	PERPHENAZINE-M (DESALKYL-)	AC	**401** 233 **141** 99	649
1760	PETHIDINE		**247** 218 172 **71**	410
1885	PETHIDINE-M (NOR-)		**233** **158** **57**	378
2205	PETHIDINE-M (HO-)	AC	**305** 230 188 **71**	535
2240	PETHIDINE-M (NOR-)	AC	**275** 232 202 **187** 158 57	468
2600	PETHIDINE-M (NOR-HO-)	2AC	**333** 290 245 **203** 57	586
1800	PETHIDINE-M (DESETHYL-)	(ME)	**233** 218 **158** **71**	380
1680	PHENACETIN		**179** 137 109 **108**	254
<1000*	PHENACETIN-M (HYDROQUINONE)		**110** 81	135
1240	PHENACETIN-M (AMINOPHENOL)		**109** 80 52	131
1280	PHENACETIN-M (P-PHENETIDINE)		**137** **108** 80 65	178
1780	PHENACETIN-M (DESETHYL-)		**151** **109** 80	206
1395*	PHENACETIN-M (HYDROQUINONE)	2AC	**194** 152 **110**	286
1755	PHENACETIN-M (HO-)	AC	**237** 195 **153** 124	390
1765	PHENACETIN-M (P-AMINOPHENOL)	2AC	**193** 151 **109**	283
2045	PHENALLYMAL		**244** **215** 141 104	401
1845	PHENAZONE		**188** 96 77	276
1855	PHENAZONE-M (HO-)		**204** 120 **85** 56	309
2095	PHENAZONE-M (HO-)	AC	**246** 204 119 **57**	408
2280	PHENAZOPYRIDINE		**213** 136 **108** 81	334
1890	PHENCYCLIDINE		**243** **200** 91 84	400
1480	PHENDIMETRAZINE		**191** 85 **57**	279
1830	PHENDIMETRAZINE-M (NOR-HO-)		**193** 107 **71** 56	282
1810	PHENDIMETRAZINE-M (NOR-)	AC	**219** 176 113 **100** 58	349
2200	PHENDIMETRAZINE-M (NOR-HO-)	2AC	**277** 234 113 86 **56**	473
1280	P-PHENETIDINE		**137** **108** 80 65	178
1680	P-PHENETIDINE	AC	**179** 137 109 **108**	254
2235	PHENGLUTARIMIDE		**288** **216** 98 **86**	498

RI	NAME	DERIVATIVE	TYPICAL IONS	PAGE
2370	PHENGLUTARIMIDE-M (DESETHYL-)		**260** **189**	436
2530	PHENGLUTARIMIDE-M (DESETHYL-)	AC	**302** 260 **189**	530
1805	PHENIRAMINE		**182** **169** 72 **58**	263
2250	PHENIRAMINE-M (NOR-)	AC	**268** 225 182 **169**	455
1440	PHENMETRAZINE		**177** **71** 57	251
1830	PHENMETRAZINE-M (HO-)		**193** 107 **71** 56	282
1810	PHENMETRAZINE	AC	**219** 176 **113** 86 **71**	349
2200	PHENMETRAZINE-M (HO-)	2AC	**277** 234 113 86 **56**	473
1965	PHENOBARBITAL		**232** **204** 161 117	375
2295	PHENOBARBITAL-M (HO-)		**248** 220 **219** 148	413
1860	PHENOBARBITAL	2ME	**260** **232** 175 146 118	438
1895	PHENOBARBITAL	ME	**246** **218** 146 117	406
----	PHENOBARBITAL-M (HO-)	3ME	**290** **261** 233 176 148	505
2010	PHENOTHIAZINE		**199** 167	296
2550	PHENOTHIAZINE-M (HO-)	AC	**257** **215** 183	431
1495*	PHENOXYACETIC ACID METHYLESTER		**166** **107** 77	229
----	PHENOXYMETHYLPENICILLIN -M/ARTIFACT		**187** **172** 143	275
2440*	PHENPROCOUMON		**280** **251** 189 121	481
2475*	PHENPROCOUMON	AC	**322** 280 **251** 189 121	566
2335*	PHENPROCOUMON	ME	**294** 265 **203** **91**	514
1170	PHENTERMINE		**134** 91 65 **58**	172
1510	PHENTERMINE	AC	**191** 177 **100** 86 **58**	280
2180	N-PHENYLALPHANAPHTHYLAMINE		**219** 109	348
2375	PHENYLBUTAZONE		**308** 252 **183** 77	539
2435	PHENYLBUTAZONE ARTIFACT		**324** **183** 119 **77**	569
0000	PHENYLBUTAZONE-M (HO-)		**324** **205** 149 119 **93**	570
2700	PHENYLBUTAZONE-M (HO-)	AC	**366** **324** 211 119 **93**	621
2290	PHENYLBUTAZONE	(ME)	**322** 266 **183** 77	567
2545	PHENYLBUTAZONE-M (HO-) ISOMER 1	2ME	**352** 272 213 149 119	609
2720	PHENYLBUTAZONE-M (HO-) ISOMER 2	2ME	**352** 309 190 160 77	609
2110	PHENYLEPHRINE	3AC	**293** **233** 191 149 **86**	511
0000	PHENYLMERCURIC ACETATE		**327** 238 **93** 63	575
1880	PHENYLMETHYLBARBITAL		**218** **132** 104 78	343
1790	PHENYLMETHYLBARBITAL	2ME	**246** **132** 104	410
1550*	O-PHENYLPHENOL		**170** 141	242
2350	PHENYTOIN		**252** 223 209 **180** 104 77	423
2795	PHENYTOIN-M (HO-)		**268** 239 **196** 120 104	455

RI	NAME	DERIVATIVE	TYPICAL IONS	PAGE
2300	PHENYTOIN	AC	**294** 252 223 **208** 180 104	513
2730	PHENYTOIN-M (HO-)	(ME)2AC	**366** **324** 224	621
2775	PHENYTOIN-M (HO-)	2AC	**352** **310** 268 224 196	608
2245	PHENYTOIN	ME	**266** 237 209 **180** 104 77	452
2240	PHYSOSTIGMINE		**218** **174** 160 94	344
1835	PHYSOSTIGMINE-M/ARTIFACT		**218** **174** 160 94	343
3870	PIMOZIDE		**461** **230** 187 133 82	666
1950	PIMOZIDE-M 1		**134** 106 79 67	172
2120*	PIMOZIDE-M 2		**262** **203** 183	440
2230*	PIMOZIDE-M 3		**276** **203** 183	469
2290	PIMOZIDE-M 4		**231** **134** 106 79	373
2415	PIMOZIDE-M 5		**217** **134** 106 79	342
1730	PIMOZIDE-M 1	2AC	**218** 176 **134** 106	346
2150*	PIMOZIDE-M 2	AC	**304** 244 216 **203** 183	534
2750	PIMOZIDE-M 5	2AC	**301** **259** 216 134 82	529
2770	PIMOZIDE-M 5	AC	**259** 216 134 125 **82**	435
	PINDOLOL		**248** 204 **133** 72	413
2250	PINDOLOL ARTIFACT		**260** 133 **127** 86	436
2750	PINDOLOL	2AC	**332** **200** 186 140 98	584
3040	PIPAMPERONE		**331** 164 123 **84**	582
1490*	PIPAMPERONE-M 1		**180** 125 123 95 **56**	256
3250	PIPAMPERONE-M (HO-)		**347** 292 165 154 **123**	604
2340	PIPAMPERONE-M (DESALKYL-HO-) -H2O	AC	**251** **209** 165 82	422
3290	PIPAMPERONE-M (HO-)	AC	**389** 292 165 **123**	641
1750	PIPERAZINE	2AC	**170** 85 69 **56**	243
1520	PIRACETAM		**142** **98** 84 70	195
3005	PIRENZEPIN		**351** 211 **113** 70	607
3560	PIRITRAMIDE		**386** 345 301 138	639
2340	PIZOTIFEN		**295** 233 197 96 58	515
1945*	POLICHLORINATED BIPHENYL (4CL)		**290** 220 **149**	503
2155*	POLICHLORINATED BIPHENYL (5CL)		**324** **290** 254 220 184	568
2220*	POLICHLORINATED BIPHENYL (6CL)		**358** **288** 218	614
2240*	POLICHLORINATED BIPHENYL (7CL)		**392** **322** 252	642
2245*	POLYCHLOROCAMPHENE		**410** **376** **341** 195 **89**	652
0000	POLYETHYLENE GLYCOL		133 119 89 **59** **45**	171
2650	PRAZEPAM		**324** 295 **269** 91 **55**	569
2520	PRAZEPAM-M		**270** **242** 77	459
2245	PRAZEPAM-M	HYAC	**273** **230** 154 105 77	463
2050	PRAZEPAM-M	HY	**231** **230** 154 105 77	375

RI	NAME	DERIVATIVE	TYPICAL IONS	PAGE
2410	PRAZEPAM	HY	**285** 270 105 77 **56**	494
2800*	PREDNISOLONE		**300** **122** 91	526
3400*	PREDNISOLONE	3AC	**372** 314 147 **122**	629
2560	PRENYLAMINE		**329** **328** **239** 167 **58**	579
2925	PRENYLAMINE	AC	**371** **281** 239 100 **58**	626
2290	PRIDINOL		**295** **180** 113 **98**	515
2220	PRIDINOL -H2O		**277** 163 **110**	471
2250	PRIDINOL-M (AMINO-) -H2O	AC	**251** 208 **192** 84	422
2615	PRIDINOL-M (HO-) -H2O	AC	**335** **292** 209 **110**	588
2645	PRIDINOL-M (AMINO-HO-) -H2O	2AC	**309** **208**	542
2980	PRIDINOL-M (DI-HO-) -H2O	2AC	**393** 309 **208**	643
1850	PRILOCAINE		**220** **86**	350
2060	PRILOCAINE	AC	**262** **156** 128 107 **86**	442
2260	PRIMIDONE		**218** **190** 161 146 117	345
1935	PRIMIDONE-M (DIAMIDE)		**163** 148 103 91	226
1965	PRIMIDONE-M (PHENOBARBITAL)		**232** **204** 161 117	375
2115	PRIMIDONE	AC	**260** 232 189 **146** 117	437
1555	PROBARBITAL		**169** 156 **141** 98	238
1485	PROBARBITAL	2ME	**197** 184 **169** 112	294
2270	PROCAINAMIDE		**235** 120 **99** **86**	384
2025	PROCAINE		**164** 120 **99** **86**	226
1985	PROCAINE-M (PABA)	MEAC	**193** 151 **120** 92 65	284
1550	PROCAINE-M (PABA)	ME	**151** **120** 92 65	208
2970	PROCHLORPERAZINE		**373** 141 **113** **70**	629
2100	PROCHLORPERAZINE-M (RING)		**233** 198	378
2990	PROCHLORPERAZINE-M (AMINO-)	AC	**332** 233 **100**	585
3500	PROCHLORPERAZINE-M (NOR-)	AC	**401** 233 **141** 99	649
2195	PROCYCLIDINE		**287** 269 **204** **84**	495
2540	PROCYCLIDINE-M (HO-) -H2O	AC	**327** 186 129 105 **84**	575
2640	PROCYCLIDINE-M (AMINO-HO-) -H2O	2AC	**315** 255 **196** 84	556
2335	PROFENAMINE		**312** 213 **199** **100**	547
2450	PROFENAMINE-M (BIS-DESETHYL-)	AC	**298** **212** 180 100 58	522
2515	PROFENAMINE-M (DESETHYL-)	AC	**326** **212** 128 **72**	573
2880	PROFENAMINE-M (DESETHYL-HO-)	2AC	**384** **270** 128 **72**	637
2780*	PROGESTERONE		**314** 272 **124**	553
2315	PROMAZINE		**284** 199 86 **58**	489
2010	PROMAZINE-M (RING)		**199** 167	296
2405	PROMAZINE-M (NOR-)		**270** 238 213 **199** 44	458
2685	PROMAZINE-M (HO-)		**300** 254 215 86 **58**	525

RI	NAME	DERIVATIVE	TYPICAL IONS	PAGE
2705	PROMAZINE-M (SULFOXIDE)		**300** 284 **212** **58**	526
2550	PROMAZINE-M (HO-RING)	AC	**257** **215** 183	431
2710	PROMAZINE-M (HO-)	AC	**342** 257 215 86 **58**	599
2805	PROMAZINE-M (NOR-)	AC	**312** 198 180 **114**	549
3195	PROMAZINE-M (NOR-HO-)	2AC	**370** 328 214 **114** 86	625
2270	PROMETHAZINE		**284** 213 199 **72**	489
2010	PROMETHAZINE-M (RING)		**199** 167	296
2250	PROMETHAZINE-M (NOR-)		**270** **213** 198 180 **58**	458
2580	PROMETHAZINE-M (NOR-HO-)		**286** **212** 180 **58**	494
2590	PROMETHAZINE-M (HO-)		**300** **229** 214 196 **72**	525
2710	PROMETHAZINE-M (SULFOXIDE)		**300** 284 **213** **72**	526
2450	PROMETHAZINE-M (BIS-DESMETHYL-)	AC	**298** **212** 180 100 58	522
2540	PROMETHAZINE-M (NOR-)	AC	**312** **212** 114 **58**	548
2550	PROMETHAZINE-M (HO-RING)	AC	**257** **215** 183	431
2690	PROMETHAZINE-M (HO-)	AC	**342** **256** 214 **72**	598
3015	PROMETHAZINE-M (NOR-HO-)	2AC	**370** 270 **228** 114 **58**	625
----	PROMETHAZINE-M (NOR-SULFOXIDE)	AC	**328** 312 **212** 100 **58**	579
2300	PROPAFENONE -H2O		**323** 294 **98** 91	567
1830*	PROPAFENONE-M (PHENOL)		**226** 194 **121**	363
2720	PROPAFENONE-M (HO-) -H2O		**339** 310 **98** 91	593
2760	PROPAFENONE ARTIFACT		**353** 324 **128** 121 98 91	609
2215*	PROPAFENONE-M (HO-PHENOL)	AC	**284** **242** **137** 91	490
2580*	PROPAFENONE-M (HO-METHOXY-PHENOL)	AC	**314** 272 **167** 91	553
2715*	PROPAFENONE-M (DESAMINO-HO-)	2AC	**384** **159** 121 91	637
2930	PROPAFENONE -H2O	AC	**365** 224 **140** **98**	619
2950*	PROPAFENONE-M (DESAMINO-DI-HO-)	3AC	**442** 308 **159** **91**	663
3050	PROPAFENONE-M (HO-) -H2O	2AC	**423** 381 **140** 98 **91**	657
1875	PROPALLYLONAL		**209** **167** 124	321
1770	PROPALLYLONAL-M (DESBROMO-OXO-)		**226** 184 **169** 141	363
1745	PROPALLYLONAL	2ME	**237** **195** 138	390
----	PROPALLYLONAL-M (DESBROMO-DIHYDRO-HO-)	2ME	**241** 214 198 183 **169**	397
----	PROPALLYLONAL-M (DESBROMO-OXO-)	2ME	**239** 212 197 **169** 112	394
1840	PROPIVANE		**277** **205** 99 **86** 58	470
1585	PROPOXUR		**209** 152 **110**	320
1390*	PROPOXUR-M 1	AC	**194** 152 **110**	286
1680*	PROPOXUR-M 2	2AC	**210** 168 **126**	325
2205	PROPOXYPHENE		**265** **208** 115 **58**	447
1755*	PROPOXYPHENE ARTIFACT		**208** 130 **115** 91	317
2240	PROPOXYPHENE-M (NOR-) -H2O		**251** **217** **119**	420
2400	PROPOXYPHENE-M (NOR-) N-PROP.		**307** **220** **100** **57**	537
2555	PROPOXYPHENE-M (NOR-) -H2O N-PROP.		**307** **234** **105** 100 91	537
2365	PROPOXYPHENE-M (NOR-) -H2O	AC	**293** **220** 205	511
2395	PROPOXYPHENE-M	(HY)	**281** **190** **119** **105** 56	486
2160	PROPRANOLOL		**259** 144 **100** **72**	433
1545*	PROPRANOLOL-M (NAPHTHOL)		**144** 115	198

RI	NAME	DERIVATIVE	TYPICAL IONS	PAGE
2065*	PROPRANOLOL-M (DESAMINO-HO-)		**218** **144** 115	344
2220	PROPRANOLOL -H2O		**241** **98** **56**	396
1555*	PROPRANOLOL-M (NAPHTHOL)	AC	**186** **144** 115	274
1900*	PROPRANOLOL-M (HO-NAPHTHOL)	2AC	**244** 202 **160**	402
2195*	PROPRANOLOL-M (DESAMINO-HO-)	2AC	**302** **159** 144 115	530
2330	PROPRANOLOL -H2O	AC	**283** 198 181 **140** 127 98	488
2565*	PROPRANOLOL-M (DESAMINO-DI-HO-)	3AC	**360** 318 **159**	615
2605	PROPRANOLOL	2AC	**343** **283** **200** 140 98	600
2750	PROPRANOLOL-M (HO-) -H2O ISOMER 1	2AC	**341** 197 **140** 98	597
2900	PROPRANOLOL-M (HO-) -H2O ISOMER 2	2AC	**341** 197 **140** 98	597
2940	PROPRANOLOL-M (HO-)	3AC	**401** **341** 186 **140** 98	649
1170	PROPYLHEXEDRINE		**155** 140 **58**	212
1475	PROPYLHEXEDRINE-M (HO-)		**171** 156 **58**	244
1570	PROPYLHEXEDRINE	AC	**197** 182 140 **100** 58	293
1915	PROPYLHEXEDRINE-M (HO-)	2AC	**255** 240 195 **100** **58**	427
1910	PROPYPHENAZONE		**230** **215** 56	369
1765	PROPYPHENAZONE-M (NOR-)		**216** **174** 77	339
1780	PROPYPHENAZONE-M (NOR-HO-)		**232** 190 121 **93** 77	375
1970	PROPYPHENAZONE-M (ISOPROPENYL-)		**228** **136** 95	366
2080	PROPYPHENAZONE-M (NOR-HO-PHENYL-)		**232** **190** 121 93 65	376
2090	PROPYPHENAZONE-M (NOR-DI-HO-)		**248** 206 136 109	412
2210	PROPYPHENAZONE-M (HO-PROPYL-)		**246** 231 **215** 124 56	406
2300	PROPYPHENAZONE-M (HO-PHENYL-)		**246** **231** 96 56	406
2410	PROPYPHENAZONE-M (HO-METHYL-)		**246** **231** 215 77	407
----	PROPYPHENAZONE-M (ISOPROPANOLYL-)		**246** **231** 213	407
1820	PROPYPHENAZONE-M (NOR-)	AC	**258** 216 **201** 77	432
1895	PROPYPHENAZONE-M (NOR-HO-)	AC	**274** 232 214 **190**	465
2165	PROPYPHENAZONE-M (NOR-HO-PHENYL-)	AC	**316** 274 **232** 217 190	557
2240	PROPYPHENAZONE-M (HO-METHYL-)	AC	**288** 273 **245** 232 190	500
2305	PROPYPHENAZONE-M (HO-PROPYL-)	AC	**288** 245 228 **215** 56	500
2530	PROPYPHENAZONE-M (HO-PHENYL-)	AC	**288** 273 246 **231** 56	500
1735	PROPYPHENAZONE-M (NOR-)	ME	**230** **215** 200 185 77	372
----	PROPYPHENAZONE-M (HO-PHENYL-)	ME	**260** **245** 215 122 56	438
----	PROPYPHENAZONE-M (HOOC-)	ME	**274** **215** 56	466
----	PROPYPHENAZONE-M (NOR-HO-PHENYL-)	2ME	**260** **245** 230 215	438
2670	PROQUAZONE		**278** **235** 221 77	475
2350	PROTHIPENDYL		**285** 227 214 **200** 86 **58**	491
2045	PROTHIPENDYL-M (RING)		**200** 168 155	300
----	PROTHIPENDYL-M (HO-)		**301** 230 **216** 86 **58**	528
----	PROTHIPENDYL-M (SULFOXIDE)		301 285 **216** 84 **58**	528
2780	PROTHIPENDYL-M (HO-)	AC	**343** 230 **216** 86 **58**	600
2830	PROTHIPENDYL-M (BIS-NOR-)	AC	**299** 227 213 **200** 100	524
2880	PROTHIPENDYL-M (NOR-)	AC	**313** 227 213 **200** **114** 100	550
3070	PROTHIPENDYL-M (NOR-HO-)	2AC	**371** 258 216 **114** 100	627
2250	PROTRIPTYLINE		**263** **191** 84 70	445
2690	PROTRIPTYLINE	AC	**305** **191** 114	535
2780	PROTRIPTYLINE-M (NOR-)	AC	**291** 218 **191** 100 86	506

RI	NAME	DERIVATIVE	TYPICAL IONS	PAGE
2895	PROTRIPTYLINE-M (HO-)	AC	**363** 321 249 **207** 114	617
2080	PROXYPHYLLINE		**238** **194** 180 137 109	391
2180	PROXYPHYLLINE	AC	**280** 237 220 193 180	482
1460	PYRAZINAMIDE		**123** **80** 53	156
<1000	PYRIDINE		**79** 52	74
1520	PYRITHYLDIONE		**167** 152 139 **98** **83**	232
0000	PYRITINOL		**368** 199 **166** 151 106	623
1800	PYRITINOL-M		**207**	314
0000	PYRITINOL-M		**199** **151** 122 106	297
0000	PYRITINOL	3ME	**410** **165** **136**	653
3025*	QUINESTROL		**364** 338 295 **270** 213	618
2790	QUINIDINE		**324** 189 173 **136**	569
2940	QUINIDINE-M		**338** 323 **152** 138	592
2950	QUINIDINE-M (N-OXIDE)		**340** 324 189 **152** 136	595
2750	QUINIDINE	AC	**366** 307 189 **136**	621
2935	QUINIDINE-M (N-OXIDE)	AC	**382** 189 **152**	636
3185	QUINIDINE-M (HO-)	2AC	**424** **365** 305 194	657
3350	QUINIDINE-M (DI-HO-DIHYDRO-)	3AC	**484** **425** 365 254 194	667
2790	QUININE		**324** 189 **136**	569
2750	QUININE	AC	**366** 309 189 **136**	621
0000	RESERPINE		**608** 397 365 195	668
1460	SALICYLAMIDE		**137** **120** 92 65	178
1660	SALICYLAMIDE	AC	**179** 137 **120** 92	255
1860	SALICYLAMIDE-M (HO-)	2AC	**237** **195** 153 **136** 108	390
1295*	SALICYLIC ACID		**138** 120 **92** 64	182
----	SALICYLIC ACID GLYCINE CONJUGATE		**195** 177 149 **120** 92 65	288
1545*	SALICYLIC ACID	AC	**180** 138 **120** 92	256
1350*	SALICYLIC ACID	ET	**166** **120** 92 65	231
1200*	SALICYLIC ACID	ME	**152** 120 **92** 65	210
1810	SALICYLIC ACID GLYCINE CONJUGATE	ME	**209** **121** 92 65	323
----	SALICYLIC ACID GLYCINE CONJUGATE	2ME	**223** **135** 90 77	360
2315	SCOPOLAMINE		**303** 285 154 138 **94**	532
2230	SCOPOLAMINE -H2O		**285** 154 138 **94**	491
2450	SCOPOLAMINE	AC	**345** 285 154 138 **94**	602
1795	SECOBARBITAL		**209** **195** **168** 167 141	320
1665	SECOBARBITAL-M (DESALLYL-)		**169** 154 **129**	238
1970	SECOBARBITAL-M (HO-) -H2O		**236** **168** 167 70	387
1690	SECOBARBITAL	2ME	**248** **196** 181 138 111	414
----	SECOBARBITAL-M (DESETHYL)	3ME	**240** 225 211 **197** 183	395

RI	NAME	DERIVATIVE	TYPICAL IONS	PAGE
2055	SIGMODAL		**237** 193 **167** 122 78	389
1910	SIGMODAL	2ME	**265** **195** 138	450
1690	SIMAZINE		**201** 186 173 84 **72**	303
0000	SOTALOL		**272** 239 199 122 **72**	462
2675	SOTALOL -H2O	AC	**296** 217 **175** 133 84	518
1785	SPARTEINE		**234** 193 137 **98**	381
3000*	SQUALENE		**410** 136 95 82 **69**	652
2170*	STEARIC ACID		**284** 256 **129** 73 **56**	489
2130*	STEARIC ACID	ME	**298** 255 **143** 87 **74**	522
2300*	STRESSHORMONE (HYDROXYANDROSTENE)		**274** **259** 241 148 94	465
2860*	STRESSHORMONE (HYDROXYANDROSTENE)	AC	**316** 256 241 215	557
3120	STRYCHNINE		**334**	587
0000	SUBLIMATE		**272** **202**	462
2660	SULFAMETHIAZOLE	ME	**284** 156 **92** 65	490
2690	SULFAMETHOXAZOL-M (SULFANILAMIDE)	AC	**214** **172** 156 92	336
2185	SULFANILAMIDE		**172** 156 108 92 **65**	246
2690	SULFANILAMIDE	AC	**214** **172** 156 92	336
2285	SULFINPYRAZONE		**278** 105 **77**	474
3415	SULFORIDAZINE		**402** **277** 198 **98**	649
3180	SULFORIDAZINE-M (RING)		**277** 198	472
3800	SULFORIDAZINE-M (NOR-)	AC	**430** 277 **154** 84	660
2890*	SULINDAC		**312** **297** 265 233 117	548
3220*	SULINDAC	ME	**370** 354 295 248 **233**	625
----	SULPIRIDE ARTIFACT		**135** **98**	174
2175	SYNEPHRINE	3AC	**293** 233 191 **149** **86**	511
1705	TALBUTAL		**167** 153 124 97	233
1600	TALBUTAL	2ME	**234** **195** 181 138 111	383
2625	TEMAZEPAM		**300** **271** 256 239	525
2320	TEMAZEPAM-M		**268** 239 233 205 **77**	454
2245	TEMAZEPAM-M	HYAC	**273** **230** 154 105 77	463
2050	TEMAZEPAM-M	HY	**231** **230** 154 105 77	375
2100	TEMAZEPAM	HY	**245** 228 193 105 **77**	405
2620*	TESTOSTERONE		**288** 246 **124**	499

RI	NAME	DERIVATIVE	TYPICAL IONS	PAGE
2490	TETRABENAZINE		**317** 274 **261** 191	559
2500	TETRABENAZINE-M (O-DESMETHYL-HO-)		**319** 274 232 **205** 191	561
2510	TETRABENAZINE-M (O-BIS-DESMETHYL-)	AC	**331** **296** 232 **191** 177	583
2585	TETRABENAZINE-M (O-DESMETHYL-HO-)	AC	**361** **302** 274 246 205	616
2665	TETRABENAZINE-M (O-BIS-DESMETHYL-HO-)	2AC	**389** 330 **302** 288 233 191	640
1945*	TETRACHLOROBIPHENYL		**290** 220 **149**	503
----*	2.3.7.8-TETRACHLORODIBENZO-P-DIOXIN		**320** 257 189	563
<1000*	TETRACHLOROMETHANE		**117** 82 47	147
2470*	TETRAHYDROCANNABINOL		**314** 299 271 231	552
2400*	TETRAHYDROCANNABINOL	AC	**356** 313 **297** 231	612
2620*	TETRAHYDROCANNABINOL-M (NOR-9-HOOC-)	2ME	**372** 357 **313** 245	629
2400	TETRAZEPAM		**288** **253**	499
2570	TETRAZEPAM-M (HO-)		**304** 285 275 **235**	533
2650	TETRAZEPAM-M/ARTIFACT (TRI-HO-) -2H2O		**300** **272** 255	525
2415	TETRAZEPAM-M (HO-) ISOMER 1	HYAC	**307** **248** 234 220 194	538
2605	TETRAZEPAM-M (HO-) ISOMER 2	HYAC	**307** **248** 207 194	539
2635	TETRAZEPAM-M (HO-)	AC	**346** 304 **287**	603
2790	TETRAZEPAM-M/ARTIFACT (TRI-HO-) -2H2O	AC	**342** **300** 272	599
2200	TETRAZEPAM	HY	**249** 234 220 **207**	416
2330	TETRAZEPAM-M (HO-) ISOMER 1	HY	**265** 253 220 207 **194**	449
2575	TETRAZEPAM-M (HO-) ISOMER 2	HY	**265** 253 220 207 **194**	449
1830	TETRYZOLINE		**200** 185 171	299
1900	TETRYZOLINE-M 1	AC	**229** 157 **115** **98**	368
2000	TETRYZOLINE-M 2	AC	**242** 200 157 **115** **98**	398
2110	TETRYZOLINE	AC	**242** **200** 185 86	398
2400	TETRYZOLINE	2AC	**284** 242 **199**	490
2440	THALIDOMIDE		**258** 173 111 104 **75**	432
2500	THEBACONE		**341** 298 242 162	596
2435	THEBACONE-M (DIHYDRO-)	AC	**343** 300 226 70	600
2545	THEBACONE-M (O-DESMETHYL-DIHYDRO-)	2AC	**371** **329** 288 164 70	626
2620	THEBACONE-M (O-DESMETHYL-)	AC	**369** **327** 284 228 162	624
2750	THEBACONE-M (NOR-DIHYDRO-)	2AC	**371** **87** 72	626
2545	THEBAINE		**311** 296	546
1980	THEOBROMINE		**180** 137 109	257
2025	THEOPHYLLINE		**180** 95 68	257
1790	THIOBUTABARBITAL		**228** 172 **156** 141 97	366
1855	THIOPENTAL		**242** 173 **172** 157	397
1740	THIOPENTAL-M (PENTOBARBITAL)		**197** **156** **141**	293
1630	THIOPENTAL-M (PENTOBARBITAL)	2ME	**225** **184** 169	363

RI	NAME	DERIVATIVE	TYPICAL IONS	PAGE
1825	THIOPENTAL	2ME	**200** 185 97 69	303
----	THIOPENTAL-M (HOOC-)	3ME	**314** 283 241 **200** 185	554
3470	THIOPROPAZATE		**445** 246 185 **98** **70**	663
2100	THIOPROPAZATE-M (RING)		**233** 198	378
3360	THIOPROPAZATE-M (DESACETYL-)		**403** 372 **246** 143	649
2990	THIOPROPAZATE-M (AMINO-)	AC	**332** 233 **100**	585
3500	THIOPROPAZATE-M (DESALKYL-)	AC	**401** 233 **141** 99	649
3575	THIOPROPERAZINE		**446** **320** 127 **113** **70**	663
3200	THIOPROPERAZINE-M (RING)		**306** 198	536
3125	THIORIDAZINE		**370** 126 **98** 70	624
3500	THIORIDAZINE-M (OXO-)		**384** 258 244 **112**	637
3490	THIORIDAZINE-M (NOR-)	AC	**398** 356 **154** 84	646
2090	TIABENDAZOLE		**201** 174	303
2820	TIAPRIDE		**328** **326** 311 213 **86**	578
2580	TIAPRIDE-M (O-DESMETHYL-)		**314** 86 **58**	552
2590	TIAPRIDE-M (O-DESMETHYL-N-OXIDE) -(C2H5)2NOH		**241**	396
1865*	TIAPROFENIC ACID		**260** **216** 201 **139** 77	435
2180*	TIAPROFENIC ACID	ME	**274** 231 **215** 105 77	466
2110	TICLOPIDINE		**263** 125 **110**	444
1835	TILIDINE		**273** **176** **97** 82	463
1520*	TILIDINE-M (PHENYLCYCLOHEXENONE)		**172** 104 **68**	245
1820	TILIDINE-M (NOR-)		**259** **83** 68	433
1840	TILIDINE-M (BIS-NOR-)		**245** **83** **69**	402
----	TILIDINE-M (BIS-NOR-HO-)		**261** 244 103 **85** 69	439
----	TILIDINE-M (BIS-NOR-OXIME-)		**259** **186** 168	434
----	TILIDINE-M (NITRO-)		**275** 258 184 **103**	467
1550*	TILIDINE-M/ARTIFACT	AC	**212** **170**	329
2100	TILIDINE-M (BIS-NOR-)	AC	**287** 244 **111** **69**	497
2165	TILIDINE-M (NOR-)	AC	**301** 258 **125** **83** 69	528
2280	TILIDINE-M/ARTIFACT	2AC	**271** 211 **169**	461
2275	TIMOLOL ARTIFACT		**328** **313** 187 **86** 57	577
2290	TIMOLOL	AC	**358** **343** 284 86 **56**	614
3555	TIOTIXENE		**443** **221** **113** **70**	663
1730	TOCAINIDE		**192** 176 147 121 **57**	281
2040	TOCAINIDE	AC	**234** 147 **121** 106 87	383
2175	TOLAZOLINE-M (HO-DIHYDRO-)	2AC	**262** 161 **118** 91	442
1820	TOLIPROLOL ARTIFACT		**235** 220 127 108 **56**	383
2155	TOLIPROLOL	2AC	**307** **247** 190 140 **72**	538
1885	TOLMETINE		**212** 198 122 91	328

RI	NAME	DERIVATIVE	TYPICAL IONS	PAGE
2265	TOLMETINE	ET	**285** **212** 119 91	493
2235	TOLMETINE	ME	**271** **212** **83**	461
<1000*	TOLUENE		**92** **91** 65	104
2245*	TOXAPHENE (TM)		**410** **376** **341** 195 **89**	652
1945	TRAMADOL		**263** **58**	444
1905	TRAMADOL -H2O		**245** **184** **58**	402
1975	TRAMADOL-M (O-DESMETHYL-) -H2O		**231** **184** **58**	373
1995	TRAMADOL-M (O-DESMETHYL-)		249 204 97 **58**	414
2000	TRAMADOL-M (O-DESMETHYL-) -H2O	AC	**273** **184** **58**	463
2295	TRAMADOL-M (N-DESMETHYL-) -H2O	AC	**273** **200** **86** 58	464
2465	TRAMADOL-M (BIS-DESMETHYL-) -H2O	2AC	**301** 228 186 **86**	529
1230	TRANYLCYPROMINE		**133** **132** 115 **56**	171
1635	TRANYLCYPROMINE	AC	**175** **132** **116** 84 56	249
3345	TRAZODONE		**371** **278** 231 205 176 **70**	626
2020	TRAZODONE-M 1	2AC	**227** 185 **143**	365
2265	TRAZODONE-M 2	AC	**238** 195 **166** 154	391
2355	TRAZODONE-M 3 ISOMER 1	2AC	**296** 254 **182** 154	517
2525	TRAZODONE-M 3 ISOMER 2	2AC	**296** 254 **182** 154	518
3380	TRAZODONE-M 4	AC	**429** 414 336 **205**	659
1980	TRIADIMEFON		**293** **208** 181 128 **57**	510
2200	TRIAMPHOS		**294** 251 **160** 135	512
3080	TRIAZOLAM		**342** 313 279 238	598
3000	TRIAZOLAM-M (ALPHA-HO-)		**358** **328** 293 265 239	614
3200	TRIAZOLAM-M (ALPHA-HO-)	AC	**400** **357** 329 239	647
2865	TRIAZOLAM-M	HY	**331** **296** 139 111	583
1505	TRICHLORFON		**220** 185 145 **109** 79	350
<1000*	TRICHLOROETHANOL		**148** 119 **113** 82 **77**	201
<1000*	TRICHLOROETHYLENE		**130** 95 60	167
1440*	2.4.5-TRICHLOROPHENOL		**196** 132 97	291
1420*	TRICHLOROPHENOL		**196** 132 91	291
2060*	TRICOSANE		**288** 252 218 146 114	498
2685	TRIFLUOPERAZINE		**407** 267 **113** **70**	650
2190	TRIFLUOPERAZINE-M (RING)		**267** 235	453
2765	TRIFLUOPERAZINE-M (AMINO-)	AC	**366** 267 **100**	621
3145	TRIFLUOPERAZINE-M (NOR-)	AC	**435** **267** **141** 99	661
2700	TRIFLUPERIDOL		**409** **271** 258 123	651

RI	NAME	DERIVATIVE	TYPICAL IONS	PAGE
1490*	TRIFLUPERIDOL-M 1		**180** 125 123 95 **56**	256
1570	TRIFLUPERIDOL-M 2		**223** 154 127	357
1950	TRIFLUPERIDOL-M 3		**257** 223 173 145 **56**	430
1970	TRIFLUPERIDOL-M 4		**245** 227 **56**	403
2035	TRIFLUPERIDOL-M 4	AC	**287** 269 244 227 99 **57**	496
2240	TRIFLUPROMAZINE		**352** 267 86 **58**	607
2190	TRIFLUPROMAZINE-M (RING)		**267** 235	453
2720	TRIFLUPROMAZINE-M (HO-)	AC	**410** 368 283 **58**	652
2740	TRIFLUPROMAZINE-M (NOR-)	AC	**380** 267 156 **114** 100	635
2765	TRIFLUPROMAZINE-M (BIS-NOR-)	AC	**366** 267 **100**	621
3120	TRIFLUPROMAZINE-M (NOR-HO-)	2AC	**438** **323** 156 **114**	662
2250	TRIHEXYPHENIDYL		**301** **218** **98**	527
2500	TRIHEXYPHENIDYL-M (HO-)		**317** 299 **218** **98**	559
2095*	TRIHEXYPHENIDYL-M -2H2O -CO2	AC	**242** 200 **182** 167	398
2555	TRIHEXYPHENIDYL-M (DI-HO-) -H2O ISO 1	2AC	**399** 357 **98**	646
2640	TRIHEXYPHENIDYL-M (AMINO-HO-) -H2O	2AC	**315** 255 **196** 84	556
2665	TRIHEXYPHENIDYL-M (DI-HO-) -H2O ISO 2	2AC	**399** 338 194 98	647
2965	TRIHEXYPHENIDYL-M (TRI-HO-) -H2O	3AC	**457** **398** 336 194 **156**	665
1080	TRIMETHADIONE		**143** 128 **58**	196
2590	TRIMETHOPRIM		**290** 259 123	504
2700	TRIMETHOPRIM	AC	**332** **290** 275	584
3000	TRIMETHOPRIM	2AC	**374** **332** 317 275	630
2260	TRIMETOZINE		**281** **195**	484
2225	TRIMIPRAMINE		**294** **249** 235 **58**	512
1930	TRIMIPRAMINE-M (RING)		**195** 180	287
2575	TRIMIPRAMINE-M (HO-)		**310** 265 **250** 224 **58**	544
2535	TRIMIPRAMINE-M (HO-RING)	AC	**253** **211**	425
2650	TRIMIPRAMINE-M (HO-)	AC	**352** **265** 215 99 84 **58**	608
2670	TRIMIPRAMINE-M (NOR-HO-) -H2O	AC	**320** **206** 128	564
3155	TRIMIPRAMINE-M (NOR-HO-)	2AC	**380** **266** 224 128	635
3555	TRIMIPRAMINE-M (NOR-DI-HO-)	3AC	**438** **324** 240 **128** 86	662
1730	TRYPTAMINE		**160** **130** 103 77	222
----	TRYPTOPHAN	ME2AC	**302** 243 201 **130**	531
1730	TRYPTOPHAN-M (TRYPTAMINE)		**160** **130** 103 77	222
2150	TRYPTOPHAN	MEAC	**260** 201 **130**	437
----	TRYPTOPHAN-M (HYDROXY INDOLE ACETIC ACID)	ME	**205** **146**	313
----	TRYPTOPHAN-M (INDOLE ACETIC ACID)	ME	**189** **130**	278
----	TRYPTOPHAN-M (INDOLE FORMIC ACID)	ME	**175** **144** 116	250
----	TRYPTOPHAN-M (INDOLE LACTIC ACID)	ME	**219** **130**	349
----	TRYPTOPHAN-M (INDOLE PYRUVIC ACID)	2ME	**231** 216 188 129	375
1745	TYRAMINE		**137** **108** 77	179
1950	TYRAMINE	2AC	**221** 162 **120** 107	355
0000	UNDERGROUND OV-17		**452** **394** **315** **198** **135**	664

RI	NAME	DERIVATIVE	TYPICAL IONS	PAGE
0000	UNDERGROUND OV-101		**355 281 207** 73	611
0000	UNDERGROUND UCC-W-982		**429 355 281 207** 73	659
1150*	VALPROIC ACID		**144** 115 **102 73**	198
----*	VANILLIN MANDELIC ACID	2ME	**226 167** 139	364
3150	VERAPAMIL		**454** 438 **303** 260 59	665
1855	VILOXAZINE		**237 138** 100 **56**	389
2325	VILOXAZINE-M (DI-OXO-)		**265 138** 100 **56**	447
2220	VILOXAZINE	AC	**279 142 100** 86 56	479
2610	VILOXAZINE-M (HO-)	2AC	**337** 295 **142 100**	591
2405	VIMINOL		**344** 315 287 259 125	601
2785	VIMINOL-M/ARTIFACT	AC	**394** 335 **125**	643
1765	VINBARBITAL		**195** 152 **141** 134 69	287
1670	VINBARBITAL	2ME	**223** 166 138	360
1745	VINYLBITAL		**154** 83	211
1665	VINYLBITAL-M (DESVINYL-)		**169** 154 **129**	238
1995	VINYLBITAL-M (HO-)		**195** 179 **154** 83	288
1655	VINYLBITAL	2ME	**223** 209 **182** 97	360
1720	VINYLBITAL	(ME)	**209** 195 **168** 83	323
----	VINYLBITAL-M (DESVINYL-)	3ME	**240** 225 211 **197** 183	395
0000	WARFARIN		**308 181** 146 **131 103**	540
2650*	WARFARIN-M (DIHYDRO-)	MEAC	**366 292** 121	620
2540*	WARFARIN	ME	**322 279** 121 91	567
2550*	WARFARIN-M (DIHYDRO-) -H2O	ME	**306 292** 263 249 121	536
2840*	WARFARIN-M (HO-)	2ME	**352 309**	609
2020	XYLOMETAZOLINE		**244** 229 214 119 91	401
2260	XYLOMETAZOLINE	AC	**286** 271 229 214 128	495
2270	ZIMELIDINE		**316** 238 193 70 **58**	556
2040	ZOMEPIRAC		**246** 211 136	406
1835	ZOMEPIRAC	ME	**305 246** 139 111	535

10 Table II: List of Retention Indices of Measured Compounds

10.1 Explanatory Notes

The measured compounds are listed in order of ascending retention indices (OV-101) in this section. Table II can be employed for the tentative identification of GC peaks. Such identification should always be confirmed by mass spectrometry (7.3). The entry for metabolites or derivatives common to different substances includes all possible parent compounds.

The title of the list is printed at the top of each page together with the first or last substance, the page number is printed at the bottom.

The first column contains the retention indices, the second column the compound name (INN for drugs, common names for pesticides, chemical names for chemicals) and the third column contains the derivatives. If necessary, a synonym index (e.g. ABDA, 1984; Negwer, 1978; Perkow, 1983; Windholz et al., 1983) should be employed in conjunction with this list. Additional information from CAS is accessible through the list of common names (Part 2, 5.1). The fourth column lists fragment ions typical for the compound. The ions under which the mass spectrum is listed in Part 2 are printed boldface. The fifth column indicates the page on which the mass spectrum is reproduced under its most massive ion, in order to facilitate finding it.

10.2 Table II: List of Retention Indices

RI	NAME	DERIVATIVE	TYPICAL IONS	PAGE
<1000	AMYLNITRITE		**85** 70 57 **41**	84
<1000	BENZYLAMINE		**107** 91 77	129
<1000	PYRIDINE		**79** 52	74
<1000*	ACETIC ACID		**60** **43**	47
<1000*	ACETONE		**58** **43**	19
<1000*	BENZENE		**78**	73
<1000*	CHLORAL HYDRATE-M (TRICHLOROETHANOL)		**148** 119 **113** 82 **77**	201
<1000*	CHLOROFORM		**118** **83**	147
<1000*	CYCLOHEXANOL		**100** **82** **57**	116
<1000*	DICHLOROMETHANE		**84** **49**	81
<1000*	DIMETHYLSULFOXIDE		**78** **63** 45	73
<1000*	DIOXANE		**88** 58	100
<1000*	ETHANOL		**46** **45** **31**	5
<1000*	ETHYLACETATE		**88** 73 70 **61** **43**	100
<1000*	ETHYLENEGLYCOL		**62** 43 **33**	48
<1000*	HYDROQUINONE		**110** 81	135
<1000*	ISOBUTANOL		**74** 55 **43**	70
<1000*	ISOPROPANOL		**60** **45**	47
<1000*	METHYLATED BENZENES 106/N=2 120/N=3 134/N=4		**134** **120** **106** 105 91 **57**	172
<1000*	METHYLPENTYNOL		**83** **69**	78
<1000*	PHENACETIN-M (HYDROQUINONE)		**110** 81	135
<1000*	TETRACHLOROMETHANE		**117** 82 47	147
<1000*	TOLUENE		**92** **91** 65	104
<1000*	TRICHLOROETHANOL		**148** 119 **113** 82 **77**	201
<1000*	TRICHLOROETHYLENE		**130** 95 60	167
<1000*	ETHYLENEGLYCOL	2AC	**116** **86** **43**	146
<1000*	CARBROMAL-M (ETHYL-HO-BUTYRIC ACID)	ME	**117** **87** 69 57	147
1020*	METALDEHYDE		**131** 117 **89**	169
1080	TRIMETHADIONE		**143** 128 **58**	196
1110	PARAMETHADIONE		**157** **129** 57	217
1115	CARBROMAL ARTIFACT		**157** **129** **57**	217
1120	ETHADIONE		**157** 70 **58**	218
1125	HEPTAMINOL		**130** 127 **59** 56 **44**	168
1140	DIMPYLATE ARTIFACT 1		**166** **151** 138	229
1150*	VALPROIC ACID		**144** 115 **102** **73**	198
1155*	DIMETHYLPHENOL		**122** 107	154
1160	AMPHETAMINE		**135** 120 **91** 65 **44**	174
1160	AMPHETAMINIL-M/ARTIFACT (AMPHETAMINE)		**135** 120 **91** 65 **44**	174
1160	ANILINE		**93** 66	105
1160	FENETHYLLINE-M (AMPHETAMINE)		**135** 120 **91** 65 **44**	174
1170	PHENTERMINE		**134** 91 65 **58**	172
1170	PROPYLHEXEDRINE		**155** 140 **58**	212
1180*	BENZOIC ACID METHYLESTER		**136** **105** 77	176
1180	DIMETHYLANILINE		**121** 106	152
1180	LIDOCAINE-M (DIMETHYLANILINE)		**121** 106	152
1195	METHAMPHETAMINE		**134** **91** **58**	172
1200*	METHYLSALICYLATE		**152** 120 **92** 65	210
1200*	ACETYLSALICYLIC ACID-M (DESACETYL-)	ME	**152** 120 **92** 65	210
1200*	SALICYLIC ACID	ME	**152** 120 **92** 65	210
1210	ACECARBROMAL ARTIFACT 1		**180** 129 **69**	256
1210	METHENAMINE		**140** 112	185
1215	CARBROMAL-M/ARTIFACT (CARBROMIDE)		**165** 150 114 **69**	226

RI	NAME	DERIVATIVE	TYPICAL IONS	PAGE
1225*	BENZOIC ACID ETHYLESTER		**150** 122 **105** 77	204
1225	ETHOSUXIMIDE		**141** **113** 70 **55**	188
1230	CLOMETHIAZOLE		**161** **112** 85	223
1230	ETILAMFETAMINE		**163** 148 **91** **72**	225
1230	TRANYLCYPROMINE		**133** **132** 115 **56**	171
1235*	BENZOIC ACID		**122** **105** 77	155
1235	CHLORMEZANONE ARTIFACT		**152**	208
1235	CLOMETHIAZOLE-M (DESCHLORO-HOOC-)		**157** 128 **112** 85	218
1240	AMANTADINE		**151** **94**	206
1240	P-AMINOPHENOL		**109** 80 52	131
1240	BUCETIN-M (AMINOPHENOL)		**109** 80 52	131
1240	LACTYLPHENETIDINE-M (AMINOPHENOL)		**109** 80 52	131
1240	PARACETAMOL-M (AMINOPHENOL)		**109** 80 52	131
1240	PHENACETIN-M (AMINOPHENOL)		**109** 80 52	131
1250	DIMEPHENOPANE		**163** **148** 117 91 **72**	225
1250	FENFLURAMINE		**230** 216 **159** **72**	369
1250	PENTOREX		**148** **58**	201
1260	CLOMETHIAZOLE-M (DESCHLORO-2-HO-)		**143** **128** 100	196
1270	HYDROXYSCATOL		**147** **146**	201
1270	MEMANTINE		**179** **163** 122 107 91	253
1275*	BENZOIC ACID BUTYLESTER		**178** **163** 135 105 91 77	252
1275*	DICHLORVOS		**220** 185 145 **109** 79	350
1280	BUCETIN-M (P-PHENETIDINE)		**137** **108** 80 65	178
1280	LACTYLPHENETIDINE-M (P-PHENETIDINE)		**137** **108** 80 65	178
1280	PHENACETIN-M (P-PHENETIDINE)		**137** **108** 80 65	178
1280	P-PHENETIDINE		**137** **108** 80 65	178
1285	DIETHYLALLYLACETAMIDE		**155** **140** 126 **69** **55**	212
1290	M-AMINOPHENOL		**109** **80**	132
1290	P-AMINOSALICYLIC ACID-M (M-AMINOPHENOL)		**109** **80**	132
1290	CYCLAMATE-M	AC	**141** 98 **57**	193
1295*	ACETYLSALICYLIC ACID-M (DESACETYL-)		**138** 120 **92** 64	182
1295*	SALICYLIC ACID		**138** 120 **92** 64	182
1315	CLOMETHIAZOLE-M (DESCHLORO-2-HO-)	AC	**185** 143 128 **125**	272
1320*	DICHLOROPHENOL		**162** 126 98	224
1320*	2.4-DICHLOROPHENOXYACETIC ACID-M		**162** 126 98	224
1320*	DICHLORPROP-M (DICHLOROPHENOL)		**162** 126 98	224
1320	LABETALOL ARTIFACT		**149** 132 117 **91** 57	203
1325	ETHOSUXIMIDE-M (3-HO-)		**157** **129** 86 **71**	218
1335*	DIPHENHYDRAMINE-M	HY(ME)	**198** **167** **121**	296
1340	CARBROMAL-M (HO-CARBROMIDE)		**194** 181 **165** **150** 69	284
1350	BEMEGRIDE		**155** 127 113 83 **55**	212
1350	INDOLE		**117** 90 63	147
1350*	ACETYLSALICYLIC ACID-M (DESACETYL-)	ET	**166** **120** 92 65	231
1350*	SALICYLIC ACID	ET	**166** **120** 92 65	231
1355	CHLORPHENTERMINE		**168** 125 107 **58**	236
1355	METAMFEPRAMONE		**177** **175** 152 120 **72**	251
1360	CAFEDRINE-M (NORPSEUDOEPHEDRINE)		**105** 77 **44**	125
1360	D-NORPSEUDOEPHEDRINE		**105** 77 **44**	125
1370	ETHOSUXIMIDE-M (HO-ETHYL-)		**157** 142 **113** 69	218
1375	CLOMETHIAZOLE-M (HO-)		**177** **128** 100	251
1375	EPHEDRINE		**146** 105 77 **58**	200
1375	METHYLEPHEDRINE-M (NOR-)		**146** 105 77 **58**	200

RI	NAME	DERIVATIVE	TYPICAL IONS	PAGE
1380	ACETANILIDE		**135** **93**	174
1380	CARBROMAL-M (DESBROMO-)		**143** **130** **113** 87 71	197
1380	CLOMETHIAZOLE-M (DESCHLORO-1-HO-)		**143** **113** 85	197
1380	NICOTINE		**162** 133 **84**	224
1380*	BENCYCLANE-M (OXO-) ISOMER 1	HY	**218** 190 **127** **99**	347
1390*	P-CHLOROPHENOL		**128** 100 65	163
1390*	CLOFIBRATE-M (P-CHLOROPHENOL)		**128** 100 65	163
1390*	CLOFIBRIC ACID-M (P-CHLOROPHENOL)		**128** 100 65	163
1390*	PROPOXUR-M 1	AC	**194** 152 **110**	286
1390	NICOTINIC ACID	ME	**137** **106** 78	181
1395*	ETHINAMATE		**167** **124** **95** 81	231
1395*	HYDROQUINONE	2AC	**194** 152 **110**	286
1395*	PHENACETIN-M (HYDROQUINONE)	2AC	**194** 152 **110**	286
1400	BENZAMIDE		**121** **105** 77	152
1400*	CHLOROCRESOL		**142** **107** 77	194
1400*	DIMPYLATE ARTIFACT 2		**198** 170 **138** 111	294
1415*	BENCYCLANE-M (OXO-) ISOMER 2	HY	**218** 200 128 **109** 81	347
1420*	CHLOROXYLENOL		**156** **121** 91 77	213
1420*	TRICHLOROPHENOL		**196** 132 91	291
1420	BARBITAL	2ME	**184** **169** 126 112	271
1420	METHARBITAL	ME	**184** **169** 126 112	271
1425	MEXILETINE		**179** 122 105 91 **58**	253
1430	METHYLEPHEDRINE		**151** **119** 106 **72**	206
1440*	FENOPROP-M (TRICHLOROPHENOL)		**196** 132 97	291
1440	MORAZONE-M/ARTIFACT (PHENMETRAZINE)		**177** **71** 57	251
1440	PHENMETRAZINE		**177** **71** 57	251
1440*	2.4.5-TRICHLOROPHENOL		**196** 132 97	291
1450*	CHLOROXYLENOL	AC	**198** **156** 121 91	295
1455	METHARBITAL		**170** **155** 126 112	243
1455	BARBITAL	ME	**170** **155** 126 112	243
1455	P-NITROPHENOL	ME	**153** 123 92 77	211
1455	PARATHION-ETHYL-M (P-NITROPHENOL)	ME	**153** 123 92 77	211
1460	2.2'-BIPYRIDYL		**156** 128 78	211
1460	ETHENZAMIDE-M (DESETHYL-)		**137** **120** 92 65	178
1460	LIDOCAINE-M (DIMETHYLHYDROXYANILINE)		**137** 122 107	179
1460*	MCPA		**200** **165** 141 111	298
1460	PYRAZINAMIDE		**123** **80** 53	156
1460	SALICYLAMIDE		**137** **120** 92 65	178
1465	COCAINE-M (METHYLECGONINE)		**199** 168 96 **82**	296
1470*	DIMETHYLBROMOPHENOL		**200** **121** 91 77	299
1475	PROPYLHEXEDRINE-M (HO-)		**171** 156 **58**	244
1480	PHENDIMETRAZINE		**191** 85 **57**	279
1480	CLOMETHIAZOLE-M (DESCHLORO-DI-HO-) -H2O	AC	**183** 170 141 **128**	267
1485*	MANDELIC ACID		**166** **107** 79	229
1485	PROBARBITAL	2ME	**197** 184 **169** 112	294
1490*	BENPERIDOL-M 1		**180** 125 123 95 **56**	256
1490*	BROMPERIDOL-M 1		**180** 125 123 95 **56**	256
1490*	DROPERIDOL-M 1		**180** 125 123 95 **56**	256
1490*	FLUANISONE-M 1		**180** 125 123 95 **56**	256
1490*	HALOPERIDOL-M 1		**180** 125 123 95 **56**	256
1490*	MELPERONE-M 1		**180** 125 123 95 **56**	256
1490*	MOPERONE-M 1		**180** 125 123 95 **56**	256

RI	NAME	DERIVATIVE	TYPICAL IONS	PAGE
1490*	PIPAMPERONE-M 1		**180** 125 123 95 **56**	256
1490*	TRIFLUPERIDOL-M 1		**180** 125 123 95 **56**	256
1495*	DIETHYLPHTHALATE		**222** 177 **149**	356
1495*	PHENOXYACETIC ACID METHYLESTER		**166** **107** 77	229
1495	METHYLEPHEDRINE	AC	**221** **162** 117 **72**	354
1495*	METHYLPARABEN	ME	**166** **135** 107	231
1500	BARBITAL		**167** **156** **141**	231
1500	CLOMETHIAZOLE-M (HO-)	AC	**219** 183 **141** **128**	349
1500	P-NITROPHENOL	AC	**181** 139 109 **65**	262
1500	PARATHION-ETHYL-M (P-NITROPHENOL)	AC	**181** 139 109 **65**	262
1500*	CLOFIBRATE-M (CLOFIBRIC ACID)	ME	**228** 169 **128**	368
1500*	CLOFIBRIC ACID	ME	**228** 169 **128**	368
1505	AMFEPRAMONE		**205** **203** 188 105 **100**	311
1505	TRICHLORFON		**220** 185 145 **109** 79	350
1505	AMPHETAMINE	AC	**177** 118 **86**	252
1505	AMPHETAMINIL	AC	**177** 118 **86**	252
1505	FENETHYLLINE-M (AMPHETAMINE)	AC	**177** 118 **86**	252
1505	ALLOBARBITAL	2ME	**236** **195** **138** 80	388
1510	ACECARBROMAL ARTIFACT 2		**165** **113** 98 69	227
1510	BROMISOVAL ARTIFACT		**137** 120 100	179
1510*	MCPB		**228** 169 142 **107**	366
1510*	METHYLPARABEN		**152** **121** 93 65	208
1510	FENFLURAMINE-M (DESETHYL-)	AC	**245** 226 **159** **86**	404
1510	PHENTERMINE	AC	**191** 177 **100** 86 **58**	280
1510*	P-CHLOROPHENOXYACETIC ACID	ME	**200** 141	302
1510*	MECLOFENOXATE-M	ME	**200** 141	302
1515	CARBROMAL		**208** 191 **165** **69**	317
1515*	IONOL		**220** **205** 57	350
1515	LAUDAMONIUM AMINE 1		**213** 91 71 **58**	332
1520	2.4-DINITROPHENOL		**184** 154 107 91	268
1520	PIRACETAM		**142** **98** 84 70	195
1520	PYRITHYLDIONE		**167** 152 139 **98** **83**	232
1520*	TILIDINE-M (PHENYLCYCLOHEXENONE)		**172** 104 **68**	245
1520*	O-CHLOROPHENOL-M (HO-)	2AC	**228** 186 **144**	367
1520	DOXYLAMINE-M	HY	**183** **182** 167	268
1520	NARCONUMAL	2ME	**238** 220 **195** 138 111	391
1525	METHYPRYLONE		**183** 155 **140** 98 **83**	266
1530	P-NITROPHENOL		**139** 109 93 65	183
1530	PARATHION-ETHYL-M (P-NITROPHENOL)		**139** 109 93 65	183
1530	HEPTAMINOL	2AC	**172** **169** 114 95 **86**	247
1535*	MEPROBAMATE ARTIFACT 1		**84**	81
1535	NICETHAMIDE		**178** **177** 149 **106** 78	252
1540	BROMISOVAL		**222** **163** 70 **55**	356
1540*	CLOFIBRATE		**242** 169 **128**	397
1540*	MECOPROP		**214** 155 **141** 125	335
1540	METHYPRYLONE-M (HO-)		**181** 166 **153** 98 **83**	260
1540	PENTETRAZOL		**138** 109 82 **55**	182
1540	APROBARBITAL	2ME	**238** **195** 138 111	391
1545*	ACETYLSALICYLIC ACID		**180** 138 **120** 92	256
1545*	NAPHTHOL		**144** 115	198
1545*	PROPRANOLOL-M (NAPHTHOL)		**144** 115	198
1545*	SALICYLIC ACID	AC	**180** 138 **120** 92	256

RI	NAME	DERIVATIVE	TYPICAL IONS	PAGE
1550*	O-PHENYLPHENOL		**170** 141	242
1550*	TILIDINE-M/ARTIFACT	AC	**212** **170**	329
1550	P-AMINOBENZOIC ACID	ME	**151** **120** 92 65	208
1550	BENZOCAINE-M (PABA)	ME	**151** **120** 92 65	208
1550	PROCAINE-M (PABA)	ME	**151** **120** 92 65	208
1555	CHLORMEZANONE-M/ARTIFACT		**169** **139** 111	237
1555	PROBARBITAL		**169** 156 **141** 98	238
1555*	NAPHTHOL	AC	**186** **144** 115	274
1555*	PROPRANOLOL-M (NAPHTHOL)	AC	**186** **144** 115	274
1560	CRIMIDINE		**171** 156 **142** 93	244
1560	NARCONUMAL		**209** **181** 167 124 97	320
1560*	ORPHENADRINE-M		**182** **167** 108 107	263
1560	DOXYLAMINE-M ARTIFACT -H2O	HY	**181** **180** 152	262
1565*	P-HYDROXYPHENYLACETIC ACID		**152** **107**	208
1565	BUTABARBITAL	2ME	**211** 184 **169**	328
1570	TRIFLUPERIDOL-M 2		**223** 154 127	357
1570	PROPYLHEXEDRINE	AC	**197** 182 140 **100** 58	293
1575	ETHENZAMIDE		**165** 150 **120** 92	227
1575	MEFENOREX		**91** **84** 56	102
1575	METHAMPHETAMINE	AC	**191** **100** **58**	280
1580*	CLOFIBRATE-M (CLOFIBRIC ACID) ARTIFACT		**168** **128**	236
1580*	CLOFIBRIC ACID ARTIFACT		**168** **128**	236
1580*	ETHYLPARABEN		**166** 138 **121**	229
1580	FENFLURAMINE	AC	**254** 216 **159** 114 **72**	426
1580	PENTOREX	AC	**148** 131 **100** **58**	202
1585	FENPROPOREX		**97** 57	108
1585	OMETHOATE		**213** **156** **110** 79 58	332
1585	PROPOXUR		**209** 152 **110**	320
1585	BUTOBARBITAL	2ME	**212** 184 **169** 112	332
1590	PEMOLINE	2ME	**204** 190 **118** 90	310
1595	ALLOBARBITAL		**208** 193 **167** 141 **124** 80	317
1595	COCAINE-M (METHYLECGONINE)	AC	**241** **182** 96 **82**	396
1595	AMOBARBITAL	2ME	**239** 225 **184** **169**	393
1600	CROTAMITON		**203** 188 120 **69**	306
1600*	DICHLORPROP		**234** **199** 175 145 111	381
1600	MOPERONE-M 2		**169** 91	238
1600	MEMANTINE	AC	**221** 164 150 122 107	354
1600	P-AMINOSALICYLIC ACID	ME	**167** **135** 107 79	235
1600	TALBUTAL	2ME	**234** **195** 181 138 111	383
1605	NICOTINAMIDE		**122** 106 78	155
1610	APROBARBITAL		**210** 195 **167** 124	324
1610*	GUAIFENESIN		**198** **124** 109	294
1610	IDOBUTAL	2ME	**223** **195** 181 169 138	359
1620	CROTYLBARBITAL		**210** 181 **156** **141** **55**	324
1620	NEALBARBITAL	2ME	**250** 209 195 **169** 57	419
1625	METRONIDAZOLE		**171** 124 **81** 54	244
1630	DOXYLAMINE	HY	**199** 184	298
1630	BUTALBITAL	(ME)	**223** 195 **182** 181 155	360
1630	PENTOBARBITAL	2ME	**225** **184** 169	363
1630	THIOPENTAL-M (PENTOBARBITAL)	2ME	**225** **184** 169	363
1635	TRANYLCYPROMINE	AC	**175** **132** **116** 84 56	249
1640*	CLOFIBRATE-M (CLOFIBRIC ACID)		**214** 168 **128** 86 65	335

RI	NAME	DERIVATIVE	TYPICAL IONS	PAGE
1640*	CLOFIBRIC ACID		**214** 168 **128** 86 65	335
1640	AMANTADINE	AC	**193 136** 94	283
1645*	BENZATROPINE	HY	**184 105** 77	270
1645*	DIPHENHYDRAMINE	HY	**184 105** 77	270
1645*	DIPHENYLPYRALINE	HY	**184 105** 77	270
1645	BARBITURIC ACID	3ME	**170** 113 98 82	244
1650	DIPROPYLBARBITAL		**170 141** 98	242
1650	HALOPERIDOL-M 2		**189** 154 127	276
1650	ISONIAZID		**137** 106 **78**	179
1650*	CHLORPHENOXAMINE	HY	**232 217** 139 **77**	377
1650*	CLEMASTINE	HY	**232 217** 139 **77**	377
1650*	MECLOXAMINE	HY	**232 217** 139 **77**	377
1655	BUTABARBITAL		**183 156 141**	266
1655	BUTALBITAL	2ME	**237** 209 **196** 195 169	390
1655	VINYLBITAL	2ME	**223** 209 **182** 97	360
1660	ETHENZAMIDE-M (DESETHYL-)	AC	**179** 137 **120** 92	255
1660	SALICYLAMIDE	AC	**179** 137 **120** 92	255
1660	BENZOIC ACID GLYCINE CONJUGATE	ME	**193** 134 **105** 77	284
1660	HIPPURIC ACID	ME	**193** 134 **105** 77	284
1665	BUTOBARBITAL		**184** 167 **156 141**	269
1665	SECOBARBITAL-M (DESALLYL-)		**169** 154 **129**	238
1665	VINYLBITAL-M (DESVINYL-)		**169** 154 **129**	238
1665	METRONIDAZOLE	AC	**213** 171 **87**	335
1670	ATRAZINE-M (DESETHYL-DESCHLORO-METHOXY-)		**183 168** 141 70 **58**	266
1670	VINBARBITAL	2ME	**223** 166 138	360
1675	CROTETHAMIDE		**226** 181 **154 86** 69	363
1675	ETILAMFETAMINE	AC	**205 114** 91 **72**	312
1680	ATRAZINE-M (DESETHYL-)		**187 172** 70 **58**	274
1680	BECLAMIDE ARTIFACT		**161** 117 106 91 **55**	223
1680*	BENZYLPHENOL ISOMER 1		**184** 165 106 78	269
1680	PHENACETIN		**179** 137 109 **108**	254
1680	BUCETIN-M (P-PHENETIDINE)	AC	**179** 137 109 **108**	254
1680	LACTYLPHENETIDINE-M (P-PHENETIDINE)	AC	**179** 137 109 **108**	254
1680	P-PHENETIDINE	AC	**179** 137 109 **108**	254
1680*	PROPOXUR-M 2	2AC	**210** 168 **126**	325
1685	DIMPYLATE ARTIFACT 3		**152 137** 109 84	208
1685	FENCAMFAMINE		**215** 186 98 84 **58**	337
1690	BUTALBITAL		**209** 181 **168** 167 **141**	320
1690*	HEXACHLOROBENZENE		**282** 247 212 177 142	486
1690	MESCALINE		**211 181**	325
1690	SIMAZINE		**201** 186 173 84 **72**	303
1690	SECOBARBITAL	2ME	**248 196** 181 138 111	414
1700*	BUTYLPARABEN		**194 138 121**	285
1700	IDOBUTAL		**181 167** 124	261
1700*	KETAMINE-M (DESAMINO-HO-) -H2O		**204 169** 139	308
1700*	BENZATROPINE	HYAC	**226** 184 **165** 105 **77**	364
1700*	DIPHENHYDRAMINE	HYAC	**226** 184 **165** 105 **77**	364
1700*	DIPHENYLPYRALINE	HYAC	**226** 184 **165** 105 **77**	364
1700*	ORPHENADRINE ARTIFACT	HY	**196 195** 165 91 77	292
1705*	KAVAIN -CO2		**186** 128 95	273
1705	TALBUTAL		**167** 153 124 97	233
1710	AMOBARBITAL		**211** 198 **197 156 141**	326

RI	NAME	DERIVATIVE	TYPICAL IONS	PAGE
1710	LAUDAMONIUM AMINE 2		**241** 91 **58**	395
1710*	CHLORPHENOXAMINE ARTIFACT -H2O	HY	**214** **179** 139	336
1710*	CLEMASTINE ARTIFACT -H2O	HY	**214** **179** 139	336
1710*	MECLOXAMINE ARTIFACT -H2O	HY	**214** **179** 139	336
1710*	MYRISTIC ACID	ME	**242** 185 87 **74**	399
1715	COTININE		**176** 118 **98**	250
1715	NICOTINE-M (COTININE)		**176** 118 **98**	250
1715*	ADIPHENINE-M/ARTIFACT (HOOC-)	(ME)	**226** **167** 152	364
1720	ACECARBROMAL		**191** **149** 113 **69**	279
1720	ATRAZINE		**215** **200** 173 **58**	337
1720	BECLAMIDE		**197** 162 148 106 **91**	293
1720*	BENZYLPHENOL ISOMER 2		**184** 165 106 91 77	269
1720*	MEPROBAMATE ARTIFACT 2		**101** **84** 56	123
1720	NEALBARBITAL		**223** 181 167 **141** **57**	357
1720	VINYLBITAL	(ME)	**209** 195 **168** 83	323
1725	CROPROPAMIDE		**240** 195 **168** **100** 69	394
1725	DIMETHOATE		**229** 125 93 **87**	368
1725	BRALLOBARBITAL	2ME	**235** 193	386
1730	TOCAINIDE		**192** 176 147 121 **57**	281
1730	TRYPTAMINE		**160** **130** 103 77	222
1730	TRYPTOPHAN-M (TRYPTAMINE)		**160** **130** 103 77	222
1730	CHLORPHENTERMINE	AC	**225** **166** 100 86 **58**	363
1730	DROPERIDOL-M 2	2AC	**218** 176 **134** 106	346
1730	PIMOZIDE-M 1	2AC	**218** 176 **134** 106	346
1735	P-AMINOSALICYLIC ACID	2ME	**181** 149 121	262
1735	METHOHEXITAL	ME	**261** **235** 195 178 **81**	440
1735	PROPYPHENAZONE-M (NOR-)	ME	**230** **215** 200 185 77	372
1740*	LINDANE		**288** 252 217 **181** 109	498
1740	METHYLPHENIDATE		**150** 91 **84**	205
1740	PENTOBARBITAL		**197** **156** **141**	293
1740	THIOPENTAL-M (PENTOBARBITAL)		**197** **156** **141**	293
1740	CAFEDRINE-M (NORPSEUDOEPHEDRINE)	2AC	**235** 176 **129** 107 **86**	385
1740	D-NORPSEUDOEPHEDRINE	2AC	**235** 176 **129** 107 **86**	385
1745	BENZOIC ACID GLYCINE CONJUGATE		**161** 117 **105** 77	223
1745	HIPPURIC ACID		**161** 117 **105** 77	223
1745	TYRAMINE		**137** **108** 77	179
1745	VINYLBITAL		**154** 83	211
1745	METARAMINOL -H2O	2AC	**233** 93 **69**	379
1745	HEXETHAL	2ME	**210** 184 **169** 112 55	325
1745	PROPALLYLONAL	2ME	**237** **195** 138	390
1750	HALOPERIDOL-M 3		**223** 189 **84** **56**	357
1750*	BENCYCLANE-M (OXO-)	HYAC	**260** 218 200 127 **91**	436
1750*	ORPHENADRINE	HYAC	**240** **180** 165	395
1750	PIPERAZINE	2AC	**170** 85 69 **56**	243
1750	AMOBARBITAL-M (HO-)	2ME	**270** 255 **184** 169 **137**	460
1750*	HOMOVANILLIC ACID	ME	**196** **137** 107	292
1750*	LEVODOPA-M (HOMOVANILLIC ACID)	ME	**196** **137** 107	292
1755	AMPHETAMINIL		**132** 105	170
1755*	PROPOXYPHENE ARTIFACT		**208** 130 **115** 91	317
1755	BUCETIN-M (HO-P-PHENETIDINE)	2AC	**237** 195 **153** 124	390
1755	LACTYLPHENETIDINE-M (HO-P-PHENETIDINE)	2AC	**237** 195 **153** 124	390
1755	PHENACETIN-M (HO-)	AC	**237** 195 **153** 124	390

RI	NAME	DERIVATIVE	TYPICAL IONS	PAGE
1760	BUTETAMATE		**263** 248 191 99 **86**	443
1760	DIMETHYLPHENYLTHIAZOLANIMIN		**206** 132 118 83 **58**	313
1760*	FENOPROP		**268** **233** 209 181	454
1760*	KETAMINE-M (DESAMINO-HO-)		**222** 187 **113**	356
1760*	MYRISTIC ACID		**228** 185 **129** 73 **56**	366
1760*	PENTACHLOROPHENOL		**264** 228 200 165	446
1760	PETHIDINE		**247** 218 172 **71**	410
1760*	ORPHENADRINE	HY	**198** 180 165 119 **77**	295
1765	PROPYPHENAZONE-M (NOR-)		**216** **174** 77	339
1765	VINBARBITAL		**195** 152 **141** 134 69	287
1765	P-AMINOPHENOL	2AC	**193** 151 **109**	283
1765	BUCETIN-M (P-AMINOPHENOL)	2AC	**193** 151 **109**	283
1765	LACTYLPHENETIDINE-M (P-AMINOPHENOL)	2AC	**193** 151 **109**	283
1765	PARACETAMOL	AC	**193** 151 **109**	283
1765	PHENACETIN-M (P-AMINOPHENOL)	2AC	**193** 151 **109**	283
1770	PROPALLYLONAL-M (DESBROMO-OXO-)		**226** 184 **169** 141	363
1775	CYCLOPENTOBARBITAL	2ME	**221** 196 **67**	356
1780*	DISULFOTON		**274** 186 125 97 **88**	465
1780	MEPHENYTOIN		**218** **189** **104**	343
1780	METHOHEXITAL		**262** 246 233 **221** **79**	440
1780	PARACETAMOL		**151** **109** 80	206
1780	PHENACETIN-M (DESETHYL-)		**151** **109** 80	206
1780	PROPYPHENAZONE-M (NOR-HO-)		**232** 190 121 **93** 77	375
1780	MEXILETINE	AC	**221** **122** **100** 77 58	355
1785*	MEPROBAMATE		**144** 114 96 **83** **55**	198
1785	SPARTEINE		**234** 193 137 **98**	381
1790	LIDOCAINE-M (DESETHYL-)		**206** 149 **58**	313
1790	MECLOFENOXATE		**257** 111 **58**	429
1790	THIOBUTABARBITAL		**228** 172 **156** 141 97	366
1790*	NORFENEFRINE-M (DESAMINO-HO-)	3AC	**280** **220** 178 **136** 123	482
1790	PHENYLMETHYLBARBITAL	2ME	**246** **132** 104	410
1795	BRALLOBARBITAL-M (DESBROMO-OXO-)		**224** 181 **167** 141 124	360
1795	SECOBARBITAL		**209** **195** **168** 167 141	320
1795	EPHEDRINE	2AC	**249** **189** **100** **58**	415
1795	METHYLEPHEDRINE-M (NOR-)	2AC	**249** **189** **100** **58**	415
1800	BENZYLNICOTINATE		**213** 168 106 **91**	332
1800	CARBAMAZEPINE-M (ACRIDINE)		**179** 151	254
1800	HALOPERIDOL-M 4		**211** 139 **84** **56**	326
1800	LOPERAMIDE-M		**211** 139 **84** **56**	326
1800	MORAZONE-M		**204** **92**	308
1800	PYRITINOL-M		**207**	314
1800	PETHIDINE-M (DESETHYL-)	(ME)	**233** 218 **158** **71**	380
1805	NARCOBARBITAL		**223** 181 138 124	357
1805	PHENIRAMINE		**182** **169** 72 **58**	263
1805	HEXOBARBITAL	ME	**250** **235** 169 81	419
1810	MORAZONE-M/ARTIFACT (PHENMETRAZINE)	AC	**219** 176 **113** 86 **71**	349
1810	PHENDIMETRAZINE-M (NOR-)	AC	**219** 176 113 **100** 58	349
1810	PHENMETRAZINE	AC	**219** 176 **113** 86 **71**	349
1810	ACETYLSALICYLIC ACID-M	ME	**209** **121** 92 65	323
1810	SALICYLIC ACID GLYCINE CONJUGATE	ME	**209** **121** 92 65	323
1815	MORAZONE-M/ARTIFACT		**188** 105 **77**	275
1815*	PENTACHLOROPHENOL	ME	**278** 263 235	476

RI	NAME	DERIVATIVE	TYPICAL IONS	PAGE
1820	BENZOCAINE		**165** 137 **120** 92 65	227
1820	CAFFEINE		**194** **109** 82 67 55	285
1820*	2.4-DICHLOROPHENOXYACETIC ACID (2.4-D)		**220** 175 **162** 133 111	350
1820	LOBELINE		**120** **105** 77	150
1820	TILIDINE-M (NOR-)		**259** **83** 68	433
1820	TOLIPROLOL ARTIFACT		**235** 220 127 108 **56**	383
1820	PROPYPHENAZONE-M (NOR-)	AC	**258** 216 **201** 77	432
1820	P-AMINOBENZOIC ACID	ET	**165** 137 **120** 92 65	227
1825	ALPRENOLOL		**249** 234 205 100 **72**	414
1825*	DITAZOL-M (BENZIL)		**210** **105** 77	324
1825	ISONIAZID	2AC	**221** 179 **161** 137 106	355
1825	THIOPENTAL	2ME	**200** 185 97 69	303
1830	AMOBARBITAL-M (HO-) -H2O		**224** 195 156 **141** **69**	361
1830	GLUTETHIMIDE		**217** **189** 160 132 117	341
1830	INSTILLAGEL (TM) INGREDIENT		**232** **218** 132 85 **71**	375
1830	MORAZONE-M		**193** 107 **71** 56	282
1830	PHENDIMETRAZINE-M (NOR-HO-)		**193** 107 **71** 56	282
1830	PHENMETRAZINE-M (HO-)		**193** 107 **71** 56	282
1830*	PROPAFENONE-M (PHENOL)		**226** 194 **121**	363
1830	TETRYZOLINE		**200** 185 171	299
1835	BRALLOBARBITAL-M (DESBROMO-HO-DIHYDRO-)		**183** **139** 95 67	266
1835	HEXETHAL		**211** **156** **141** 55	326
1835	KETAMINE		**237** 209 **180** 152	388
1835	MELPERONE-M 2		**112**	137
1835	PHYSOSTIGMINE-M/ARTIFACT		**218** **174** 160 94	343
1835	TILIDINE		**273** **176** **97** 82	463
1835	ZOMEPIRAC	ME	**305** **246** 139 111	535
1840	ISONIAZID ACETONE DERIVATE		**177** 162 106 **78**	251
1840	PROPIVANE		**277** **205** 99 **86** 58	470
1840	TILIDINE-M (BIS-NOR-)		**245** **83** **69**	402
1840*	BENACTYZINE-M (HOOC-)	ME	**242** **183** 105 77	400
1845	MORAZONE-M/ARTIFACT (PHENAZONE)		**188** 96 77	276
1845	PHENAZONE		**188** 96 77	276
1845	CYCLOBARBITAL	2ME	**264** **235** 169	446
1850	BRALLOBARBITAL		**207** 165 124	315
1850	BROMPERIDOL-M 2		**233** 154 127	377
1850	DICHLORQUINOLINOL		**213** 185 150	333
1850	DIURON		**219** **187** 174 124 59	347
1850*	NOXIPTYLINE-M		**208** 180 165	317
1850	PRILOCAINE		**220** **86**	350
1850*	ETODROXIZINE ARTIFACT	HY	**216** 139 **105** 77	341
1850*	HYDROXYZINE ARTIFACT	HY	**216** 139 **105** 77	341
1850*	MECLOZINE ARTIFACT	HY	**216** 139 **105** 77	341
1855	AMINOPHENAZONE-M (DESAMINO-HO-)		**204** 120 **85** 56	309
1855	HEXOBARBITAL		**236** **221** **157** 155 81	387
1855	PARATHION-METHYL		**263** 233 125 **109** 79	444
1855	PHENAZONE-M (HO-)		**204** 120 **85** 56	309
1855	THIOPENTAL		**242** 173 **172** 157	397
1855	VILOXAZINE		**237** **138** 100 **56**	389
1860	P-AMINOSALICYLIC ACID-M ACETYL CONJUGATE		**151** **109** 80	207
1860	M-AMINOPHENOL	AC	**151** **109** 80	207
1860	SALICYLAMIDE-M (HO-)	2AC	**237** **195** 153 **136** 108	390

RI	NAME	DERIVATIVE	TYPICAL IONS	PAGE
1860	METHYLPHENOBARBITAL	ME	**260** **232** 175 146 118	438
1860	PHENOBARBITAL	2ME	**260** **232** 175 146 118	438
1865	CYCLOPENTOBARBITAL		**193** 169 **67**	282
1865	GLUTETHIMIDE-M (HO-ETHYL-)		**233** 205 189 **146** 104	378
1865*	TIAPROFENIC ACID		**260** **216** 201 **139** 77	435
1865*	GUAIFENESIN	2AC	**282** **159**	487
1870*	BORNYL SALICYLATE		**274** **137** 121 **81**	465
1870	DIPHENHYDRAMINE		**255** **165** 152 73 **58**	427
1870	OXYPERTINE-M (PHENYLPIPERAZINE)	AC	**204** 161 **132** 56	310
1875	GLUTETHIMIDE-M (HO-PHENYL-)		**233** **204** 176 148 133	378
1875	LIDOCAINE		**234** **86** 72 58	381
1875	MOPERONE-M 3		**185** 156	272
1875	PROPALLYLONAL		**209** **167** 124	321
1880	BUTOBARBITAL-M (OXO-)		**226** 198 **156** **141**	364
1880	PHENYLMETHYLBARBITAL		**218** **132** 104 78	343
1880*	FLURBIPROFEN	ME	**258** **199** 183 170	433
1885	LACTYLPHENETIDINE		**209** 137 109 **108**	321
1885	PETHIDINE-M (NOR-)		**233** **158** **57**	378
1885	TOLMETINE		**212** 198 122 91	328
1885*	CLOROFENE	AC	**260** **218** 183 140	437
1885	LIDOCAINE-M (DIMETHYLHYDROXYANILINE)	2AC	**221** 179 **137**	355
1890	BROMPERIDOL-M 3		**267** **233** 127 94 **56**	452
1890	DIPHENHYDRAMINE-M (HO-)		**213** **183** 167 **58**	333
1890	MELPERONE		**263** 125 **112**	444
1890	PARAOXON		**275** **149** **109** 99 81	467
1890	PARATHION-ETHYL-M (PARAOXON)		**275** **149** **109** 99 81	467
1890	PENTOBARBITAL-M (HO-) -H2O		**224** 195 **156** **141** **69**	361
1890	PHENCYCLIDINE		**243** **200** 91 84	400
1890*	ETODROXIZINE	HYAC	**260** 200 **165** 105	437
1890*	HYDROXYZINE	HYAC	**260** 200 **165** 105	437
1890*	MECLOZINE	HYAC	**260** 200 **165** 105	437
1895	AMINOPHENAZONE		**231** 123 97 **56**	373
1895*	DIPHENHYDRAMINE-M (DI-HO-)		**244** **213** **167**	401
1895	METHYLPHENOBARBITAL		**246** **218** 146 117	406
1895	PROPYPHENAZONE-M (NOR-HO-)	AC	**274** 232 214 **190**	465
1895	PHENOBARBITAL	ME	**246** **218** 146 117	406
1900	BROMACIL		**260** 231 **205** 188 162	435
1900	ETAMIVAN		**223** **151** 72	358
1900*	FLURBIPROFEN		**244** **199** 183 170	401
1900*	MELITRACENE-M (RING)		**208** **193** 178	318
1900	MELPERONE-M 3 -H2O		**261** 125 123 **112**	438
1900	NIFENALOL ARTIFACT		**236** 221 191 **151** 77	387
1900	ORPHENADRINE-M (NOR-)		**255** **180** 165 86	427
1900	PARATHION-ETHYL-M (AMINO-)		**261** **125** **109** 80	439
1900	FENPROPOREX	AC	**139** **97**	184
1900	LIDOCAINE-M (DIMETHYLHYDROXYANILINE)	3AC	**263** 221 **179** 137	445
1900*	OXPRENOLOL-M (DESAMINO-HO-)	2AC	**308** 249 **159** 99	540
1900*	PROPRANOLOL-M (HO-NAPHTHOL)	2AC	**244** 202 **160**	402
1900	TETRYZOLINE-M 1	AC	**229** 157 **115** **98**	368
1900*	ETODROXIZINE	HY(ME)	**232** 201 165 **105** 77	377
1900*	HYDROXYZINE	HY(ME)	**232** 201 165 **105** 77	377
1900*	MECLOZINE	HY(ME)	**232** 201 165 **105** 77	377

RI	NAME	DERIVATIVE	TYPICAL IONS	PAGE
1905	DIMETACRINE-M (RING)		**209** **194**	321
1905	TRAMADOL -H2O		**245** **184** **58**	402
1910*	FENSULFOTHION IMPURITY		**292** 156 140 125 97	507
1910	PROPYPHENAZONE		**230** **215** 56	369
1910	SIGMODAL	2ME	**265** **195** 138	450
1915	AMOBARBITAL-M (HO-)		**227** 195 157 **156** **141**	365
1915	BUPRANOLOL ARTIFACT		**283** **268** 142 86 70	487
1915*	DIBUTYLPHTHALATE		**278** 222 205 **149**	474
1915	PROPYLHEXEDRINE-M (HO-)	2AC	**255** 240 195 **100** **58**	427
1915	HEPTABARBITAL	2ME	**249** 169 133	417
1920	BUTOBARBITAL-M (HO-)		**213** 199 **156** **141**	333
1920	DOXYLAMINE		**270** **200** 183 167 71 **58**	458
1920	PANTHENOL		**205** **175** 157 **133** 102	311
1920	PANTHENOL ARTIFACT		**189** 159 145 **71**	276
1920	PENFLURIDOL-M 1		**257** 222 167	429
1920*	GUAIFENESIN-M (O-DESMETHYL-)	3AC	**310** 268 204 **159**	545
1920*	OXPRENOLOL-M (DESAMINO-HO-DESALKYL-)	3AC	**310** 268 204 **159**	545
1925	BUTABARBITAL-M (HO-)		**213** 199 181 **156** **141**	333
1925	AMIPHENAZOLE	2ME	**219** **191** 147 121 77	349
1930	DESIPRAMINE-M (RING)		**195** 180	287
1930	IMIPRAMINE-M (RING)		**195** 180	287
1930	LOFEPRAMINE-M (RING)		**195** 180	287
1930	TRIMIPRAMINE-M (RING)		**195** 180	287
1935	ORPHENADRINE		**181** **165** 73 **58**	261
1935	PRIMIDONE-M (DIAMIDE)		**163** 148 103 91	226
1935	MEFENOREX	AC	**253** 162 **120**	425
1940	BUTALBITAL-M (OXO-)		**240** **168** 167 141	394
1940*	MALATHION		**330** 285 **173** **127** 93	581
1940	PARACETAMOL-M (METHOXY-)	AC	**223** 181 **139**	358
1945*	ALDRIN		**362** 327 291 263 **261**	617
1945	AMINOPHENAZONE-M (BIS-NOR-) ARTIFACT		**180** **119** 91	257
1945	METAMIZOL-M (BIS-DESALKYL-) ARTIFACT		**180** **119** 91	257
1945	NIFENAZONE-M (DESACYL-) ARTIFACT		**180** **119** 91	257
1945*	POLICHLORINATED BIPHENYL (4CL)		**290** 220 **149**	503
1945*	TETRACHLOROBIPHENYL		**290** 220 **149**	503
1945	TRAMADOL		**263** **58**	444
1950*	CLOROFENE		**218** 183 140	344
1950	DROPERIDOL-M 2		**134** 106 79 67	172
1950	PIMOZIDE-M 1		**134** 106 79 67	172
1950	TRIFLUPERIDOL-M 3		**257** 223 173 145 **56**	430
1950	ISONIAZID	AC	**179** 137 **106** 78	255
1950	TYRAMINE	2AC	**221** 162 **120** 107	355
1950	CETOBEMIDONE	ME	**261** **204** **70**	440
1955	AMINOPHENAZONE-M (BIS-NOR-)		**203** 93 **84** **56**	306
1955	METAMIZOL-M (BIS-DESALKYL-)		**203** 93 **84** **56**	306
1955	NIFENAZONE-M (DESACYL-)		**203** 93 **84** **56**	306
1955	PENTOBARBITAL-M (HO-)		**227** 197 195 **156** **141**	365
1960	LACTYLPHENETIDINE	AC	**251** **137** 109 108	421
1960	NIFLUMIC ACID	ME	**296** 263 236 168 145	519
1965*	PALMITIC ACID		**256** 129 73 **56**	428
1965	PHENOBARBITAL		**232** **204** 161 117	375
1965	PRIMIDONE-M (PHENOBARBITAL)		**232** **204** 161 117	375

RI	NAME	DERIVATIVE	TYPICAL IONS	PAGE
1970	CYCLOBARBITAL		**236** **207** 141	387
1970*	DOXEPIN-M (N-OXIDE) -(CH3)2NOH		**234** 219 165	382
1970	PARATHION-ETHYL		**291** 137 **109** 97	505
1970	PROPYPHENAZONE-M (ISOPROPENYL-)		**228** **136** 95	366
1970	SECOBARBITAL-M (HO-) -H2O		**236** **168** 167 70	387
1970	TRIFLUPERIDOL-M 4		**245** 227 **56**	403
1970	ETAMIVAN	AC	**265** 223 195 **151** 72	447
1975*	AMITRIPTYLINE-M (N-OXIDE) -(CH3)2NOH		**232** 217 202	376
1975*	AMITRIPTYLINOXIDE -(CH3)2NOH		**232** 217 202	376
1975	CYCLOPHOSPHAMIDE ARTIFACT		**224** **175** 147 69	361
1975	TRAMADOL-M (O-DESMETHYL-) -H2O		**231** **184** **58**	373
1975	LACTYLPHENETIDINE-M (O-DESETHYL-)	2AC	**265** **223** 151 **109**	448
1980	AMINOPHENAZONE-M (NOR-)		**217** 123 98 **83** **56**	341
1980	BUNITROLOL ARTIFACT		**260** **245** 86 70 57	435
1980	CHLORPYRIFOS		**349** 314 286 **197** **97**	606
1980	METAMIZOL-M (DESALKYL-)		**217** 123 98 **83** **56**	341
1980	THEOBROMINE		**180** 137 109	257
1980	TRIADIMEFON		**293** **208** 181 128 **57**	510
1985	CARBAMAZEPINE-M/ARTIFACT		**193** 165	282
1985	IMIPRAMINE-M (HO-RING) -H2O		**193** 165	282
1985	OPIPRAMOL-M (RING)		**193** 165	282
1985	OXPRENOLOL ARTIFACT		**277** 262 248 148 **56**	471
1985	P-AMINOBENZOIC ACID	MEAC	**193** 151 **120** 92 65	284
1985	BENZOCAINE-M (PABA)	MEAC	**193** 151 **120** 92 65	284
1985	PROCAINE-M (PABA)	MEAC	**193** 151 **120** 92 65	284
1990	P-AMINOBENZOIC ACID	ETAC	**207** 165 137 **120** 92	316
1990	BENZOCAINE	AC	**207** 165 137 **120** 92	316
1990*	DIFLUNISAL	2ME	**278** 247 204 188 175	476
1995*	BROMOPHOS		**364** **329** 211 **125**	618
1995	METAMIZOL		**215** **123** 56	337
1995	TRAMADOL-M (O-DESMETHYL-)		**249** 204 97 **58**	414
1995	VINYLBITAL-M (HO-)		**195** 179 **154** 83	288
1995	P-AMINOSALICYLIC ACID ACETYL CONJUGATE	ME	**209** 167 **135**	323
2000*	AMITRIPTYLINE-M (HO-N-OXIDE) -H2O -(CH3)2NOH		**230** 215	370
2000*	AMITRIPTYLINOXIDE-M (HO-) -H2O -(CH3)2NOH		**230** 215	370
2000	DROPERIDOL-M 3 -H2O		**241** **112**	395
2000*	NOXIPTYLINE-M -H2O		**206** **178** 152	314
2000	TETRYZOLINE-M 2	AC	**242** 200 157 **115** **98**	398
2000	TRAMADOL-M (O-DESMETHYL-) -H2O	AC	**273** **184** **58**	463
2005	FENCAMFAMINE-M (DESETHYL-)	AC	**229** **170** **142**	369
2005	ORPHENADRINE-M	HYAC	**239** **180** 165	393
2010	ALIMEMAZINE-M (RING)		**199** 167	296
2010	DIXYRAZINE-M (RING)		**199** 167	296
2010	PECAZINE-M (RING)		**199** 167	296
2010	PERAZINE-M (RING)		**199** 167	296
2010	PHENOTHIAZINE		**199** 167	296
2010	PROMAZINE-M (RING)		**199** 167	296
2010	PROMETHAZINE-M (RING)		**199** 167	296
2020	BUCETIN		**223** 205 **179** 137 109 **108**	358
2020	CHLORPHENAMINE		**203** 167 72 **58**	307
2020	DIMETACRINE-M (N-OXIDE) -(CH3)2NOH		**249** **234** 194	415
2020	PENOXALIN		**281** **252**	483

RI	NAME	DERIVATIVE	TYPICAL IONS	PAGE
2020	XYLOMETAZOLINE		**244** 229 214 119 91	401
2020	TRAZODONE-M 1	2AC	**227** 185 **143**	365
2025	CARBAMAZEPINE-M (ACRIDINE-CHO)		**207** **179** 151	315
2025	PROCAINE		**164** 120 **99** **86**	226
2025	THEOPHYLLINE		**180** 95 68	257
2030	BUTANILICAINE		**223** 141 **98** 86 **57**	358
2030	NORMETHADONE-M (NOR-)		**263** 220	444
2030	AMBROXOL-M/ARTIFACT	AC	**317** 304 **275**	559
2030*	METHOXYHYDROXYPHENYLGLYCOL (MHPG)	3AC	**310** 268 208 **166** 153	545
2030	FLURAZEPAM-M (DESALKYL-)	HY	**249** 154 122 95	416
2035	NEFOPAM		**253** 225 **179** 165 **58**	424
2035	TRIFLUPERIDOL-M 4	AC	**287** 269 244 227 99 **57**	496
2040	BRALLOBARBITAL-M (OXO-)		**223**	358
2040	ETIDOCAINE		**276** **259** 245 **128** 86	469
2040	METHADONE-M		**277** 262 248 165	471
2040	ZOMEPIRAC		**246** 211 136	406
2040	TOCAINIDE	AC	**234** 147 **121** 106 87	383
2045	ISOPYRIN		**245** 230 137 83 **56**	403
2045	PHENALLYMAL		**244** **215** 141 104	401
2045	PROTHIPENDYL-M (RING)		**200** 168 155	300
2050	CAMAZEPAM-M	HY	**231** **230** 154 105 77	375
2050	CHLORDIAZEPOXIDE	HY	**231** **230** 154 105 77	375
2050	CLORAZEPATE	HY	**231** **230** 154 105 77	375
2050	DIAZEPAM-M	HY	**231** **230** 154 105 77	375
2050	KETAZOLAM-M	HY	**231** **230** 154 105 77	375
2050	MEDAZEPAM-M	HY	**231** **230** 154 105 77	375
2050	OXAZEPAM	HY	**231** **230** 154 105 77	375
2050	OXAZOLAM-M	HY	**231** **230** 154 105 77	375
2050	PRAZEPAM-M	HY	**231** **230** 154 105 77	375
2050	TEMAZEPAM-M	HY	**231** **230** 154 105 77	375
2055	HEXOBARBITAL-M (OXO-)		**250** **235** 193 156 **95**	417
2055	NIFLUMIC ACID -CO2		**238** **237** 217 168 145	390
2055	SIGMODAL		**237** 193 **167** 122 78	389
2055	DOXYLAMINE-M (HO-)	AC	**239** **196** 71 **58**	393
2055	MOPERONE-M 3	AC	**227** **185**	365
2055	PANTHENOL	3AC	**331** 211 **169** 115 109	583
2060	KETAZOLAM-M ARTIFACT 1		**240** **239** 205	394
2060	OXAZEPAM ARTIFACT 1		**240** **239** 205	394
2060*	TRICOSANE		**288** 252 218 146 114	498
2060	DROPERIDOL-M 4	3AC	**276** 234 192 **150**	470
2060	GLUTETHIMIDE-M (HO-ETHYL-)	AC	**275** 247 233 **189** **187**	467
2060	PRILOCAINE	AC	**262** **156** 128 107 **86**	442
2065	CYCLOPHOSPHAMIDE		**260** **211** **175** 147 69	436
2065*	PROPRANOLOL-M (DESAMINO-HO-)		**218** **144** 115	344
2065	METARAMINOL	3AC	**293** **233** 191 86 **69**	511
2070	BENZOCTAMINE		**249** **218** 191 178	415
2070	HEPTABARBITAL		**221** **141**	352
2070	KETAZOLAM-M ARTIFACT 2		**254** **253** 219	425
2070	OXAZEPAM ARTIFACT 2		**254** **253** 219	425
2070	BUNITROLOL	AC	**275** 119 98 **86** 56	468
2070	LEVODOPA-M	2AC	**251** 209 **150** 137	421
2075	CETOBEMIDONE		**247** 218 190 **70**	411

RI	NAME	DERIVATIVE	TYPICAL IONS	PAGE
2075	8-CHLOROTHEOPHYLLINE		**214** 157 129 68	335
2075	MEPIVACAINE		**246 98** 70	406
2080	PROPYPHENAZONE-M (NOR-HO-PHENYL-)		**232 190** 121 93 65	376
2080	PROXYPHYLLINE		**238 194** 180 137 109	391
2080	NEFOPAM-M (NOR-)	AC	**281 208** 194 179 87	485
2085	ATROPINE -H2O		**271** 140 **124** 96 82	460
2085	CAMYLOFINE		**320** 235 204 135 **86**	563
2085	HYOSCYAMINE -H2O		**271** 140 **124** 96 82	460
2085	NIFLUMIC ACID		**282** 263 **237** 168 145	486
2085	FENCAMFAMINE	AC	**257 170 142** 58	430
2085	METHYLPHENIDATE	AC	**275** 126 **84**	468
2085	NORFENEFRINE	3AC	**279 220** 165 73 **55**	478
2085	PARACETAMOL	3AC	**277 235** 193 151 **109**	473
2090	PROPYPHENAZONE-M (NOR-DI-HO-)		**248** 206 136 109	412
2090	TIABENDAZOLE		**201** 174	303
2090*	KETOPROFEN	ME	**268 209** 191 105 77	456
2095	CHLORPHENOXAMINE		**303** 214 **178** 165 **58**	531
2095*	DIFLUNISAL		**250** 232 **206** 175	417
2095	METOCLOPRAMIDE-M		**71 58**	58
2095	AMINOPHENAZONE-M (DESAMINO-HO-)	AC	**246** 204 119 **57**	408
2095	BUCETIN	AC	**265** 205 **137** 109 108	448
2095	CETOBEMIDONE	AC	**289** 247 190 **70**	503
2095	PHENAZONE-M (HO-)	AC	**246** 204 119 **57**	408
2095*	TRIHEXYPHENIDYL-M -2H2O -CO2	AC	**242** 200 **182** 167	398
2100	CHLORPROMAZINE-M (RING)		**233** 198	378
2100	NAPHAZOLINE		**210 209** 141	324
2100	PERPHENAZINE-M (RING)		**233** 198	378
2100	PROCHLORPERAZINE-M (RING)		**233** 198	378
2100	THIOPROPAZATE-M (RING)		**233** 198	378
2100	DOXYLAMINE-M (DI-HO-)	AC	**257** 180 71 **58**	431
2100	TILIDINE-M (BIS-NOR-)	AC	**287** 244 **111 69**	497
2100	CAMAZEPAM	HY	**245** 228 193 105 **77**	405
2100	DIAZEPAM	HY	**245** 228 193 105 **77**	405
2100	KETAZOLAM	HY	**245** 228 193 105 **77**	405
2100	TEMAZEPAM	HY	**245** 228 193 105 **77**	405
2105	BROMPHENIRAMINE		**247** 167 72 **58**	411
2105	NORMETHADONE		**295** 263 224 165 72 **58**	514
2105	MOPERONE-M 5	AC	**215** 173	338
2110	TICLOPIDINE		**263** 125 **110**	444
2110	BUCETIN-M (O-DESETHYL-)	2AC	**279** 237 177 **109**	478
2110	PHENYLEPHRINE	3AC	**293 233** 191 149 **86**	511
2110	TETRYZOLINE	AC	**242 200** 185 86	398
2110*	BORNYL SALICYLATE	ME	**288 135** 81	501
2110*	LINOLEIC ACID	ME	**294** 95 **81** 67	514
2115	DIPHENYLPYRALINE		**281 167** 114 **99**	483
2115	LAUDAMONIUM AMINE 3		**289 134 91**	501
2115	LIDOCAINE-M (DESETHYL-)	AC	**248** 128 **100 58**	413
2115	PRIMIDONE	AC	**260** 232 189 **146** 117	437
2120*	ASCORBIC ACID		**176 116** 85	250
2120	BENCYCLANE		**289 198** 102 86 **58**	502
2120	DICYCLOVERINE		**309** 294 99 **86**	541
2120*	FLUSPIRILENE-M 1		**262 203** 183	440

RI	NAME	DERIVATIVE	TYPICAL IONS	PAGE
2120*	PENFLURIDOL-M 2		**262** **203** 183	440
2120*	PIMOZIDE-M 2		**262** **203** 183	440
2125	ETOFYLLINE		**224** 194 **180** 109	361
2130*	METHYLSTEARATE		**298** 255 **143** 87 **74**	522
2130	METOPROLOL		**267** 252 223 **100** **72**	453
2130*	GLUCOSE	5AC	**331** **157** 115 **97**	583
2130	ACEMETACIN ARTIFACT 1	ME	**233** **174**	381
2130	INDOMETACIN ARTIFACT	ME	**233** **174**	381
2130*	STEARIC ACID	ME	**298** 255 **143** 87 **74**	522
2135	BRALLOBARBITAL-M (HO-DIHYDRO-)		**182** 138	263
2135	DICLOFENAC		**277** 242 **214** 179 89	471
2140	METOPROLOL ARTIFACT		**279** 264 127 **72**	477
2140	FLUANISONE-M (HO-PHENYL-PIPERAZINE)	2AC	**262** 220 **148**	442
2145	METHORPHAN		**271** 150 70 **58**	460
2145*	BENZOCTAMINE-M (HO-METHYL-)	AC	**278** **250** 191	476
2145	EPHEDRINE-M (HO-)	3AC	**307** **247** 163 86 **58**	538
2145	HYDROXYEPHEDRINE	3AC	**307** **247** 163 86 **58**	538
2150	NOMIFENSINE		**238** **194** 178 165	391
2150	PENBUTOLOL ARTIFACT		**303** **288** 160 **86** 57	531
2150	ETILEFRINE	3AC	**307** **247** 205 163 100 **58**	538
2150*	FLUSPIRILENE-M 1	AC	**304** 244 216 **203** 183	534
2150*	PENFLURIDOL-M 2	AC	**304** 244 216 **203** 183	534
2150*	PIMOZIDE-M 2	AC	**304** 244 216 **203** 183	534
2150	TRYPTOPHAN	MEAC	**260** 201 **130**	437
2155	METHAQUALONE		**250** **235** 132 91	418
2155*	PENTACHLOROBIPHENYL		**324** **290** 254 220 184	568
2155*	POLICHLORINATED BIPHENYL (5CL)		**324** **290** 254 220 184	568
2155	HALOPERIDOL-M 4 -H2O	AC	**235** 193 189	386
2155	TOLIPROLOL	2AC	**307** **247** 190 140 **72**	538
2160	METHADONE		**309** 294 165 **72**	542
2160	PROPRANOLOL		**259** 144 **100** **72**	433
2160	ISOPYRIN-M (NOR-HO-) -H2O	2AC	**313** 271 **229** **57**	550
2160	MESCALINE	AC	**253** **194** 181	425
2165	MELPERONE-M 4		**307** 246 123 **112**	536
2165	METHAQUALONE-M (2-CARBOXY-) -CO2		**236** **219** 132 91	387
2165	PROPYPHENAZONE-M (NOR-HO-PHENYL-)	AC	**316** 274 **232** 217 190	557
2165	TILIDINE-M (NOR-)	AC	**301** 258 **125** **83** 69	528
2165	FLUNITRAZEPAM-M (NOR-AMINO-)	HY	**230** 211	372
2170	AMIPHENAZOLE		**191** 149 121 104 77	279
2170	CYCLOBARBITAL-M (HO-)		**234** **205** 156 141	382
2170	LORAZEPAM ARTIFACT		**274** **239**	465
2170	LORMETAZEPAM ARTIFACT		**274** **239**	465
2170*	STEARIC ACID		**284** 256 **129** 73 **56**	489
2170	KETAMINE	AC	**279** **216** 208 180 152	478
2175	DICLOBENIL		**171** 136 100	244
2175	SYNEPHRINE	3AC	**293** 233 191 **149** **86**	511
2175	TOLAZOLINE-M (HO-DIHYDRO-)	2AC	**262** 161 **118** 91	442
2180	DROFENINE		**317** 173 99 **86**	558
2180	MECLOXAMINE		**317** 215 179 **72**	558
2180	N-PHENYLALPHANAPHTHYLAMINE		**219** 109	348
2180	OXELADIN		**335** 320 219 **144** **86**	587
2180	PROXYPHYLLINE	AC	**280** 237 220 193 180	482

RI	NAME	DERIVATIVE	TYPICAL IONS	PAGE
2180	LORAZEPAM	HY	**265** **230** 139 111	449
2180	LORMETAZEPAM-M (NOR-)	HY	**265** **230** 139 111	449
2180*	FLURBIPROFEN-M (HO-)	2ME	**288** **229**	501
2180*	TIAPROFENIC ACID	ME	**274** 231 **215** 105 77	466
2185	MEFEXAMIDE		**280** 263 155 99 **86**	480
2185	SULFANILAMIDE		**172** 156 108 92 **65**	246
2190	CHLOROPYRAMINE		**289** 231 **125** 72 **58**	502
2190	CYCLOBARBITAL-M (OXO-)		**250** **221** 193 179 150	418
2190	FLUPHENAZINE-M (RING)		**267** 235	453
2190	HOMOFENAZINE-M (RING)		**267** 235	453
2190	TRIFLUOPERAZINE-M (RING)		**267** 235	453
2190	TRIFLUPROMAZINE-M (RING)		**267** 235	453
2190*	DIETHYLSTILBESTROL	2ME	**296** 267 159 121	519
2195	OXYMETAZOLINE		**260** **245** 217 81	436
2195	PROCYCLIDINE		**287** 269 **204** **84**	495
2195	BROMPHENIRAMINE-M (NOR-)	AC	**346** 260 **247** 180 169	603
2195	FLURAZEPAM-M (DESALKYL-)	HYAC	**291** **249** 123 95	506
2195*	PROPRANOLOL-M (DESAMINO-HO-)	2AC	**302** **159** 144 115	530
2195	DICLOFENAC	ME	**309** 277 242 **214**	543
2200	COCAINE		**303** 198 **182** **82**	531
2200	TRIAMPHOS		**294** 251 **160** 135	512
2200	ETOFYLLINE	AC	**266** 180 151 **87**	451
2200	PHENDIMETRAZINE-M (NOR-HO-)	2AC	**277** 234 113 86 **56**	473
2200	PHENMETRAZINE-M (HO-)	2AC	**277** 234 113 86 **56**	473
2200	TETRAZEPAM	HY	**249** 234 220 **207**	416
2205	AMITRIPTYLINE		**277** 215 **202** **58**	471
2205	PROPOXYPHENE		**265** **208** 115 **58**	447
2205	HYDROXYPETHIDINE	AC	**305** 230 188 **71**	535
2205	PENBUTOLOL	2AC	**375** **315** 158 98 **56**	631
2205	PETHIDINE-M (HO-)	AC	**305** 230 188 **71**	535
2210	CHLORMEZANONE		**209** **152** 98	321
2210	ETAMIPHYLLINE		**279** 99 **86** 58	477
2210	ETODROXIZINE-M 1		**280** 201 165	480
2210	MIANSERIN		**264** **193** 178 72	446
2210	PROPYPHENAZONE-M (HO-PROPYL-)		**246** 231 **215** 124 56	406
2210	CLOBAZAM-M (NOR-)	HY	**242** 206 166 77	399
2215	ADIPHENINE		**311** 239 **167** 99 **86**	546
2215	ATROPINE		**289** 140 **124** 94 83	502
2215	HYOSCYAMINE		**289** 140 **124** 94 83	502
2215	IMIPRAMINE		**280** **235** 193 85 **58**	480
2215*	PROPAFENONE-M (HO-PHENOL)	AC	**284** **242** **137** 91	490
2220	CHLORCYCLIZINE		**300** 165 **99** 56	524
2220	ETODROXIZINE-M 2		**300** 165 **99** 56	524
2220*	HEXACHLOROBIPHENYL		**358** **288** 218	614
2220*	POLICHLORINATED BIPHENYL (6CL)		**358** **288** 218	614
2220	PRIDINOL -H2O		**277** 163 **110**	471
2220	PROPRANOLOL -H2O		**241** **98** **56**	396
2220	ETIFELMIN	AC	**279** 220 205 191 **112**	479
2220	VILOXAZINE	AC	**279** **142** **100** 86 56	479
2220	LORMETAZEPAM	HY	**279** **244** 229	479
2225	DESIPRAMINE		**266** 235 **195** 71 **44**	450
2225	IMIPRAMINE-M (NOR-)		**266** 235 **195** 71 **44**	450

RI	NAME	DERIVATIVE	TYPICAL IONS	PAGE
2225	LOFEPRAMINE-M (DESALKYL-)		**266** 235 **195** 71 **44**	450
2225	TRIMIPRAMINE		**294** **249** 235 **58**	512
2225	CLOBAZAM	HY	**274** **257** 231 215 77	466
2225	NITRAZEPAM-M	HY	**212** **211** 195 107 77	331
2225	CLORAZEPATE ISOMER 1	ME	**284** **283**	490
2230	ETHOXYPHENYLDIETHYLPHENYL BUTYRAMINE		**325** **252** 237 115	571
2230*	FLUSPIRILENE-M 2		**276** **203** 183	469
2230*	PENFLURIDOL-M 3		**276** **203** 183	469
2230*	PIMOZIDE-M 3		**276** **203** 183	469
2230	SCOPOLAMINE -H2O		**285** 154 138 **94**	491
2235	AMITRIPTYLINE-M (HO-) -H2O		**275** **215** 202 **58**	467
2235	AMITRIPTYLINOXIDE-M (DESOXO-HO-) -H2O		**275** **215** 202 **58**	467
2235*	KAVAIN		**230** **186** 128 98 91	370
2235	MEDAZEPAM		**270** **242** **207** 165	458
2235	PHENGLUTARIMIDE		**288** **216** 98 **86**	498
2235	HALOPERIDOL-M 4	AC	**253** **189** 139 **57**	425
2235	LOPERAMIDE-M	AC	**253** **189** 139 **57**	425
2235	TOLMETINE	ME	**271** **212** **83**	461
2240	DOXEPIN		**279** 165 **58**	477
2240*	HEPTACHLOROBIPHENYL		**392** **322** 252	642
2240	METHAQUALONE-M (2-FORMYL-)		**264** **235** 132 91	446
2240	METHITURAL		**288** 214 171 155 **74**	499
2240	METIPRANOLOL ARTIFACT		**321** 306 194 **152** **72**	564
2240	METOPROLOL-M (HO-ETHYL-) ARTIFACT		**277** 262 114 **72**	472
2240	PENTIFYLLINE		**264** 193 **180** 137 109	446
2240	PHYSOSTIGMINE		**218** **174** 160 94	344
2240*	POLICHLORINATED BIPHENYL (7CL)		**392** **322** 252	642
2240	PROPOXYPHENE-M (NOR-) -H2O		**251** **217** **119**	420
2240	TRIFLUPROMAZINE		**352** 267 86 **58**	607
2240	PENFLURIDOL-M 5	AC	**321** 303 278 99 **57**	565
2240	PETHIDINE-M (NOR-)	AC	**275** 232 202 **187** 158 57	468
2240	PROPYPHENAZONE-M (HO-METHYL-)	AC	**288** 273 **245** 232 190	500
2245	ISOTHIPENDYL		**285** **214** 200 181 **72**	491
2245*	KETOPROFEN		**254** **208** 131 **105** 77	426
2245*	POLYCHLOROCAMPHENE		**410** **376** **341** 195 **89**	652
2245*	TOXAPHENE (TM)		**410** **376** **341** 195 **89**	652
2245	CAMAZEPAM-M	HYAC	**273** **230** 154 105 77	463
2245	CHLORDIAZEPOXIDE	HYAC	**273** **230** 154 105 77	463
2245	CLORAZEPATE	HYAC	**273** **230** 154 105 77	463
2245	DIAZEPAM-M	HYAC	**273** **230** 154 105 77	463
2245	KETAZOLAM-M	HYAC	**273** **230** 154 105 77	463
2245	MEDAZEPAM-M	HYAC	**273** **230** 154 105 77	463
2245	OXAZEPAM	HYAC	**273** **230** 154 105 77	463
2245	OXAZOLAM	HYAC	**273** **230** 154 105 77	463
2245	PRAZEPAM-M	HYAC	**273** **230** 154 105 77	463
2245	TEMAZEPAM-M	HYAC	**273** **230** 154 105 77	463
2245	PHENYTOIN	ME	**266** 237 209 **180** 104 77	452
2250	BAMIPINE		**280** **180** **97**	480
2250*	FENSULFOTHION		**308** **293** 141 125 97	539
2250	HALOPERIDOL-M 5		**239** 189 139 **100** **56**	392
2250	PINDOLOL ARTIFACT		**260** 133 **127** 86	436
2250	PROMETHAZINE-M (NOR-)		**270** **213** 198 180 **58**	458

RI	NAME	DERIVATIVE	TYPICAL IONS	PAGE
2250	PROTRIPTYLINE		**263** **191** 84 70	445
2250	TRIHEXYPHENIDYL		**301** **218** **98**	527
2250	GLUTETHIMIDE-M (HO-PHENYL-)	AC	**275** **233** 204 189 176	468
2250	NEFOPAM-M (HO-) ISOMER 1	AC	**311** 238 **195** 165 87	547
2250	PHENIRAMINE-M (NOR-)	AC	**268** 225 182 **169**	455
2250	PRIDINOL-M (AMINO-) -H2O	AC	**251** 208 **192** 84	422
2250	COCAINE-M (BENZOYLECGONINE)	ET	**317** 272 **196** 82	560
2250	BROMAZEPAM	HY	**276** **247** 198 168	470
2255	AMITRIPTYLINE-M (NOR-)		**263** **202** 58 **44**	445
2255	BROMAZEPAM-M (HO-) ARTIFACT		**285** **206** 179	491
2255	DEXTRORPHAN		**257** 200 150 **59**	430
2255	LEVORPHANOL		**257** 200 150 **59**	430
2255	METHORPHAN -M (O-DESMETHYL-)		**257** 200 150 **59**	430
2255	NORTRIPTYLINE		**263** **202** 58 **44**	445
2260	BORNAPRINE		**329** 314 257 171 **86**	579
2260	BUPIVACAINE		**286** **243** **140** 96 84	494
2260	PRIMIDONE		**218** **190** 161 146 117	345
2260	TRIMETOZINE		**281** **195**	484
2260	BROMPERIDOL-M 4	AC	**293** 279 **251** 222	511
2260	OXPRENOLOL -H2O	AC	**289** 188 **72**	503
2260	XYLOMETAZOLINE	AC	**286** 271 229 214 128	495
2265	FLURAZEPAM-M (DESALKYL-HO-)		**286** 258 223 75	494
2265	CETOBEMIDONE-M (METHOXY-)	AC	**319** 220 **70**	562
2265	DIPHENHYDRAMINE-M (NOR-)	AC	**283** 241 **167** **101** 86	488
2265	TRAZODONE-M 2	AC	**238** 195 **166** 154	391
2265	TOLMETINE	ET	**285** **212** 119 91	493
2270	BENACTYZINE		**327** **239** 182 105 **86**	574
2270	DOXEPIN-M (NOR-)		**265** **204** 178 44	447
2270	NOXIPTYLINE		**224** **208** 71 **58**	361
2270	PROCAINAMIDE		**235** 120 **99** **86**	384
2270	PROMETHAZINE		**284** 213 199 **72**	489
2270	ZIMELIDINE		**316** 238 193 70 **58**	556
2270	AMINOPHENAZONE-M (BIS-NOR-)	AC	**245** 203 84 **56**	405
2270	METAMIZOL-M (BIS-DESALKYL-)	AC	**245** 203 84 **56**	405
2270	NIFENAZONE-M (DESACYL-)	AC	**245** 203 84 **56**	405
2275	HEPTABARBITAL-M (HO-)		**266** 237 **219** **141** 93	450
2275	TIMOLOL ARTIFACT		**328** **313** 187 **86** 57	577
2275	ATROPINE	AC	**331** 140 **124** 94 83	583
2275	HYOSCYAMINE	AC	**331** 140 **124** 94 83	583
2280	BIPERIDEN		**311** **218** **98**	546
2280	CHLORPROTHIXENE-M (NOR-HO-)		**317** 247 **44**	558
2280	MEDAZEPAM-M (NOR-)		**256** **228** 193 165	428
2280	PENTAZOCINE		**285** **217** 110 **70**	491
2280	PHENAZOPYRIDINE		**213** 136 **108** 81	334
2280	ALPRENOLOL -H2O	AC	**273** **200** 126 98 **72**	464
2280	DEXTRORPHAN	AC	**299** 231 150 **59**	524
2280	LEVORPHANOL	AC	**299** 231 150 **59**	524
2280	METHORPHAN -M (O-DESMETHYL-)	AC	**299** 231 150 **59**	524
2280	TILIDINE-M/ARTIFACT	2AC	**271** 211 **169**	461
2285	CARBAMAZEPINE		**236** **193** 165	388
2285	MELITRACENE		**291** 217 **202** **58**	505
2285	SULFINPYRAZONE		**278** 105 **77**	474

RI	NAME	DERIVATIVE	TYPICAL IONS	PAGE
2285	NEFOPAM-M (HO-) ISOMER 2	AC	**311** 268 208 195 **178**	547
2285	CLONAZEPAM-M (AMINO-)	HY	**246** 211 139 111 107	409
2290	BENPERIDOL-M 2		**231** **134** 106 79	373
2290	DIMETINDENE		**292** **218** **58**	507
2290	METOPROLOL-M (HO-PHENYL-) ARTIFACT		**295** 280 250 127 86 **72**	515
2290	PIMOZIDE-M 4		**231** **134** 106 79	373
2290	PRIDINOL		**295** **180** 113 **98**	515
2290	TIMOLOL	AC	**358** **343** 284 86 **56**	614
2290	PHENYLBUTAZONE	(ME)	**322** 266 **183** 77	567
2295*	DIETHYLSTILBESTROL		**268** 239 159 145 107	454
2295	LAUDAMONIUM AMINE 4		**317** **134** **91**	558
2295	PHENOBARBITAL-M (HO-)		**248** 220 **219** 148	413
2295	TRAMADOL-M (N-DESMETHYL-) -H2O	AC	**273** **200** **86** 58	464
2295	FLURAZEPAM-M (BIS-DESETHYL-) -H2O	HY	**274** 246 **211**	466
2300	HEPTABARBITAL-M (HO-) -H2O		**248** **219** 157 141 **93**	413
2300	PROPAFENONE -H2O		**323** 294 **98** 91	567
2300	PROPYPHENAZONE-M (HO-PHENYL-)		**246** **231** 96 56	406
2300*	STRESSHORMONE (HYDROXYANDROSTENE)		**274** **259** 241 148 94	465
2300	DOXYLAMINE-M (NOR-)	AC	**298** **183** 167	521
2300	LORAZEPAM	HYAC	**307** 265 **230**	538
2300	LORMETAZEPAM-M (NOR-)	HYAC	**307** 265 **230**	538
2300	PHENYTOIN	AC	**294** 252 223 **208** 180 104	513
2305	FENCAMFAMINE-M (DESETHYL-HO-)	2AC	**287** 228 168 **142**	497
2305	NIFENALOL	2AC	**308** **248** 206 114 **72**	540
2305	PROPYPHENAZONE-M (HO-PROPYL-)	AC	**288** 245 228 **215** 56	500
2310	BAMETHAN -H2O	2AC	**275** **233** 191 148 98	468
2310*	FLURBIPROFEN-M (HO-METHOXY-)	2ME	**318** 259 215	561
2315	ALIMEMAZINE		**298** **198** 100 84 **58**	521
2315	BENZATROPINE		**307** 201 **167** 140 124 **83**	537
2315	DIMETACRINE		**294** 279 **86** 58	513
2315	PROMAZINE		**284** 199 86 **58**	489
2315	SCOPOLAMINE		**303** 285 154 138 **94**	532
2315	CLONIDINE	2AC	**313** 278 236 **194** **58**	550
2320	CAMAZEPAM-M		**268** 239 233 205 **77**	454
2320	CLORAZEPATE-M		**268** 239 233 205 **77**	454
2320	DIAZEPAM-M		**268** 239 233 205 **77**	454
2320	KETAZOLAM-M		**268** 239 233 205 **77**	454
2320	OXAZEPAM		**268** 239 233 205 **77**	454
2320	OXAZOLAM-M		**268** 239 233 205 **77**	454
2320	TEMAZEPAM-M		**268** 239 233 205 **77**	454
2325	CLONAZEPAM-M (AMINO-HO-) ARTIFACT		**255** **220**	427
2325	LORAZEPAM-M (HO-) ARTIFACT		**290** **255**	504
2325	VILOXAZINE-M (DI-OXO-)		**265** **138** 100 **56**	447
2330	BAMETHAN	3AC	**335** **275** **233** 191 148	587
2330	METOPROLOL -H2O	AC	**291** 140 98 **72**	506
2330	PENTAZOCINE	AC	**327** 312 **259** 110 70	575
2330	PROPRANOLOL -H2O	AC	**283** 198 181 **140** 127 98	488
2330	TETRAZEPAM-M (HO-) ISOMER 1	HY	**265** 253 220 207 **194**	449
2335	PROFENAMINE		**312** 213 **199** **100**	547
2335	BROMPERIDOL-M 5	AC	**297** 279 254 183 99 **57**	520
2335	FLUNITRAZEPAM-M (NOR-)	HY	**260** 241 123	437
2335*	PHENPROCOUMON	ME	**294** 265 **203** **91**	514

RI	NAME	DERIVATIVE	TYPICAL IONS	PAGE
2340	CYPROHEPTADINE		**287** 215 96	496
2340	PIZOTIFEN		**295** 233 197 96 58	515
2340	DOXEPIN-M (HO-DIHYDRO-)	AC	**339** **211** 165 **58**	594
2340	PIPAMPERONE-M (DESALKYL-HO-) -H2O	AC	**251** **209** 165 82	422
2345	MAZINDOL		**266** 231	450
2350	ANTAZOLINE		**182** 91 **84**	263
2350	FLUSPIRILENE-M 3		**259** **71**	434
2350	PHENYTOIN		**252** 223 209 **180** 104 77	423
2350	PROTHIPENDYL		**285** 227 214 **200** 86 **58**	491
2350	PENTAZOCINE-M	AC	**323** **109** 94	568
2355	LEVALLORPHAN		**283** 256 176 157 85	487
2355	OXYPERTINE-M (HO-PHENYLPIPERAZINE)	2AC	**262** 220 **148**	442
2355	TRAZODONE-M 3 ISOMER 1	2AC	**296** 254 **182** 154	517
2360	METHAQUALONE-M (2-HO-METHYL-)		**266** **235** 132 91	450
2360*	DOXEPIN-M (HO-N-OXIDE) -(CH3)2NOH	AC	**292** **250** **233** 165	508
2360	LORAZEPAM-M (HO-)	HY	**281** **246**	485
2365	ISOPYRIN-M (NOR-)	2AC	**315** **273** 231 **123** 70	556
2365	PROPOXYPHENE-M (NOR-) -H2O	AC	**293** **220** 205	511
2365	NITRAZEPAM	HY	**242** 241 195 165 105 77	399
2370*	ALLYLESTRENOL		**300** 259 **241** 201 91	524
2370	BENCYCLANE-M (HO-)		**214** 185 102 86 **58**	336
2370	PHENGLUTARIMIDE-M (DESETHYL-)		**260** **189**	436
2370	BUPRANOLOL	AC	**298** 142 112 **86**	521
2370	ORCIPRENALINE	4AC	**379** **319** **277** 235 72	634
2370	FLUNITRAZEPAM	HY	**274** 257 211	466
2375	ADEPTOLON (TM) INGREDIENT		**347** 275 **169** 86 **72**	604
2375	AZATADINE		**290** 246 232 96 **70**	504
2375	BROMHEXINE		**374** 305 293 **262** 112 **70**	629
2375	CODEINE		**299** 229 162 124	522
2375	PENTAZOCINE ARTIFACT (+H2O)		**303** 288 **230** 58	532
2375	PHENYLBUTAZONE		**308** 252 **183** 77	539
2375	MORPHINE	ME	**299** 229 162 124	522
2380	AMITRIPTYLINE-M (HO-)		**293** 275 215 **202** **58**	510
2380	AMITRIPTYLINOXIDE-M (DESOXO-HO-)		**293** 275 215 **202** **58**	510
2380*	BUTYLOCTADECANOATE		**340** 285 267 **57**	595
2380	HYDROXYZINE-M	AC	**285** **226** 191 84	493
2380	MECLOZINE-M	AC	**285** **226** 191 84	493
2380	PENTAZOCINE-M (DESALKYL-)	2AC	**301** **87** 72	528
2385*	DIISOBUTYLADIPATE		**258** **185** **129** 111	432
2385	BORNAPRINE-M (HO-) ISOMER 1	AC	**387** **372** 214 142 **86**	639
2385	FLURAZEPAM-M (HO-ETHYL-)	HY	**293** **262** 166 109	512
2385	BROMAZEPAM ISOMER 1	ME	**329** **250** 208 179	580
2390	AMITRIPTYLINE-M (NOR-HO-)		**279** 261 **218** 203 58 **44**	477
2390	ATENOLOL ARTIFACT		**278** **263** 127 86 **72** 56	475
2390	MAPROTILINE		**277** 70 59 **44**	472
2390	MEPINDOLOL		**262** **147** 114 100 72	441
2390	NORTRIPTYLINE-M (HO-)		**279** 261 **218** 203 58 **44**	477
2390	LEVALLORPHAN	AC	**325** 298 257 176 **85**	571
2390	OXPRENOLOL	2AC	**349** **289** **200** 98 **72**	606
2390	ACEMETACIN ARTIFACT 2	ME	**291** 233 **174** 159 131	507
2395	AMINOPHENAZONE-M (NOR-)	AC	**259** 217 123 **56**	434
2395	METAMIZOL-M (DESALKYL-)	AC	**259** 217 123 **56**	434

RI	NAME	DERIVATIVE	TYPICAL IONS	PAGE
2395	PROPOXYPHENE-M	(HY)	**281** **190** **119** **105** 56	486
2400	BENZYDAMINE		**309** **224** 91 85 **58**	542
2400*	CANNABIDIOL		**314** 246 **231** 174	551
2400	DIHYDROCODEINE-M (O-DESMETHYL-)		**287**	496
2400	DIHYDROMORPHINE		**287**	496
2400	HYDROCODONE-M (O-DESMETHYL-DIHYDRO-)		**287**	496
2400	HYDROMORPHONE-M (DIHYDRO-)		**287**	496
2400	METHAQUALONE-M (2-CARBOXY-)		**280** **235** 146 132	480
2400	PROPOXYPHENE-M (NOR-) N-PROP.		**307** **220** **100** **57**	537
2400	TETRAZEPAM		**288** **253**	499
2400	ISOPYRIN	AC	**287** 244 137 **56**	497
2400*	TETRAHYDROCANNABINOL	AC	**356** 313 **297** 231	612
2400	TETRYZOLINE	2AC	**284** 242 **199**	490
2405	FLUSPIRILENE-M 4		**245** **57**	403
2405	PROMAZINE-M (NOR-)		**270** 238 213 **199** 44	458
2405	VIMINOL		**344** 315 287 259 125	601
2405	CLOBAZAM-M (NOR-HO-METHOXY-)	HY	**288**	501
2410*	CHLORPROTHIXENE-M (N-OXIDE) -(CH3)2NOH		**270** 255 **234** 202 117	458
2410*	CLOPENTHIXOL-M (N-OXIDE) -C6H14N2O2		**270** 255 **234** 202 117	458
2410	DIHYDROCODEINE		**301** 164	527
2410	MEPIVACAINE-M (HO-)		**262** **98** 96 70	441
2410	METHAQUALONE-M (2')		**262** **98** 96 70	441
2410	PROPYPHENAZONE-M (HO-METHYL-)		**246** **231** 215 77	407
2410	PRAZEPAM	HY	**285** 270 105 77 **56**	494
2415	BENPERIDOL-M 3		**217** **134** 106 79	342
2415	PIMOZIDE-M 5		**217** **134** 106 79	342
2415	TETRAZEPAM-M (HO-) ISOMER 1	HYAC	**307** **248** 234 220 194	538
2420	BUPHENINE		**176** 121 91 71	250
2420	CHLORAMBUCIL		**303** **268** 118	532
2420	ETHYLMORPHINE		**313** 284 162 124	549
2420	BENZOCTAMINE-M (NOR-)	AC	**277** **249** 191 178	473
2425	PENBUTOLOL-M (HO-) ARTIFACT		**319** **304** 178 **86** 57	561
2425*	MAPROTILINE-M (HO-PROPYL-)	AC	**306** **278** 191	536
2425	OXAZEPAM ISOMER 1	2ME	**314** **271** 239 205	554
2430	DIAZEPAM		**284** **256** 221	489
2430	KETAZOLAM ARTIFACT		**284** **256** 221	489
2430	KETAZOLAM-M		**284** **256** 221	489
2430	CLORAZEPATE ISOMER 2	ME	**284** **256** 221	489
2435	PENTOXIFYLLINE		**278** **221** 193 180 109	475
2435	PHENYLBUTAZONE ARTIFACT		**324** **183** 119 **77**	569
2435	DIHYDROCODEINE	AC	**343** 300 226 70	600
2435	PENTAZOCINE ARTIFACT (+H2O)	AC	**345** 330 **272** 87	602
2435	THEBACONE-M (DIHYDRO-)	AC	**343** 300 226 70	600
2440	HYDROCODONE		**299** 242 185 96 59	523
2440	LORAZEPAM		**302** 274 **239** **75**	529
2440*	PHENPROCOUMON		**280** **251** 189 121	481
2440	THALIDOMIDE		**258** 173 111 104 **75**	432
2440	METHAQUALONE-M (2-HO-METHYL-)	AC	**308** **265** 235	541
2445	CLEMASTINE		**217** **214** 179 128 **84**	342
2445	HYDROMORPHONE		**285** 228	492
2445	FLUANISONE-M/ARTIFACT	AC	**292** 250 178 **154** 123	508
2450	ACEBUTOLOL ARTIFACT (PHENOL)		**221** **151** 136	353

RI	NAME	DERIVATIVE	TYPICAL IONS	PAGE
2450	FENDILINE		**315** 181 167 132 **105**	554
2450	LEVOBUNOLOL ARTIFACT		**303** **288** 162 **86** 57	532
2450*	METHOXYCHLOR		**344** **308** 274 238 **227**	601
2450	NOMIFENSINE-M (HO-)		**254** 210 194 **86**	426
2450*	CANNABIDIOL	2AC	**398** 355 297 **231** 121	645
2450*	DIETHYLSTILBESTROL	2AC	**352** 310 **268** 239 107	608
2450	MEPIVACAINE-M (HO-)	AC	**304** **98** 96 70	534
2450	PROFENAMINE-M (BIS-DESETHYL-)	AC	**298** **212** 180 100 58	522
2450	PROMETHAZINE-M (BIS-DESMETHYL-)	AC	**298** **212** 180 100 58	522
2450	SCOPOLAMINE	AC	**345** 285 154 138 **94**	602
2455	CLOMIPRAMINE		**314** **269** 85 **58**	551
2455	CODEINE-M (O-DESMETHYL-)		**285** 268 162 124	492
2455	ETHYLMORPHINE-M (O-DESETHYL-)		**285** 268 162 124	492
2455	HEROIN-M (MORPHINE)		**285** 268 162 124	492
2455	MORPHINE		**285** 268 162 124	492
2455	DIPROPHYLLINE	2AC	**338** 236 194 **180** 159	592
2460	APRINDINE		**322** 249 209 113 **86**	565
2460	AZINPHOS-METHYL		**317** **160** 132 93 **77**	559
2460	DIBENZEPIN-M (NOR-)		**281** **210** 72 **58**	484
2460	FLURAZEPAM-M (BIS-DESETHYL-) -H2O	HYAC	**316** 273 **246** 211	557
2460	ISOPRENALINE	4AC	**365** **319** 277 193 **84**	619
2460	LEVOBUNOLOL	AC	**333** **318** 259 200 **86**	586
2465	DIBENZEPIN		**224** 180 71 **58**	362
2465	BORNAPRINE-M (HO-) ISOMER 2	AC	**387** **372** 214 142 **86**	640
2465	FLURAZEPAM-M (HO-ETHYL-)	HYAC	**335** 275 **262** 166 109	588
2465	TRAMADOL-M (BIS-DESMETHYL-) -H2O	2AC	**301** 228 186 **86**	529
2470	BROMAZEPAM-M (HO-)		**313** 284 206 179	549
2470	FENCARBAMIDE		**326** 196 **169** 99 **86**	572
2470	FLURAZEPAM-M (DESALKYL-)		**288** 260	499
2470*	TETRAHYDROCANNABINOL		**314** 299 271 231	552
2470*	BENZOCTAMINE-M (DI-HO-)	2AC	**336** 266 **249** 191	590
2470	MEDAZEPAM-M (NOR-)	AC	**298** **297** 256 **228** 193	522
2470	NOMIFENSINE	AC	**280** **222** 194 178	482
2470	CLONAZEPAM	HY	**276** **241** 195 165 139 111	470
2470	LORMETAZEPAM-M (HO-)	HY	**295** **260** 245	516
2475*	ANDROSTERONE		**290** 272 257 244	504
2475*	PHENPROCOUMON	AC	**322** 280 **251** 189 121	566
2480*	CHLORPROTHIXENE-M (N-OXIDE-SULFOX.) -(CH3)2NOH		**286** 271 234 **203**	494
2480	METOPROLOL	2AC	**351** 291 **200** 98 **72**	607
2480	IMIPRAMINE-M (HO-)	ME	**310** 265 85 **58**	546
2485	MIANSERIN-M (HO-)		**280** 236 **209** 72	481
2485	BENOXAPROFEN	ME	**315** **256** 119 91	556
2485	LORAZEPAM ISOMER 1	2ME	**348** 305 **75**	605
2485	NITRAZEPAM ISOMER 1	ME	**295** **294** 248 91	516
2490	DISOPYRAMIDE		**193** 165	283
2490	METHAQUALONE-M (3'CARBOXY-)		**280** **235** 146 132	480
2490	TETRABENAZINE		**317** 274 **261** 191	559
2490	BROMAZEPAM	HYAC	**318** 289 275 **247** **121**	561
2500	CHLORPROMAZINE		**318** 272 232 86 **58**	560
2500*	DOXEPIN-M (HO-N-OXIDE) -(CH3)2NOH		**250** 231 203	418
2500	FLECAINIDE		**301** 218 **125** 97	527
2500	FLUSPIRILENE-M 5		**245** **71** **57**	404

RI	NAME	DERIVATIVE	TYPICAL IONS	PAGE
2500	METHAQUALONE-M (4'CARBOXY-)		**280** **235** 146 132	480
2500	METIXENE		**309** 197 165 **99**	542
2500	OXAZEPAM ARTIFACT 3		**298** **240** 203	521
2500	TETRABENAZINE-M (O-DESMETHYL-HO-)		**319** 274 232 **205** 191	561
2500	THEBACONE		**341** 298 242 162	596
2500	TRIHEXYPHENIDYL-M (HO-)		**317** 299 **218** **98**	559
2500	CODEINE	AC	**341** 282 229 204 162	597
2505	NOMIFENSINE-M (HO-METHOXY-) ISOMER 1		**284** 241 **210** 86	489
2505	PENTOXIFYLLINE-M (HO-)		**280** 236 193 **180** 109	481
2505	NORMETHADONE-M (HO-)	AC	**353** **294** 72 **58**	609
2510	CHLORPROTHIXENE		**315** 255 **221** 58	554
2510	TETRABENAZINE-M (O-BIS-DESMETHYL-)	AC	**331** **296** 232 **191** 177	583
2515	MOXAVERINE		**307** **292** 248 91	537
2515	FLECAINIDE	AC	**456** **301** 218 126 **84**	665
2515	PROFENAMINE-M (DESETHYL-)	AC	**326** **212** 128 **72**	573
2520	CLORAZEPATE GC ARTIFACT		**270** **242** 77	459
2520	DIAZEPAM-M		**270** **242** 77	459
2520	KETAZOLAM-M		**270** **242** 77	459
2520	MEDAZEPAM-M		**270** **242** 77	459
2520	NORDAZEPAM		**270** **242** 77	459
2520	OXAZOLAM-M		**270** **242** 77	459
2520	PRAZEPAM-M		**270** **242** 77	459
2520	OXPRENOLOL-M (HO-) -H2O ISOMER 1	2AC	**347** 305 200 **72**	604
2520	PENBUTOLOL-M (HO-)	2AC	**391** **376** 158 86 **56**	642
2525	METHAQUALONE-M (6-HO-)		**266** **251** 249 132 91	451
2525	TRAZODONE-M 3 ISOMER 2	2AC	**296** 254 **182** 154	518
2525	LORAZEPAM ISOMER 2	2ME	**330** 316 274 239 **75**	582
2530	DOXEPIN-M (HO-DIHYDRO-)		**297** 71 **58**	519
2530	ETHYLMORPHINE	AC	**355** 327 204 162 124	611
2530	METHAQUALONE-M (4'HO-)	AC	**308** **265** 235	541
2530	PHENGLUTARIMIDE-M (DESETHYL-)	AC	**302** 260 **189**	530
2530	PROPYPHENAZONE-M (HO-PHENYL-)	AC	**288** 273 246 **231** 56	500
2535	CHLORDIAZEPOXIDE ARTIFACT (DESOXO-)		**283** **282**	487
2535	DOXEPIN-M (HO-) ISOMER 1		**295** 178 165 **58**	515
2535	HEROIN-M (6-ACETYL-MORPHINE)		**327** 268 162 124	574
2535	DESIPRAMINE-M (HO-RING)	AC	**253** **211**	425
2535	IMIPRAMINE-M (HO-RING)	AC	**253** **211**	425
2535	LOFEPRAMINE-M (HO-RING)	AC	**253** **211**	425
2535	TRIMIPRAMINE-M (HO-RING)	AC	**253** **211**	425
2540	CLOMIPRAMINE-M (HO-) ISOMER 1		**330** **285** 245 85 **58**	581
2540	CLOTIAZEPAM		**318** **289**	560
2540*	DIISOOCTYLPHTHALATE		**390** **279** 167 **149**	641
2540	DOXEPIN-M (NOR-HO-)		**281** 238 165 **44**	484
2540	LEVOMEPROMAZINE		**328** 228 185 100 **58**	577
2540	OXAZOLAM		**328** 283 **251** 70	577
2540	OXYCODONE		**315** 258 230 140 70	555
2540	BENZOCTAMINE	AC	**291** **263** **218** 191	506
2540*	CANNABINOL	AC	**352** **337** 295 238	608
2540	DICLOFENAC-M (HO-)	AC	**335** **293** 258 230	588
2540	DOXEPIN-M (HO-) ISOMER 1	AC	**337** **257** **58**	591
2540	PROCYCLIDINE-M (HO-) -H2O	AC	**327** 186 129 105 **84**	575
2540	PROMETHAZINE-M (NOR-)	AC	**312** **212** 114 **58**	548

RI	NAME	DERIVATIVE	TYPICAL IONS	PAGE
2540	BROMAZEPAM ISOMER 2	ME	**329** 300 250	580
2540*	WARFARIN	ME	**322** **279** 121 91	567
2545*	MESTEROLONE		**304** 218 200	533
2545	PECAZINE		**310** 199 112 96 **58**	543
2545	PENTAZOCINE-M (HO-)		**301** 268 **217** 110 70	527
2545	THEBAINE		**311** 296	546
2545	CETOBEMIDONE-M (NOR-)	2AC	**317** **261** 218 70 **58**	559
2545	DIHYDROCODEINE-M (O-DESMETHYL-)	2AC	**371** **329** 288 164 70	626
2545	DIHYDROMORPHINE	2AC	**371** **329** 288 164 70	626
2545	HYDROCODONE-M (O-DESMETHYL-DIHYDRO-)	2AC	**371** **329** 288 164 70	626
2545	HYDROMORPHONE-M (DIHYDRO-)	2AC	**371** **329** 288 164 70	626
2545	THEBACONE-M (O-DESMETHYL-DIHYDRO-)	2AC	**371** **329** 288 164 70	626
2545	OXYPHENBUTAZONE ISOMER 1	2ME	**352** 272 213 149 119	609
2545	PHENYLBUTAZONE-M (HO-) ISOMER 1	2ME	**352** 272 213 149 119	609
2550*	ESTRADIOL		**272** 213 172 160 146	462
2550	INDOMETACIN		**313** **139** 111	549
2550	ALIMEMAZINE-M (HO-RING)	AC	**257** **215** 183	431
2550	DIXYRAZINE-M (HO-RING)	AC	**257** **215** 183	431
2550	PECAZINE-M (HO-RING)	AC	**257** **215** 183	431
2550	PERAZINE-M (HO-RING)	AC	**257** **215** 183	431
2550	PHENOTHIAZINE-M (HO-)	AC	**257** **215** 183	431
2550	PROMAZINE-M (HO-RING)	AC	**257** **215** 183	431
2550	PROMETHAZINE-M (HO-RING)	AC	**257** **215** 183	431
2550*	WARFARIN-M (DIHYDRO-) -H2O	ME	**306** **292** 263 249 121	536
2555*	CANNABINOL		**310** **295** 238 223	543
2555	LOXAPINE		**327** **257** 83 **70**	574
2555	PERICIAZINE-M (RING)		**224** 192	362
2555	PROPOXYPHENE-M (NOR-) -H2O N-PROP.		**307** **234** **105** 100 91	537
2555	LEVORPHANOL-M (HO-)	2AC	**357** 315 298 231 **57**	613
2555	OXYCODONE	AC	**357** 314 298 240	613
2555	TRIHEXYPHENIDYL-M (DI-HO-) -H2O ISO 1	2AC	**399** 357 **98**	646
2555	FLURAZEPAM	HY	**348** **86**	605
2555	CLONAZEPAM ISOMER 1	ME	**329** 294 248	581
2560	DOXEPIN-M (HO-) ISOMER 2		**295** 178 165 **58**	516
2560	METHAQUALONE-M (4'OMER 2		**295** 178 165 **58**	516
2560	NADOLOL ARTIFACT		**321** 277 236 120 **86**	565
2560	PRENYLAMINE		**329** **328** **239** 167 **58**	579
2560	DITAZOL-M (BIS-DESALKYL-)	AC	**278** **236** 105	476
2560*	GUAIFENESIN-M	AC	**328** 245 170 **159**	578
2560	OXYCODONE ENOL	2AC	**399** 357 314 240	646
2560	PENTOXIFYLLINE-M (HO-)	AC	**322** 262 193 **180**	566
2565	IMIPRAMINE-M (HO-)		**296** 251 85 **58**	517
2565	BORNAPRINE-M (HO-) ISOMER 3	AC	**387** **372** 214 142 **86**	640
2565*	PROPRANOLOL-M (DESAMINO-DI-HO-)	3AC	**360** 318 **159**	615
2570	AZINPHOS-ETHYL		**345** **186** 160 **132** 77	602
2570*	MAPROTILINE-M (DI-HO-)		**280** **252** 207	481
2570	TETRAZEPAM-M (HO-)		**304** 285 275 **235**	533
2570	LEVOBUNOLOL -H2O	AC	**315** **259** 200 160 **57**	556
2570	OXPRENOLOL-M (HO-) -H2O ISOMER 2	2AC	**347** 305 204 **72**	605
2570	OXYCODONE-M (DIHYDRO-)	2AC	**401** **359** 242 70	648
2575	TRIMIPRAMINE-M (HO-)		**310** 265 **250** 224 **58**	544
2575	AMIPHENAZOLE	2AC	**275** 233 **191** 121	469

RI	NAME	DERIVATIVE	TYPICAL IONS	PAGE
2575	TETRAZEPAM-M (HO-) ISOMER 2	HY	**265** 253 220 207 **194**	449
2575	OXAZEPAM ISOMER 2 -H2O	2ME	**296** **295** 267 239 205	519
2580	KETOTIFEN		**309** 237 208 96 70	542
2580	MIDAZOLAM		**325** **310**	571
2580	PROMETHAZINE-M (NOR-HO-)		**286** **212** 180 **58**	494
2580	TIAPRIDE-M (O-DESMETHYL-)		**314** 86 **58**	552
2580*	ANDROSTERONE	AC	**332** **272** 257	584
2580	CARBAMAZEPINE-M	AC	**251** **209** 180	423
2580	MIANSERIN-M (HO-)	AC	**322** 278 **209** 72	566
2580*	PROPAFENONE-M (HO-METHOXY-PHENOL)	AC	**314** 272 **167** 91	553
2585	DOXEPIN-M (HO-) ISOMER 2	AC	**337** **257** **58**	591
2585	TETRABENAZINE-M (O-DESMETHYL-HO-)	AC	**361** **302** 274 246 205	616
2590	NOMIFENSINE-M (HO-METHOXY-) ISOMER 2		**284** 241 210 **86**	490
2590	PROMETHAZINE-M (HO-)		**300** **229** 214 196 **72**	525
2590	TIAPRIDE-M (O-DESMETHYL-N-OXIDE) -(C2H5)2NOH		**241**	396
2590	TRIMETHOPRIM		**290** 259 123	504
2595	CHLOROQUINE		**319** 290 245 **86** 58	561
2595	HYDROMORPHONE	AC	**327** 285 228 162	575
2595	MIANSERIN-M (NOR-)	AC	**292** 248 193 **100**	508
2600	CINCHONIDINE		**294** **136**	513
2600	CINCHONINE		**294** **136**	513
2600	LEVOMEPROMAZINE-M (NOR-)		**314** 229 **213** **72**	552
2600	ALIMEMAZINE-M (HO-)	AC	**356** 228 214 **100** **58**	612
2600	PETHIDINE-M (NOR-HO-)	2AC	**333** 290 245 **203** 57	586
2600	CAMAZEPAM-M (METHYLOXAZEPAM)	ME	**314** **271** 255	554
2605	PROPRANOLOL	2AC	**343** **283** **200** **140** 98	600
2605	TETRAZEPAM-M (HO-) ISOMER 2	HYAC	**307** **248** 207 194	539
2610	CLOBAZAM		**300** 283 255 231 181 77	525
2610*	CUMATETRALYL		**292** 188 130 121 91	508
2610	FLUNITRAZEPAM		**313** 285 266 238	550
2610	METOCLOPRAMIDE		**299** **184** **99** **86**	523
2610	IMIPRAMINE-M (HO-)	AC	**338** 251 **211** 85 **58**	592
2610	NEFOPAM-M (NOR-DI-HO-) -H2O ISOMER 1	2AC	**337** 295 266 **87**	591
2610	VILOXAZINE-M (HO-)	2AC	**337** 295 **142** **100**	591
2615	FLUNITRAZEPAM-M (AMINO-)		**283** 255	487
2615	CLOBAZAM-M (NOR-HO-METHOXY-)	HYAC	**330** **288**	582
2615	PRIDINOL-M (HO-) -H2O	AC	**335** **292** 209 **110**	588
2620	HEROIN		**369** **327** 310 268 162	623
2620*	TESTOSTERONE		**288** 246 **124**	499
2620	BIPERIDEN-M (HO-)	AC	**369** 327 269 112 **98** 84	623
2620	CODEINE-M (O-DESMETHYL-)	2AC	**369** **327** 310 268 162	623
2620	ETHYLMORPHINE-M (O-DESETHYL-)	2AC	**369** **327** 310 268 162	623
2620	HYDROCODONE-M (O-DESMETHYL-) ENOL	2AC	**369** **327** 284 228 162	624
2620	HYDROMORPHONE ENOL	2AC	**369** **327** 284 228 162	624
2620	MORPHINE	2AC	**369** **327** 310 268 162	623
2620	THEBACONE-M (O-DESMETHYL-)	AC	**369** **327** 284 228 162	624
2620*	TETRAHYDROCANNABINOL-M (NOR-9-HOOC-)	2ME	**372** 357 **313** 245	629
2625	ACEPROMETHAZINE		**326** 255 222 **72**	572
2625	CAMAZEPAM-M (METHYLOXAZEPAM)		**300** **271** 256 239	525
2625	OXAPADOL		**278** 248 219 105 77	475
2625	TEMAZEPAM		**300** **271** 256 239	525
2630	CHLORAMPHENICOL	2AC	**273** **212** 170 **153** 118	464

RI	NAME	DERIVATIVE	TYPICAL IONS	PAGE
2635	TETRAZEPAM-M (HO-)	AC	**346** 304 **287**	603
2640	METOPROLOL-M (O-DESMETHYL-)	3AC	**379** **319** **200** 140 **72**	634
2640	NEFOPAM-M (NOR-DI-HO-) -H2O ISOMER 2	2AC	**337** 295 195 **87**	592
2640	PROCYCLIDINE-M (AMINO-HO-) -H2O	2AC	**315** 255 **196** 84	556
2640	TRIHEXYPHENIDYL -M (AMINO-HO-) -H2O	2AC	**315** 255 **196** 84	556
2645	BIPERIDEN-M (HO-)		**327** **218** 114 **98**	574
2645	PRIDINOL-M (AMINO-HO-) -H2O	2AC	**309** **208**	542
2650	ALIMEMAZINE-M (HO-)		**314** 228 214 **100** **58**	552
2650	FLURAZEPAM-M (BIS-DESETHYL-) -H2O		**313**	550
2650	PRAZEPAM		**324** 295 **269** 91 **55**	569
2650	TETRAZEPAM-M/ARTIFACT (TRI-HO-) -2H2O		**300** **272** 255	525
2650	NADOLOL	3AC	**435** **420** 301 **86** 56	661
2650	TRIMIPRAMINE-M (HO-)	AC	**352** **265** 215 99 84 **58**	608
2650*	WARFARIN-M (DIHYDRO-)	MEAC	**366** **292** 121	620
2650	CLOBAZAM-M (NOR-HO-)	HY	**258**	432
2655	BISACODYL-M (BIS-DESACETYL-)		**277** 199	474
2655	BISACODYL	HY	**277** 199	474
2660	BROMHEXINE-M (HO-)		**390** 293 **262** **128** 86	641
2660	CLOTIAZEPAM-M (OXO-)		**332** **303**	584
2660	FLURAZEPAM-M (HO-ETHYL-)		**332** **288** 273 211	584
2660	AMITRIPTYLINE-M (NOR-)	AC	**305** **232** 219 202 86	535
2660	METIPRANOLOL -H2O	AC	**333** 248 152 **140** 98	586
2660	NORTRIPTYLINE	AC	**305** **232** 219 202 86	535
2660	SULFAMETHIAZOLE	ME	**284** 156 **92** 65	490
2665	ALIMEMAZINE-M (SULFOXIDE)		**314** 298 **212** 199 **58**	552
2665	AMBROXOL		**376** 279 **262** **114** **70**	631
2665	BROMHEXINE-M (NOR-HO-)		**376** 279 **262** **114** **70**	631
2665	NORMETHADONE-M (NOR-)	2AC	**365** 323 **267** 193 **86**	619
2665	TETRABENAZINE-M (O-BIS-DESMETHYL-HO-)	2AC	**389** 330 **302** 288 233 191	640
2665	TRIHEXYPHENIDYL-M (DI-HO-) -H2O ISO 2	2AC	**399** 338 194 98	647
2670	BROMAZEPAM		**315** 286 259 **236** 208 179	555
2670	PROQUAZONE		**278** **235** 221 77	475
2670	AMITRIPTYLINE-M (NOR-HO-) -H2O	AC	**303** **230** 215 202 86	533
2670	AMITRIPTYLINOXIDE-M (DESOXO-NOR-HO-) -H2O	AC	**303** **230** 215 202 86	533
2670	DESIPRAMINE	AC	**308** **208** 193 114	541
2670	IMIPRAMINE-M (NOR-)	AC	**308** **208** 193 114	541
2670	LOFEPRAMINE-M (DESALKYL-)	AC	**308** **208** 193 114	541
2670	METIPRANOLOL	2AC	**393** 333 **200** 140 98	642
2670	NORTRIPTYLINE-M (HO-) -H2O	AC	**303** **230** 215 202 86	533
2670	TRIMIPRAMINE-M (NOR-HO-) -H2O	AC	**320** **206** 128	564
2675	SOTALOL -H2O	AC	**296** 217 **175** 133 84	518
2680	BISACODYL-M (METHOXY-BIS-DESACETYL-)		**307** 276 229 199	537
2680	FENBUTRAZATE		**367** 261 **190** 91 **69**	622
2680	OXYCODONE-M (NOR-) ENOL	3AC	**427** **385** 343 87	658
2680	PENTOXIFYLLINE-M (DI-HO-)	2AC	**380** 251 **181** 180	634
2685	PROMAZINE-M (HO-)		**300** 254 215 86 **58**	525
2685	TRIFLUOPERAZINE		**407** 267 **113** **70**	650
2685*	BENZOCTAMINE-M (DI-HO-METHOXY-)	2AC	**366** 324 **296**	620
2685	LONAZOLAC	ME	**326** **267** 232 164 77	573
2690	ACETYLSULFANILAMIDE		**214** **172** 156 92	336
2690	CARTEOLOL ARTIFACT		**304** **289** 163 84 **57**	534
2690	FENPIPRAMIDE		**322** **211** 112 **98**	565

RI	NAME	DERIVATIVE	TYPICAL IONS	PAGE
2690	FLUNITRAZEPAM-M (NOR-AMINO-)		**269** 241	457
2690	ACEPROMETHAZINE-M (DIHYDRO-)	AC	**370 299** 224 **72**	625
2690	PROMETHAZINE-M (HO-)	AC	**342 256** 214 **72**	598
2690	PROTRIPTYLINE	AC	**305 191** 114	535
2690	SULFAMETHOXAZOL-M (SULFANILAMIDE)	AC	**214 172** 156 92	336
2690	SULFANILAMIDE	AC	**214 172** 156 92	336
2690	NITRAZEPAM ISOMER 2	ME	**276 275 249** 231	470
2700*	DIISONONYLPHTHALATE		**418** 362 **293 149**	655
2700	TRIFLUPERIDOL		**409 271** 258 123	651
2700	CARTEOLOL	AC	**334** 319 163 **86 57**	587
2700	DOXEPIN-M (NOR-)	AC	**307 234** 219 86	539
2700	ETODROXIZINE-M (N-DESALKYL-)	AC	**328** 242 **201** 165 **85**	578
2700	HYDROXYZINE-M (N-DESALKYL-)	AC	**328** 242 **201** 165 **85**	578
2700	MECLOZINE-M (N-DESALKYL-)	AC	**328** 242 **201** 165 **85**	578
2700	OXYPHENBUTAZONE	AC	**366 324** 211 119 **93**	621
2700	PHENYLBUTAZONE-M (HO-)	AC	**366 324** 211 119 **93**	621
2700	TRIMETHOPRIM	AC	**332 290** 275	584
2705	CLOTIAZEPAM-M (HO-)		**316 287**	557
2705	FLUNITRAZEPAM-M (NOR-)		**299** 272 252 **224**	523
2705	PROMAZINE-M (SULFOXIDE)		**300** 284 **212 58**	526
2705	MAZINDOL	AC	**326** 284 **256** 220	573
2710	MOPERONE -H2O		**337** 214 188 **123**	590
2710	PROMETHAZINE-M (SULFOXIDE)		**300** 284 **213 72**	526
2710	ALIMEMAZINE-M (NOR-)	AC	**326 212** 180 **128** 86	573
2710	LEVORPHANOL-M (NOR-)	2AC	**327** 285 **87** 72	576
2710	METHORPHAN -M (BIS-DESMETHYL-)	2AC	**327** 285 **87** 72	576
2710	PROMAZINE-M (HO-)	AC	**342** 257 215 86 **58**	599
2715	FLUANISONE-M (O-DESMETHYL-)		**342 194** 165 123	598
2715	NALOXONE		**327** 286 242	575
2715	FLUNITRAZEPAM-M (NOR-AMINO-)	HY2AC	**314** 272 **230**	553
2715*	PROPAFENONE-M (DESAMINO-HO-)	2AC	**384 159** 121 91	637
2715	CARBAMAZEPINE-M CYSTEINE-CONJUGATE	(ME)	**326** 283 **180** 152	573
2720	ACEPROMAZINE-M (DIHYDRO-) -H2O		**310** 225 86 **58**	544
2720	FENTANYL		**336 245** 189 146	589
2720	PROPAFENONE-M (HO-) -H2O		**339** 310 **98** 91	593
2720*	NORETHISTERONE	AC	**340 298** 283 91 **56**	596
2720	TRIFLUPROMAZINE-M (HO-)	AC	**410** 368 283 **58**	652
2720	OXYPHENBUTAZONE ISOMER 2	2ME	**352** 309 190 160 77	609
2720	PHENYLBUTAZONE-M (HO-) ISOMER 2	2ME	**352** 309 190 160 77	609
2725	BENZOCTAMINE-M (NOR-HO-) ISOMER 1	2AC	**335** 293 **265**	588
2725	FLURAZEPAM-M (HO-ETHYL-)	AC	**374** 346 **314** 287	630
2730	FLUSPIRILENE-M 4	AC	**287 245 57**	497
2730	LORAZEPAM	2AC	**345** 307 265 **230**	603
2730	METOPROLOL-M (HO-ETHYL-)	3AC	**409** 349 **200** 140 **72**	652
2730	PHENYTOIN-M (HO-)	(ME)2AC	**366 324** 224	621
2735	LEVOMEPROMAZINE-M (HO-)		**344 100 58**	601
2735	LORMETAZEPAM		**334 305**	586
2735	METOCLOPRAMIDE	AC	**341** 269 226 **184 99 86**	597
2740	CLOBAZAM-M (NOR-)		**286** 244 215 77	495
2740	TRIFLUPROMAZINE-M (NOR-)	AC	**380** 267 156 **114** 100	635
2745	LEVOMEPROMAZINE-M (HO-)	AC	**386** 312 **212** 114 100 **58**	639
2750*	BENZBROMARONE		**422 344** 279 264 173	656

RI	NAME	DERIVATIVE	TYPICAL IONS	PAGE
2750	CHLORPROTHIXENE-M (HO-DIHYDRO-)		**333** 247 **58**	585
2750	LEVOMEPROMAZINE-M (NOR-HO-)		**330** 258 **245** 86 **72**	581
2750	BENPERIDOL-M 3	2AC	**301** **259** 216 134 82	529
2750	BISACODYL-M (METHOXY-DESACETYL-)	AC	**349** 307 **277** 199	606
2750	DIHYDROCODEINE-M (NOR-)	2AC	**371** **87** 72	626
2750	HYDROCODONE-M (NOR-DIHYDRO-)	2AC	**371** **87** 72	626
2750	MEPINDOLOL	2AC	**346** **286** **184** 140 98	604
2750	NOXIPTYLINE-M (NOR-HO-) -H2O	AC	**320** **205** **178** 100	564
2750	PECAZINE-M (HO-)	AC	**368** 326 215 **112** **58**	623
2750	PIMOZIDE-M 5	2AC	**301** **259** 216 134 82	529
2750	PINDOLOL	2AC	**332** **200** 186 140 98	584
2750	PROPRANOLOL-M (HO-) -H2O ISOMER 1	2AC	**341** 197 **140** 98	597
2750	QUINIDINE	AC	**366** 307 189 **136**	621
2750	QUININE	AC	**366** 309 189 **136**	621
2750	THEBACONE-M (NOR-DIHYDRO-)	2AC	**371** **87** 72	626
2755	ACEPROMAZINE		**326** 241 86 **58**	572
2760	NITRAZEPAM		**281** 253 234 222 206	484
2760	PROPAFENONE ARTIFACT		**353** 324 **128** 121 98 91	609
2760	HYDROCODONE-M (NOR-)	AC	**327** 241 **87** 72	576
2760	MAPROTILINE-M (NOR-)	AC	**305** **277** 218 191	535
2760	MELITRACENE-M (NOR-)	AC	**319** **246** 231 86	563
2760	OXYMETAZOLINE	2AC	**344** **302** 287 230 203	602
2760	CLONAZEPAM ISOMER 2	ME	**329** 302 294 248	581
2765	MEQUITAZINE		**322** 212 198 180 **124**	566
2765	ACEPROMAZINE-M (DIHYDRO-)	AC	**370** 310 225 86 **58**	625
2765	ALIMEMAZINE-M (BIS-NOR-)	AC	**312** **212** 114	548
2765	DIXYRAZINE-M (AMINO-)	AC	**312** **212** 114	548
2765	FLUPHENAZINE-M (AMINO-)	AC	**366** 267 **100**	621
2765	HOMOFENAZINE-M (AMINO-)	AC	**366** 267 **100**	621
2765	TRIFLUOPERAZINE-M (AMINO-)	AC	**366** 267 **100**	621
2765	TRIFLUPROMAZINE-M (BIS-NOR-)	AC	**366** 267 **100**	621
2770	BENPERIDOL-M 3	AC	**259** 216 134 125 **82**	435
2770	PIMOZIDE-M 5	AC	**259** 216 134 125 **82**	435
2775	DIMETINDENE-M (NOR-)	AC	**320** 218 **100** 86 58	564
2775	PHENYTOIN-M (HO-)	2AC	**352** **310** 268 224 196	608
2780	FLURAZEPAM		**387** 315 99 **86**	639
2780*	PROGESTERONE		**314** 272 **124**	553
2780*	ESTRADIOL	2AC	**356** **314** 172 146	612
2780	PROTHIPENDYL-M (HO-)	AC	**343** 230 **216** 86 **58**	600
2780	PROTRIPTYLINE-M (NOR-)	AC	**291** 218 **191** 100 86	506
2780	LORAZEPAM-M (HO-METHOXY-)	HY	**311** 281 **246**	547
2785	NITRAZEPAM-M (AMINO-)		**251** 223 222	421
2785	VIMINOL-M/ARTIFACT	AC	**394** 335 **125**	643
2790	PERAZINE		**339** 199 141 113 **70**	594
2790	QUINIDINE		**324** 189 173 **136**	569
2790	QUININE		**324** 189 **136**	569
2790	BENZOCTAMINE-M (NOR-HO-) ISOMER 2	2AC	**335** 307 **265** 207	588
2790	BORNAPRINE-M (DESETHYL-HO-) ISOMER 1	2AC	**401** **358** 142 112 84 **58**	648
2790	TETRAZEPAM-M/ARTIFACT (TRI-HO-) -2H2O	AC	**342** **300** 272	599
2795	FLUANISONE		**356** 218 205 **162** 123	612
2795	PHENYTOIN-M (HO-)		**268** 239 **196** 120 104	455
2795	FLUNITRAZEPAM-M (AMINO-)	HY	**244** 227	402

RI	NAME	DERIVATIVE	TYPICAL IONS	PAGE
2800*	AMIADARONE ARTIFACT		**420 294** 265 **142** 121	656
2800	CLOMIPRAMINE-M (HO-) ISOMER 2		**330 285** 245 85 **58**	582
2800	MOPERONE		**355** 217 **204 123**	610
2800*	PREDNISOLONE		**300 122** 91	526
2800	AMITRIPTYLINE-M (NOR-DI-HO-) -H2O	2AC	**361** 319 **277**	616
2800	CHLORPROTHIXENE-M (HO-DIHYDRO-)	AC	**375** 247 **58**	631
2800	DIBENZEPIN-M (NOR-)	AC	**323** 250 237 **209** 100	568
2800	MAPROTILINE	AC	**319 291** 218 100	563
2800	NORTRIPTYLINE-M (DI-HO-) -H2O	2AC	**361** 319 **277 87**	616
2805	CLOMIPRAMINE-M (HO-) ISOMER 1	AC	**372** 327 **285** 245 85 **58**	628
2805	PROMAZINE-M (NOR-)	AC	**312** 198 180 **114**	549
2810	NALOXONE-M (DIHYDRO-)	2AC	**413** 371 242 **82**	653
2815	LORCAINIDE		**370 355** 245 127 **91**	624
2820	CARAZOLOL ARTIFACT		**310 183** 154 127 86	544
2820	CHLORDIAZEPOXIDE		**299 282**	523
2820	PAPAVERINE		**339 324** 154	594
2820	TIAPRIDE		**328 326** 311 213 **86**	578
2820*	MAPROTILINE-M (DI-HO-)	2AC	**364** 336 **294** 207	618
2820	MIDAZOLAM-M (HO-)	AC	**383** 340 **310**	636
2825	DIBENZEPIN-M (TER-NOR-)	AC	**295** 236 **223** 195	516
2825	FENDILINE	AC	**357** 162 120 **105** 72	613
2825	NALOXONE	ME	**341** 300 256	598
2830	FENETHYLLINE		**341 250** 207 91	596
2830	MIDAZOLAM-M (HO-)		**339 310**	594
2830	FLUANISONE-M (O-DESMETHYL-)	AC	**384** 246 **233 123**	637
2830	PROTHIPENDYL-M (BIS-NOR-)	AC	**299** 227 213 **200** 100	524
2830	NALOXONE	2ET	**383 270**	637
2835	BISACODYL		**361** 319 **277** 199	616
2835	INDOMETACIN	ME	**371** 312 **139** 111	627
2840	CLONAZEPAM		**315** 286 280 240 234 205	555
2840	NALOXONE	AC	**369 327** 286 242	624
2840*	WARFARIN-M (HO-)	2ME	**352 309**	609
2845	CLONAZEPAM-M (AMINO-)	HY2AC	**330** 288 **246** 211	582
2845	DITAZOL-M (BIS-DESALKYL-HO-)	2AC	**336** 294 **252** 121	590
2850	ACEBUTOLOL -H2O		**318** 303 140 **98**	560
2850	BROMOPRIDE		**343 293** 195 178 **58**	599
2850	NOMIFENSINE-M (HO-) ISOMER 1	2AC	**338** 310 **280** 268 238 226	593
2850	NORMETHADONE-M (NOR-DIHYDRO-) -H2O	AC	**307 266** 193 **86**	539
2860*	STRESSHORMONE (HYDROXYANDROSTENE)	AC	**316** 256 241 215	557
2865	TRIAZOLAM-M	HY	**331 296** 139 111	583
2870	CLOTIAZEPAM-M (HO-)	AC	**376** 316 **271** 256	632
2870	DIBENZEPIN-M (BIS-NOR-)	AC	**309** 236 **223** 195 100	543
2870	FLUNITRAZEPAM-M (AMINO-)	HY2AC	**328** 286 244 **205**	578
2875	BENZOCTAMINE-M (NOR-HO-METHOXY-)	2AC	**365** 323 **295**	619
2875	BORNAPRINE-M (DESETHYL-HO-) ISOMER 2	2AC	**401 358** 169 128 84 **58**	648
2875	ACEMETACIN	ME	**429 371** 312 **139** 111	659
2880	CLONAZEPAM-M (AMINO-)		**285** 256 250 222 111	492
2880	NOMIFENSINE-M (HO-) ISOMER 2	2AC	**338** 308 **280** 268 194	593
2880	PROFENAMINE-M (DESETHYL-HO-)	2AC	**384 270** 128 **72**	637
2880	PROTHIPENDYL-M (NOR-)	AC	**313** 227 213 **200 114** 100	550
2885	NALOXONE	2ME	**355** 256 82	611
2890*	SULINDAC		**312 297** 265 233 117	548

RI	NAME	DERIVATIVE	TYPICAL IONS	PAGE
2890	BENZOCTAMINE-M (HO-)	2AC	**349** 321 **279** 207	606
2890	BORNAPRINE-M (DESETHYL-HO-) ISOMER 3	2AC	**401** **358** 169 128 84 **58**	649
2890	NALOXONE	MEAC	**383** 340 324 242	636
2895	CLOZAPINE		**326** 256 **243** 227 192 70	572
2895	PROTRIPTYLINE-M (HO-)	AC	**363** 321 249 **207** 114	617
2900	CHAVICINE		**285** 201 173 **115** 84	493
2900	DITAZOL		**324** 293 249 165 77	570
2900	HYDROXYZINE		**374** 299 **201** 165	630
2900	CLOBAZAM-M (HO-)	AC	**358** **316** 299 271	615
2900	OXYCODONE-M (NOR-DIHYDRO-)	2AC	**387** **343** 258 87 72	640
2900	PROPRANOLOL-M (HO-) -H2O ISOMER 2	2AC	**341** 197 **140** 98	597
2905	CLOMIPRAMINE-M (HO-) ISOMER 2	AC	**372** 327 **285** 245 85 **58**	628
2905	CLOBAZAM-M (HO-METHOXY-)	HY	**320** 240 206	564
2920	ACEPROMETHAZINE-M (METHOXY-DIHYDRO-) -H2O		**340** 271 238 **72**	595
2920	DEXTROMORAMIDE		**392** **265** 128 **100**	642
2925	PRENYLAMINE	AC	**371** **281** 239 100 **58**	626
2930	ALIMEMAZINE-M (NOR-HO-)	2AC	**384** 228 214 196 **128**	638
2930	BROMHEXINE-M (HO-)	2AC	**474** 417 **335** 304 264	666
2930	CHLORPROTHIXENE-M (NOR-DIHYDRO-)	AC	**345** 270 **231** 114 58	603
2930	ETHYLMORPHINE-M (NOR-)	2AC	**383** 341 237 209 **87** 72	636
2930	PROPAFENONE -H2O	AC	**365** 224 **140** **98**	619
2935	CLONAZEPAM-M (AMINO-HO-)		**283** 255 220	488
2935	BROMHEXINE-M (NOR-HO-) ISOMER 1	2AC	**460** 417 279 **262** **81**	665
2935	ETODROXIZINE M/ARTIFACT	HYAC	**280** **201** 165	483
2935	HYDROXYZINE-M/ARTIFACT	HYAC	**280** **201** 165	483
2935	LOXAPINE-M (HO-)	AC	**385** 315 **83** **70**	638
2935	OXYCODONE-M (NOR-DIHYDRO-)	3AC	**429** **387** **242** 87 72	659
2935	QUINIDINE-M (N-OXIDE)	AC	**382** 189 **152**	636
2940*	ESTRIOL		**288** 213 172 160 146	500
2940	HALOPERIDOL		**375** **237** **224** 189 123	631
2940	LEVOMEPROMAZINE-M (SULFOXIDE)		**344** 328 **242** 229 100 **58**	602
2940	QUINIDINE-M		**338** 323 **152** 138	592
2940	ACEPROMETHAZINE-M (NOR-)	AC	**354** **254** 114 72 **58**	610
2940	PROPRANOLOL-M (HO-)	3AC	**401** **341** 186 **140** 98	649
2945	CHLORPROTHIXENE-M (NOR-)	AC	**343** **270** 235 **221** 86	600
2945	CODEINE-M (NOR-)	2AC	**369** 327 223 **87** 72	624
2945	NORCODEINE	2AC	**369** 327 223 **87** 72	624
2950	ETHAVERINE		**395** **366** 73	644
2950	QUINIDINE-M (N-OXIDE)		**340** 324 189 **152** 136	595
2950	FLUNITRAZEPAM-M (AMINO-)	AC	**325** 297 255	571
2950*	PROPAFENONE-M (DESAMINO-DI-HO-)	3AC	**442** 308 **159** **91**	663
2955	MICONAZOLE		**414** **333** **159** 121 81	654
2955	CODEINE-M (N-O-BIS-DESMETHYL-)	3AC	**397** 355 209 **87** 72	645
2955	ETHYLMORPHINE-M (N-O-BIS-DESALKYL-)	3AC	**397** 355 209 **87** 72	645
2955	HEROIN-M (NOR-MORPHINE)	3AC	**397** 355 209 **87** 72	645
2955	MORPHINE-M (NOR-)	3AC	**397** 355 209 **87** 72	645
2960	CAFEDRINE		**339** **249** 105 **70**	594
2960	CAMAZEPAM		**371** 283 **271** 256 227 **72**	626
2960	DITAZOL-M (BIS-DESALKYL-HO-)	MEAC	**308** 266 **135**	541
2960	METIXENE-M (NOR-)	AC	**337** **197**	592
2965	HALOPERIDOL	AC	**357** 206 **192** 123	613
2965	TRIHEXYPHENIDYL-M (TRI-HO-) -H2O	3AC	**457** **398** 336 194 **156**	665

RI	NAME	DERIVATIVE	TYPICAL IONS	PAGE
2970	PROCHLORPERAZINE		**373** 141 **113** **70**	629
2970	DITAZOL-M (DESALKYL-HO-)	ME2AC	**394** **352** 266 135	644
2970	LEVOMEPROMAZINE-M (NOR-)	AC	**356** 242 228 **128**	613
2970	NOMIFENSINE-M (HO-METHOXY-)	2AC	**368** 310 **268** 224	623
2975	ATENOLOL -H2O	AC	**290** 205 188 **140** 98	505
2980	PRIDINOL-M (DI-HO-) -H2O	2AC	**393** 309 **208**	643
2985	DITAZOL	2AC	**408** 322 262 **87**	651
2985	NITRAZEPAM-M (AMINO-)	HY2AC	**296** 254 **212** 211	518
2985	PECAZINE-M (NOR-)	AC	**338** **212** 198 98	593
2990	CHLORPROMAZINE-M (BIS-NOR-)	AC	**332** 233 **100**	585
2990	PERPHENAZINE-M (AMINO-)	AC	**332** 233 **100**	585
2990	PROCHLORPERAZINE-M (AMINO-)	AC	**332** 233 **100**	585
2990	THIOPROPAZATE-M (AMINO-)	AC	**332** 233 **100**	585
2995	CLOMIPRAMINE-M (NOR-)	AC	**342** 240 **114**	599
2995	CLOTIAZEPAM-M (DI-HO-)	2AC	**434** **374** **332** 319 291	660
2995	DOXEPIN-M (NOR-HO-) ISOMER 1	2AC	**365** **292** 250 233 **86**	619
2995	MAPROTILINE-M (HO-ETHANEDIYL-)	2AC	**377** **291** 218 191 100	632
3000*	CHOLESTEROL -H2O		**368** 353 260 147	622
3000	CLOBAZAM-M (HO-)		**316** 299 271	557
3000*	SQUALENE		**410** 136 95 82 **69**	652
3000	TRIAZOLAM-M (ALPHA-HO-)		**358** **328** 293 265 239	614
3000	ACEPROMAZINE-M (HO-DIHYDRO-)	2AC	**428** **343** 154 86 **58**	659
3000	CLOBAZAM-M (NOR-HO-)	HYAC	**300** **258**	526
3000	HYDROXYZINE	AC	**416** 355 299 **201** 165	654
3000	TRIMETHOPRIM	2AC	**374** **332** 317 275	630
3005	PIRENZEPIN		**351** 211 **113** 70	607
3005	FLUPENTIXOL-M (DIHYDRO-)	AC	**478** 418 **265** 185 125 98	667
3005	MIANSERIN-M (NOR-HO-)	2AC	**350** 265 209 **100**	607
3010*	ESTRIOL	3AC	**414** **372** 330 270 160	654
3015	AMBROXOL	2AC	**460** **417** 279 **262** **81** 70	665
3015	BROMHEXINE-M (NOR-HO-) ISOMER 2	2AC	**460** **417** 279 **262** **81** 70	665
3015	PROMETHAZINE-M (NOR-HO-)	2AC	**370** 270 **228** 114 **58**	625
3020	DITAZOL-M (DESALKYL-HO-)	3AC	**422** 380 338 **252** 87	657
3020	MIDAZOLAM-M (DI-HO-)	2AC	**441** **399** 383 340 326 **310**	662
3020	NOXIPTYLINE-M (NOR-DI-HO-) -H2O	2AC	**378** **336** 220 **178** 100	633
3025*	QUINESTROL		**364** 338 295 **270** 213	618
3025	ACEPROMETHAZINE-M (HO-)	AC	**384** **313** 256 **72**	638
3025	FLURAZEPAM-M (BIS-DESETHYL-)	AC	**373** 314 286 **273** 246	629
3030	MELITRACENE-M (NOR-HO-DIHYDRO-)	2AC	**379** 265 **223** 114	634
3035	DOXEPIN-M (NOR-HO-) ISOMER 2	2AC	**365** **292** 250 233 **86**	620
3035	FLUNITRAZEPAM-M (NOR-AMINO-)	AC	**311** 283 241	547
3040	MECLOZINE		**390** 285 189 **105**	641
3040	PIPAMPERONE		**331** 164 123 **84**	582
3040	ACEPROMAZINE-M (HO-)	AC	**384** 256 86 **58**	638
3045	FLUPENTIXOL	AC	**302** 265 234 **185**	531
3050	FLUPHENAZINE		**437** **280** 143 113 **70**	661
3050	OXPRENOLOL-M (HO-) ISOMER 1	3AC	**407** **347** 305 204 **72**	650
3050	PROPAFENONE-M (HO-) -H2O	2AC	**423** 381 **140** 98 **91**	657
3055	FLUPENTIXOL		**302** 265 234 80	529
3055	OPIPRAMOL		**363** **218** 193 70	617
3055	FLUPENTIXOL-M (DESALKYL-DIHYDRO-)	AC	**434** 265 **185** **141** 99	660
3060	PARACETAMOL-M CONJUGATE	AC	**438** 396 **246** 204 **162**	662

RI	NAME	DERIVATIVE	TYPICAL IONS	PAGE
3065	DESIPRAMINE-M (HO-)	2AC	**366** 266 **114**	622
3065	IMIPRAMINE-M (NOR-HO-)	2AC	**366** 266 **114**	622
3065	LOFEPRAMINE-M (DESALKYL-HO-)	2AC	**366** 266 **114**	622
3070	CHLORPROMAZINE-M (NOR-)	AC	**346** 232 **114** 86	604
3070	PROTHIPENDYL-M (NOR-HO-)	2AC	**371** 258 216 **114** 100	627
3080	NIFENAZONE		**308** 202 **56**	540
3080	TRIAZOLAM		**342** 313 279 238	598
3085*	CHOLESTEROL		**386** 368 353 301 275	639
3090	DIMETINDENE-M (NOR-HO-)	2AC	**378** 276 234 **100** 86	633
3095	MAPROTILINE-M (HO-ANTHRYL-)	2AC	**377 349** 307 234	633
3100	BROTIZOLAM		**392** 363 316 291 245	642
3100	ACEBUTOLOL -H20	AC	**360** 259 230 **151** 98	616
3100	OXPRENOLOL-M (HO-) ISOMER 2	3AC	**407** 347 200 140 **72**	651
3105	CLOZAPINE-M (NOR-)		**312** 269 256 **243** 192 85	548
3110	MOPERONE-M 4		**329** 234 185 **123**	580
3110	FENETHYLLINE	AC	**383** 292 **250** 207	636
3120	STRYCHNINE		**334**	587
3120	TRIFLUPROMAZINE-M (NOR-HO-)	2AC	**438 323** 156 **114**	662
3125	THIORIDAZINE		**370** 126 **98** 70	624
3130	CARAZOLOL -H2O	AC	**322 220 140** 98	566
3135	FLUNARIZINE		**404 287 203** 201	650
3145	ACEPROMAZINE-M (NOR-)	AC	**354** 241 **114** 100	610
3145	FLUPHENAZINE-M (DESALKYL-)	AC	**435 267 141** 99	661
3145	TRIFLUOPERAZINE-M (NOR-)	AC	**435 267 141** 99	661
3150	VERAPAMIL		**454** 438 **303** 260 59	665
3150	ACEPROMAZINE-M (NOR-DIHYDRO-) -H2O	AC	**338 114** 100	593
3150	MAPROTILINE-M (NOR-HO-)	2AC	**363 335** 293 **207 100**	617
3150	NITRAZEPAM-M (AMINO-)	AC	**293** 265 223 222	512
3155	ETODROXIZINE		**418 299 201** 165	655
3155	TRIMIPRAMINE-M (NOR-HO-)	2AC	**380 266** 224 128	635
3165	HOMOFENAZINE		**451 433 280** 248 167 **58**	664
3165	ACEPROMETHAZINE-M (METHOXY-DIHYDRO-)	AC	**400 329** 270 **72**	647
3165	BROMHEXINE-M (NOR-HO-) ISOMER 3	2AC	**460 417** 279 262 **81**	666
3170	FLUPHENAZINE	AC	**479 419 280** 185 125 70	667
3170	OPIPRAMOL	AC	**405** 345 218 **193**	650
3175	PERAZINE-M (HO-)		**355** 215 155 141 113 **70**	611
3180	SULFORIDAZINE-M (RING)		**277** 198	472
3185	QUINIDINE-M (HO-)	2AC	**424 365** 305 194	657
3190	BUTAPERAZINE		**409** 269 141 **113 70**	651
3190	CLONAZEPAM-M (AMINO-)	AC	**327** 299 292 256 220	577
3190	PERAZINE-M (HO-)	AC	**397** 214 141 113 **70 58**	645
3195	CARBAMAZEPINE-M	AC	**340 297** 205 **179**	596
3195	CHLORPROTHIXENE-M (NOR-HO-DIHYDRO-)	2AC	**403** 289 **247** 114 86	650
3195	PROMAZINE-M (NOR-HO-)	2AC	**370** 328 214 **114** 86	625
3200	THIOPROPERAZINE-M (RING)		**306** 198	536
3200	DITAZOL-M (HO-)	ME2AC	**438** 352 266 135 87	662
3200*	MAPROTILINE-M (TRI-HO-)	3AC	**422 394** 352 **310** 223	657
3200	TRIAZOLAM-M (ALPHA-HO-)	AC	**400 357** 329 239	647
3205	ACEPROMETHAZINE-M (NOR-HO-)	2AC	**412 254** 114 100 **58**	653
3205	CLOMIPRAMINE-M (NOR-HO-)	2AC	**400** 358 **300** 258 244 **114**	648
3210	DEXTROMORAMIDE-M (HO-)	AC	**450** 407 **323** 194 128 **100**	664
3210	PERAZINE-M (NOR-)	AC	**367** 238 **199** 141 99	622

RI	NAME	DERIVATIVE	TYPICAL IONS	PAGE
3210	ACENOCOUMAROL	ME	**367** 310 193 121 72	622
3220	DIXYRAZINE		**427** 352 **212** 187	658
3220	LEVOMEPROMAZINE-M (NOR-HO-)	2AC	**414** 372 300 258 244 **128**	654
3220	CARBAMAZEPINE-M	(AC)	**361** 232 218 207 **193**	616
3220*	SULINDAC	ME	**370** 354 295 248 **233**	625
3225	DICLOFENAC-M	AC	**413** 371 **336** 60	653
3240	HOMOFENAZINE-M (DESALKYL-)	AC	**449** **267** 112	664
3250	PIPAMPERONE-M (HO-)		**347** 292 165 154 **123**	604
3250	DITAZOL-M (HO-)	2AC	**424** 338 252 **87**	658
3255	CLOBAZAM-M (HO-METHOXY-)		**346** 316 301 271 245	603
3260	HOMOFENAZINE	AC	**493** **433** 280 **167** 87	667
3265	PERICIAZINE		**365** 264 223 142 **114**	618
3270	DEXTROMORAMIDE-M (METHOXY-)		**422** **323** 194 128 **100**	657
3275	BRUCINE		**394** 379 355	643
3290	PIPAMPERONE-M (HO-)	AC	**389** 292 165 **123**	641
3310*	CYPROTERONE -H2O		**356** 246 **175**	612
3320*	CYPROTERONE-M/ARTIFACT 1	AC	**374** 356 **339** 175	630
3330*	CYPROTERONE-M/ARTIFACT 2	AC	**372** 354 **339**	628
3340*	CYPROTERONE	AC	**416** 356 **313** 246 175	655
3340	FLUSPIRILENE	AC	**517** **475** **286** **72**	668
3345	TRAZODONE		**371** **278** 231 205 176 **70**	626
3350	METONITAZENE		**382** 352 121 **86**	635
3350	PENFLURIDOL		**523** **292** 201 109	668
3350	DIXYRAZINE-M (O-DESALKYL-)	AC	**425** 365 199 **185** 98	658
3350	QUINIDINE-M (DI-HO-DIHYDRO-)	3AC	**484** **425** 365 254 194	667
3355	DIXYRAZINE-M (N-DESALKYL-)	AC	**381** 339 199 **141** 99	635
3360	BUPRENORPHINE ARTIFACT		**435** 410 **378** 84 **55**	661
3360	PERPHENAZINE		**403** 372 **246** 143	649
3360	THIOPROPAZATE-M (DESACETYL-)		**403** 372 **246** 143	649
3370	DROPERIDOL	ME	**393** **246** 165 **123**	643
3380	TRAZODONE-M 4	AC	**429** 414 336 **205**	659
3390	PERICIAZINE	AC	**407** 263 224 184 **156** 114	651
3400	CLOPENTHIXOL		**400** **221** **143** 100 70	647
3400	LABETALOL	3AC	**409** 376 **335** 160 133	652
3400	PERAZINE-M	AC	**397** 355 199 **100**	645
3400*	PREDNISOLONE	3AC	**372** 314 147 **122**	629
3410	BUPRENORPHINE	AC	**509** 453 **421** 84 55	668
3415	DIPHENOXYLATE		**452** **377** **246** 165	664
3415	SULFORIDAZINE		**402** **277** 198 **98**	649
3415	PECAZINE-M (NOR-HO-)	2AC	**396** 354 **228** 214 98	644
3440	BENPERIDOL		**381** **363** **230** 134 109 82	635
3445	LYSERGIDE (LSD)		**323** **221** 181	567
3445	OXYPERTINE		**379** 217 **175** 132 70	633
3450	CLOPENTHIXOL-M (DESALKYL-DIHYDRO-)	AC	**400** **268** **141** 99	648
3450	LOXAPINE-M (NOR-HO-)	2AC	**413** **207** 112	654
3460	CLOPENTHIXOL	AC	**442** 221 **185** 98 87	663
3470	THIOPROPAZATE		**445** 246 185 **98** **70**	663
3470	PERPHENAZINE	AC	**445** 246 185 **98** **70**	663
3490	CLOPENTHIXOL-M (DESALKYL-)	AC	**398** **268** **141** 99	646
3490	CLOZAPINE-M (NOR-)	2AC	**396** 310 298 227 192	645
3490	THIORIDAZINE-M (NOR-)	AC	**398** 356 **154** 84	646
3500	THIORIDAZINE-M (OXO-)		**384** 258 244 **112**	637

RI	NAME	DERIVATIVE	TYPICAL IONS	PAGE
3500	PERPHENAZINE-M (DESALKYL-)	AC	**401** 233 **141** 99	649
3500	PROCHLORPERAZINE-M (NOR-)	AC	**401** 233 **141** 99	649
3500	THIOPROPAZATE-M (DESALKYL-)	AC	**401** 233 **141** 99	649
3530	DIXYRAZINE	AC	**469** 229 212 **199**	666
3555	TIOTIXENE		**443 221 113 70**	663
3555	TRIMIPRAMINE-M (NOR-DI-HO-)	3AC	**438 324** 240 **128** 86	662
3560	PIRITRAMIDE		**386** 345 301 138	639
3575	THIOPROPERAZINE		**446 320** 127 **113 70**	663
3650	CLOZAPINE-M (NOR-)	AC	**354** 243 192 112	610
3800	BUTAPERAZINE-M (NOR-)	AC	**437 269 141** 99	661
3800	SULFORIDAZINE-M (NOR-)	AC	**430** 277 **154** 84	660
3870	PIMOZIDE		**461 230** 187 133 82	666

11 Table III: List of Potential Poisons in Order of Molecular Mass

11.1 Explanatory Notes

In this section drugs, poisons and common chemicals are listed in order of ascending molecular mass. This list is intended to be used in conjunction with accurate mass measurements as an aid to identification using in the absence of reference spectra (2.4.5). Consideration of the other data listed in Table 11-1 makes identification possible in most cases (7.5 and 11.2).

The list comprises about 6000 drugs, poisons and common chemicals selected from lists of drugs (ABDA, 1984) and of pesticides (Perkow, 1983). These together contain most of the drugs and pesticides known. In order to avoid complications in selection compounds were only included if they were likely to be available e.g. in the household. The compounds are arranged in order of ascending molecular mass. Compounds of the same molecular mass are listed in alphabetical order.

The title of the list is printed at the top of each page together with the first or last substance. The page number is printed at the bottom. The first column contains the accurate molecular masses calculated using the atomic masses of the most abundant isotopes of the elements (5). The second column contains the empirical formulas and the third column the compound name (INN for drugs, common names for pesticides or short chemical names). If necessary a synonym index (e.g. ABDA, 1984; Negwer, 1978; Perkow, 1983; Windholz et al., 1983) should be used, they are necessary in any case for structural and other information. The fourth column contains the category to which the compounds belong. This facilitates the identification of compounds by the aid of clinical symptoms. "MS" is printed in the fifth column, if mass spectra of the compound or its derivatives or metabolites are included in Part 2. The page numbers of the spectra reproduced in Part 2 are indicated in the alphabetical list (9).

11.2 Example for Illustrating the Identification of Unknown Compounds Using Table III

Case report:
A child suspected of intoxication with unknown pesticides was admitted to an anti-poison center. He had no typical symptoms and the ingestion of pesticides was doubtful. A stomach lavage was carried out as a preventively measure and the gastric contents were analyzed.

Procedure:
A standard extract of the gastric contents (2.2.2.1) was analyzed by computerized gas chromatography. The CMPs 1-4 (Tab. 2-1) indicated the presence of a compound with the fragment ions 217 and 58. The underlying mass spectrum could not be identified in the absence of a reference spectrum. Because the compound was detected in the gastric contents it ought to be a parent compound. It contained nitrogen, because it was detectable by GC with nitrogen-sensitive detection (N-FID) and its molecular ion (M^+) was odd-numbered. The mass spectrum (A in Fig. 11-1) contains the probable M^+ at 215 AMU with the isotopic abundances typical for an organic monochloro compound (B in Fig. 11-1). Identification was attempted from Table III in 11.3. The Table contains two monochloro compounds with nitrogen at the molecular mass of 215 (C in Fig. 11-1). They have different elemental compositions ($C_8H_{10}N_3ClS$, $C_8H_{14}N_5Cl$) and hence different molecular masses (215.02840, 215.09377). Measurement of the accurate mass of the M^+ (2.4.5) allows calculation of the elemental composition and differentiation between the compounds. In this case the molecular mass was 215.0937 AMU. Hence the herbicide Atrazine was the most likely compound. The observed fragmentation pattern correlates with its structure. The isopropylamino group leads to ion 58 (C_3H_8N) and to ion 200 ($C_7H_{11}N_5Cl$) by loss of a methyl group, to ion 173 ($C_5H_8N_5Cl$) by loss of the isopropyl group and to 158 ($C_5H_7N_4Cl$) by loss of the isopropylamino group. Ethyl amino triazine leads to ions 68 and 69 ($C_3H_4N_2$, $C_3H_5N_2$).

The information that ingestion of a pesticide was suspected corroborates the identification.

However, such an identification should always be confirmed by comparing the mass spectrum with that of the pure reference substance. It is our experience that in almost all cases the identification obtained using the procedure described above is thus confirmed.

Table 11-1 summarizes criteria for the identification of unknown drugs or poisons using gas chromatography with nitrogen-sensitive detection (GC with N-FID), mass spectrometry with electron-impact ionization (MSB with EI), accurate mass measurement and a selection of drug and poison molecular masses (Maurer and Pfleger, 1981b).

Tab. 11-1: Criteria for the identification of unknown compounds using GC with N-FID, MS with EI, accurate mass measurement and a selection of molecular masses (Table III)

Criterion		see
Nitrogen?	GC with N-FID	2.3
Chlorine, Bromine, Sulfur?	MS with EI (Isotope distribution)	Fig. 11-1, B
Fragmentation pattern	MS with EI	3.2
Elemental composition	Accurate mass measurement	2.4.5

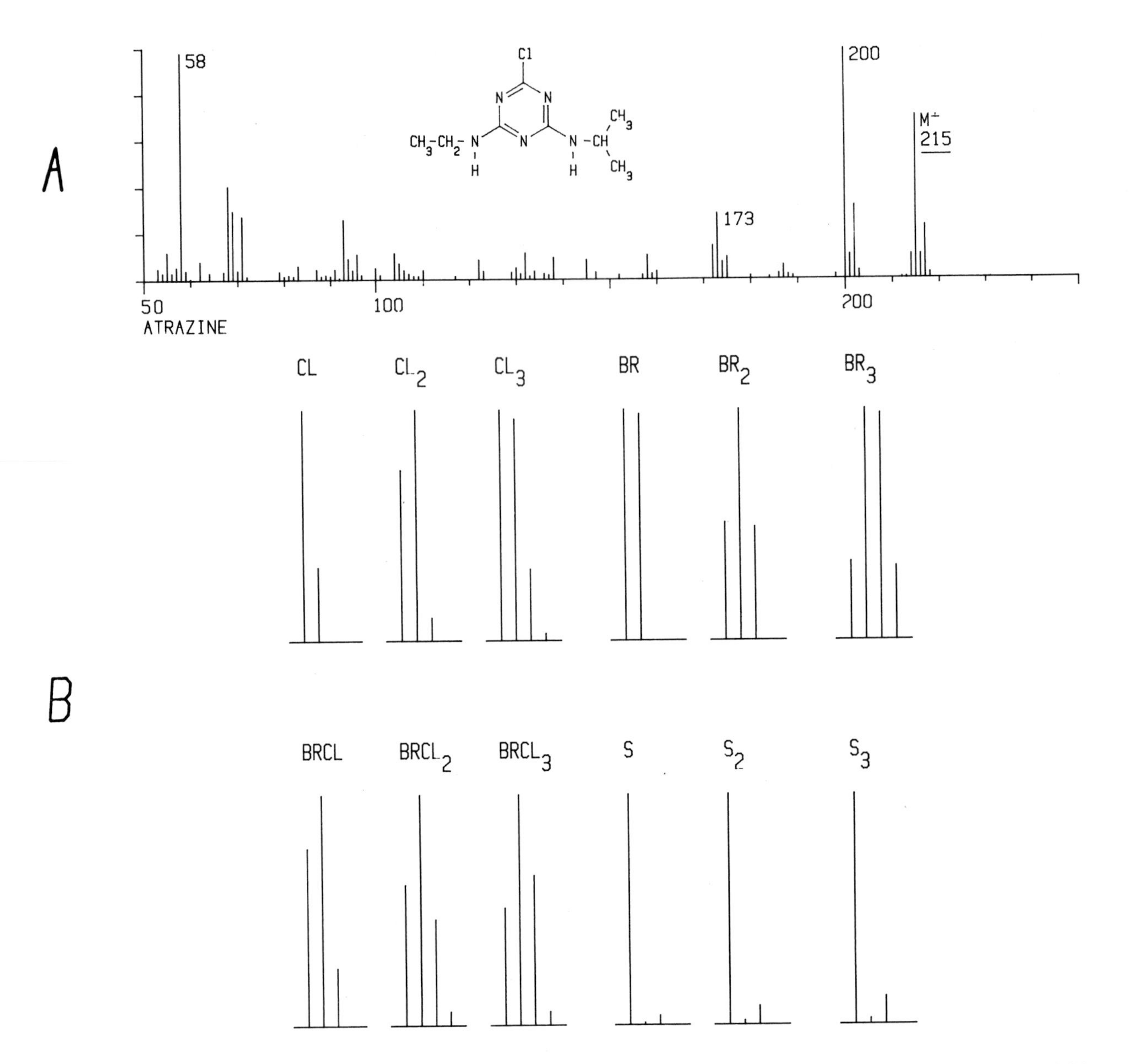

C

214.97521

TABLE III: LIST OF MOLECULAR MASSES

MASS	FORMULA		NAME	CATEGORY	MS
214.97521	$C_5H_7NO_4CL_2$		DICHLOROACETYLSERINE	CYTOSTATIC	
215.02840	$C_8H_{10}N_3CLS$	⟵	TIAMENIDINE	ANTIHYPERTENSIVE	
215.03646	$C_7H_9N_3O_3S$		SULFACARBAMIDE	ANTIBIOTIC	
215.06948	$C_{11}H_9N_3O_2$		NAFTAZONE	HEMOSTATIC	
215.08071	$C_{10}H_9N_5O$		KINETIN	CHEMICAL	
215.09377	$C_8H_{14}N_5CL$	⟵	ATRAZINE	HERBICIDE	
215.09463	$C_{13}H_{13}NO_2$		ACETAMIDOMETHYLNAPHTHOL	VITAMINE	
215.10586	$C_{12}H_{13}N_3O$		FENYRIPOL	MUSCLE RELAXANT	
215.11875	$C_9H_{18}N_3OP$		METEPA	CHEMICAL	
215.13101	$C_{14}H_{17}NO$		PHENYLDIALLYLACETAMIDE	HYPNOTIC	
215.13439	$C_{11}H_{21}NOS$		CYCLOATE	HERBICIDE	
215.14225	$C_{13}H_{17}N_3$		TRAMAZOLINE	VASOCONSTRICTOR	
215.16740	$C_{15}H_{21}N$		FENCAMFAMINE	STIMULANT	MS
215.18853	$C_{12}H_{25}NO_2$		BUTOCTAMIDE	HYPNOTIC	
216.03171	$C_6H_8N_4O_3S$		NITHIAZIDE	TRICHOMONACIDE	

Fig. 11-1: A: Mass spectrum of Atrazine, B: isotope distribution of chlorine, bromine and sulfur, C: from Table III (11.3)

11.3 Table III: List of Molecular Masses

With cooperation of Hildegard Pflеger

MASS	FORMULA	NAME	CATEGORY	MS
16.03130	CH_4	METHANE	CHEMICAL	
17.02655	H_3N	AMMONIA	CHEMICAL	
18.01057	H_2O	WATER	SOLVENT	
26.01565	C_2H_2	ACETYLENE	CHEMICAL	
27.01090	CHN	PRUSSIC ACID	INSECTICIDE	
27.99492	CO	CARBON MONOXIDE	CHEMICAL	
28.03130	C_2H_4	ETHYLENE	NARCOTIC	
29.99799	NO	NITRIC OXIDE	CHEMICAL	
30.01057	CH_2O	FORMALDEHYDE	DESINFICIENT	
30.04695	C_2H_6	ETHANE	CHEMICAL	
31.04220	CH_5N	METHYLAMINE	CHEMICAL	
32.02622	CH_4O	METHANOL	SOLVENT	
32.03745	H_4N_2	HYDRAZINE	CHEMICAL	
33.02146	H_3NO	HYDROXYLAMINE	CHEMICAL	
33.98772	H_2S	HYDROGEN SULFIDE	CHEMICAL	
33.99724	PH_3	PHOSPHINE	INSECTICIDE	
34.00548	H_2O_2	HYDROGENE PEROXIDE	DESINFICIENT	
34.02188	CH_3F	FLUOROMETHANE	CHEMICAL	
35.97668	HCL	HYDROGEN CHLORIDE	CHEMICAL	
41.02655	C_2H_3N	ACETONITRILE	CHEMICAL	
42.01057	C_2H_2O	KETENE	CHEMICAL	
42.02180	CH_2N_2	CYANAMIDE	HERBICIDE	
	CH_2N_2	DIAZOMETHANE	CHEMICAL	
42.04695	C_3H_6	CYCLOPROPANE	NARCOTIC	
	C_3H_6	PROPYLENE	CHEMICAL	
43.04220	C_2H_5N	ETHYLENIMINE	CHEMICAL	
43.98983	CO_2	CARBON DIOXIDE	RESPIRAT.STIMULANT	
44.00106	N_2O	NITROUS OXIDE	NARCOTIC	
44.02622	C_2H_4O	ACETALDEHYDE	CHEMICAL	
	C_2H_4O	ETHYLENE OXIDE	INSECTICIDE	
44.06260	C_3H_8	PROPANE	CHEMICAL	
45.02146	CH_3NO	FORMAMIDE	CHEMICAL	
45.05785	C_2H_7N	DIMETHYLAMINE	CHEMICAL	
	C_2H_7N	ETHYLAMINE	CHEMICAL	
45.99290	NO_2	NITROGEN DIOXIDE	CHEMICAL	
46.00548	CH_2O_2	FORMIC ACID	DESINFICIENT	
46.04187	C_2H_6O	DIMETHYL ETHER	CHEMICAL	
	C_2H_6O	ETHANOL	SOLVENT	MS
49.99233	CH_3CL	METHYL CHLORIDE	LOCAL ANESTHETIC	
53.02655	C_3H_3N	ACRYLONITRILE	INSECTICIDE	
54.04695	C_4H_6	BUTADIENE	CHEMICAL	
55.04220	C_3H_5N	PROPIONITRILE	CHEMICAL	
56.02621	C_3H_4O	ACROLEIN	HERBICIDE	
56.06260	C_4H_8	BUTENE	CHEMICAL	
	C_4H_8	CYCLOBUTANE	CHEMICAL	
	C_4H_8	ISOBUTYLENE	CHEMICAL	
57.05785	C_3H_7N	ALLYLAMINE	CHEMICAL	
58.00548	$C_2H_2O_2$	GLYOXAL	DESINFICIENT	
58.04187	C_3H_6O	ACETONE	SOLVENT	MS
	C_3H_6O	ALLYL ALCOHOL	HERBICIDE	
	C_3H_6O	PROPYLENE OXIDE	CHEMICAL	
58.07825	C_4H_{10}	BUTANE	CHEMICAL	

MASS	FORMULA	NAME	CATEGORY	MS
59.04835	CH_5N_3	GUANIDINE	ENDOG.BIOMOLECULE	
59.07350	C_3H_9N	ISOPROPYLAMINE	CHEMICAL	
	C_3H_9N	PROPYLAMINE	CHEMICAL	
	C_3H_9N	TRIMETHYLAMINE	CHEMICAL	
60.02113	$C_2H_4O_2$	ACETIC ACID	ORGANIC ACID	MS
	$C_2H_4O_2$	METHYL FORMATE	CHEMICAL	
60.03236	CH_4N_2O	UREA	ENDOG.BIOMOLECULE	
60.05752	C_3H_8O	ISOPROPANOL	SOLVENT	MS
	C_3H_8O	PROPANOL	SOLVENT	
61.05276	C_2H_7NO	ETHANOLAMINE	SOLVENT	
61.99233	C_2H_3CL	VINYL CHLORIDE	CHEMICAL	
62.03678	$C_2H_6O_2$	ETHYLENE GLYCOL	ANTIFREEZY	MS
63.96190	O_2S	SULFUR DIOXIDE	CHEMICAL	
64.00798	C_2H_5CL	ETHYL CHLORIDE	NARCOTIC	
66.04695	C_5H_6	CYCLOPENTADIENE	CHEMICAL	
68.02621	C_4H_4O	FURAN	CHEMICAL	
68.03745	$C_3H_4N_2$	IMIDAZOLE	CHEMICAL	
	$C_3H_4N_2$	PYRAZOLE	CHEMICAL	
68.06260	C_5H_8	ISOPRENE	CHEMICAL	
69.05785	C_4H_7N	BUTYRONITRILE	CHEMICAL	
70.00303	CHF_3	FLUOROFORM	CHEMICAL	
70.04187	C_4H_6O	CROTONALDEHYDE	CHEMICAL	
	C_4H_6O	DIVINYL ETHER	NARCOTIC	
	C_4H_6O	METHYL VINYL KETONE	SOLVENT	
70.07825	C_5H_{10}	CYCLOPENTANE	CHEMICAL	
71.03711	C_3H_5NO	ACRYLAMIDE	CHEMICAL	
71.07350	C_4H_9N	PYRROLIDINE	CHEMICAL	
72.02113	$C_3H_4O_2$	PROPIOLACTONE	CHEMICAL	
72.05752	C_4H_8O	ETHYL METHYL KETONE	SOLVENT	
	C_4H_8O	TETRAHYDROFURAN	CHEMICAL	
72.09390	C_5H_{12}	PENTANE	CHEMICAL	
72.99862	C_2H_3NS	METHYL ISOTHIOCYANATE	PESTICIDE	
73.05276	C_3H_7NO	DIMETHYLFORMAMIDE	CHEMICAL	
73.06400	$C_2H_7N_3$	METHYLGUANIDINE	CHEMICAL	
73.08915	$C_4H_{11}N$	BUTYLAMINE	CHEMICAL	
	$C_4H_{11}N$	DIETHYLAMINE	CHEMICAL	
74.00040	$C_2H_2O_3$	GLYOXALIC ACID	DESINFICIENT	
74.03678	$C_3H_6O_2$	PROPIONIC ACID	ORGANIC ACID	
74.07317	$C_4H_{10}O$	BUTANOL	SOLVENT	
	$C_4H_{10}O$	DIETHYL ETHER	NARCOTIC	
75.01427	C_2H_5NS	THIOACETAMIDE	CHEMICAL	
75.03203	$C_2H_5NO_2$	ACETOHYDROXYAMICACIDE	ENZYME INHIBITOR	
	$C_2H_5NO_2$	ETHYL NITRITE	CORONARY DILATOR	
	$C_2H_5NO_2$	GLYCINE	AMINO ACID	
76.02728	$CH_4N_2O_2$	HYDROXYCARBAMIDE	CYTOSTATIC	
76.05243	$C_3H_8O_2$	PROPYLENE GLYCOL	SOLVENT	
77.02992	C_2H_7NS	CYSTEAMINE	CHEMICAL	
77.94507	H_3AS	ARSINE	CHEMICAL	
78.01171	$C_2H_3FO_2$	FLUOROACETIC ACID	RODENTICIDE	
78.01394	C_2H_6OS	DIMETHYL SULFOXIDE	SOLVENT	MS
78.04695	C_6H_6	BENZENE	SOLVENT	MS
79.04220	C_5H_5N	PYRIDINE	CHEMICAL	MS

MASS	FORMULA	NAME	CATEGORY	MS
80.03745	$C_4H_4N_2$	PYRAZINE	CHEMICAL	
	$C_4H_4N_2$	PYRIDAZINE	CHEMICAL	
82.07825	C_6H_{10}	CYCLOHEXENE	CHEMICAL	
83.95336	CH_2CL_2	DICHLOROMETHANE	SOLVENT	MS
84.00337	C_4H_4S	THIOPHENE	DESINFICIENT	
84.04360	$C_2H_4N_4$	AMITROL	HERBICIDE	
84.06875	$C_4H_8N_2$	METHYLIMIDAZOLINE	CHEMICAL	
84.09390	C_6H_{12}	CYCLOHEXANE	SOLVENT	
85.08915	$C_5H_{11}N$	PIPERIDINE	CHEMICAL	
86.08440	$C_4H_{10}N_2$	PIPERAZINE	ANTHELMINTIC	
86.10955	C_6H_{14}	HEXANE	SOLVENT	
87.06841	C_4H_9NO	BUTYRAMIDE	CHEMICAL	
	C_4H_9NO	DIMETHYLACETAMIDE	CHEMICAL	
	C_4H_9NO	MORPHOLINE	CHEMICAL	
	C_4H_9NO	n.n-DIMETHYLACETAMIDE	SOLVENT	
88.01605	$C_3H_4O_3$	PYRUVIC ACID	ENDOG.BIOMOLECULE	
88.05243	$C_4H_8O_2$	BUTYRIC ACID	ORGANIC ACID	
	$C_4H_8O_2$	DIOXANE	SOLVENT	
	$C_4H_8O_2$	ETHYL ACETATE	SOLVENT	MS
88.08882	$C_5H_{12}O$	PENTANOL	SOLVENT	
89.04768	$C_3H_7NO_2$	ALANINE	AMINO ACID	
	$C_3H_7NO_2$	URETHAN	CYTOSTATIC	
89.08406	$C_4H_{11}NO$	AMINOISOBUTANOL	CHEMICAL	
	$C_4H_{11}NO$	DEANOL	ATARACTIC	
89.99531	$C_2H_2O_4$	OXALIC ACID	ORGANIC ACID	
90.03170	$C_3H_6O_3$	DIHYDROXYACETONE	CHEMICAL	
	$C_3H_6O_3$	LACTIC ACID	ORGANIC ACID	
90.06808	$C_4H_{10}O_2$	BUTANEDIOL	SOLVENT	
91.02694	$C_2H_5NO_3$	ETHYL NITRATE	CHEMICAL	
91.99320	$C_2H_4O_2S$	THIOGLYCOLIC ACID	ORGANIC ACID	
92.04735	$C_3H_8O_3$	GLYCEROL	LAXATIVE	
92.06260	C_7H_8	TOLUENE	SOLVENT	
93.05785	C_6H_7N	ANILINE	CHEMICAL	MS
93.94181	CH_3BR	METHYL BROMIDE	INSECTICIDE	
94.04187	C_6H_6O	PHENOL	DESINFICIENT	
96.05752	C_6H_8O	PENTOL	SOLVENT	
97.96901	$C_2H_4CL_2$	ETHYLENE CHLORIDE	SOLVENT	
98.07317	$C_6H_{10}O$	CYCLOHEXANONE	SOLVENT	
99.01427	C_4H_5NS	ALLYL ISOTHIOCYANATE	COUNTERIRRITANT	
99.03203	$C_4H_5NO_2$	SUCCINIMIDE	ANTIOXALURIC	
99.04326	$C_3H_5N_3O$	CYACETACIDE	TUBERCULOSTATIC	
100.00952	$C_3H_4N_2S$	AMINOTHIAZOLE	THYREOSTATIC	
100.02728	$C_3H_4N_2O_2$	HYDANTOIN	CHEMICAL	
100.05243	$C_5H_8O_2$	ACETYLACETONE	CHEMICAL	
	$C_5H_8O_2$	ANGELIC ACID	SEDATIVE	
	$C_5H_8O_2$	ETHYL ACRYLATE	CHEMICAL	
	$C_5H_8O_2$	GLUTARAL	DESINFICIENT	
100.08882	$C_6H_{12}O$	CYCLOHEXANOL	SOLVENT	MS
	$C_6H_{12}O$	METHYL BUTYL KETONE	SOLVENT	
	$C_6H_{12}O$	PINACOLONE	CHEMICAL	
100.12520	C_7H_{16}	HEPTANE	SOLVENT	
101.12045	$C_6H_{15}N$	DIISOPROPYLAMINE	CHEMICAL	

MASS	FORMULA	NAME	CATEGORY	MS
101.12045	$C_6H_{15}N$	DIPROPYLAMINE	CHEMICAL	
102.00926	$C_2H_2F_4$	NORFLURANE	NARCOTIC	
102.03170	$C_4H_6O_3$	ACETIC ANHYDRIDE	CHEMICAL	
102.04293	$C_3H_6N_2O_2$	CYCLOSERINE	ANTIBIOTIC	
102.06808	$C_5H_{10}O_2$	ETHYL PROPIONATE	SOLVENT	
	$C_5H_{10}O_2$	ISOPROPYL ACETATE	SOLVENT	
	$C_5H_{10}O_2$	ISOVALERIC ACID	SEDATIVE	
	$C_5H_{10}O_2$	METHYL BUTYRATE	FLAVORING	
	$C_5H_{10}O_2$	PIVALIC ACID	ORGANIC ACID	
	$C_5H_{10}O_2$	PROPYL ACETATE	SOLVENT	
	$C_5H_{10}O_2$	TETRAHYDROFURFURYL ALCOHOL	SOLVENT	
	$C_5H_{10}O_2$	VALERIC ACID	ORGANIC ACID	
102.10447	$C_6H_{14}O$	HEXANOL	SOLVENT	
103.03818	$C_2H_5N_3O_2$	BIURET	CHEMICAL	
103.04220	C_7H_5N	BENZONITRILE	SOLVENT	
103.06333	$C_4H_9NO_2$	AMINOBUTYRIC ACID (GABA)	ANTIHYPERTENSIVE	
103.09971	$C_5H_{13}NO$	DIMEPRANOL	CHEMICAL	
104.01096	$C_3H_4O_4$	MALONIC ACID	CHEMICAL	
104.03343	$CH_4N_4O_2$	NITROGUANIDINE	CHEMICAL	
104.04735	$C_4H_8O_3$	HYDROXYBUTYRIC ACID	NARCOTIC	
	$C_4H_8O_3$	METHYL LACTATE	SOLVENT	
104.06260	C_8H_8	STYRENE	CHEMICAL	
104.06597	$C_5H_{12}S$	AMYL MERCAPTAN	CHEMICAL	
	$C_5H_{12}S$	ISOAMYL MERCAPTAN	CHEMICAL	
104.08373	$C_5H_{12}O_2$	NEOPENTYL GLYCOL	CHEMICAL	
	$C_5H_{12}O_2$	PENTANEDIOL	CHEMICAL	
105.04259	$C_3H_7NO_3$	SERINE	AMINO ACID	
105.06122	$C_4H_{11}NS$	CAPTAMINE	DERMATIC	
105.07898	$C_4H_{11}NO_2$	DIETHANOLAMINE	DERMATIC	
106.00885	$C_3H_6O_2S$	THIOLACTIC ACID	CHEMICAL	
106.01854	C_4H_7OCL	CHLOROETHYL VINYL ETHER	SOLVENT	
106.03784	$C_2H_6N_2O_3$	AMINOETHYL NITRATE	CORONARY DILATOR	
106.04187	C_7H_6O	BENZALDEHYDE	FLAVORING	
106.06300	$C_4H_{10}O_3$	DIETHYLENE GLYCOL	ANTIFREEZY	
106.07825	C_8H_{10}	ETHYLBENZENE	SOLVENT	
	C_8H_{10}	XYLENE	SOLVENT	
106.98634	$C_2H_5NS_2$	METHAM	NEMATOCIDE	
107.03711	C_6H_5NO	NICOTINALDEHYDE	DERMATIC	
107.07350	C_7H_9N	BENZYLAMINE	CHEMICAL	
	C_7H_9N	TOLUIDINE	CHEMICAL	
107.95746	C_2H_5BR	ETHYL BROMIDE	NARCOTIC	
108.02113	$C_6H_4O_2$	QUINONE	CHEMICAL	
108.02450	$C_3H_8O_2S$	THIOGLYCEROL	CHEMICAL	
108.05752	C_7H_8O	BENZYL ALCOHOL	DESINFICIENT	
	C_7H_8O	CRESOL	DESINFICIENT	
108.06875	$C_6H_8N_2$	AMINOPICOLINE	ANALGESIC	
	$C_6H_8N_2$	PHENYLHYDRAZINE	CHEMICAL	
	$C_6H_8N_2$	PICOLAMINE	ANALGESIC	
109.05276	C_6H_7NO	AMINOPHENOL	CHEMICAL	MS
	C_6H_7NO	NICOTINYL ALCOHOL	VASODILATOR	
109.96901	$C_3H_4CL_2$	DICHLOROPROPENE	NEMATOCIDE	
110.01346	$C_3H_7O_2CL$	CHLOROPROPANEDIOL	CHEMICAL	

MASS	FORMULA	NAME	CATEGORY	MS
110.03678	$C_6H_6O_2$	HYDROQUINONE	CHEMICAL	MS
	$C_6H_6O_2$	RESORCINOL	DERMATIC	
110.05318	C_7H_7F	FLUOROTOLUENE	SOLVENT	
111.03203	$C_5H_5NO_2$	MECRILATE	ADHESIVE	
111.04326	$C_4H_5N_3O$	CYTOSINE	ENDOG.BIOMOLECULE	
	$C_4H_5N_3O$	IMEXONE	CYTOSTATIC	
111.04843	C_6H_6NF	FLUOROANILINE	CHEMICAL	
111.07965	$C_5H_9N_3$	BETAZOLE	DIAGNOSTIC AID	
	$C_5H_9N_3$	HISTAMINE	RUBEFACIENT	
111.98466	$C_3H_6CL_2$	DICHLOROPROPANE	NEMATOCIDE	
112.00798	C_6H_5CL	CHLOROBENZENE	SOLVENT	
112.02728	$C_4H_4N_2O_2$	MALEIC HYDRAZIDE	PLANT GROWTH REGU.	
	$C_4H_4N_2O_2$	URACIL	ENDOG.BIOMOLECULE	
112.05243	$C_6H_8O_2$	SORBIC ACID	PRESERVATIVE	
113.02253	$C_3H_3N_3O_2$	AZOMYCIN	ANTIBIOTIC	
113.05891	$C_4H_7N_3O$	CREATININE	ENDOG.BIOMOLECULE	
113.08406	$C_6H_{11}NO$	CAPROLACTAM	CHEMICAL	
	$C_6H_{11}NO$	TETRAMIN	CYTOSTATIC	
113.12045	$C_7H_{15}N$	NANOFIN	GANGLIOPLEGIC	
113.96392	$C_2H_4OCL_2$	DICHLOROMETHYLETHER	CHEMICAL	
114.02517	$C_4H_6N_2S$	AMINOMETHYLTHIAZOLE	THYREOSTATIC	
	$C_4H_6N_2S$	THIAMAZOL	THYREOSTATIC	
114.04293	$C_4H_6N_2O_2$	MUSCIMOL	SEDATIVE	
114.06808	$C_6H_{10}O_2$	ETHYL METHACRYLATE	CHEMICAL	
114.07931	$C_5H_{10}N_2O$	XINOMILIN	------------	
114.10447	$C_7H_{14}O$	CYMAROSE	SUGAR	
	$C_7H_{14}O$	HEPTANONE	SOLVENT	
114.14085	C_8H_{18}	OCTANE	CHEMICAL	
115.04557	C_5H_9NS	BUTYL ISOTHIOCYANATE	COUNTERIRRITANT	
115.06333	$C_5H_9NO_2$	PROLINE	AMINO ACID	
115.13610	$C_7H_{17}N$	METHYLHEXANEAMINE	SYMPATHOMIMETIC	
	$C_7H_{17}N$	TUAMINOHEPTANE	VASOCONSTRICTOR	
116.01096	$C_4H_4O_4$	FUMARIC ACID	DERMATIC	
	$C_4H_4O_4$	MALEIC ACID	ORGANIC ACID	
116.04082	$C_4H_8N_2S$	TIOSINAMINE	DERMATIC	
116.04735	$C_5H_8O_3$	LEVULINIC ACID	CHEMICAL	
	$C_5H_8O_3$	METHYLOXOBUTYRIC ACID	ORGANIC ACID	
116.06260	C_9H_8	INDENE	CHEMICAL	
116.08373	$C_6H_{12}O_2$	BUTYLACETATE	CHEMICAL	
	$C_6H_{12}O_2$	CAPROIC ACID	ORGANIC ACID	
	$C_6H_{12}O_2$	ETHYLBUTYRATE	FLAVORING	
	$C_6H_{12}O_2$	ISOAMYL FORMATE	FLAVORING	
116.09496	$C_5H_{12}N_2O$	TETRAMETHYLUREA	SOLVENT	
116.12012	$C_7H_{16}O$	HEPTANOL	SOLVENT	
116.13135	$C_6H_{16}N_2$	HEXANEDIAMINE	CHEMICAL	
117.02484	C_4H_7NOS	HOMOCYSTEINE THIOLACTONE	PROTEC.LIVER THER.	
117.05383	$C_3H_7N_3O_2$	GLYCOCYAMINE	CARDIOTONIC	
117.05785	C_8H_7N	INDOLE	CHEMICAL	MS
117.07898	$C_5H_{11}NO_2$	AMYL NITRITE	VASODILATOR	MS
	$C_5H_{11}NO_2$	VALINE	AMINO ACID	
117.11536	$C_6H_{15}NO$	DIETHYLAMINOETHANOL	ANTIHIST./-ALLERG.	
117.91438	$CHCL_3$	CHLOROFORM	SOLVENT	MS

MASS	FORMULA	NAME	CATEGORY	MS
117.99023	$C_3H_2O_5$	MESOXALIC ACID	ANTIDIABETIC	
118.02661	$C_4H_6O_4$	SUCCINIC ACID	ORGANIC ACID	
118.04187	C_8H_6O	BENZOFURAN	CHEMICAL	
118.05310	$C_7H_6N_2$	BENZIMIDAZOLE	CHEMICAL	
118.06300	$C_5H_{10}O_3$	DIETHYL CARBONATE	SOLVENT	
	$C_5H_{10}O_3$	ETHYL LACTATE	SOLVENT	
118.09938	$C_6H_{14}O_2$	ACETAL	HYPNOTIC	
	$C_6H_{14}O_2$	HEXAMETHYLENE GLYCOL	CHEMICAL	
	$C_6H_{14}O_2$	HEXYLENE GLYCOL	CHEMICAL	
119.02186	$C_3H_5NO_4$	HADACIDIN	CYTOSTATIC	
119.05824	$C_4H_9NO_3$	AMINOHYDROXYBUTYRIC ACID	ANTIEPILEPTIC	
	$C_4H_9NO_3$	HYDROXYMETHYLSARCOSINE	DESINFICIENT	
	$C_4H_9NO_3$	THREONINE	AMINO ACID	
119.93451	CCL_2F_2	DICHLORODIFLUOROMETHANE	PROPELLANT	
119.95746	C_3H_5BR	ALLYL BROMIDE	CHEMICAL	
120.02450	$C_4H_8O_2S$	SULFOLANE	SOLVENT	
120.03574	$C_3H_8N_2OS$	NOXYTIOLINE	DESINFICIENT	
120.04226	$C_4H_8O_4$	ERYTHROSE	SUGAR	
	$C_4H_8O_4$	THREOSE	SUGAR	
120.04360	$C_5H_4N_4$	PURINE	CHEMICAL	
120.05349	$C_3H_8N_2O_3$	OXYMETHUREA	DESINFICIENT	
120.05752	C_8H_8O	ACETOPHENONE	HYPNOTIC	
120.09390	C_9H_{12}	CUMENE	NARCOTIC	
121.00199	$C_3H_7NS_2$	FERBAM	FUNGIST./ANTIMYC.	
	$C_3H_7NS_2$	ZIRAM	FUNGIST./ANTIMYC.	
121.01975	$C_3H_7NO_2S$	CYSTEINE	AMINO ACID	
121.07389	$C_4H_{11}NO_3$	TROMETAMOL (TRIS)	BUFFERING AGENT	
121.08915	$C_8H_{11}N$	DIMETHYLANILINE	SOLVENT	MS
	$C_8H_{11}N$	PHENETHYLAMINE	CHEMICAL	
	$C_8H_{11}N$	XYLIDINE	CHEMICAL	
122.03678	$C_7H_6O_2$	BENZOIC ACID	PRESERVATIVE	MS
	$C_7H_6O_2$	RESORCYLIC ACID	ANTIRHEUMATIC	
122.04015	$C_4H_{10}O_2S$	THIODIGLYCOL	CYTOSTATIC	
122.04801	$C_6H_6N_2O$	NICOTINAMIDE	VITAMINE	MS
122.05791	$C_4H_{10}O_4$	ERYTHRITOL	CORONARY DILATOR	
122.07317	$C_8H_{10}O$	PHENYLETHANOL	PRESERVATIVE	
	$C_8H_{10}O$	XYLENOL	SOLVENT	
123.00871	$C_3H_6NO_2CL$	LANSTANE	FUNGIST./ANTIMYC.	
123.03203	$C_6H_5NO_2$	NICOTINIC ACID	VASODILATOR	MS
	$C_6H_5NO_2$	NITROBENZENE	CHEMICAL	
123.04326	$C_5H_5N_3O$	PYRAZINAMIDE	TUBERCULOSTATIC	MS
123.07965	$C_6H_9N_3$	AMPYZIN	STIMULANT	
124.00166	$C_3H_8OS_2$	DIMERCAPROL	ANTIDOTE	
124.01942	$C_3H_8O_3S$	DIMERCAPTOPROPANESULFONIC ACID	ANTIDOTE	
124.03467	C_7H_8S	THIOCRESOL	DESINFICIENT	
124.05243	$C_7H_8O_2$	GUAIACOL	ANTITUSSIVE	
	$C_7H_8O_2$	MEQUINOL	DERMATIC	
	$C_7H_8O_2$	ORCINOL	CHEMICAL	
124.06366	$C_6H_8N_2O$	CETOHEXAZINE	HYPNOTIC	
	$C_6H_8N_2O$	DIAMINOPHENOL	CHEMICAL	
	$C_6H_8N_2O$	NICARBAZINE (DIMETHYLPYRIMIDINOL)	FUNGIST./ANTIMYC.	
124.08882	$C_8H_{12}O$	ETHINYLCYCLOHEXANOL	HYPNOTIC	

MASS	FORMULA	NAME	CATEGORY	MS
125.01467	$C_2H_7NO_3S$	TAURINE	ENDOG.BIOMOLECULE	
125.04768	$C_6H_7NO_2$	MEPIROXOL	ANTICHOLESTEREMIC	
125.12045	$C_8H_{15}N$	TROPANE	CHEMICAL	
125.99868	$C_2H_6O_4S$	DIMETHYL SULFATE	CHEMICAL	
	$C_2H_6O_4S$	ISETHIONIC ACID	DESINFICIENT	
126.02363	C_7H_7CL	BENZYL CHLORIDE	CHEMICAL	
126.02925	$C_4H_5F_3O$	FLUROXENE	NARCOTIC	
126.03170	$C_6H_6O_3$	MALTOL	FLAVORING	
	$C_6H_6O_3$	PHLOROGLUCIN	ANTISPASMOTIC	
	$C_6H_6O_3$	PYROGALLOL	DESINFICIENT	
126.04293	$C_5H_6N_2O_2$	THYMINE	ENDOG.BIOMOLECULE	
126.05416	$C_4H_6N_4O$	ORAZAMIDE	PROTEC.LIVER THER.	
126.06539	$C_3H_6N_6$	MELAMINE	CHEMICAL	
127.00919	C_5H_5NOS	PYRITHIONE	FUNGIST./ANTIMYC.	
127.13610	$C_8H_{17}N$	CONIINE	ANALGESIC	
127.97957	$C_3H_6OCL_2$	DICHLOROPROPANOL	SOLVENT	
128.00289	C_6H_5OCL	CHLOROPHENOL	DESINFICIENT	MS
128.00444	$C_4H_4N_2OS$	THIOURACIL	THYREOSTATIC	
128.02219	$C_4H_4N_2O_3$	BARBITURIC ACID	CHEMICAL	MS
128.04082	$C_5H_8N_2S$	METHYLMETHIMAZOLE	THYREOSTATIC	
128.06260	$C_{10}H_8$	AZULENE	ANTIINFLAMMATORY	
	$C_{10}H_8$	NAPHTHALENE	DESINFICIENT	
128.08373	$C_7H_{12}O_2$	CYCLOHEXANECARBOXYLIC ACID	SOLUBILIZER ETC.	
128.12012	$C_8H_{16}O$	OCTANAL	CHEMICAL	
128.13135	$C_7H_{16}N_2$	CIMEMOXINE	ANTIDEPRESSANT	
129.01744	$C_3H_3N_3O_3$	CYANURIC ACID	CHEMICAL	
129.03384	$C_4H_4N_3OF$	FLUCYTOSINE	FUNGIST./ANTIMYC.	
129.04259	$C_5H_7NO_3$	DIMETHADIONE	ANTIEPILEPTIC	
129.05785	C_9H_7N	ISOQUINOLINE	CHEMICAL	
	C_9H_7N	QUINOLINE	ANTIMALARIAL	
129.10144	$C_4H_{11}N_5$	METFORMINE	ANTIDIABETIC	
129.15175	$C_8H_{19}N$	OCTODRINE	VASOCONSTRICTOR	
129.91438	C_2HCL_3	TRICHLOROETHYLENE	NARCOTIC	
130.01786	$C_4H_3N_2O_2F$	FLUOROURACIL	CYTOSTATIC	
130.02661	$C_5H_6O_4$	CITRACONIC ACID	ANTIOXIDANT	
130.06300	$C_6H_{10}O_3$	KETHOXAL	VIRUCIDE	
	$C_6H_{10}O_3$	METHYLOXOVALERIC ACID	THER.RENAL INSUFF.	
	$C_6H_{10}O_3$	PROPIONIC ACID	CHEMICAL	
130.11061	$C_6H_{14}N_2O$	PENTYLUREA	SEDATIVE	
130.13577	$C_8H_{18}O$	OCTANOL	SOLVENT	
131.05824	$C_5H_9NO_3$	HYDROXYPROLINE	AMINO ACID	
131.06948	$C_4H_9N_3O_2$	CREATINE	ENDOG.BIOMOLECULE	
131.09463	$C_6H_{13}NO_2$	AMINOCAPROIC ACID	ANTIFIBRINOLYTIC	
	$C_6H_{13}NO_2$	ISOLEUCINE	AMINO ACID	
	$C_6H_{13}NO_2$	LEUCINE	AMINO ACID	
131.93003	$C_2H_3CL_3$	TRICHLOROETHANE	SOLVENT	
132.00588	$C_4H_4O_5$	OXALACETIC ACID	ENDOG.BIOMOLECULE	
132.01983	$C_3H_4OF_4$	TETRAFLUOROPROPANOL	CHEMICAL	
132.04226	$C_5H_8O_4$	GLUTARIC ACID	ENDOG.BIOMOLECULE	
132.04360	$C_6H_4N_4$	PTERIDINE	CHEMICAL	
132.05349	$C_4H_8N_2O_3$	ASPARAGINE	AMINO ACID	
132.05751	C_9H_8O	CINNAMALDEHYDE	FLAVORING	

MASS	FORMULA	NAME	CATEGORY	MS
132.07865	$C_6H_{12}O_3$	DIMETHYLDIOXOLANEMETHANOL	SOLVENT	
	$C_6H_{12}O_3$	PARALDEHYDE	HYPNOTIC	
132.08988	$C_5H_{12}N_2O_2$	ORNITHINE	ENDOG.BIOMOLECULE	
132.09390	$C_{10}H_{12}$	TETRAHYDRONAPHTHALENE	SOLVENT	
132.11503	$C_7H_{16}O_2$	DIETHYLPROPANEDIOL	MUSCLE RELAXANT	
133.01975	$C_4H_7NO_2S$	TIMONACIC	PROTEC.LIVER THER.	
133.03751	$C_4H_7NO_4$	ASPARTIC ACID	AMINO ACID	
133.05276	C_8H_7NO	MANDELO NITRILE	FLAVORING	
133.07389	$C_5H_{11}NO_3$	HYDROXYETHYLLACTAMIDE	SOLUBILIZER ETC.	
133.08915	$C_9H_{11}N$	TRANYLCYPROMINE	ANTIDEPRESSANT	MS
134.02152	$C_4H_6O_5$	MALIC ACID	ENDOG.BIOMOLECULE	
134.05791	$C_5H_{10}O_4$	DESOXYRIBOSE	SUGAR	
134.07317	$C_9H_{10}O$	ANOL	CHEMICAL	
	$C_9H_{10}O$	CINNAMYL ALCOHOL	CHEMICAL	
	$C_9H_{10}O$	PROPIOPHENONE	CHEMICAL	
134.09430	$C_6H_{14}O_3$	DIPROPYLENE GLYCOL	DESINFICIENT	
134.10955	$C_{10}H_{14}$	CYMENE	SOLVENT	
135.01427	C_7H_5NS	PHENYL ISOTHIOCYANATE	COUNTERIRRITANT	
135.03540	$C_4H_9NO_2S$	MECYSTEINE	ANTITUSSIVE	
135.05449	$C_5H_5N_5$	ADENINE	VITAMINE	
135.06841	C_8H_9NO	ACETANILIDE	ANALGESIC	MS
135.10480	$C_9H_{13}N$	AMPHETAMINE	STIMULANT	MS
135.95238	C_3H_5OBR	BROMOACETONE	POISON GAS	
136.03065	$C_3H_8N_2O_2S$	TAURULTAM	------------	
136.03851	$C_5H_4N_4O$	ALLOPURINOL	URICOSURIC	
	$C_5H_4N_4O$	HYPOXANTHINE	ENDOG.BIOMOLECULE	
136.05243	$C_8H_8O_2$	ANISALDEHYDE	CHEMICAL	
	$C_8H_8O_2$	BENZYL FORMATE	RUBEFACIENT	
	$C_8H_8O_2$	METHYL BENZOATE	CHEMICAL	
136.07356	$C_5H_{12}O_4$	PENTAERYTHRITOL	CHEMICAL	
136.08881	$C_9H_{12}O$	PHENYLPROPANOL	CHOLERETIC	
	$C_9H_{12}O$	TOLYLETHANOL	CHOLERETIC	
136.10005	$C_8H_{12}N_2$	BETAHISTINE	VASODILATOR	
	$C_8H_{12}N_2$	MEBANAZINE	ANTIDEPRESSANT	
	$C_8H_{12}N_2$	PHENELZINE	ANTIDEPRESSANT	
136.12520	$C_{10}H_{16}$	ADAMANTINE	VIRUCIDE	
	$C_{10}H_{16}$	CAMPHENE	ANTISPASMOTIC	
	$C_{10}H_{16}$	LIMONENE	SOLVENT	
	$C_{10}H_{16}$	PINENE	DESINFICIENT	
137.04768	$C_7H_7NO_2$	AMINOBENZOIC ACID	DERMATIC	MS
	$C_7H_7NO_2$	CARBANILIC ACID	ORGANIC ACID	
	$C_7H_7NO_2$	METHYL NICOTINATE	RUBEFACIENT	MS
	$C_7H_7NO_2$	SALICYLAMIDE	ANALGESIC	MS
137.05891	$C_6H_7N_3O$	ISONIAZID	TUBERCULOSTATIC	MS
137.08406	$C_8H_{11}NO$	DIMETHYLAMINOPHENOL	ANTIDOTE	
	$C_8H_{11}NO$	METYRIDINE	ANTHELMINTIC	
	$C_8H_{11}NO$	PHENETIDINE	CHEMICAL	MS
	$C_8H_{11}NO$	PHENYLETHANOLAMINE	SYMPATHOMIMETIC	
	$C_8H_{11}NO$	TYRAMINE	VASOCONSTRICTOR	MS
137.09530	$C_7H_{11}N_3$	ISAXONIN	------------	
137.96620	$C_2H_7O_2AS$	CACODYLIC ACID	HERBICIDE	
138.00820	$C_3H_7O_4P$	FOSFOMYCINE	ANTIBIOTIC	

MASS	FORMULA	NAME	CATEGORY	MS
138.03170	$C_7H_6O_3$	HYDROXYBENZOIC ACID	PRESERVATIVE	
	$C_7H_6O_3$	SALICYLIC ACID	DERMATIC	MS
138.04293	$C_6H_6N_2O_2$	NICOXAMATE	------------	
138.06808	$C_8H_{10}O_2$	VERATROLE	DESINFICIENT	
138.09055	$C_6H_{10}N_4$	PENTETRAZOLE	STIMULANT	MS
139.02694	$C_6H_5NO_3$	OXINIACIC ACID	ANTICHOLESTEREMIC	
139.94547	CH_5O_3AS	METHYLARSINIC ACID	TONIC	
139.98746	$C_2H_5O_5P$	PHOSPHONOACETIC ACID	VIRUCIDE	
140.04735	$C_7H_8O_3$	FLAMENOL	ANTISPASMOTIC	
140.10620	$C_6H_{12}N_4$	METHENAMINE	DESINFICIENT	MS
141.00134	$C_2H_8NO_2SP$	METHAMIDOPHOS	INSECTICIDE	
141.01910	$C_2H_8NO_4P$	AMINOPHOS	TONIC	
141.02484	C_6H_7NOS	CEPHEM	CHEMICAL	
141.05383	$C_5H_7N_3O_2$	DIMETRIDAZOLE	ANTIBIOTIC	
141.07898	$C_7H_{11}NO_2$	ETHOSUXIMIDE	ANTIEPILEPTIC	MS
	$C_7H_{11}NO_2$	METHYLPENTINOL CARBAMATE	HYPNOTIC	
141.15175	$C_9H_{19}N$	CYCLOPENTAMINE	VASOCONSTRICTOR	
	$C_9H_{19}N$	ISOMETHEPTENE	ANTISPASMOTIC	
141.95884	$C_3H_4O_2CL_2$	DALAPON	HERBICIDE	
142.00146	$C_4H_2N_2O_4$	ALLOXAN	CYTOSTATIC	
142.01854	C_7H_7OCL	CHLOROCRESOL	DESINFICIENT	MS
142.02009	$C_5H_6N_2OS$	METHYLTHIOURACIL	THYREOSTATIC	
142.07423	$C_6H_{10}N_2O_2$	PIRACETAM	DYNAMIC	MS
142.13577	$C_9H_{18}O$	NONANAL	CHEMICAL	
143.04049	C_6H_9NOS	CEPHAM	CHEMICAL	
143.05824	$C_6H_9NO_3$	TRIMETHADIONE	ANTIEPILEPTIC	MS
143.13101	$C_8H_{17}NO$	VALNOCTAMIDE	TRANQUILIZER	
	$C_8H_{17}NO$	VALPROMIDE	ANTIEPILEPTIC	
143.97431	$C_2H_6O_3CLP$	CHLOROETHYLPHOSPHONIC ACID	CHEMICAL	
	$C_2H_6O_3CLP$	ETHEPHONE	PLANT GROWTH REGU.	
144.03419	C_7H_9OCL	ETHCLORVYNOL	HYPNOTIC	
144.04226	$C_6H_8O_4$	ETHYL HYDROGENEFUMARATE	DERMATIC	
144.05752	$C_{10}H_8O$	NAPHTOL	DESINFICIENT	
144.10111	$C_5H_{12}N_4O$	TIFORMIN	ANTIDIABETIC	
144.11503	$C_8H_{16}O_2$	BUTYL BUTYRATE	SOLVENT	
	$C_8H_{16}O_2$	CAPRYLIC ACID	FUNGIST./ANTIMYC.	
	$C_8H_{16}O_2$	VALPROIC ACID	ANTIEPILEPTIC	MS
144.15142	$C_9H_{20}O$	NONANOL	CHEMICAL	
144.16265	$C_8H_{20}N_2$	OCTAMOXINE	ANTIDEPRESSANT	
144.99460	$C_3H_3N_3O_2S$	AMINONITROTHIAZOLE	TRICHOMONACIDE	
145.05276	C_9H_7NO	CHINOLINOL	DESINFICIENT	
145.11028	$C_7H_{15}NO_2$	EMYLCAMATE	TRANQUILIZER	
145.14666	$C_8H_{19}NO$	HEPTAMINOL	CARDIOTONIC	MS
145.96901	$C_6H_4CL_2$	DICHLOROBENZENE	SOLVENT	
146.02153	$C_5H_6O_5$	KETOGLUTARIC ACID	ENDOG.BIOMOLECULE	
146.03678	$C_9H_6O_2$	COUMARIN	FLAVORING	
146.05791	$C_6H_{10}O_4$	ACEBURIC ACID	ANALGESIC	
	$C_6H_{10}O_4$	ADIPIC ACID	ORGANIC ACID	
	$C_6H_{10}O_4$	ETHYLENE GLYCOL DIACETATE	SOLVENT	MS
	$C_6H_{10}O_4$	ISOSORBIDE	DIURETIC	
	$C_6H_{10}O_4$	SORBIDE (BIS-DEHYRATED SORBITOL)	SUGAR	
146.06914	$C_5H_{10}N_2O_3$	GLUTAMINE	DYNAMIC	

MASS	FORMULA	NAME	CATEGORY	MS
146.10553	$C_6H_{14}N_2O_2$	LYSINE	AMINO ACID	
147.03540	$C_5H_9NO_2S$	OMONASTEINE	MUCOLYTIC	
147.05316	$C_5H_9NO_4$	GLUTAMIC ACID	AMINO ACID	
147.92495	$C_2H_3OCL_3$	TRICHLOROETHANOL	NARCOTIC	MS
148.05243	$C_9H_8O_2$	CINNAMIC ACID	ANTHELMINTIC	
148.07356	$C_6H_{12}O_4$	DIGITOXOSE	SUGAR	
	$C_6H_{12}O_4$	KETOXAL	VIRUCIDE	
	$C_6H_{12}O_4$	MEVALONIC ACID	ENDOG.BIOMOLECULE	
	$C_6H_{12}O_4$	PANTOIC ACID	ORGANIC ACID	
148.08882	$C_{10}H_{12}O$	ANETHOLE	STOMACHIC	
	$C_{10}H_{12}O$	CUMINALDEHYDE	CHEMICAL	
148.10005	$C_9H_{12}N_2$	NORNICOTINE	PESTICIDE	
149.02992	C_8H_7NS	BENZYL ISOTHIOCYANATE	DESINFICIENT	
	C_8H_7NS	BENZYL THIOCYANATE	RUBEFACIENT	
149.04366	$C_3H_7N_3O_4$	ALANOSINE	CYTOSTATIC	
149.05105	$C_5H_{11}NO_2S$	METHIONINE	AMINO ACID	
	$C_5H_{11}NO_2S$	PENICILLAMINE	ANTIDOTE	
149.08406	$C_9H_{11}NO$	CATHIONE	------------	
149.10519	$C_6H_{15}NO_3$	TRIETHANOLAMINE	SOLUBILIZER ETC.	
149.12045	$C_{10}H_{15}N$	METHAMPHETAMINE	STIMULANT	MS
	$C_{10}H_{15}N$	ORTETAMINE	ANOREXIC	
	$C_{10}H_{15}N$	PHENPROMETHAMINE	VASOCONSTRICTOR	
	$C_{10}H_{15}N$	PHENTERMINE	ANOREXIC	MS
150.01644	$C_4H_6O_6$	TARTARIC ACID	BUFFERING AGENT	
150.02517	$C_7H_6N_2S$	AMINOBENZOTHIAZOLE	CHEMICAL	
150.03170	$C_8H_6O_3$	PIPERONAL	PESTICIDE	
150.03507	$C_5H_{10}O_3S$	HYDROXYMETHYLTHIOBUTYRIC ACID	THER.RENAL INSUFF.	
150.05282	$C_5H_{10}O_5$	APIOSE	SUGAR	
	$C_5H_{10}O_5$	ARABINOSE	SUGAR	
	$C_5H_{10}O_5$	RIBOSE	SUGAR	
	$C_5H_{10}O_5$	XYLOSE	SUGAR	
	$C_5H_{10}O_5$	XYLULOSE	SUGAR	
150.06808	$C_9H_{10}O_2$	ETHYL BENZOATE	SOLVENT	MS
	$C_9H_{10}O_2$	PAROXYPROPIONE	HORMONE	
150.07931	$C_8H_{10}N_2O$	DEFENURONE	HERBICIDE	
150.10447	$C_{10}H_{14}O$	CARVACROL	ANTHELMINTIC	
	$C_{10}H_{14}O$	CARVONE	STOMACHIC	
	$C_{10}H_{14}O$	PROPYL CRESOL	DESINFICIENT	
	$C_{10}H_{14}O$	THYMOL	DESINFICIENT	
150.11570	$C_9H_{14}N_2$	PHENIPRAZINE	STIMULANT	
151.04941	$C_5H_5N_5O$	GUANINE	DIAGNOSTIC AID	
151.06333	$C_8H_9NO_2$	AMINOMETHYLBENZOIC ACID	ANTIFIBRINOLYTIC	
	$C_8H_9NO_2$	CRESOTAMIDE	ANALGESIC	
	$C_8H_9NO_2$	ETHYL NICOTINATE	RUBEFACIENT	
	$C_8H_9NO_2$	METACETAMOL	ANALGESIC	
	$C_8H_9NO_2$	PARACETAMOL	ANALGESIC	MS
151.07456	$C_7H_9N_3O$	PHENICARBAZIDE	ANALGESIC	
151.09971	$C_9H_{13}NO$	CATHINE (NORPSEUDOEPHEDRINE)	ANOREXIC	MS
	$C_9H_{13}NO$	GEPEFRIN	SYMPATHOMIMETIC	
	$C_9H_{13}NO$	HYDROXYAMPHETAMINE	STIMULANT	
	$C_9H_{13}NO$	NOREPHEDRINE	VASOCONSTRICTOR	
151.13610	$C_{10}H_{17}N$	AMANTADINE	ANTIPARKINSONIAN	MS

MASS	FORMULA	NAME	CATEGORY	MS
151.87541	CCL_4	TETRACHLOROMETHANE	SOLVENT	MS
152.01567	$C_5H_4N_4S$	MERCAPTOPURINE	CYTOSTATIC	
	$C_5H_4N_4S$	TISOPURINE	URICOSURIC	
152.03343	$C_5H_4N_4O_2$	OXIPURINOL	URICOSURIC	
	$C_5H_4N_4O_2$	XANTHINE	ENDOG.BIOMOLECULE	
152.04082	$C_7H_8N_2S$	PHENYLTHIOUREA	CHEMICAL	
152.04735	$C_8H_8O_3$	MANDELIC ACID	ANTISEPTIC	MS
	$C_8H_8O_3$	METHYL SALICYLATE	RUBEFACIENT	MS
	$C_8H_8O_3$	METHYLPARABEN	PRESERVATIVE	MS
	$C_8H_8O_3$	PHENOXYACETIC ACID	FUNGIST./ANTIMYC.	
	$C_8H_8O_3$	RESORCINOL MONOACETATE	DERMATIC	
	$C_8H_8O_3$	VANILLIN	FLAVORING	
152.05858	$C_7H_8N_2O_2$	HYDROXYMETHYLNICOTINAMIDE	CHOLERETIC	
152.06848	$C_5H_{12}O_5$	XYLITOL	SUGAR	
152.12012	$C_{10}H_{16}O$	CAMPHOR	RUBEFACIENT	
	$C_{10}H_{16}O$	CITRAL	FLAVORING	
	$C_{10}H_{16}O$	FENCHONE	COUNTERIRRITANT	
	$C_{10}H_{16}O$	HOMOCAMFIN	STIMULANT	
153.04259	$C_7H_7NO_3$	PARAAMINOSALICYLIC ACID	TUBERCULOSTATIC	MS
153.06506	$C_5H_7N_5O$	HYDRACARBAZINE	DIURETIC	
153.07898	$C_8H_{11}NO_2$	BUCRILATE	ADHESIVE	
	$C_8H_{11}NO_2$	DOPAMINE	SYMPATHOMIMETIC	
	$C_8H_{11}NO_2$	ENBUCRILATE	ADHESIVE	
	$C_8H_{11}NO_2$	NICOTINALDEHYDE DIMETHYLACETAL	RUBEFACIENT	
	$C_8H_{11}NO_2$	NORFENEFRINE	SYMPATHOMIMETIC	MS
	$C_8H_{11}NO_2$	OCTOPAMINE	SYMPATHOMIMETIC	
153.15175	$C_{10}H_{19}N$	BUTYNAMINE	ANTIHYPERTENSIVE	
	$C_{10}H_{19}N$	DROPEMPINE	GANGLIOPLEGIC	
154.02661	$C_7H_6O_4$	GENTISIC ACID	ANTIRHEUMATIC	
	$C_7H_6O_4$	PATULIN	ANTIBIOTIC	
	$C_7H_6O_4$	RESORCYLIC ACID	ANTIRHEUMATIC	
154.03784	$C_6H_6N_2O_3$	ACIPIMOX	ANTICHOLESTEREMIC	
154.04301	$C_8H_7O_2F$	FLUOROPHENYLACETIC ACID	CHEMICAL	
154.06713	$C_4H_{12}N_2OFP$	DIMEFOX	INSECTICIDE	
154.07825	$C_{12}H_{10}$	BIPHENYL	FUNGIST./ANTIMYC.	
154.12185	$C_7H_{14}N_4$	GUANCIDINE	ANTIHYPERTENSIVE	
154.13577	$C_{10}H_{18}O$	BORNEOL	RUBEFACIENT	
	$C_{10}H_{18}O$	CINEOL	EXPECTORANT	
	$C_{10}H_{18}O$	CITRONELLAL	NATURAL SUBSTANCE	
	$C_{10}H_{18}O$	GERANIOL	ANTHELMINTIC	
	$C_{10}H_{18}O$	LINALOOL	NATURAL SUBSTANCE	
	$C_{10}H_{18}O$	MENTHONE	CHOLERETIC	
155.02686	$C_5H_{11}NCL_2$	CHLORMETHINE	CYTOSTATIC	
155.05824	$C_7H_9NO_3$	ALLOMETHADIONE	ANTIEPILEPTIC	
	$C_7H_9NO_3$	ALOXIDONE	ANTIEPILEPTIC	
155.06948	$C_6H_9N_3O_2$	HISTIDINE	AMINO ACID	
	$C_6H_9N_3O_2$	MEDAZOMIDE	ANTITUSSIVE	
155.09463	$C_8H_{13}NO_2$	ARECOLINE	ANTHELMINTIC	
	$C_8H_{13}NO_2$	BEMEGRIDE	RESPIRAT.STIMULANT	MS
155.13101	$C_9H_{17}NO$	DIETHYLALLYLACETAMIDE	HYPNOTIC	MS
155.16740	$C_{10}H_{21}N$	CYCLEXEDRINE	SYMPATHOMIMETIC	
	$C_{10}H_{21}N$	PEMPIDINE	GANGLIOPLEGIC	

MASS	FORMULA	NAME	CATEGORY	MS
155.16740	$C_{10}H_{21}N$	PROPYLHEXEDRINE	ANOREXIC	MS
155.94360	C_2H_5I	ETHYL JODIDE	CHEMICAL	
156.01711	$C_5H_4N_2O_4$	NIFUROXIME	ANTIBIOTIC	
	$C_5H_4N_2O_4$	OROTIC ACID	URICOSURIC	
156.03419	C_8H_9OCL	CHLOROXYLENOL	DESINFICIENT	MS
156.06875	$C_{10}H_8N_2$	BIPYRIDYL	CHEMICAL	MS
156.08988	$C_7H_{12}N_2O_2$	ECTYLUREA	SEDATIVE	
156.15142	$C_{10}H_{20}O$	CIMEPANOL	CHOLERETIC	
	$C_{10}H_{20}O$	CITRONELLOL	NATURAL SUBSTANCE	
	$C_{10}H_{20}O$	MENTHOL	FLAVORING	
157.03751	$C_6H_7NO_4$	METHOXYMETHYLNITROFURAN	FUNGIST./ANTIMYC.	
157.07389	$C_7H_{11}NO_3$	ETHADIONE	ANTIEPILEPTIC	
	$C_7H_{11}NO_3$	PARAMETHADIONE	ANTIEPILEPTIC	MS
157.11028	$C_8H_{15}NO_2$	DIHYDROARECOLIN	CHEMICAL	
	$C_8H_{15}NO_2$	OXANAMIDE	TRANQUILIZER	
	$C_8H_{15}NO_2$	TRANEXAMIC ACID	HEMOSTATIC	
157.13274	$C_6H_{15}N_5$	BUFORMIN	ANTIDIABETIC	
157.18305	$C_{10}H_{23}N$	DIPROBUTIN	ANTIPARKINSONIAN	
157.97238	$C_4H_8CL_2S$	DICHLORODIETHYLSULFIDE	POISON GAS	
158.03678	$C_{10}H_6O_2$	NAPHTHOQUINONE	CHEMICAL	
158.04399	$C_4H_6N_4O_3$	ALLANTOIN	DERMATIC	
158.09430	$C_8H_{14}O_3$	BUTYRIC ANHYDRIDE	CHEMICAL	
158.16707	$C_{10}H_{22}O$	DECANOL	CHEMICAL	
	$C_{10}H_{22}O$	DIAMYLETHER	SOLVENT	
159.03540	$C_6H_9NO_2S$	CITIOLONE	PROTEC.LIVER THER.	
159.06841	$C_{10}H_9NO$	DRINIDENE	ANALGESIC	
	$C_{10}H_9NO$	ECHINOPSINE	TONIC	
159.10480	$C_{11}H_{13}N$	PARGYLINE	ANTIHYPERTENSIVE	
159.12593	$C_8H_{17}NO_2$	OCTANOHYDROXAMIC ACID	ANTIBIOTIC	
160.05243	$C_{10}H_8O_2$	METHYLCHROMONE	VASODILATOR	
160.07490	$C_8H_8N_4$	HYDRALAZINE	ANTIHYPERTENSIVE	
160.08479	$C_6H_{12}N_2O_3$	SUCCINIC ACID DIMETHYLHYDRAZIDE	PLANT GROWTH REGU.	
160.10005	$C_{10}H_{12}N_2$	TOLAZOLINE	VASODILATOR	MS
161.00660	C_6H_8NCLS	CLOMETHIAZOLE	HYPNOTIC	MS
161.07015	$C_7H_7N_5$	FENAMOLE	ANTIRHEUMATIC	
161.08406	$C_{10}H_{11}NO$	ABIKOVIROMYCIN	VIRUCIDE	
161.10519	$C_7H_{15}NO_3$	CARNITINE	VITAMINE	
161.12045	$C_{11}H_{15}N$	ALFETAMINE	ANALGESIC	
	$C_{11}H_{15}N$	CYPENAMINE	ANTIDEPRESSANT	
161.90421	$C_2HO_2CL_3$	TRICHLOROACETIC ACID	DERMATIC	
162.01731	$C_6H_{10}OS_2$	ALLICIN	STOMACHIC	
162.02854	$C_5H_{10}N_2S_2$	DAZOMET	NEMATOCIDE	
	$C_5H_{10}N_2S_2$	PICADEX	ANTHELMINTIC	
162.03170	$C_9H_6O_3$	PHLOROGLUCINOL	ANTISPASMOTIC	
	$C_9H_6O_3$	UMBELLIFERONE	DERMATIC	
162.04293	$C_8H_6N_2O_2$	FENADIAZOLE	HYPNOTIC	
162.04630	$C_5H_{10}N_2O_2S$	METHOMYL	INSECTICIDE	
162.05282	$C_6H_{10}O_5$	DIETHYL DICARBONATE	PRESERVATIVE	
	$C_6H_{10}O_5$	STREPTOSE	SUGAR	
162.05582	$C_5H_{11}N_2O_2P$	TABUN	POISON GAS	
162.06808	$C_{10}H_{10}O_2$	SAFROLE	DESINFICIENT	
162.07931	$C_9H_{10}N_2O$	AMINOREX	ANOREXIC	MS

MASS	FORMULA	NAME	CATEGORY	MS
162.08921	$C_7H_{14}O_4$	CYMAROSE	SUGAR	
162.10044	$C_6H_{14}N_2O_3$	DESOXYSTREPTAMINE	SUGAR	
162.11570	$C_{10}H_{14}N_2$	ANABASINE	INSECTICIDE	
	$C_{10}H_{14}N_2$	NICOTINE	INSECTICIDE	MS
162.12560	$C_8H_{18}O_3$	DIMETHYLOXYDIPROPANOL	CHOLERETIC	
	$C_8H_{18}O_3$	TERBUPROL	CHOLERETIC	
162.89946	CNO_2CL_3	CHLOROPICRIN	NEMATOCIDE	
162.99393	$C_4H_5NO_4S$	ACESULFAM	SWEETENER	
	$C_4H_5NO_4S$	METHYLOXATHIAZINONE DIOXIDE	SWEETENER	
163.02694	$C_8H_5NO_3$	CARSALAM	ANALGESIC	
163.03032	$C_5H_9NO_3S$	ACETYLCYSTEINE	ANTIDOTE	
	$C_5H_9NO_3S$	TIOPROMINE	ANTIDOTE	
163.08446	$C_6H_{13}NO_4$	MYCOSAMINE	SUGAR	
163.09971	$C_{10}H_{13}NO$	PHENYLBUTYRAMIDE	ANTICHOLESTEREMIC	
163.13610	$C_{11}H_{17}N$	DIMEPHENOPANE	SYMPATHOMIMETIC	MS
	$C_{11}H_{17}N$	DIMETAMFETAMINE	STIMULANT	
	$C_{11}H_{17}N$	ETILAMFETAMINE	ANOREXIC	MS
	$C_{11}H_{17}N$	MEPHENTERMINE	SYMPATHOMIMETIC	
	$C_{11}H_{17}N$	PENTOREX	ANOREXIC	MS
	$C_{11}H_{17}N$	XYLOPROPAMINE	SYMPATHOMIMETIC	
163.87541	C_2CL_4	TETRACHLOROETHYLENE	SOLVENT	
163.91986	$C_2H_3O_2CL_3$	CHLORAL HYDRATE	HYPNOTIC	MS
163.96073	$C_3H_4OCL_2F_2$	METHOXYFLUORANE	NARCOTIC	
164.06848	$C_6H_{12}O_5$	RHAMNOSE	SUGAR	
	$C_6H_{12}O_5$	SORBITANE	PHARMACEUTICAL AID	
164.08373	$C_{10}H_{12}O_2$	EUGENOL	DESINFICIENT	
	$C_{10}H_{12}O_2$	PHENYLBUTYRIC ACID	ANTICHOLESTEREMIC	
164.09496	$C_9H_{12}N_2O$	FENURON	HERBICIDE	
164.11877	$C_9H_{14}N_3$	TETRIDAMINE	ANALGESIC	
164.12012	$C_{11}H_{16}O$	FENIPENTOL	CHOLERETIC	
165.07898	$C_9H_{11}NO_2$	ATROLACTAMIDE	ANTIEPILEPTIC	
	$C_9H_{11}NO_2$	BENZOCAINE	LOCAL ANESTHETIC	MS
	$C_9H_{11}NO_2$	ETHENZAMIDE	ANALGESIC	MS
	$C_9H_{11}NO_2$	PARAPROPAMOL	ANALGESIC	
	$C_9H_{11}NO_2$	PHENYLALANINE	AMINO ACID	
165.11536	$C_{10}H_{15}NO$	EPHEDRINE	SYMPATHOMIMETIC	MS
	$C_{10}H_{15}NO$	HORDENINE	SYMPATHOMIMETIC	
	$C_{10}H_{15}NO$	PHOLEDRINE	SYMPATHOMIMETIC	
	$C_{10}H_{15}NO$	PSEUDOEPHEDRINE	VASOCONSTRICTOR	
165.12660	$C_9H_{15}N_3$	TETRIDAMINE	ANALGESIC	
165.89106	$C_2H_2CL_4$	TETRACHLOROETHANE	SOLVENT	
166.02661	$C_8H_6O_4$	PHTHALIC ACID	CHEMICAL	
166.05647	$C_8H_{10}N_2S$	ETHIONAMIDE	TUBERCULOSTATIC	
166.06300	$C_9H_{10}O_3$	APOCYNIN	CARDIOTONIC	
	$C_9H_{10}O_3$	ETHYL SALICYLATE	RUBEFACIENT	MS
	$C_9H_{10}O_3$	ETHYLPARABEN	PRESERVATIVE	MS
166.11061	$C_9H_{14}N_2O$	FENOXYPROPAZINE	ANTIDEPRESSANT	
	$C_9H_{14}N_2O$	PHENOXYPROPAZINE	ENZYME INHIBITOR	
167.02657	$C_5H_5N_5S$	TIOGUANINE	CYTOSTATIC	
167.05824	$C_8H_9NO_3$	ORTHOCAINE	LOCAL ANESTHETIC	
	$C_8H_9NO_3$	PYRIDOXAL	VITAMINE	
167.06948	$C_7H_9N_3O_2$	AMINOSALICYLIC ACID HYDRAZIDE	TUBERCULOSTATIC	

MASS	FORMULA	NAME	CATEGORY	MS
167.09463	$C_9H_{13}NO_2$	ETHINAMATE	HYPNOTIC	**MS**
	$C_9H_{13}NO_2$	METARAMINOL	SYMPATHOMIMETIC	**MS**
	$C_9H_{13}NO_2$	PHENYLEPHRINE	VASOCONSTRICTOR	**MS**
	$C_9H_{13}NO_2$	PYRITHYLDIONE	HYPNOTIC	**MS**
	$C_9H_{13}NO_2$	SYNEPHRINE	SYMPATHOMIMETIC	**MS**
167.16740	$C_{11}H_{21}N$	MECAMYLAMINE	GANGLIOPLEGIC	
167.98812	$C_7H_4O_3S$	TIOXOLONE	DERMATIC	
168.00904	$C_7H_5N_2OCL$	ZOXAZOLAMINE	MUSCLE RELAXANT	
168.02834	$C_5H_4N_4O_3$	URIC ACID	ENDOG.BIOMOLECULE	
168.03419	C_9H_9OCL	CLORINDANOL	ANTIBIOTIC	
168.04226	$C_8H_8O_4$	DEHYDROACETIC ACID	FUNGIST./ANTIMYC.	
	$C_8H_8O_4$	FUMIGATIN	ANTIBIOTIC	
	$C_8H_8O_4$	HOMOGENTISIC ACID	ENDOG.BIOMOLECULE	
	$C_8H_8O_4$	VANILLIC ACID	ORGANIC ACID	
168.07865	$C_9H_{12}O_3$	TRIMETHOXYBENZENE	ANTISPASMOTIC	
168.08988	$C_8H_{12}N_2O_2$	PYRIDOXAMINE	VITAMINE	
168.11503	$C_{10}H_{16}O_2$	ASCARIDOLE	ANTHELMINTIC	
	$C_{10}H_{16}O_2$	CICROTOIC ACID	CHOLERETIC	
	$C_{10}H_{16}O_2$	IRIDOMYRMECIN	ANTIBIOTIC	
168.99306	$C_7H_4NO_2CL$	CHLORZOXAZONE	MUSCLE RELAXANT	
169.01401	$C_3H_8NO_5P$	GLYPHOSATE	HERBICIDE	
169.07389	$C_8H_{11}NO_3$	NOREPINEPHRINE	SYMPATHOMIMETIC	
	$C_8H_{11}NO_3$	OXIDOPAMINE	SYMPATHOMIMETIC	
	$C_8H_{11}NO_3$	PYRIDOXOL	VITAMINE	
169.08513	$C_7H_{11}N_3O_2$	IPRONIDAZOLE	ANTIBIOTIC	
169.11028	$C_9H_{15}NO_2$	ACECLIDINE	PARASYMP.-MIMETIC	
	$C_9H_{15}NO_2$	DIHYPRYLONE	SEDATIVE	
169.93132	$C_2CL_2F_4$	CRYOFLUORANE	PROPELLANT	
170.02153	$C_7H_6O_5$	GALLIC ACID	ORGANIC ACID	
170.03792	$C_8H_7O_3F$	FLUOROHYDROXYPHENYLACETIC ACID	THYREOSTATIC	
170.05139	$C_7H_{10}N_2OS$	PROPYLTHIOURACIL	THYREOSTATIC	
170.05791	$C_8H_{10}O_4$	PENICILLIC ACID	ANTIBIOTIC	
170.07317	$C_{12}H_{10}O$	PHENYLPHENOL	DESINFICIENT	**MS**
170.09430	$C_9H_{14}O_3$	CASTELAMARIN	NATURAL SUBSTANCE	
170.10553	$C_8H_{14}N_2O_2$	ETIRACETAM	------------	
170.13068	$C_{10}H_{18}O_2$	SOBREROL	RESPIRAT.STIMULANT	
170.96426	$C_7H_3NCL_2$	DICHLOBENIL	HERBICIDE	
170.98539	$C_4H_7NO_2CL_2$	DICHLOROISOPROPYLMETHANE	HYPNOTIC	
171.02177	$C_5H_{11}NOCL_2$	CHLOROMETHINE OXIDE	CYTOSTATIC	
171.03540	$C_7H_9NO_2S$	TIZOPROLIC ACID	ANTICHOLESTEREMIC	
	$C_7H_9NO_2S$	TOLUENESULFONAMIDE	DESINFICIENT	
171.04663	$C_6H_9N_3OS$	METHIOPRIM	CYTOSTATIC	
171.05633	$C_7H_{10}N_3CL$	CIMIDINE	RODENTICIDE	**MS**
171.06439	$C_6H_9N_3O_3$	METRONIDAZOLE	TRICHOMONACIDE	**MS**
171.08954	$C_8H_{13}NO_3$	DIETHADIONE	ANALGESIC	
171.11201	$C_6H_{13}N_5O$	MOROXYDINE	VIRUCIDE	
171.17355	$C_9H_{21}N_3$	GUANOCTINE	ANTIHYPERTENSIVE	
171.19870	$C_{11}H_{25}N$	IPROHEPTIN	ANTIHIST./-ALLERG.	
	$C_{11}H_{25}N$	METRON S	ANTIHIST./-ALLERG.	
172.00079	$C_6H_4O_6$	TETROQUINONE	DERMATIC	
172.01368	$C_3H_9O_6P$	GLYCEROPHOSPHORIC ACID	TONIC	
172.02893	$C_7H_9O_3P$	HYDROXYBENZYLPHOSPHINIC ACID	TONIC	

MASS	FORMULA	NAME	CATEGORY	MS
172.03065	$C_6H_8N_2O_2S$	SULFANILAMIDE	ANTIBIOTIC	MS
172.05243	$C_{11}H_8O_2$	MENADIONE	VITAMINE	
172.10995	$C_9H_{16}O_3$	HEXOCYCLONIC ACID	STIMULANT	
172.14633	$C_{10}H_{20}O_2$	CAPRIC ACID	ORGANIC ACID	
	$C_{10}H_{20}O_2$	TERPIN	EXPECTORANT	
172.98951	$C_4H_3N_3O_3S$	FORMINITRAZOLE	TRICHOMONACIDE	
173.01467	$C_6H_7NO_3S$	SULFANILIC ACID	ANTIBIOTIC	
173.04366	$C_5H_7N_3O_4$	AZASERINE	FUNGIST./ANTIMYC.	
173.06074	$C_8H_{12}NOCL$	ALLIDOCHLOR	HERBICIDE	
173.06881	$C_7H_{11}NO_4$	OXACEPROL	ANTIRHEUMATIC	
173.08406	$C_{11}H_{11}NO$	VITAMIN K5	VITAMINE	
173.10519	$C_8H_{15}NO_3$	ACETYLLEUCIN	AMINO ACID	
	$C_8H_{15}NO_3$	ACEXAMIC ACID	DERMATIC	
173.99868	$C_6H_6O_4S$	PHENOLSULFONIC ACID	LOCAL ANESTHETIC	
174.03170	$C_{10}H_6O_3$	JUGLONE	HEMOSTATIC	
	$C_{10}H_6O_3$	LAWSONE	DERMATIC	
174.06808	$C_{11}H_{10}O_2$	MENADIOL	VITAMINE	
174.08921	$C_8H_{14}O_4$	DIMETHOXANE	PRESERVATIVE	
174.11168	$C_6H_{14}N_4O_2$	ARGININE	AMINO ACID	
175.02225	$C_7H_{10}NCLS$	CLOPROTHIAZOLE	FUNGIST./ANTIMYC.	
175.04807	$C_6H_9NO_5$	ACETYLASPARAGIC ACID	DYNAMIC	
175.06333	$C_{10}H_9NO_2$	CARFIMATE	TRANQUILIZER	
	$C_{10}H_9NO_2$	INDOLE ACETIC ACID	PLANT GROWTH REGU.	MS
175.09569	$C_6H_{13}N_3O_3$	CITRULLINE	AMINO ACID	
175.09971	$C_{11}H_{13}NO$	BENZALAMIDE	ANTICHOLESTEREMIC	
175.11095	$C_{10}H_{13}N_3$	DEBRISOQUINE	ANTIHYPERTENSIVE	
	$C_{10}H_{13}N_3$	PHENAMAZOLIN	VASOCONSTRICTOR	
175.13610	$C_{12}H_{17}N$	BUTIXIRATE (AMINE)	ANALGESIC	
175.95625	$C_4H_7OCL_3$	CHLOROBUTANOL	PRESERVATIVE	
175.97957	$C_7H_6OCL_2$	DICHLOROBENZYL ALCOHOL	DESINFICIENT	
176.03209	$C_6H_8O_6$	ASCORBIC ACID	VITAMINE	MS
	$C_6H_8O_6$	GLUCUROLACTONE	ANTIDOTE	
176.04735	$C_{10}H_8O_3$	ERYTHROCENTAURIN	NATURAL SUBSTANCE	
	$C_{10}H_8O_3$	HYMECROMONE	CHOLERETIC	
176.05858	$C_9H_8N_2O_2$	PEMOLINE	STIMULANT	MS
176.06023	$C_7H_{13}O_3P$	CYCLOHEXENYLHYDROXYMETHYLPHOSPHIN.ACID	TONIC	
176.08373	$C_{11}H_{12}O_2$	METHYLPHENYLBUTINDIOL	HYPNOTIC	
176.09496	$C_{10}H_{12}N_2O$	COTININE	STIMULANT	MS
	$C_{10}H_{12}N_2O$	SEROTONIN	ENDOG.BIOMOLECULE	
176.10486	$C_8H_{16}O_4$	METALDEHYDE	PESTICIDE	MS
177.00958	$C_5H_7NO_4S$	TIDIACIC	PROTEC.LIVER THER.	
177.04597	$C_6H_{11}NO_3S$	ALLIIN	AMINO ACID	
177.05383	$C_8H_7N_3O_2$	LUMINOL	CHEMICAL	
177.06122	$C_{10}H_{11}NS$	PHENYLPROPYL ISOTHIOCYANATE	COUNTERIRRITANT	
177.07898	$C_{10}H_{11}NO_2$	TUBERIN	TUBERCULOSTATIC	
177.11536	$C_{11}H_{15}NO$	METAMFEPRAMONE	ANOREXIC	MS
	$C_{11}H_{15}NO$	PHENMETRAZINE	SYMPATHOMIMETIC	MS
177.12660	$C_{10}H_{15}N_3$	BETANIDINE	ANTIHYPERTENSIVE	
	$C_{10}H_{15}N_3$	MODALINE	ANTIDEPRESSANT	
177.98086	$C_4H_3OCLF_4$	ALIFLURANE	NARCOTIC	
178.01452	$C_5H_7N_2O_3CL$	ACIVICIN	-----------	
178.02661	$C_9H_6O_4$	NINHYDRIN	CHEMICAL	

MASS	FORMULA	NAME	CATEGORY	MS
178.04774	$C_6H_{10}O_6$	GLUCONOLACTONE	CHEMICAL	
178.04908	$C_7H_6N_4O_2$	MELIZAME	SWEETENER	
178.05647	$C_9H_{10}N_2S$	ETISAZOLE	FUNGIST./ANTIMYC.	
178.07423	$C_9H_{10}N_2O_2$	PHENACEMIDE	ANTIEPILEPTIC	
178.07760	$C_6H_{14}N_2O_2S$	HEXAHYDROAZEPINSULFONAMIDE	STIMULANT	
178.08413	$C_7H_{14}O_5$	DIGITALOSE	SUGAR	
	$C_7H_{14}O_5$	THEVETOSE	SUGAR	
178.09938	$C_{11}H_{14}O_2$	BUTYL BENZOATE	SOLVENT	MS
178.11061	$C_{10}H_{14}N_2O$	BUPICOMIDE	ANTIHYPERTENSIVE	
	$C_{10}H_{14}N_2O$	NICETHAMIDE	CARDIOTONIC	MS
178.12051	$C_8H_{18}O_4$	TRIGLYME	SOLVENT	
178.13577	$C_{12}H_{18}O$	PENTYLCRESOL	DESINFICIENT	
179.01379	C_9H_6NOCL	CLOXIQUINE	FUNGIST./ANTIMYC.	
179.02523	$C_5H_9NO_4S$	CARBOCISTEINE	EXPECTORANT	
179.05824	$C_9H_9NO_3$	HIPPURIC ACID	ENDOG.BIOMOLECULE	MS
	$C_9H_9NO_3$	SALACETAMIDE	ANALGESIC	
179.06162	$C_6H_{13}NO_3S$	CYCLAMATE (ACID)	SWEETENER	MS
179.06948	$C_8H_9N_3O_2$	ACETYLPICOLINOHYDRAZIDE	CYTOSTATIC	
179.07350	$C_{13}H_9N$	ACRIDINE	CHEMICAL	
179.07937	$C_6H_{13}NO_5$	GLUCOSAMINE	ANTIRHEUMATIC	
179.09463	$C_{10}H_{13}NO_2$	DIHYDROTUBERIN	TUBERCULOSTATIC	
	$C_{10}H_{13}NO_2$	HOMARYLAMINE	ANTITUSSIVE	
	$C_{10}H_{13}NO_2$	N-ISOPROPYLSALICYLAMIDE	ANALGESIC	
	$C_{10}H_{13}NO_2$	PHENACETIN	ANALGESIC	MS
	$C_{10}H_{13}NO_2$	PHENPROBAMATE	MUSCLE RELAXANT	
	$C_{10}H_{13}NO_2$	PROPHAM	HERBICIDE	
	$C_{10}H_{13}NO_2$	RISOCAINE	LOCAL ANESTHETIC	
179.10586	$C_9H_{13}N_3O$	IPRONIAZIDE	TUBERCULOSTATIC	
179.10752	$C_7H_{18}NO_2P$	BUTAFOSFANE	TONIC	
179.13101	$C_{11}H_{17}NO$	METHOXYPHENAMINE	SYMPATHOMIMETIC	
	$C_{11}H_{17}NO$	METHYLEPHEDRINE	RESPIRAT.STIMULANT	MS
	$C_{11}H_{17}NO$	MEXILETINE	ANTIARRHYTHMIC	MS
179.16740	$C_{12}H_{21}N$	MEMANTINE	ANTIPARKINSONIAN	MS
	$C_{12}H_{21}N$	RIMANTADINE	VIRUCIDE	
179.91977	C_2HF_4BR	TEFLURANE	NARCOTIC	
179.93003	$C_6H_3CL_3$	TRICHLOROBENZENE	CHEMICAL	
180.04226	$C_9H_8O_4$	ACETOZONE	PRESERVATIVE	
	$C_9H_8O_4$	ACETYLSALICYLIC ACID	ANALGESIC	MS
	$C_9H_8O_4$	CAFFEIC ACID	NATURAL SUBSTANCE	
	$C_9H_8O_4$	ESCORIN	DIAGNOSTIC AID	
	$C_9H_8O_4$	HYDROXYPHENYLPYRUVIC ACID	DIAGNOSTIC AID	
180.04697	$C_7H_8N_4S$	ISONICOTINALDEHYDE THIOSEMICARBAZONE	TUBERCULOSTATIC	
	$C_7H_8N_4S$	NICOTHIAZONE	TUBERCULOSTATIC	
180.06339	$C_6H_{12}O_6$	FRUCTOSE	SUGAR	
	$C_6H_{12}O_6$	GALACTOSE	SUGAR	
	$C_6H_{12}O_6$	GLUCOSE	SUGAR	MS
	$C_6H_{12}O_6$	INOSITOL	TONIC	
	$C_6H_{12}O_6$	LEVULOSE	SUGAR	
	$C_6H_{12}O_6$	MANNOSE	SUGAR	
	$C_6H_{12}O_6$	PSICOSE	SUGAR	
180.06473	$C_7H_8N_4O_2$	ACETYLPYRAZINE CARBOXYLIC ACID	CARDIOTONIC	
	$C_7H_8N_4O_2$	THEOBROMINE	CARDIOTONIC	MS

MASS	FORMULA	NAME	CATEGORY	MS
180.06473	$C_7H_8N_4O_2$	THEOPHYLLINE	CARDIOTONIC	MS
180.07212	$C_9H_{12}N_2S$	PROTIONAMIDE	TUBERCULOSTATIC	
180.07865	$C_{10}H_{12}O_3$	PROPYLPARABEN	PRESERVATIVE	
180.08988	$C_9H_{12}N_2O_2$	DULCIN	SWEETENER	
181.00537	$C_5H_{11}NS_3$	THIOCYCLAM	INSECTICIDE	
181.07389	$C_9H_{11}NO_3$	ADRENALONE	SYMPATHOMIMETIC	
	$C_9H_{11}NO_3$	METHYL AMINOMANDELATE	RESPIRAT.STIMULANT	
	$C_9H_{11}NO_3$	STYRAMATE	MUSCLE RELAXANT	
	$C_9H_{11}NO_3$	TYROSINE	AMINO ACID	
181.08915	$C_{13}H_{11}N$	STILBAZOLE	FUNGIST./ANTIMYC.	
181.09502	$C_6H_{15}NO_5$	GLUCAMINE	SUGAR	
181.11028	$C_{10}H_{15}NO_2$	ETHYPICONE	HYPNOTIC	
	$C_{10}H_{15}NO_2$	ETILEFRINE	SYMPATHOMIMETIC	MS
	$C_{10}H_{15}NO_2$	HEXAPROPYMATE	HYPNOTIC	
	$C_{10}H_{15}NO_2$	HYDROXYEPHEDRINE	SYMPATHOMIMETIC	MS
181.12151	$C_9H_{15}N_3O$	AZEPEXOL	ANTIHYPERTENSIVE	
181.18305	$C_{12}H_{23}N$	DIMECAMINE	GANGLIOPLEGIC	
	$C_{12}H_{23}N$	LEPTACLINE	STIMULANT	
181.98745	$C_2H_4N_6CL_2$	CHLORAZODIN	DESINFICIENT	
182.01663	$C_4H_4OF_6$	FLUROTYL	STIMULANT	
182.05791	$C_9H_{10}O_4$	FLOPROPIONE	ANTISPASMOTIC	
	$C_9H_{10}O_4$	GLYCOL MONOSALICYLATE	RUBEFACIENT	
182.05925	$C_{10}H_6N_4$	STRINOLIN	ANALGESIC	
182.07317	$C_{13}H_{10}O$	BENZOPHENONE	CHEMICAL	
182.07904	$C_6H_{14}O_6$	MANNITOL	LAXATIVE	
	$C_6H_{14}O_6$	SORBITOL	SWEETENER	
182.09161	$C_6H_{10}N_6O$	DACARBAZINE	CYTOSTATIC	
182.09430	$C_{10}H_{14}O_3$	ANISALDEHYDE DIMETHYLACETAL	DERMATIC	
	$C_{10}H_{14}O_3$	MEPHENESINE	MUSCLE RELAXANT	
182.09843	$C_6H_{16}N_2OFP$	MIPAFOX	INSECTICIDE	
182.15315	$C_9H_{18}N_4$	GUANACLINE	ANTIHYPERTENSIVE	
182.99902	$C_7H_5NO_3S$	SACCHARIN	SWEETENER	
183.01190	$C_4H_{10}NO_3PS$	ACEPHATE	INSECTICIDE	
183.03540	$C_8H_9NO_2S$	OXISURANE	IMMUN SUPPRESSOR	
183.06956	$C_9H_{10}NO_2F$	FLUORPHENYLALANINE	VIRUCIDE	
183.08148	$C_{10}H_{14}NCL$	CHLORPHENTERMINE	ANOREXIC	MS
	$C_{10}H_{14}NCL$	CLORTERMINE	ANOREXIC	
183.08954	$C_9H_{13}NO_3$	CORBADRINE	VASOCONSTRICTOR	
	$C_9H_{13}NO_3$	EPINEPHRINE	SYMPATHOMIMETIC	
	$C_9H_{13}NO_3$	NORDEFRINE	VASOCONSTRICTOR	
183.12593	$C_{10}H_{17}NO_2$	METHYPRYLONE	HYPNOTIC	MS
183.16231	$C_{11}H_{21}NO$	UNDECENE AMIDE	FUNGIST./ANTIMYC.	
183.97143	$C_3H_2OCLF_5$	ENFLURANE	NARCOTIC	
	$C_3H_2OCLF_5$	ISOFLURANE	NARCOTIC	
183.98870	$C_3H_5N_2O_5CL$	CLONITRATE	CORONARY DILATOR	
184.06366	$C_{11}H_8N_2O$	FUBERIDAZOL	FUNGIST./ANTIMYC.	
184.06549	$C_{10}H_{13}OCL$	CHLORCARVACROL	DESINFICIENT	
	$C_{10}H_{13}OCL$	CHLOROTHYMOL	DESINFICIENT	
184.06646	$C_6H_{14}O_3FP$	FLUOSTIGMINE	PARASYMP.-MIMETIC	
184.08479	$C_8H_{12}N_2O_3$	BARBITAL	HYPNOTIC	MS
	$C_8H_{12}N_2O_3$	PRIMOCARCIN	CYTOSTATIC	
184.08882	$C_{13}H_{12}O$	BENZYL PHENOL	DESINFICIENT	MS

MASS	FORMULA	NAME	CATEGORY	MS
184.11849	$C_5H_{12}N_8$	MITOGUAZONE	CYTOSTATIC	
184.12118	$C_9H_{16}N_2O_2$	APRONALIDE	HYPNOTIC	
184.12520	$C_{14}H_{16}$	CHAMAZULENE	ANTIINFLAMMATORY	
	$C_{14}H_{16}$	ISOPROPYLAZULENE	STOMACHIC	
184.14633	$C_{11}H_{20}O_2$	UNDECYLENIC ACID	FUNGIST./ANTIMYC.	
184.16880	$C_9H_{20}N_4$	GUANAZODINE	ANTIHYPERTENSIVE	
184.97021	C_7H_4NOSCL	TICLATONE	FUNGIST./ANTIMYC.	
185.00893	$C_3H_8NO_6P$	SERINE PHOSPHATE	AMINO ACID	
185.05105	$C_8H_{11}NO_2S$	MESYLBENZYLAMINE	ANTIBIOTIC	
185.08004	$C_7H_{11}N_3O_3$	SECNIDAZOLE	TRICHOMONACIDE	
	$C_7H_{11}N_3O_3$	TERNIDAZOLE	TRICHOMONACIDE	
185.08406	$C_{12}H_{11}NO$	PIRFENIDONE	ANALGESIC	
185.10519	$C_9H_{15}NO_3$	ECGONINE	LOCAL ANESTHETIC	
	$C_9H_{15}NO_3$	PSEUDOECGONINE	LOCAL ANESTHETIC	
185.11643	$C_8H_{15}N_3O_2$	ISOCARBAMIDE	HERBICIDE	
185.14158	$C_{10}H_{19}NO_2$	PROCYMATE	TRANQUILIZER	
185.16405	$C_8H_{19}N_5$	ETOFORMIN	ANTIDIABETIC	
185.86797	$C_2H_4BR_2$	DIBROMOETHANE	NEMATOCIDE	
186.04630	$C_7H_{10}N_2O_2S$	CARBIMAZOLE	THYREOSTATIC	
	$C_7H_{10}N_2O_2S$	MAFENIDE	ANTIBIOTIC	
186.05283	$C_8H_{10}O_5$	ENDOTHAL	HERBICIDE	
186.06808	$C_{12}H_{10}O_2$	CHIMAPHILIN	DESINFICIENT	
	$C_{12}H_{10}O_2$	NAPHTHOLACETIC ACID	PLANT GROWTH REGU.	
186.07931	$C_{11}H_{10}N_2O$	AMPHENIDONE	SEDATIVE	
186.11570	$C_{12}H_{14}N_2$	AZEPINDOL	ANTIHYPERTENSIVE	
	$C_{12}H_{14}N_2$	DETOMIDINE	------------	
186.12560	$C_{10}H_{18}O_3$	CYCLOBUTOIC ACID	CHOLERETIC	
	$C_{10}H_{18}O_3$	CYCLOBUTYROL	CHOLERETIC	
186.13683	$C_9H_{18}N_2O_2$	CAPURIDE	HYPNOTIC	
186.19837	$C_{12}H_{26}O$	DODECANOL	CHEMICAL	
187.00516	$C_5H_5N_3O_3S$	AMINITROZOLE	ANTIBIOTIC	
187.07456	$C_{10}H_9N_3O$	AMRINONE	CARDIOTONIC	
187.08580	$C_9H_9N_5$	AMANOZINE	DIURETIC	
187.09971	$C_{12}H_{13}NO$	NAFOMINE	MUSCLE RELAXANT	
187.10309	$C_9H_{17}NOS$	MOLINATE	HERBICIDE	
187.11095	$C_{11}H_{13}N_3$	DEXIMAFENE	ANTIDEPRESSANT	
187.13610	$C_{13}H_{17}N$	SELEGILINE	ANTIDEPRESSANT	
188.01433	$C_7H_8O_4S$	CRESOLSULFONIC ACID	DESINFICIENT	
188.03073	$C_8H_9O_2FS$	FLUORESONE	TRANQUILIZER	
188.04332	$C_6H_8N_2O_5$	ENTEROMYCIN	ANTIBIOTIC	
188.07971	$C_7H_{12}N_2O_4$	ACEGLUTAMIDE	DYNAMIC	
188.09496	$C_{11}H_{12}N_2O$	PHENAZONE	ANALGESIC	MS
	$C_{11}H_{12}N_2O$	VASICINE	ANTIASTHMATIC	
188.12012	$C_{13}H_{16}O$	GRISANE	CHEMICAL	
188.13135	$C_{12}H_{16}N_2$	AZAQUINZOL	ANTIDEPRESSANT	
	$C_{12}H_{16}N_2$	DIMETHYLTRYPTAMINE	HALLUCINOGEN	
	$C_{12}H_{16}N_2$	ETRYPTAMINE	ANTIDEPRESSANT	
	$C_{12}H_{16}N_2$	FENPROPOREX	ANOREXIC	MS
188.14125	$C_{10}H_{20}O_3$	PROMOXOLANE	TRANQUILIZER	
188.15248	$C_9H_{20}N_2O_2$	PROPAMOCARB	FUNGIST./ANTIMYC.	
188.98289	$C_6H_4NO_4CL$	NIFURMERONE	FUNGIST./ANTIMYC.	
189.04896	$C_6H_{12}N_3PS$	THIOTEPA	CYTOSTATIC	

MASS	FORMULA	NAME	CATEGORY	MS
189.06372	$C_7H_{11}NO_5$	ACETYLGLUTAMIC ACID	DYNAMIC	
189.07898	$C_{11}H_{11}NO_2$	PHENSUXIMIDE	ANTIEPILEPTIC	MS
189.08235	$C_8H_{15}NO_2S$	PRENISTEINE	EXPECTORANT	
189.09021	$C_{10}H_{11}N_3O$	AZOLIMINE	DIURETIC	
	$C_{10}H_{11}N_3O$	CROTONIAZIDE	TUBERCULOSTATIC	
189.11536	$C_{12}H_{15}NO$	ETHYLCROTONANILIDE	DERMATIC	
189.11874	$C_9H_{19}NOS$	EPTC	HERBICIDE	
189.96058	$C_2H_6O_6S_2$	ETHANEDISULFONIC ACID	PHARMACEUTICAL AID	
189.99360	$C_6H_6O_5S$	DIHYDROXYBENZENESULFONIC ACID	ANTICHOLESTEREMIC	
189.99522	$C_8H_8OCL_2$	DICHLOROXYLENOL	DESINFICIENT	
190.03784	$C_9H_6N_2O_3$	NITROXOLINE	ANTIBIOTIC	
190.07423	$C_{10}H_{10}N_2O_2$	PROCODAZOL	IMMUN SUPPRESSOR	
190.07760	$C_7H_{14}N_2O_2S$	BUTOCARBOXIM	INSECTICIDE	MS
	$C_7H_{14}N_2O_2S$	ALDICARB	INSECTICIDE	
190.09669	$C_8H_{10}N_6$	DIHYDRALAZINE	ANTIHYPERTENSIVE	
190.09938	$C_{12}H_{14}O_2$	FENABUTENE	------------	
190.11399	$C_8H_{18}N_2OS$	PROTHIOCARB	FUNGIST./ANTIMYC.	
190.93076	$C_3H_4NO_2CL_3$	CHLORAL FORMAMIDE	HYPNOTIC	
	$C_3H_4NO_2CL_3$	TRICHLOROETHYLURETHAN	HYPNOTIC	
190.99047	$C_7H_7NOCL_2$	CLOPIDOL	FUNGIST./ANTIMYC.	
191.04299	$C_6H_9NO_6$	NITRILOTRIACETIC ACID	CHEMICAL	
191.05172	$C_9H_9N_3S$	AMIPHENAZOLE	RESPIRAT.STIMULANT	MS
191.06162	$C_7H_{13}NO_3S$	ACETYLMETHIONINE	PROTEC.LIVER THER.	
	$C_7H_{13}NO_3S$	ACETYLPENICILLAMINE	ANTIDOTE	
191.06948	$C_9H_9N_3O_2$	BENZISOXAZOLE ACETAMIDEOXIME	ANTIDEPRESSANT	
	$C_9H_9N_3O_2$	CARBENDAZIM	FUNGIST./ANTIMYC.	
191.09463	$C_{11}H_{13}NO_2$	IDROCILAMIDE	MUSCLE RELAXANT	
191.09800	$C_8H_{17}NO_2S$	METHIONINE ISOPROPYLESTER	PROTEC.LIVER THER.	
191.13101	$C_{12}H_{17}NO$	DEET	RODENTICIDE	
	$C_{12}H_{17}NO$	DIETHYLTOLUAMIDE	INSECTICIDE	
	$C_{12}H_{17}NO$	INDANOREX	ANOREXIC	
	$C_{12}H_{17}NO$	PHENDIMETRAZINE	ANOREXIC	MS
	$C_{12}H_{17}NO$	TREBENZOMIN	ANTIDEPRESSANT	
191.93976	$C_3H_4OF_3BR$	ROFLURANE	NARCOTIC	
191.95116	$C_4H_7O_2CL_3$	BUTYLCHLORALHYDRATE	SEDATIVE	
191.95888	$C_1H_6O_7P_2$	OXIDRONIC ACID	DIAGNOSTIC AID	
191.98159	$C_8H_4N_2S_2$	BITOSCANATE	ANTHELMINTIC	
192.02700	$C_6H_8O_7$	CITRIC ACID	ORGANIC ACID	
192.04543	$C_{10}H_9N_2CL$	LOFEMIZOLE	------------	
192.06339	$C_7H_{12}O_6$	HYDROXYPROPYL HYDROGENEMALEATE	------------	
	$C_7H_{12}O_6$	QUINIC ACID	ANALGESIC	
192.08988	$C_{10}H_{12}N_2O_2$	NICOPHOLINE	------------	
	$C_{10}H_{12}N_2O_2$	PROXIMPHAM	HERBICIDE	
192.11503	$C_{12}H_{16}O_2$	BENZYLISOVALERATE	DERMATIC	
	$C_{12}H_{16}O_2$	IBUFENAC	ANTIRHEUMATIC	
192.12626	$C_{11}H_{16}N_2O$	TOCAINIDE	LOCAL ANESTHETIC	MS
192.15142	$C_{13}H_{20}O$	IONONE	CHEMICAL	
192.16265	$C_{12}H_{20}N_2$	TREMORINE	CHEMICAL	
193.02525	$C_4H_8N_3O_4P$	PHOSPHOCREATININE	ENDOG.BIOMOLECULE	
193.03506	$C_7H_6NO_2F_3$	FLUCRILATE	ADHESIVE	
193.07389	$C_{10}H_{11}NO_3$	DIACETAMATE	ANALGESIC	
193.11028	$C_{11}H_{15}NO_2$	BUTAMBEN	LOCAL ANESTHETIC	

MASS	FORMULA	NAME	CATEGORY	MS
193.11028	$C_{11}H_{15}NO_2$	ISOBUTAMBEN	LOCAL ANESTHETIC	
	$C_{11}H_{15}NO_2$	METHOXYPHEDRINE	SYMPATHOMIMETIC	
	$C_{11}H_{15}NO_2$	SALSOLINE	ANTIHYPERTENSIVE	
193.12151	$C_{10}H_{15}N_3O$	GUANOXYFEN	ANTIHYPERTENSIVE	
193.14666	$C_{12}H_{19}NO$	ETAFEDRINE	SYMPATHOMIMETIC	
193.93542	$C_3H_3BRF_4$	HALOPROPANE	NARCOTIC	
194.04266	$C_6H_{10}O_7$	GALACTURONIC ACID	ENDOG.BIOMOLECULE	
194.05791	$C_{10}H_{10}O_4$	DIMETHYL PHTHALATE	RODENTICIDE	
194.06914	$C_9H_{10}N_2O_3$	ACETYLHYDRAZINO SALICYLALDEHYDE	ANTIBIOTIC	
	$C_9H_{10}N_2O_3$	AMINOHIPPURIC ACID	DIAGNOSTIC AID	
	$C_9H_{10}N_2O_3$	OLMIDINE	ANTIHYPERTENSIVE	
194.07317	$C_{14}H_{10}O$	ANTHRANOL	CHEMICAL	
	$C_{14}H_{10}O$	ANTHRONE	CHEMICAL	
194.08038	$C_8H_{10}N_4O_2$	CAFFEINE	STIMULANT	MS
	$C_8H_{10}N_4O_2$	ENPROFYLLINE	------------	
194.08440	$C_{13}H_{10}N_2$	AMINOACRIDIN	FUNGIST./ANTIMYC.	
194.09430	$C_{11}H_{14}O_3$	BUTYLPARABEN	DESINFICIENT	MS
	$C_{11}H_{14}O_3$	THYMOTIC ACID	DESINFICIENT	
	$C_{11}H_{14}O_3$	ZINGERONE	------------	
194.10553	$C_{10}H_{14}N_2O_2$	ALLOPHANOYLALLYLVALEROLACTONE	ANTIEPILEPTIC	
	$C_{10}H_{14}N_2O_2$	PHENOCOLL	ANALGESIC	
194.13068	$C_{12}H_{18}O_2$	HEXYLRESORCINOL	ANTHELMINTIC	
195.05316	$C_9H_9NO_4$	CARBAMOYLPHENOXYACETIC ACID	ANALGESIC	
195.06841	$C_{13}H_9NO$	PYRIDARONE	ANTIDEPRESSANT	
195.08954	$C_{10}H_{13}NO_3$	BURAMATE	TRANQUILIZER	
	$C_{10}H_{13}NO_3$	DIHYDROXYPHENYLMORPHOLINE	VASOCONSTRICTOR	
	$C_{10}H_{13}NO_3$	FENACETINOL	ANALGESIC	
195.10078	$C_9H_{13}N_3O_2$	AMINOMETRADINE	DIURETIC	
	$C_9H_{13}N_3O_2$	AMISOMETRADINE	DIURETIC	
195.11067	$C_7H_{17}NO_5$	MEGLUMINE	PHARMACEUTICAL AID	
195.12593	$C_{11}H_{17}NO_2$	DETERENOL	SYMPATHOMIMETIC	
	$C_{11}H_{17}NO_2$	METATEROL	------------	
195.89022	$C_2HBRCLF_3$	HALOTHANE	NARCOTIC	
195.92495	$C_6H_3OCL_3$	TRICHLOROPHENOL	DESINFICIENT	MS
195.96544	$C_6H_{10}CLBR$	CHLOROBROMOCYCLOHEXANE	FUNGIST./ANTIMYC.	
196.04034	$C_9H_9N_2OCL$	CLOMINOREX	ANOREXIC	
196.05831	$C_6H_{12}O_7$	GLUCONIC ACID	ORGANIC ACID	
196.06130	$C_5H_{13}N_2O_4P$	ALAFOSFALIN	ANTIBIOTIC	
196.06549	$C_{11}H_{13}OCL$	DOWICIDE	DESINFICIENT	
196.07356	$C_{10}H_{12}O_4$	CANTHARIDIN	RUBEFACIENT	
	$C_{10}H_{12}O_4$	HYDROXYPROPYL SALICYLATE	ANALGESIC	
196.07673	$C_{10}H_{13}N_2CL$	CHLORDIMEFORM	PESTICIDE	
	$C_{10}H_{13}N_2CL$	CHLORPHENAMIDIN	PESTICIDE	
196.08479	$C_9H_{12}N_2O_3$	ETHALLOBARBITAL	HYPNOTIC	
196.14633	$C_{12}H_{20}O_2$	LINALYL ACETATE	DESINFICIENT	
196.16880	$C_{10}H_{20}N_4$	SPIRGETINE	ANTIHYPERTENSIVE	
196.93950	$C_3HN_3O_3CL_2$	TROCLOSENE	DESINFICIENT	
197.04366	$C_7H_7N_3O_4$	NIHYDRAZONE	ANTIBIOTIC	
197.05654	$C_4H_{12}N_3O_4P$	CREATINOLFOSFATE	CARDIOTONIC	
197.06074	$C_{10}H_{12}NOCL$	BECLAMIDE	ANTIEPILEPTIC	MS
197.06881	$C_9H_{11}NO_4$	LEVODOPA	ANTIPARKINSONIAN	
197.10519	$C_{10}H_{15}NO_3$	DIOXIFEDRINE	SYMPATHOMIMETIC	

MASS	FORMULA	NAME	CATEGORY	MS
197.10519	$C_{10}H_{15}NO_3$	ETHYLNOREPINEPHRINE	SYMPATHOMIMETIC	
197.12766	$C_8H_{15}N_5O$	HYDRAZINOPYRIDAZINMETHYLAMINOPROPANOL	ANTIHYPERTENSIVE	
	$C_8H_{15}N_5O$	NOFORMICIN	VIRUCIDE	
198.02767	$C_7H_6N_2O_5$	DNOC	INSECTICIDE	
198.03891	$C_6H_6N_4O_4$	NITROFURAL	ANTIBIOTIC	
198.05599	$C_9H_{11}N_2OCL$	MONURONE	HERBICIDE	
198.07529	$C_7H_{10}N_4O_3$	CURZATE	FUNGIST./ANTIMYC.	
198.07931	$C_{12}H_{10}N_2O$	FENAZOX	PESTICIDE	
198.08921	$C_{10}H_{14}O_4$	GUAIFENESIN	SEDATIVE	MS
198.10044	$C_9H_{14}N_2O_3$	ACETYLETHYLISOCROTONOYLUREA	TRANQUILIZER	
	$C_9H_{14}N_2O_3$	METHARBITAL	ANTIEPILEPTIC	MS
	$C_9H_{14}N_2O_3$	PROBARBITAL	HYPNOTIC	MS
198.10447	$C_{14}H_{14}O$	BIPHENYLYLETHANOL	ANTICHOLESTEREMIC	
198.11570	$C_{13}H_{14}N_2$	TACRINE	ANTIDOTE	
198.14085	$C_{15}H_{18}$	GUAIAZULENE	ANTIINFLAMMATORY	
198.14806	$C_9H_{18}N_4O$	AMIDONOMYCIN	ANTIBIOTIC	
198.17321	$C_{11}H_{22}N_2O$	CYCLURONE	HERBICIDE	
198.18445	$C_{10}H_{22}N_4$	GUANETHIDINE	ANTIHYPERTENSIVE	
198.94802	$C_3H_6NO_4BR$	BRONOPOL	DESINFICIENT	
198.96145	$C_6H_6NO_2AS$	OXOPHENARSINE	ANTIBIOTIC	
199.04001	$C_9H_{10}NO_2CL$	FENCLONINE	ENZYME INHIBITOR	
199.04557	$C_{12}H_9NS$	PHENOTHIAZINE	ANTHELMINTIC	MS
199.04807	$C_8H_9NO_5$	CLAVULANIC ACID	ANTIBIOTIC	
199.06447	$C_9H_{10}NO_3F$	FLUOROTYROSINE	THYREOSTATIC	
199.07622	$C_9H_{14}NO_2P$	TOLDIMFOS	TONIC	
199.11095	$C_{12}H_{13}N_3$	GAPICOMINE	CORONARY DILATOR	
199.16846	$C_{10}H_{21}N_3O$	DIETHYLCARBAMAZINE	ANTHELMINTIC	
199.23000	$C_{13}H_{29}N$	OCTAMYLAMINE	ANTISPASMOTIC	
199.85209	C_2HCL_5	PENTACHLOROETHANE	NARCOTIC	
199.94729	$C_7H_5O_2BR$	BROMOBENZOIC ACID	CHEMICAL	
199.98362	$C_3H_5N_2O_6CL$	CLONITRATE	CORONARY DILATOR	
199.98368	C_8H_9OBR	DIMETHYLBROMOPHENOL	DESINFICIENT	MS
199.99571	$C_7H_4O_7$	MECONIC ACID	ORGANIC ACID	
199.99887	$C_7H_5N_2O_3CL$	AKLOMIDE	FUNGIST./ANTIMYC.	
200.00694	$C_6H_4N_2O_6$	DINITRORESORCINOL	CHEMICAL	
200.00721	$C_4H_3OF_7$	SEVOFLURANE	NARCOTIC	
200.02402	$C_9H_9O_3CL$	MCPA	HERBICIDE	MS
200.04332	$C_7H_8N_2O_5$	NIFURATRONE	ANTIBIOTIC	
200.05456	$C_6H_8N_4O_4$	RONIDAZOLE	ANTIBIOTIC	
200.05972	$C_8H_9N_2O_3F$	TEGAFUR	CYTOSTATIC	
200.06195	$C_8H_{12}N_2O_2S$	THIOBARBITAL	THYREOSTATIC	
200.08373	$C_{13}H_{12}O_2$	MONOBENZONE	DERMATIC	
200.09496	$C_{12}H_{12}N_2O$	HARMALOL	ANTHELMINTIC	
200.10486	$C_{10}H_{16}O_4$	CAMPHORIC ACID	DESINFICIENT	
200.13135	$C_{13}H_{16}N_2$	PETHIDINE INTERMEDIATE	ANALGESIC	
	$C_{13}H_{16}N_2$	TETRYZOLINE	VASOCONSTRICTOR	MS
200.17763	$C_{12}H_{24}O_2$	ETHYL CAPRATE	FLAVORING	
	$C_{12}H_{24}O_2$	LAURIC ACID	ORGANIC ACID	
201.00958	$C_7H_7NO_4S$	CARZENIDE	ANTISPASMOTIC	
201.03607	$C_{10}H_7N_3S$	TIABENDAZOLE	ANTHELMINTIC	MS
201.07496	$C_7H_{11}N_3O_4$	MISONIDAZOLE	TRICHOMONACIDE	
201.07812	$C_7H_{12}N_5CL$	SIMAZINE	HERBICIDE	

MASS	FORMULA	NAME	CATEGORY	MS
201.07898	$C_{12}H_{11}NO_2$	CARBARYL	INSECTICIDE	
	$C_{12}H_{11}NO_2$	FENFURAM	FUNGIST./ANTIMYC.	
201.09021	$C_{11}H_{11}N_3O$	METAMFAZONE	ANALGESIC	
	$C_{11}H_{11}N_3O$	METHYLTETRAHYDROIMIDAZOQUINAZOLINONE	THROMB.AGGR.INHIB.	
201.12660	$C_{12}H_{15}N_3$	INDANAZOLINE	VASOCONSTRICTOR	
201.96294	$C_7H_7O_2BR$	BROMOSALIGENIN	ANTIPHLOGISTIC	
201.97814	$C_6H_3N_2O_4CL$	CHLORODINITROBENZENE	CHEMICAL	
201.99933	$C_8H_{11}OBR$	BROMETHINYLCYCLOHEXANOL	HYPNOTIC	
202.03967	$C_9H_{11}O_3CL$	CHLORPHENESIN	FUNGIST./ANTIMYC.	
202.05647	$C_{11}H_{10}N_2S$	ANTAFENIT	ANTHELMINTIC	
	$C_{11}H_{10}N_2S$	NAPHTHYLTHIOUREA	RODENTICIDE	
202.06300	$C_{12}H_{10}O_3$	NAPHTHOXYACETIC ACID	CHEMICAL	
202.07423	$C_{11}H_{10}N_2O_2$	TOLIMIDONE	TO THERAPY ULCERS	
202.08546	$C_{10}H_{10}N_4O$	METAMITRONE	HERBICIDE	
202.11061	$C_{12}H_{14}N_2O$	ACETRYPTIN	ANTIHYPERTENSIVE	
202.12051	$C_{10}H_{18}O_4$	SEBACIC ACID	CHEMICAL	
202.14700	$C_{13}H_{18}N_2$	DICARBIN	ANTIDEPRESSANT	
	$C_{13}H_{18}N_2$	MEDMAIN	SEROTONINE ANTAG.	
203.00353	$C_6H_{12}NCL_3$	TRICHLORMETHIN	CYTOSTATIC	
203.05018	$C_{12}H_{10}NCL$	AMINOCHLORODIPHENYL	CHEMICAL	
203.09463	$C_{12}H_{13}NO_2$	INDOLE BUTYRIC ACID	PLANT GROWTH REGU.	
	$C_{12}H_{13}NO_2$	MESUXIMIDE	ANTIEPILEPTIC	
203.09800	$C_9H_{17}NO_2S$	LETHANE	INSECTICIDE	
203.10586	$C_{11}H_{13}N_3O$	4-AMINO-PHENAZONE	ANALGESIC	MS
	$C_{11}H_{13}N_3O$	FEPROSIDNIN	STIMULANT	
203.13101	$C_{13}H_{17}NO$	CROTAMITON	PESTICIDE	MS
203.13439	$C_{10}H_{21}NOS$	PEBULATE	HERBICIDE	
	$C_{10}H_{21}NOS$	VERNOLATE	HERBICIDE	
203.16740	$C_{14}H_{21}N$	ETICYCLIDINE	STIMULANT	
204.00925	$C_7H_8O_5S$	GUAIACOLSULFONIC ACID	EXPECTORANT	
	$C_7H_8O_5S$	SULFOGAIACOL	EXPECTORANT	
204.02700	$C_7H_8O_7$	ANHYDROMETHYLENECITRIC ACID	PHARMACEUTICAL AID	
204.03419	$C_{12}H_9OCL$	PHENYLCHLOROPHENOL	FUNGIST./ANTIMYC.	
204.07212	$C_{11}H_{12}N_2S$	DEXAMISOLE	ANTIDEPRESSANT	
	$C_{11}H_{12}N_2S$	LEVAMISOLE	ANTIRHEUMATIC	
	$C_{11}H_{12}N_2S$	TETRAMISOLE	ANTHELMINTIC	
204.08988	$C_{11}H_{12}N_2O_2$	AMIQUINSIN	ANTIHYPERTENSIVE	
	$C_{11}H_{12}N_2O_2$	ETHOTOIN	ANTIEPILEPTIC	
	$C_{11}H_{12}N_2O_2$	FENOZOLONE	STIMULANT	
	$C_{11}H_{12}N_2O_2$	METAZAMIDE	ANALGESIC	
	$C_{11}H_{12}N_2O_2$	TOZALINONE	STIMULANT	
	$C_{11}H_{12}N_2O_2$	TRYPTOPHANE	AMINO ACID	MS
204.11101	$C_8H_{16}N_2O_4$	PENTABAMATE	TRANQUILIZER	
204.11234	$C_9H_{12}N_6$	TRETAMINE	CYTOSTATIC	
204.11503	$C_{13}H_{16}O_2$	BISBUTYLENETETRAHYDROFURFUROL	PESTICIDE	
204.12626	$C_{12}H_{16}N_2O$	BUFOTENINE	HALLUCINOGEN	
	$C_{12}H_{16}N_2O$	PSILOCIN	HALLUCINOGEN	
204.15142	$C_{14}H_{20}O$	BORNELONE	DERMATIC	
	$C_{14}H_{20}O$	CYCLOMENOL	ANTIBIOTIC	
204.17255	$C_{11}H_{24}O_3$	DIPUBROL	CHOLERETIC	
204.18378	$C_{10}H_{24}N_2O_2$	ETHAMBUTOL	TUBERCULOSTATIC	
204.18780	$C_{15}H_{24}$	CADINENE	CHOLERETIC	

MASS	FORMULA	NAME	CATEGORY	MS
204.18780	$C_{15}H_{24}$	CARYOPHYLLENE	NATURAL SUBSTANCE	
204.95198	$C_7H_5NSCL_2$	CHLORTHIAMIDE	HERBICIDE	
204.96974	$C_7H_5NO_2CL_2$	CHLORAMBEN	HERBICIDE	
204.99643	$C_7H_8NO_2CLS$	CHLORAMINE T	DESINFICIENT	
205.08513	$C_{10}H_{11}N_3O_2$	LOBENDAZOLE	ANTHELMINTIC	
205.13141	$C_9H_{19}NO_4$	PANTHENOL	DERMATIC	MS
205.13275	$C_{10}H_{15}N_5$	PHENFORMIN	ANTIDIABETIC	
	$C_{10}H_{15}N_5$	TRAPIDIL	CORONARY DILATOR	
205.14666	$C_{13}H_{19}NO$	AMFEPRAMONE	ANOREXIC	MS
205.96498	$C_6H_4N_2O_2CL_2$	DICHLORANE	FUNGIST./ANTIMYC.	
205.97311	$C_{10}H_7BR$	BROMONAPHTHALENE	CHEMICAL	
205.97453	$C_2H_8O_7P_2$	ETIDRONIC ACID	------------	
206.04352	$C_8H_{14}O_2S_2$	THIOCTIC ACID	PROTEC.LIVER THER.	
206.05791	$C_{11}H_{10}O_4$	HYDROXYMETHYLMETHOXYCHROMENONE	ANTIHIST./-ALLERG.	
206.06914	$C_{10}H_{10}N_2O_3$	CAROXAZONE	ANTIDEPRESSANT	
	$C_{10}H_{10}N_2O_3$	PARAXOZONE	------------	
206.08777	$C_{11}H_{14}N_2S$	DIMETHYLPHENYLTHIAZOLANIMIN	EXPECTORANT	MS
	$C_{11}H_{14}N_2S$	PYRANTEL	ANTHELMINTIC	
	$C_{11}H_{14}N_2S$	TIQUINAMIDE	TO THERAPY ULCERS	
206.09430	$C_{12}H_{14}O_3$	FUROFENAC	ANALGESIC	
206.10553	$C_{11}H_{14}N_2O_2$	ETHYLPHENACEMIDE	ANTIEPILEPTIC	
206.13068	$C_{13}H_{18}O_2$	IBUPROFEN	ANTIRHEUMATIC	
	$C_{13}H_{18}O_2$	PENTYL PHENYLACETATE	RUBEFACIENT	
206.14191	$C_{12}H_{18}N_2O$	ISOPROTURON	HERBICIDE	
	$C_{12}H_{18}N_2O$	OXOTREMORINE	CHEMICAL	
	$C_{12}H_{18}N_2O$	PIVALYLBENZHYDRAZINE	CORONARY DILATOR	
206.16707	$C_{14}H_{22}O$	IRONE	NATURAL SUBSTANCE	
206.17830	$C_{13}H_{22}N_2$	DICYCLOHEXYLCARBODIIMIDE	CHEMICAL	
207.01433	$C_7H_4NO_3F_3$	TFM	PESTICIDE	
207.02588	$C_7H_{14}NOBR$	IBROTAMIDE	HYPNOTIC	
207.04663	$C_9H_9N_3OS$	BENZTHIAZURONE	HERBICIDE	
207.08954	$C_{11}H_{13}NO_3$	HYDRASTININE	HEMOSTATIC	
	$C_{11}H_{13}NO_3$	NICOTAFURYL	RUBEFACIENT	
	$C_{11}H_{13}NO_3$	SALICYLOYLMORPHOLINE	CHOLERETIC	
	$C_{11}H_{13}NO_3$	TOLOXATONE	ANTIDEPRESSANT	
207.10078	$C_{10}H_{13}N_3O_2$	GUABENXAN	ANTIHYPERTENSIVE	
	$C_{10}H_{13}N_3O_2$	GUANOXAN	ANTIHYPERTENSIVE	
	$C_{10}H_{13}N_3O_2$	PHENYLETHYLSEMIOXAMAZIDE	CHEMICAL	
207.12593	$C_{12}H_{17}NO_2$	BUTACETIN	ANALGESIC	
	$C_{12}H_{17}NO_2$	CICLOPIROX	FUNGIST./ANTIMYC.	
	$C_{12}H_{17}NO_2$	HEXYLNICOTINATE	RUBEFACIENT	
	$C_{12}H_{17}NO_2$	PENTALAMIDE	FUNGIST./ANTIMYC.	
	$C_{12}H_{17}NO_2$	PROMECARB	INSECTICIDE	
207.13716	$C_{11}H_{17}N_3O$	MEOBENTIN	ANTIARRHYTHMIC	
207.93302	$C_6H_2O_4CL_2$	CHLORANILIC ACID	CHEMICAL	
208.01289	$C_9H_8N_2S_2$	ANTIENIT	ANTHELMINTIC	
208.01942	$C_{10}H_8O_3S$	NAPHTHALENESULFONIC ACID	CHEMICAL	
208.05243	$C_{14}H_8O_2$	ANTHRAQUINONE	PESTICIDE	
208.08479	$C_{10}H_{12}N_2O_3$	ALLOBARBITAL	HYPNOTIC	MS
	$C_{10}H_{12}N_2O_3$	KYNURENINE	AMINO ACID	
208.10005	$C_{14}H_{12}N_2$	BENDAZOL	VASODILATOR	
	$C_{14}H_{12}N_2$	BENZALDEHYDRAZIN	DERMATIC	

MASS	FORMULA	NAME	CATEGORY	MS
208.10005	$C_{14}H_{12}N_2$	NEOCUPROINE	DIAGNOSTIC AID	
208.10995	$C_{12}H_{16}O_3$	GUAIACOL VALERATE	CHEMICAL	
	$C_{12}H_{16}O_3$	ISOPENTYL SALICYLATE	RUBEFACIENT	
208.12118	$C_{11}H_{16}N_2O_2$	CARBENZID	ANTIDEPRESSANT	
	$C_{11}H_{16}N_2O_2$	PILOCARPINE	PARASYMP.-MIMETIC	
208.15756	$C_{12}H_{20}N_2O$	AMITEROL	BRONCHODILATOR	
209.07198	$C_{10}H_{12}N_3CL$	TOLONIDINE	ANTIHYPERTENSIVE	
209.09530	$C_{13}H_{11}N_3$	ACRIFLAVINE	DESINFICIENT	
	$C_{13}H_{11}N_3$	PROFLAVINE	DESINFICIENT	
209.10519	$C_{11}H_{15}NO_3$	BENZODIOXANYLAMINOPROPANOL	VASOCONSTRICTOR	
	$C_{11}H_{15}NO_3$	ETOSALAMIDE	ANALGESIC	
	$C_{11}H_{15}NO_3$	ISOPROPYLPHENYLMETHYLCARBAMATE	PESTICIDE	
	$C_{11}H_{15}NO_3$	LACTYLPHENETIDINE	ANALGESIC	MS
	$C_{11}H_{15}NO_3$	OXYFENAMATE	TRANQUILIZER	
	$C_{11}H_{15}NO_3$	PROPOXUR	INSECTICIDE	MS
209.12766	$C_9H_{15}N_5O$	MINOXIDIL	ANTIHYPERTENSIVE	
209.14158	$C_{12}H_{19}NO_2$	BAMETHAN	VASODILATOR	MS
	$C_{12}H_{19}NO_2$	DIMETHOXYMETHYLAMPHETAMINE	HALLUCINOGEN	
	$C_{12}H_{19}NO_2$	OCRILATE	ADHESIVE	
209.15281	$C_{11}H_{19}N_3O$	DIMETHIRIMOL	FUNGIST./ANTIMYC.	
	$C_{11}H_{19}N_3O$	ETHIRIMOL	FUNGIST./ANTIMYC.	
210.00339	$C_7H_6N_4S_2$	CITENAZONE	VIRUCIDE	
210.01644	$C_9H_6O_6$	TRIMELLITIC ACID	CHEMICAL	
210.01961	$C_9H_7N_2O_2CL$	CHLORACETAMINOBENZAXAZOL	URICOSURIC	
210.04293	$C_{12}H_6N_2O_2$	PHANQUINONE	ANTIBIOTIC	
210.04630	$C_9H_{10}N_2O_2S$	SULBENOX	------------	
	$C_9H_{10}N_2O_2S$	THIBENZAZOLINE	THYREOSTATIC	
210.05283	$C_{10}H_{10}O_5$	DIMETHOXYPHENYLGLYOXYLIC ACID	DERMATIC	
210.06808	$C_{14}H_{10}O_2$	BENZIL	CHEMICAL	MS
210.08921	$C_{11}H_{14}O_4$	GUAIACOLETHYLGLYCOLATE	EXPECTORANT	
210.09055	$C_{12}H_{10}N_4$	DIAMINOPHENAZINE	CHEMICAL	
210.10044	$C_{10}H_{14}N_2O_3$	APROBARBITAL	HYPNOTIC	MS
	$C_{10}H_{14}N_2O_3$	CROTYLBARBITAL	HYPNOTIC	MS
	$C_{10}H_{14}N_2O_3$	DOLCENTAL	HYPNOTIC	
	$C_{10}H_{14}N_2O_3$	BISHYDROXYETHYLNITROSOANILINE	CYTOSTATIC	
210.10447	$C_{15}H_{14}O$	FLAVANE	CHEMICAL	
	$C_{15}H_{14}O$	LACTAROVIOLIN	NATURAL SUBSTANCE	
210.11570	$C_{14}H_{14}N_2$	NAPHAZOLINE	VASOCONSTRICTOR	MS
210.15929	$C_9H_{18}N_6$	ALTRETAMINE	CYTOSTATIC	
210.17321	$C_{12}H_{22}N_2O$	PEXANTEL	ANTHELMINTIC	
211.02292	$C_7H_5N_3O_5$	NITROMIDE	ANTIBIOTIC	
211.04001	$C_{10}H_{10}NO_2CL$	CHLORTHENOXAZIN	ANALGESIC	
211.05931	$C_8H_9N_3O_4$	NICORANDIL	CORONARY DILATOR	
211.07639	$C_{11}H_{14}NOCL$	FENACLON	ANTIEPILEPTIC	
	$C_{11}H_{14}NOCL$	PROPACHLOR	HERBICIDE	
211.08446	$C_{10}H_{13}NO_4$	METHYLDOPA	ANTIHYPERTENSIVE	
211.11095	$C_{13}H_{13}N_3$	NITRIN	CHEMICAL	
211.11278	$C_{12}H_{18}NCL$	MEFENOREX	ANOREXIC	MS
211.12084	$C_{11}H_{17}NO_3$	DIMETANE	INSECTICIDE	
	$C_{11}H_{17}NO_3$	DIOXETHEDRINE	SYMPATHOMIMETIC	
	$C_{11}H_{17}NO_3$	ISOPRENALINE	SYMPATHOMIMETIC	MS
	$C_{11}H_{17}NO_3$	MESCALINE	HALLUCINOGEN	MS

MASS	FORMULA	NAME	CATEGORY	MS
211.12084	$C_{11}H_{17}NO_3$	METHOXAMINE	SYMPATHOMIMETIC	
	$C_{11}H_{17}NO_3$	ORCIPRENALINE	SYMPATHOMIMETIC	MS
211.13208	$C_{10}H_{17}N_3O_2$	ISOLAN	INSECTICIDE	
211.13610	$C_{15}H_{17}N$	BENETHAMINE	PHARMACEUTICAL AID	
	$C_{15}H_{17}N$	DIBEMETHINE	ANALGESIC	
211.14331	$C_9H_{17}N_5O$	ATRATONE	HERBICIDE	
211.95704	$C_4H_8N_2S_4$	MANEB	FUNGIST./ANTIMYC.	
	$C_4H_8N_2S_4$	NABAM	FUNGIST./ANTIMYC.	
	$C_4H_8N_2S_4$	ZINEB	FUNGIST./ANTIMYC.	
212.02402	$C_{10}H_9O_3CL$	CLORIDANIC ACID	CHOLERETIC	
212.03526	$C_9H_9N_2O_2CL$	CHLORPHENACEMIDE	ANTIEPILEPTIC	
212.06848	$C_{10}H_{12}O_5$	ASPERLIN	ANTIBIOTIC	
	$C_{10}H_{12}O_5$	GLYCEROL SALICYLATE	DERMATIC	
	$C_{10}H_{12}O_5$	PROPYL GALLATE	ANTIOXIDANT	
212.07164	$C_{10}H_{13}N_2OCL$	CHLORTOLURONE	HERBICIDE	
	$C_{10}H_{13}N_2OCL$	LOZILUREA	------------	
212.08373	$C_{14}H_{12}O_2$	BENZOIN	CHEMICAL	
	$C_{14}H_{12}O_2$	BENZYL BENZOATE	DESINFICIENT	
	$C_{14}H_{12}O_2$	CRESOL BENZOATE	DESINFICIENT	
212.09496	$C_{13}H_{12}N_2O$	BENZOYLPHENYLHYDRAZINE	FUNGIST./ANTIMYC.	
	$C_{13}H_{12}N_2O$	HARMINE	STIMULANT	
212.09834	$C_{10}H_{16}N_2OS$	ALBUTOIN	ANTIEPILEPTIC	
212.10486	$C_{11}H_{16}O_4$	GUAIETOLIN	EXPECTORANT	
212.10620	$C_{12}H_{12}N_4$	CHRYSOIDINE	DESINFICIENT	
	$C_{12}H_{12}N_4$	DIAMINOAZOBENZENE	DESINFICIENT	
212.11609	$C_{10}H_{16}N_2O_3$	BUTABARBITAL	HYPNOTIC	MS
	$C_{10}H_{16}N_2O_3$	BUTOBARBITAL	HYPNOTIC	MS
	$C_{10}H_{16}N_2O_3$	DIPROPYLBARBITAL	HYPNOTIC	MS
212.13135	$C_{14}H_{16}N_2$	ANILINOETHANE	CHEMICAL	
	$C_{14}H_{16}N_2$	TOLIDINE	CHEMICAL	
212.97482	$C_9H_5NOCL_2$	DICHLORCHINOLINOL	ANTIBIOTIC	
212.97892	C_8H_8NOBR	BROMOACETANILIDE	ANALGESIC	
213.00718	$C_5H_9N_3O_2CL_2$	CARMUSTINE	CYTOSTATIC	
213.02247	$C_5H_{12}NO_4SP$	OMETHOATE	INSECTICIDE	MS
213.05566	$C_{10}H_{12}NO_2CL$	BACLOFEN	ANTISPASMOTIC	
	$C_{10}H_{12}NO_2CL$	CARBANOLATE	INSECTICIDE	
	$C_{10}H_{12}NO_2CL$	CHLORPROPHAM	HERBICIDE	
213.07898	$C_{13}H_{11}NO_2$	BENZYL NICOTINATE	RUBEFACIENT	MS
	$C_{13}H_{11}NO_2$	SALICYLANILIDE	FUNGIST./ANTIMYC.	
213.09204	$C_{11}H_{16}NOCL$	CLORPRENALINE	SYMPATHOMIMETIC	
213.10011	$C_{10}H_{15}NO_4$	KAINIC ACID	ANTHELMINTIC	
213.10145	$C_{11}H_{11}N_5$	PHENAZOPYRIDINE	DESINFICIENT	MS
213.10482	$C_8H_{15}N_5S$	DESMETRYN	HERBICIDE	
213.12258	$C_8H_{15}N_5O_2$	OXDRALAZINE	ANTIHYPERTENSIVE	
213.12660	$C_{13}H_{15}N_3$	QUIPAZINE	------------	
213.14773	$C_{10}H_{19}N_3O_2$	GUANADREL	ANTIHYPERTENSIVE	
213.98707	$C_7H_6N_2O_2S_2$	HOLOMYCIN	ANTIBIOTIC	
214.01606	$C_6H_6N_4O_3S$	NIRIDAZOLE	ANTIBIOTIC	
214.02575	$C_7H_7N_4O_2CL$	8-CHLOROTHEOPHYLLINE	HYPNOTIC	MS
214.03967	$C_{10}H_{11}O_3CL$	CLOFIBRIC ACID	ANTICHOLESTEREMIC	MS
	$C_{10}H_{11}O_3CL$	MECOPROP	HERBICIDE	MS
214.04122	$C_8H_{10}N_2O_3S$	ACETYLSULFANILAMIDE	ANTIBIOTIC	MS

MASS	FORMULA	NAME	CATEGORY	MS
214.04122	$C_8H_{10}N_2O_3S$	SULFACETAMIDE	ANTIBIOTIC	
	$C_8H_{10}N_2O_3S$	TOLYLSULFONYLMETHYLNITROSAMIDE	CHEMICAL	
214.05091	$C_9H_{11}N_2O_2CL$	MONOLINURONE	HERBICIDE	
214.05245	$C_7H_{10}N_4O_2S$	SULFAGUANIDINE	ANTIBIOTIC	
214.06300	$C_{13}H_{10}O_3$	PHENYL SALICYLATE	DESINFICIENT	
214.06637	$C_{10}H_{14}O_3S$	TOLMESOXIDE	ANTIHYPERTENSIVE	
214.07606	$C_{11}H_{15}O_2CL$	METAGLYCODOL	TRANQUILIZER	
	$C_{11}H_{15}O_2CL$	PHENAGLYCODOL	TRANQUILIZER	
214.08883	$C_8H_{14}N_4OS$	METRIBUZIN	HERBICIDE	
214.11061	$C_{13}H_{14}N_2O$	FENYRAMIDOL	MUSCLE RELAXANT	
	$C_{13}H_{14}N_2O$	HARMALINE	STIMULANT	
	$C_{13}H_{14}N_2O$	METHOXYHARMALAN	SEROTONINE ANTAG.	
214.14700	$C_{14}H_{18}N_2$	TEFAZOLINE	VASOCONSTRICTOR	
214.15690	$C_{12}H_{22}O_3$	CICLATATE	ANTISPASMOTIC	
214.22967	$C_{14}H_{30}O$	MYRISTYL ALCOHOL	PHARMACEUTICAL AID	
214.97521	$C_5H_7NO_4CL_2$	DICHLOROACETYLSERINE	CYTOSTATIC	
215.02840	$C_8H_{10}N_3CLS$	TIAMENIDINE	ANTIHYPERTENSIVE	
215.03646	$C_7H_9N_3O_3S$	SULFACARBAMIDE	ANTIBIOTIC	
215.06948	$C_{11}H_9N_3O_2$	NAFTAZONE	HEMOSTATIC	
215.08071	$C_{10}H_9N_5O$	KINETIN	CHEMICAL	
215.09377	$C_8H_{14}N_5CL$	ATRAZINE	HERBICIDE	MS
215.09463	$C_{13}H_{13}NO_2$	ACETAMIDOMETHYLNAPHTHOL	VITAMINE	
215.10586	$C_{12}H_{13}N_3O$	FENYRIPOL	MUSCLE RELAXANT	
215.11875	$C_9H_{18}N_3OP$	METEPA	CHEMICAL	
215.13101	$C_{14}H_{17}NO$	PHENYLDIALLYLACETAMIDE	HYPNOTIC	
215.13439	$C_{11}H_{21}NOS$	CYCLOATE	HERBICIDE	
215.14225	$C_{13}H_{17}N_3$	TRAMAZOLINE	VASOCONSTRICTOR	
215.16740	$C_{15}H_{21}N$	FENCAMFAMINE	STIMULANT	MS
215.18853	$C_{12}H_{25}NO_2$	BUTOCTAMIDE	HYPNOTIC	
216.03171	$C_6H_8N_4O_3S$	NITHIAZIDE	TRICHOMONACIDE	
216.04226	$C_{12}H_8O_4$	AMMOIDIN	DERMATIC	
216.05687	$C_8H_{12}N_2O_3S$	AMINOPENICILLANIC ACID	ANTIBIOTIC	
216.06656	$C_9H_{13}N_2O_2CL$	TERBACIL	HERBICIDE	
216.07865	$C_{13}H_{12}O_3$	ALLENOLIC ACID	CHEMICAL	
	$C_{13}H_{12}O_3$	METHYLNAPHTHOXYACETATE	HERBICIDE	
	$C_{13}H_{12}O_3$	NAPHTHYL LACTATE	DESINFICIENT	
216.08988	$C_{12}H_{12}N_2O_2$	CYCLAZODONE	ANALGESIC	
	$C_{12}H_{12}N_2O_2$	FORMYLPHENAZONE	ANALGESIC	
	$C_{12}H_{12}N_2O_2$	TETRANTOIN	ANTIEPILEPTIC	
216.09325	$C_9H_{16}N_2O_2S$	TAZOLOL	BETA-ADR.BLOCKER	
216.09709	$C_6H_{12}N_6O_3$	TRIMETHYLOLMELAMINE	CYTOSTATIC	
216.11101	$C_9H_{16}N_2O_4$	BISORCIC	STIMULANT	
216.12626	$C_{13}H_{16}N_2O$	ADRENOGLOMERULOTROPIN	HORMONE	
	$C_{13}H_{16}N_2O$	OXANTEL	ANTHELMINTIC	
216.13616	$C_{11}H_{20}O_4$	ETHYL DIETHYLMALONATE	CHEMICAL	
216.97201	$C_6H_8NO_3AS$	ARSANILIC ACID	ANTIBIOTIC	
216.97384	$C_7H_8NO_2BR$	BROCRESINE	ENZYME INHIBITOR	
217.00612	$C_9H_9NOCL_2$	PROPANIL	HERBICIDE	
217.01918	$C_7H_{14}NCL_3$	NOVEMBICHIN	CYTOSTATIC	
217.02312	$C_8H_{11}NO_2S_2$	SULFANILYLETHANETHIOL	FUNGIST./ANTIMYC.	
217.04251	$C_{10}H_{13}NCL_2$	ANILINE MUSTARD	CHEMICAL	
217.06737	$C_{11}H_{11}N_3S$	TINAZOLIN	VASOCONSTRICTOR	

MASS	FORMULA	NAME	CATEGORY	MS
217.07727	$C_9H_{15}NO_3S$	CAPTOPRIL	ANTIHYPERTENSIVE	
217.09029	$C_{13}H_{12}NOF$	MNFA	INSECTICIDE	
217.11028	$C_{13}H_{15}NO_2$	FENIMIDE	TRANQUILIZER	
	$C_{13}H_{15}NO_2$	GLUTETHIMIDE	HYPNOTIC	MS
	$C_{13}H_{15}NO_2$	METHASTYRIDONE	ANTIDEPRESSANT	
	$C_{13}H_{15}NO_2$	OXOHEXAHYDROMETHANOFUROPYRIDOAZEPIN	TONIC	
	$C_{13}H_{15}NO_2$	PYRACARBOLID	FUNGIST./ANTIMYC.	
217.14666	$C_{14}H_{19}NO$	ETHOXYQUIN	ANTIOXIDANT	
217.15004	$C_{11}H_{23}NOS$	SUTAN	HERBICIDE	
217.18305	$C_{15}H_{23}N$	PROLINTANE	STIMULANT	
217.98851	$C_7H_6O_6S$	SULFOSALICYLIC ACID	CHEMICAL	
217.99803	$C_7H_7O_6P$	FOSFOSAL	ANALGESIC	
218.04984	$C_{13}H_{11}OCL$	CLOROFENE	DESINFICIENT	MS
218.06599	$C_7H_{14}N_4S_2$	METALLIBURE	HORMONE	
218.06914	$C_{11}H_{10}N_2O_3$	PHENYLMETHYLBARBITURIC ACID	ANTIEPILEPTIC	
218.07904	$C_9H_{14}O_6$	TRIACETIN	FUNGIST./ANTIMYC.	
218.10553	$C_{12}H_{14}N_2O_2$	IMINOPHENIMIDE	HYPNOTIC	
	$C_{12}H_{14}N_2O_2$	ISOPROPYLPHENYLHYDANTOIN	ANTIEPILEPTIC	
	$C_{12}H_{14}N_2O_2$	MEPHENYTOIN	ANTIEPILEPTIC	MS
	$C_{12}H_{14}N_2O_2$	METETOIN	ANTIEPILEPTIC	
	$C_{12}H_{14}N_2O_2$	PRIMIDONE	ANTIEPILEPTIC	MS
	$C_{12}H_{14}N_2O_2$	QUAZODINE	CARDIOTONIC	
218.10890	$C_9H_{18}N_2O_2S$	THIOFANOX	INSECTICIDE	
218.12666	$C_9H_{18}N_2O_4$	MEPROBAMATE	TRANQUILIZER	MS
218.14191	$C_{13}H_{18}N_2O$	FENOXAZOLINE	VASOCONSTRICTOR	
219.04107	$C_7H_{10}N_3O_3CL$	ORNIDAZOLE	TRICHOMONACIDE	
219.06776	$C_7H_{13}N_3O_3S$	OXAMYL	INSECTICIDE	
219.07728	$C_7H_{14}N_3O_3P$	UREDEPA	CYTOSTATIC	
219.10480	$C_{16}H_{13}N$	PHENYLNAPHTHYLAMINE	PRESERVATIVE	
219.11067	$C_9H_{17}NO_5$	PANTOTHENIC ACID	VITAMINE	
219.12593	$C_{13}H_{17}NO_2$	ALMINOPROFEN	ANALGESIC	
	$C_{13}H_{17}NO_2$	ENCYPRATE	ANTIDEPRESSANT	
	$C_{13}H_{17}NO_2$	PETHIDINE INTERMEDIATE	ANALGESIC	
219.16231	$C_{14}H_{21}NO$	PROFADOL	ANALGESIC	
	$C_{14}H_{21}NO$	ZYLOFURAMINE	STIMULANT	
219.94590	$C_4H_7O_4CL_2P$	DICHLORVOS	INSECTICIDE	MS
219.95731	$C_4H_7N_2O_2CL_3$	MECLORALUREA	TRANQUILIZER	
219.96940	$C_8H_6O_3CL_2$	DICAMBA	HERBICIDE	
	$C_8H_6O_3CL_2$	DICHLOROPHENOXYACETIC ACID (2.4-D)	HERBICIDE	MS
220.02911	$C_{12}H_9O_2CL$	SULPHENONE	PESTICIDE	
220.03718	$C_{11}H_8O_5$	PURPUROGALLIN	CHEMICAL	
220.08479	$C_{11}H_{12}N_2O_3$	HYDROXYTRYPTOPHAN	ENDOG.BIOMOLECULE	
220.10342	$C_{12}H_{16}N_2S$	MORANTEL	ANTHELMINTIC	
	$C_{12}H_{16}N_2S$	XYLAZINE	ANALGESIC	
220.10995	$C_{13}H_{16}O_3$	ETHYLETHOXYCINNAMATE	ANTISPASMOTIC	
	$C_{13}H_{16}O_3$	PIBECARB	HEMOSTATIC	
220.14633	$C_{14}H_{20}O_2$	BUTIBUFEN	ANALGESIC	
220.15756	$C_{13}H_{20}N_2O$	PRILOCAINE	LOCAL ANESTHETIC	MS
220.18272	$C_{15}H_{24}O$	DIBUTYLCRESOL	ANTIOXIDANT	
	$C_{15}H_{24}O$	IONOL	ANTIOXIDANT	MS
	$C_{15}H_{24}O$	SANTALOL	CHEMICAL	
221.03559	$C_{10}H_8N_3OCL$	PYRAZONE	HERBICIDE	

MASS	FORMULA	NAME	CATEGORY	MS
221.04682	$C_9H_8N_5CL$	CHLORAZANIL	DIURETIC	
221.06006	$C_{10}H_8N_3O_2F$	FLUOROPHENYLMETHYLNITROIMIDAZOLE	ANTIBIOTIC	
221.06228	$C_{10}H_{11}N_3OS$	METHABENZTHIAZURONE	HERBICIDE	
221.10519	$C_{12}H_{15}NO_3$	CARBOFURANE	INSECTICIDE	
	$C_{12}H_{15}NO_3$	METAXALONE	MUSCLE RELAXANT	
221.11643	$C_{11}H_{15}N_3O_2$	FORMETANATE	PESTICIDE	
	$C_{11}H_{15}N_3O_2$	PIVALIZID (TM)	TUBERCULOSTATIC	
221.14158	$C_{13}H_{19}NO_2$	BUFENCARB	INSECTICIDE	
	$C_{13}H_{19}NO_2$	BUTAMOXAN	TRANQUILIZER	
	$C_{13}H_{19}NO_2$	EXALAMIDE	FUNGIST./ANTIMYC.	
	$C_{13}H_{19}NO_2$	IBUPROXAM	ANALGESIC	
	$C_{13}H_{19}NO_2$	PHENAMAZIDE	ANTISPASMOTIC	
221.15281	$C_{12}H_{19}N_3O$	AMBONESTYL (TM)	ANTIARRHYTHMIC	
	$C_{12}H_{19}N_3O$	PROCARBAZINE	CYTOSTATIC	
221.17796	$C_{14}H_{23}NO$	AFFININ	INSECTICIDE	
221.88477	CH_3O_3IS	METHIODAL	DIAGNOSTIC AID	
221.98814	$C_4H_6N_4O_3S_2$	ACETAZOLAMIDE	DIURETIC	
222.00039	$C_6H_{11}N_2O_2BR$	BROMISOVAL	HYPNOTIC	MS
222.05283	$C_{11}H_{10}O_5$	GLADIOLIC ACID	FUNGIST./ANTIMYC.	
222.06743	$C_7H_{14}N_2O_4S$	BUTOXICARBOXIM	INSECTICIDE	
222.06808	$C_{15}H_{10}O_2$	FLAVONE	ANTISPASMOTIC	
	$C_{15}H_{10}O_2$	PHENYLINDANEDIONE	ANTICOAGULANT	
222.08519	$C_7H_{14}N_2O_6$	NITRAL	CORONARY DILATOR	
222.08921	$C_{12}H_{14}O_4$	APIOL	GYNECOL./OBSTRECT.	
	$C_{12}H_{14}O_4$	DIETHYL PHTHALATE	SOFTENER	MS
	$C_{12}H_{14}O_4$	DIMECROTIC ACID	CHOLERETIC	
	$C_{12}H_{14}O_4$	TETRAHYDROFURFURYL SALICYLATE	RUBEFACIENT	
222.10447	$C_{16}H_{14}O$	DYPNONE	DERMATIC	
222.11168	$C_{10}H_{14}N_4O_2$	MORINAMIDE	TUBERCULOSTATIC	
222.12291	$C_9H_{14}N_6O$	OXONAZIN	ANTIHYPERTENSIVE	
222.12560	$C_{13}H_{18}O_3$	HEXYL HYDROXYBENZOATE	DESINFICIENT	
	$C_{13}H_{18}O_3$	ISOPENTYL MANDELATE	ANTISPASMOTIC	
222.13683	$C_{12}H_{18}N_2O_2$	NICAMETATE	VASODILATOR	
	$C_{12}H_{18}N_2O_2$	ZECTRAN	INSECTICIDE	
222.14673	$C_{10}H_{22}O_5$	TETRAGLYME	SOLVENT	
222.17321	$C_{13}H_{22}N_2O$	NORURON	HERBICIDE	
222.19837	$C_{15}H_{26}O$	BISABOLOL	ANTIPHLOGISTIC	
	$C_{15}H_{26}O$	FARNESOL	NATURAL SUBSTANCE	
	$C_{15}H_{26}O$	GUAIOL	NATURAL SUBSTANCE	
	$C_{15}H_{26}O$	LEVOMENOL	ANTIPHLOGISTIC	
223.02562	$C_8H_{14}NCLS_2$	SULFALLATE	HERBICIDE	
223.03032	$C_{10}H_9NO_3S$	NAPHTHYLAMINESULFONIC ACID	HEMOSTATIC	
223.04001	$C_{11}H_{10}NO_2CL$	CHLORBUFAM	HERBICIDE	
223.05124	$C_{10}H_{10}N_3OCL$	CLAZOLIMINE	DIURETIC	
223.06096	$C_7H_{14}NO_5P$	AZODRIN	INSECTICIDE	
223.08446	$C_{11}H_{13}NO_4$	ACETYLTYROSINE	AMINO ACID	
	$C_{11}H_{13}NO_4$	BENDIOCARB	INSECTICIDE	
	$C_{11}H_{13}NO_4$	BENZACETIN	SEDATIVE	
	$C_{11}H_{13}NO_4$	DIOXACARB	INSECTICIDE	MS
	$C_{11}H_{13}NO_4$	MEPHENOXALONE	TRANQUILIZER	
223.10309	$C_{12}H_{17}NOS$	TILETAMINE	ANTIEPILEPTIC	
223.12084	$C_{12}H_{17}NO_3$	BUCETIN	ANALGESIC	MS

MASS	FORMULA	NAME	CATEGORY	MS
223.12084	$C_{12}H_{17}NO_3$	BUFEXAMAC	ANTIPHLOGISTIC	
	$C_{12}H_{17}NO_3$	BUTOXYETHYL NICOTINATE	RUBEFACIENT	
	$C_{12}H_{17}NO_3$	CERULENIN	FUNGIST./ANTIMYC.	
	$C_{12}H_{17}NO_3$	ETAMIVAN	RESPIRAT.STIMULANT	MS
	$C_{12}H_{17}NO_3$	NORBUDRINE	BRONCHODILATOR	
	$C_{12}H_{17}NO_3$	PHENISONONE	SYMPATHOMIMETIC	
	$C_{12}H_{17}NO_3$	RIMITEROL	BRONCHODILATOR	
223.15723	$C_{13}H_{21}NO_2$	DIMOXAMINE	STIMULANT	
	$C_{13}H_{21}NO_2$	GUAIACTAMINE	ANTISPASMOTIC	
	$C_{13}H_{21}NO_2$	TIGLOIDINE	ANTIPARKINSONIAN	
	$C_{13}H_{21}NO_2$	TOLIPROLOL	BETA-ADR.BLOCKER	MS
	$C_{13}H_{21}NO_2$	TROPIGLINE	ANTIPARKINSONIAN	
223.91986	$C_7H_3O_2CL_3$	TRICHLOROBENZOIC ACID	HERBICIDE	
224.01433	$C_{10}H_8O_4S$	NAPHTHOLSULFONIC ACID	CHEMICAL	
224.04498	$C_7H_{13}O_6P$	MEVINPHOS	INSECTICIDE	
224.05456	$C_8H_8N_4O_4$	NIFURADENE	ANTIBIOTIC	
224.09094	$C_9H_{12}N_4O_3$	ETOFYLLINE	CORONARY DILATOR	MS
224.10486	$C_{12}H_{16}O_4$	ASPIDINOL	ANTHELMINTIC	
	$C_{12}H_{16}O_4$	FEPENTOLIC ACID	CHOLERETIC	
224.11609	$C_{11}H_{16}N_2O_3$	BUTALBITAL	HYPNOTIC	MS
	$C_{11}H_{16}N_2O_3$	ENALLYPROPYMAL	NARCOTIC	
	$C_{11}H_{16}N_2O_3$	IDOBUTAL	HYPNOTIC	MS
	$C_{11}H_{16}N_2O_3$	NIFENALOL	BETA-ADR.BLOCKER	MS
	$C_{11}H_{16}N_2O_3$	TALBUTAL	HYPNOTIC	MS
	$C_{11}H_{16}N_2O_3$	VINBARBITAL	HYPNOTIC	MS
	$C_{11}H_{16}N_2O_3$	VINYLBITAL	HYPNOTIC	MS
224.14125	$C_{13}H_{20}O_3$	FEBUPROL	ANTICHOLESTEREMIC	
224.15248	$C_{12}H_{20}N_2O_2$	ISOMOXOLE	BRONCHODILATOR	
224.96367	$C_5H_8NO_4BR$	NIBROXANE	ANALGESIC	
225.00958	$C_9H_7NO_4S$	QUINOLINOLSULFONIC ACID	DESINFICIENT	
225.01927	$C_{10}H_8NO_3CL$	SECLAZONE	ANTIPHLOGISTIC	
225.03857	$C_8H_7N_3O_5$	DINITOLMIDE	COCCIDIOSTATIC	
	$C_8H_7N_3O_5$	FURAZOLIDONE	ANTIBIOTIC	
225.07496	$C_9H_{11}N_3O_4$	ANCITABIN	CYTOSTATIC	
225.08235	$C_{11}H_{15}NO_2S$	ETHIOFENCARB	INSECTICIDE	
	$C_{11}H_{15}NO_2S$	MERCAPTODIMETHUR	INSECTICIDE	
225.08619	$C_8H_{11}N_5O_3$	ACICLOVIR	VIRUCIDE	
225.09021	$C_{13}H_{11}N_3O$	TINUVIN P	CHEMICAL	
225.10011	$C_{11}H_{15}NO_4$	MEPHENESIN CARBAMATE	MUSCLE RELAXANT	
225.13649	$C_{12}H_{19}NO_3$	COLTEROL	BRONCHODILATOR	
	$C_{12}H_{19}NO_3$	PRENALTEROL	SYMPATHOMIMETIC	
	$C_{12}H_{19}NO_3$	TERBUTALINE	SYMPATHOMIMETIC	
225.15175	$C_{16}H_{19}N$	LEFETAMINE	ANALGESIC	
	$C_{16}H_{19}N$	POLYCAINE	LOCAL ANESTHETIC	
225.15896	$C_{10}H_{19}N_5O$	PROMETONE	HERBICIDE	
	$C_{10}H_{19}N_5O$	SECBUMETONE	HERBICIDE	
	$C_{10}H_{19}N_5O$	TERBUMETONE	HERBICIDE	
225.18411	$C_{12}H_{23}N_3O$	ESAPRAZOL	------------	
225.95884	$C_{10}H_4O_2CL_2$	DICHLONE	FUNGIST./ANTIMYC.	
225.96931	$C_8H_6N_2S_3$	OLTIPRAZ	ANTIBIOTIC	
225.97269	$C_5H_{10}N_2S_4$	PROPINEB	FUNGIST./ANTIMYC.	
226.02730	$C_6H_6N_6O_2S$	METHYLNITROIMIDAZOLYLAMINOTHIADIAZOL	ANTIBIOTIC	

MASS	FORMULA	NAME	CATEGORY	MS
226.03382	$C_7H_6N_4O_5$	NIFURALDEZONE	ANTIBIOTIC	
226.03967	$C_{11}H_{11}O_3CL$	ALCLOFENAC	ANALGESIC	
226.05091	$C_{10}H_{11}N_2O_2CL$	AMINOCHLORTHENOXAZIN	ANALGESIC	
226.06300	$C_{14}H_{10}O_3$	ANTHRAROBIN	PESTICIDE	
	$C_{14}H_{10}O_3$	DITHRANOL	DESINFICIENT	
226.06887	$C_7H_{14}O_8$	GLUCOHEPTONIC ACID	ORGANIC ACID	
226.07021	$C_8H_{10}N_4O_4$	NIFURSEMIZONE	ANTIBIOTIC	
226.07760	$C_{10}H_{14}N_2O_2S$	METHALLATAL	SEDATIVE	
226.09536	$C_{10}H_{14}N_2O_4$	ALLYLHYDROXYPROPYLBARBITURIC ACID	ANALGESIC	
	$C_{10}H_{14}N_2O_4$	CARBIDOPA	ANTIPARKINSONIAN	MS
	$C_{10}H_{14}N_2O_4$	VALOFAN	ANALGESIC	
226.09669	$C_{11}H_{10}N_6$	BENTEMAZOLE	------------	
226.10659	$C_9H_{14}N_4O_3$	NIMORAZOLE	TRICHOMONACIDE	
226.11061	$C_{14}H_{14}N_2O$	METYRAPONE	DIAGNOSTIC AID	
226.11244	$C_{13}H_{19}OCL$	CHLORHEPTYLPHENOL	DESINFICIENT	
226.11399	$C_{11}H_{18}N_2OS$	TAMITINOL	STIMULANT	
226.12051	$C_{12}H_{18}O_4$	BUTOPYRONOXYL	PESTICIDE	
226.13174	$C_{11}H_{18}N_2O_3$	AMOBARBITAL	HYPNOTIC	MS
	$C_{11}H_{18}N_2O_3$	PENTOBARBITAL	HYPNOTIC	MS
226.14700	$C_{15}H_{18}N_2$	PIRLINDOL	ANTIDEPRESSANT	
226.16813	$C_{12}H_{22}N_2O_2$	CROTETAMIDE	RESPIRAT.STIMULANT	MS
226.99047	$C_{10}H_7NOCL_2$	CHLORQUINALDOL	DESINFICIENT	
227.00258	$C_3H_5N_3O_9$	NITROGLYCEROL	CORONARY DILATOR	
227.01784	$C_7H_5N_3O_6$	TRINITROTOLUENE	CHEMICAL	
227.05172	$C_{12}H_9N_3S$	THIONINE	ANTIOXIDANT	
227.05580	$C_{11}H_8NOF_3$	FLUCARBRIL	MUSCLE RELAXANT	
227.07131	$C_{11}H_{14}NO_2CL$	BUCLOSAMIDE	FUNGIST./ANTIMYC.	
227.09463	$C_{14}H_{13}NO_2$	DIPHENANE	ANTHELMINTIC	
	$C_{14}H_{13}NO_2$	PAXAMATE	ANTIPHLOGISTIC	
227.10769	$C_{12}H_{18}NOCL$	ETOLEREX	ANOREXIC	
	$C_{12}H_{18}NOCL$	TULOBUTEROL	BRONCHODILATOR	
227.11576	$C_{11}H_{17}NO_4$	DIMETOFRINE	SYMPATHOMIMETIC	
227.12047	$C_9H_{17}N_5S$	AMETRYNE	HERBICIDE	
227.16740	$C_{16}H_{21}N$	MORPHINAN	CHEMICAL	
227.18853	$C_{13}H_{25}NO_2$	CYPRODENATE	STIMULANT	
227.23615	$C_{13}H_{29}N_3$	DODIN	FUNGIST./ANTIMYC.	
227.89128	$C_2H_4O_4CL_3P$	TRICLOFOS	HYPNOTIC	
228.00272	$C_8H_8N_2O_2S_2$	THIOLUTIN (TM)	ANTIBIOTIC	
228.01498	$C_{10}H_{13}OBR$	BROMOTHYMOL	ANTHELMINTIC	
228.03017	$C_9H_9N_2O_3CL$	BENURESTATE	ENZYME INHIBITOR	
228.04900	$C_7H_{16}O_4S_2$	SULFONAL	HYPNOTIC	
228.05532	$C_{11}H_{13}O_3CL$	MCPB	HERBICIDE	MS
228.06089	$C_{14}H_{12}OS$	TIBENZATE	INSECTICIDE	
228.06656	$C_{10}H_{13}N_2O_2CL$	METOXURONE	HERBICIDE	
228.07212	$C_{13}H_{12}N_2S$	ANTIGASTRIN	ENZYME INHIBITOR	
228.07865	$C_{14}H_{12}O_3$	BENZYL HYDROXYBENZOATE	DESINFICIENT	
	$C_{14}H_{12}O_3$	BENZYL SALICYLATE	RUBEFACIENT	
	$C_{14}H_{12}O_3$	OXYBENZONE	DERMATIC	
	$C_{14}H_{12}O_3$	TOLYL SALICYLATE	DESINFICIENT	
	$C_{14}H_{12}O_3$	TRIOXYSALEN	DERMATIC	
228.09171	$C_{12}H_{17}O_2CL$	FENPENTADIOL	TRANQUILIZER	
228.09325	$C_{10}H_{16}N_2O_2S$	THIOBUTABARBITAL	NARCOTIC	MS

MASS	FORMULA	NAME	CATEGORY	MS
228.10448	$C_9H_{16}N_4OS$	TEBUTHIURONE	HERBICIDE	
228.11503	$C_{15}H_{16}O_2$	BISPHENOL A	FUNGIST./ANTIMYC.	MS
228.12626	$C_{14}H_{16}N_2O$	COUMAZOLIN	VASOCONSTRICTOR	
228.16265	$C_{15}H_{20}N_2$	INDALPIN	ANTIDEPRESSANT	
228.20893	$C_{14}H_{28}O_2$	HEPTYL HEPTANOATE	FUNGIST./ANTIMYC.	
	$C_{14}H_{28}O_2$	MYRISTIC ACID	DERMATIC	MS
228.97384	$C_8H_8NO_2BR$	BROSOTAMIDE	ANTIEPILEPTIC	
228.97867	$C_9H_8NCLS_2$	NIMIDANE	PESTICIDE	
228.99710	$C_6H_3N_3O_7$	PICRIC ACID	DESINFICIENT	
228.99963	$C_5H_{12}NO_3S_2P$	DIMETHOATE	INSECTICIDE	MS
229.00612	$C_{10}H_9NOCL_2$	DICRYL	HERBICIDE	
229.01735	$C_9H_9N_3CL_2$	CLONIDINE	ANTIHYPERTENSIVE	MS
229.04789	$C_6H_8N_7OCL$	AMILORIDE	DIURETIC	
229.05211	$C_8H_{11}N_3O_3S$	DEXONE	FUNGIST./ANTIMYC.	
229.05864	$C_9H_{11}NO_6$	SHOWDOMYCIN	ANTIBIOTIC	
229.07389	$C_{13}H_{11}NO_3$	FAGARINE	ANTIARRHYTHMIC	
	$C_{13}H_{11}NO_3$	FENAMISAL	TUBERCULOSTATIC	
	$C_{13}H_{11}NO_3$	GUAIACOL NICOTINATE	RUBEFACIENT	
	$C_{13}H_{11}NO_3$	OSALMID	CHOLERETIC	
229.08513	$C_{12}H_{11}N_3O_2$	FURONAZIDE	TUBERCULOSTATIC	
	$C_{12}H_{11}N_3O_2$	INF	TUBERCULOSTATIC	
229.10942	$C_9H_{16}N_5CL$	PROPAZIN	HERBICIDE	
	$C_9H_{16}N_5CL$	TERBUTYLAZIN	HERBICIDE	
	$C_9H_{16}N_5CL$	TRIETAZINE	HERBICIDE	
229.11028	$C_{14}H_{15}NO_2$	ACEQUINOLINE	ANALGESIC	
	$C_{14}H_{15}NO_2$	METHFUROXAM	FUNGIST./ANTIMYC.	
229.14666	$C_{15}H_{19}NO$	FURFENOREX	ANOREXIC	
229.99168	$C_8H_7N_2O_2CLS$	DIAZOXIDE	ANTIHYPERTENSIVE	
230.01260	$C_8H_8N_4CL_2$	GUANABENZ	ANTIHYPERTENSIVE	
230.02003	$C_6H_{15}O_3S_2P$	METHYLDEMETON	INSECTICIDE	MS
230.03063	$C_{10}H_{15}OBR$	BROMOCAMPHOR	SEDATIVE	
230.03613	$C_8H_{10}N_2O_4S$	ASULAM	HERBICIDE	
230.05791	$C_{13}H_{10}O_4$	VISNAGIN	NATURAL SUBSTANCE	
230.06670	$C_{10}H_9N_2OF_3$	FLUMINOREX	ANOREXIC	
230.08777	$C_{13}H_{14}N_2S$	METIZOLINE	VASOCONSTRICTOR	
230.09430	$C_{14}H_{14}O_3$	KAVAIN	MUSCLE RELAXANT	MS
	$C_{14}H_{14}O_3$	NAPROXEN	ANALGESIC	
	$C_{14}H_{14}O_3$	PINDONE	RODENTICIDE	
230.10553	$C_{13}H_{14}N_2O_2$	METOMIDATE	HYPNOTIC	
230.13068	$C_{15}H_{18}O_2$	TETRIPROFEN	ANTIPHLOGISTIC	
230.14191	$C_{14}H_{18}N_2O$	PROPYPHENAZONE	ANALGESIC	MS
230.15181	$C_{12}H_{22}O_4$	DIISOPROPYL ADIPATE	DERMATIC	
230.17830	$C_{15}H_{22}N_2$	ETAMINIL	ANTITUSSIVE	
230.22458	$C_{14}H_{30}O_2$	GEMCADIOL	ANTICHOLESTEREMIC	
230.90053	$C_3N_3O_3CL_3$	SYMCLOSENE	DESINFICIENT	
231.01362	$C_7H_9N_3O_2S_2$	SULFATHIOUREA	ANTIBIOTIC	
231.03138	$C_7H_9N_3O_4S$	ISONIAZID METHANESULFONATE	TUBERCULOSTATIC	
231.05653	$C_9H_{13}NO_4S$	PHENETIDINOMETHANESULFONIC ACID	ANTIRHEUMATIC	
231.06439	$C_{11}H_9N_3O_3$	NITRAFUDAM	ANTIDEPRESSANT	
231.08710	$C_{11}H_{12}NOF_3$	FLUMEXADOL	ANALGESIC	
231.10078	$C_{12}H_{13}N_3O_2$	ISOCARBOXAZID	ANTIDEPRESSANT	
	$C_{12}H_{13}N_3O_2$	TRIAZIQUONE	CYTOSTATIC	

MASS	FORMULA	NAME	CATEGORY	MS
231.12348	$C_{12}H_{16}F_3N$	FENFLURAMINE	ANOREXIC	MS
231.12593	$C_{14}H_{17}NO_2$	BENZOCLIDINE	ANTISPASMOTIC	
	$C_{14}H_{17}NO_2$	INDELOXAZIN	ANTIDEPRESSANT	
231.13716	$C_{13}H_{17}N_3O$	AMINOPHENAZONE	ANALGESIC	MS
231.16231	$C_{15}H_{21}NO$	METAZOCINE	ANALGESIC	
	$C_{15}H_{21}NO$	TOFETRIDIN	ANALGESIC	
232.00579	$C_{10}H_{10}O_2CL_2$	CHLORPHENPROP-METHYL	HERBICIDE	
232.01702	$C_9H_{10}N_2OCL_2$	DIURON	HERBICIDE	MS
232.05964	$C_{10}H_8N_4O_3$	NIFURPRAZINE	DESINFICIENT	
232.06704	$C_{12}H_{12}N_2OS$	SULFINYLDIANILINE	ANTIBIOTIC	
232.07693	$C_{10}H_{16}O_4S$	CAMPHORSULFONIC ACID	RESPIRAT.STIMULANT	
232.08235	$C_{10}H_{11}N_2OF_3$	FLUOMETURON	HERBICIDE	
232.08479	$C_{12}H_{12}N_2O_3$	NALIDIXIC ACID	ANTIBIOTIC	
	$C_{12}H_{12}N_2O_3$	PHENOBARBITAL	HYPNOTIC	MS
232.08930	$C_{14}H_{15}NCL$	CHLORNAPHAZINE	CYTOSTATIC	
232.09603	$C_{11}H_{12}N_4O_2$	MOLINAZONE	ANALGESIC	
	$C_{11}H_{12}N_4O_2$	PANIDAZOLE	ANTIBIOTIC	
232.12118	$C_{13}H_{16}N_2O_2$	AMINOGLUTETHIMIDE	ANTIEPILEPTIC	
	$C_{13}H_{16}N_2O_2$	BUTYLPHENYLHYDANTOIN	ANTIEPILEPTIC	
	$C_{13}H_{16}N_2O_2$	MOFEBUTAZONE	ANALGESIC	
232.14231	$C_{10}H_{20}N_2O_4$	MEBUTAMATE	TRANQUILIZER	
232.14633	$C_{15}H_{20}O_2$	ALANTOLACTONE	ANTHELMINTIC	
	$C_{15}H_{20}O_2$	HEXAPROFEN	ANALGESIC	
	$C_{15}H_{20}O_2$	ISOPROFEN	ANTIPHLOGISTIC	
232.15756	$C_{14}H_{20}N_2O$	APTOCAINE	LOCAL ANESTHETIC	
	$C_{14}H_{20}N_2O$	PSILOCIN-ETH	HALLUCINOGEN	
	$C_{14}H_{20}N_2O$	PYRROCAINE	LOCAL ANESTHETIC	
	$C_{14}H_{20}N_2O$	SIDURON	HERBICIDE	
	$C_{14}H_{20}N_2O$	TYMAZOLINE	VASOCONSTRICTOR	
233.00104	$C_9H_9NO_2CL_2$	DILOXANIDE	ANTIBIOTIC	
233.05489	$C_9H_7N_5O_3$	FURALAZIN	DESINFICIENT	
233.09311	$C_9H_{16}N_3O_2CL$	LOMUSTINE	CYTOSTATIC	
233.10275	$C_{11}H_{14}NOF_3$	FLUDOREX	ANOREXIC	
233.10519	$C_{13}H_{15}NO_3$	MECARBINATE	ANTIHYPERTENSIVE	
233.11643	$C_{12}H_{15}N_3O_2$	BENZOFURYLOXYPROPYLGUANIDINE	ANTIHYPERTENSIVE	
233.14158	$C_{14}H_{19}NO_2$	METHYLPHENIDATE	STIMULANT	MS
	$C_{14}H_{19}NO_2$	PETHIDINE INTERMEDIATE	ANALGESIC	
	$C_{14}H_{19}NO_2$	PHACETOPERANE	STIMULANT	
	$C_{14}H_{19}NO_2$	PIPEROXAN	DIAGNOSTIC AID	
233.17796	$C_{15}H_{23}NO$	MEPTAZINOL	ANALGESIC	
233.81312	C_2CL_6	HEXACHLOROETHANE	ANTHELMINTIC	
233.84465	$C_3H_5CLBR_2$	DIBROMOCHLOROPROPANE	NEMATOCIDE	
233.97049	$C_5H_{12}O_2CLS_2P$	CHLORMEPHOS	INSECTICIDE	
233.98505	$C_9H_8O_3CL_2$	DICHLORPROP	HERBICIDE	MS
233.98659	$C_7H_7N_2O_3CLS$	SULCLAMIDE	DIURETIC	
233.99216	$C_{10}H_6N_2OS_2$	QUINOMETHIONATE	FUNGIST./ANTIMYC.	
234.00039	$C_7H_{11}N_2O_2BR$	BROMACRYLIDE	CYTOSTATIC	
234.05753	$C_{10}H_{10}N_4OS$	METISAZONE	VIRUCIDE	
234.07529	$C_{10}H_{10}N_4O_3$	DRAZIDOX	DESINFICIENT	
234.10044	$C_{12}H_{14}N_2O_3$	CYCLOPENTOBARBITAL	HYPNOTIC	MS
	$C_{12}H_{14}N_2O_3$	DIPROQUALONE	ANALGESIC	
234.10447	$C_{17}H_{14}O$	DIBENZALACETONE	DERMATIC	

MASS	FORMULA	NAME	CATEGORY	MS
234.11168	$C_{11}H_{14}N_4O_2$	EPIRIZOLE	ANALGESIC	
234.13683	$C_{13}H_{18}N_2O_2$	LENACIL	HERBICIDE	
234.17321	$C_{14}H_{22}N_2O$	AMPLICAINE	LOCAL ANESTHETIC	
	$C_{14}H_{22}N_2O$	LIDOCAINE	LOCAL ANESTHETIC	MS
	$C_{14}H_{22}N_2O$	OCTACAINE	LOCAL ANESTHETIC	
	$C_{14}H_{22}N_2O$	QUATACAINE	LOCAL ANESTHETIC	
234.20960	$C_{15}H_{26}N_2$	SPARTEINE	ANTIARRHYTHMIC	MS
234.95698	$C_5H_8NO_3CL_3$	CARBOCLORAL	HYPNOTIC	
234.97061	$C_7H_6NO_4CLS$	MONALAZON	DESINFICIENT	
235.06670	$C_{12}H_{13}NO_2S$	CARBOXIN	FUNGIST./ANTIMYC.	
	$C_{12}H_{13}NO_2S$	DOLITRONE	ANALGESIC	
	$C_{12}H_{13}NO_2S$	PHENYTHILONE	ANTISPASMOTIC	
235.09971	$C_{16}H_{13}NO$	CITENAMIDE	ANTIEPILEPTIC	
235.12084	$C_{13}H_{17}NO_3$	ROMIFENONE	DESINFICIENT	
235.13610	$C_{17}H_{17}N$	AZAPETINE	VASODILATOR	
235.15723	$C_{14}H_{21}NO_2$	AMYLOCAINE	LOCAL ANESTHETIC	
	$C_{14}H_{21}NO_2$	CARMANTADINE	ANTIPARKINSONIAN	
	$C_{14}H_{21}NO_2$	MEPRYLCAINE	LOCAL ANESTHETIC	
	$C_{14}H_{21}NO_2$	PADIMATE A	DERMATIC	
	$C_{14}H_{21}NO_2$	PENTAMOXAN	TRANQUILIZER	
235.16846	$C_{13}H_{21}N_3O$	PROCAINAMIDE	LOCAL ANESTHETIC	MS
235.94729	$C_{10}H_5O_2BR$	BROMONAPHTHOQUINONE	VIRUCIDE	
235.95366	$C_9H_4N_2S_3$	QUINOTHIONATE	PESTICIDE	
236.00379	$C_5H_8N_4O_3S_2$	METHAZOLAMIDE	ENZYME INHIBITOR	
	$C_5H_8N_4O_3S_2$	PROPAZOLAMIDE	DIURETIC	
236.01604	$C_7H_{13}N_2O_2BR$	CARBROMAL	HYPNOTIC	MS
236.02807	$C_6H_8N_2O_8$	ISOSORBIDE DINITRATE	CORONARY DILATOR	
236.07164	$C_{12}H_{13}N_2OCL$	BUTURONE	HERBICIDE	
236.07318	$C_{10}H_{12}N_4OS$	THIOACETAZONE	TUBERCULOSTATIC	
236.09094	$C_{10}H_{12}N_4O_3$	CARBAZOCHROME	HEMOSTATIC	
236.09496	$C_{15}H_{12}N_2O$	BENHEPAZONE	ANALGESIC	
	$C_{15}H_{12}N_2O$	CARBAMAZEPINE	ANTIEPILEPTIC	MS
236.11609	$C_{12}H_{16}O_3N_2$	CARBETAMIDE	HERBICIDE	
	$C_{12}H_{16}N_2O_3$	CYCLOBARBITAL	HYPNOTIC	MS
	$C_{12}H_{16}N_2O_3$	HEXOBARBITAL	HYPNOTIC	MS
236.12012	$C_{17}H_{16}O$	XENIPENTONE	ANTIPHLOGISTIC	
236.15248	$C_{13}H_{20}N_2O_2$	BUTETHAMINE	LOCAL ANESTHETIC	
	$C_{13}H_{20}N_2O_2$	DROPROPIZINE	ANTITUSSIVE	
	$C_{13}H_{20}N_2O_2$	METABUTETHAMINE	LOCAL ANESTHETIC	
	$C_{13}H_{20}N_2O_2$	PROCAINE	LOCAL ANESTHETIC	MS
	$C_{13}H_{20}N_2O_2$	SALETAMIDE	ANALGESIC	
237.03051	$C_{10}H_8N_3O_2CL$	DRAZOXOLON	FUNGIST./ANTIMYC.	
237.04174	$C_9H_8N_5OCL$	CLOGUANAMIL	ANTIBIOTIC	
237.07661	$C_8H_{16}NO_5P$	BIDRIN	INSECTICIDE	
237.07967	$C_8H_{11}N_7S$	AMBAZONE	DESINFICIENT	
237.08619	$C_9H_{11}N_5O_3$	BIOPTERIN	ENDOG.BIOMOLECULE	
237.09204	$C_{13}H_{16}NOCL$	KETAMINE	ANALGESIC	MS
237.10011	$C_{12}H_{15}NO_4$	CINTRAMIDE	TRANQUILIZER	
	$C_{12}H_{15}NO_4$	COTARNINE	HEMOSTATIC	
	$C_{12}H_{15}NO_4$	ETHOPABATE	ANTIBIOTIC	
237.11536	$C_{16}H_{15}NO$	CYHEPTAMIDE	ANTIEPILEPTIC	
237.13649	$C_{13}H_{19}NO_3$	DETANOSAL	ANALGESIC	

MASS	FORMULA	NAME	CATEGORY	MS
237.13649	$C_{13}H_{19}NO_3$	METAMIVAN	RESPIRAT.STIMULANT	
	$C_{13}H_{19}NO_3$	QUILOFLEX (TM)	MUSCLE RELAXANT	
	$C_{13}H_{19}NO_3$	VILOXAZINE	ANTIDEPRESSANT	MS
237.15175	$C_{17}H_{19}N$	DIMEFADANE	ANALGESIC	
	$C_{17}H_{19}N$	ETIFELMIN	SYMPATHOMIMETIC	MS
	$C_{17}H_{19}N$	TAMETRALINE	ANTIDEPRESSANT	
237.17288	$C_{14}H_{23}NO_2$	PIROCTONE	DERMATIC	
237.93551	$C_8H_5O_2CL_3$	FENAC	HERBICIDE	
238.03382	$C_8H_6N_4O_5$	NITROFURANTOIN	ANTIBIOTIC	
238.04774	$C_{11}H_{10}O_6$	DIPYROCETYL	ANTIRHEUMATIC	
238.07021	$C_9H_{10}N_4O_4$	ACEFYLLINE	CORONARY DILATOR	
	$C_9H_{10}N_4O_4$	NIFURIMIDE	ANTIBIOTIC	
	$C_9H_{10}N_4O_4$	THEOBROMINEACETIC ACID	CORONARY DILATOR	
	$C_9H_{10}N_4O_4$	THEOPHYLLINEACETIC ACID	CORONARY DILATOR	
238.08413	$C_{12}H_{14}O_5$	CINAMETIC ACID	CHOLERETIC	
238.09536	$C_{11}H_{14}N_2O_4$	NITROPROPOXYACETANILIDE	ANALGESIC	
238.09938	$C_{16}H_{14}O_2$	BENZYL CINNAMATE	DESINFICIENT	
238.10659	$C_{10}H_{14}N_4O_3$	PROTHEOBROMINE	CORONARY DILATOR	
	$C_{10}H_{14}N_4O_3$	PROXYPHYLLINE	CORONARY DILATOR	
238.11061	$C_{15}H_{14}N_2O$	DOXENITOIN	ANTIEPILEPTIC	
238.12051	$C_{13}H_{18}O_4$	FELOGEN	CHOLERETIC	
238.12185	$C_{14}H_{14}N_4$	ROLODINE	MUSCLE RELAXANT	
238.13174	$C_{12}H_{18}N_2O_3$	NEALBARBITAL	HYPNOTIC	MS
	$C_{12}H_{18}N_2O_3$	SECOBARBITAL	HYPNOTIC	MS
238.14298	$C_{11}H_{18}N_4O_2$	PRIMICARB	INSECTICIDE	
238.14700	$C_{16}H_{18}N_2$	METAPRAMINE	ANTIDEPRESSANT	
	$C_{16}H_{18}N_2$	NOMIFENSINE	ANTIDEPRESSANT	MS
238.95746	$C_7H_7NO_2CL_2S$	DICHLORAMINE T	PESTICIDE	
239.03492	$C_{11}H_{10}NO_3CL$	MESECLAZONE	ANALGESIC	
239.05422	$C_9H_9N_3O_5$	FURMETHOXADONE	ANTIBIOTIC	
239.10769	$C_{13}H_{18}NOCL$	AMFEBUTAMONE	ANTIDEPRESSANT	
	$C_{13}H_{18}NOCL$	LOMETRALINE	TRANQUILIZER	
	$C_{13}H_{18}NOCL$	MONALIDE	HERBICIDE	
	$C_{13}H_{18}NOCL$	PENTANOCHLOR	HERBICIDE	
239.12699	$C_{11}H_{17}N_3O_3$	EMORFAZONE	ANALGESIC	
	$C_{11}H_{17}N_3O_3$	ETHYLPIPERIDYLBARBITURIC ACID	HYPNOTIC	
239.13101	$C_{16}H_{17}NO$	DIPHENAMID	HERBICIDE	
239.14562	$C_{12}H_{21}N_3S$	TEBATIZOLE	RESPIRAT.STIMULANT	
239.15214	$C_{13}H_{21}NO_3$	ISOETARINE	BRONCHODILATOR	
	$C_{13}H_{21}NO_3$	MOPROLOL	BETA-ADR.BLOCKER	
	$C_{13}H_{21}NO_3$	SALBUTAMOL	BRONCHODILATOR	
239.16740	$C_{17}H_{21}N$	BENZPHETAMINE	ANOREXIC	
	$C_{17}H_{21}N$	DEMELVERINE	ANTISPASMOTIC	
239.92601	$C_6H_3N_2O_2CL_3$	PICLORAM	HERBICIDE	
239.97373	$C_{10}H_8OS_3$	ANETHOLTRITHIONE	CHOLERETIC	
239.98834	$C_6H_{12}N_2S_4$	THIRAM	ANTIBIOTIC	
239.99870	$C_4H_8N_4O_4S_2$	TETRAMETHYLENEDISULFOTETRAMINE	CHEMICAL	
240.00118	$C_{11}H_9O_2CLS$	TIANAFAC	ANTIRHEUMATIC	
240.02385	$C_6H_{12}N_2O_4S_2$	CYSTINE	AMINO ACID	
240.02927	$C_6H_7N_4OF_3S$	THIAZFLURONE	HERBICIDE	
240.03171	$C_8H_8N_4O_3S$	THIOFURADENE	ANTIBIOTIC	
240.04226	$C_{14}H_8O_4$	ALIZARIN	NATURAL SUBSTANCE	

MASS	FORMULA	NAME	CATEGORY	MS
240.04226	$C_{14}H_8O_4$	DANTRON	LAXATIVE	
240.05687	$C_{10}H_{12}N_2O_3S$	BENTAZONE	HERBICIDE	
240.05866	$C_{15}H_9O_2F$	FLUINDIONE	ANTICOAGULANT	
240.07462	$C_{10}H_{12}N_2O_5$	DINOSEB	HERBICIDE	
	$C_{10}H_{12}N_2O_5$	DINOTERB	HERBICIDE	
240.07865	$C_{15}H_{12}O_3$	METHYLANTHRATRIOL	NATURAL SUBSTANCE	
240.08902	$C_9H_{13}N_6CL$	CYANAZIN	HERBICIDE	
240.09325	$C_{11}H_{16}N_2O_2S$	BUTHALITAL	NARCOTIC	
240.11503	$C_{16}H_{16}O_2$	BUTIXIRATE (ACID)	ANALGESIC	
	$C_{16}H_{16}O_2$	NAPHTHONONE	ANTITUSSIVE	
	$C_{16}H_{16}O_2$	XENBUCIN	ANTICHOLESTEREMIC	
240.12224	$C_{10}H_{16}N_4O_3$	DIMETILAN	INSECTICIDE	
240.12626	$C_{15}H_{16}N_2O$	BENMOXINE	ANTIDEPRESSANT	
240.13750	$C_{14}H_{16}N_4$	BUDRALAZINE	ANTIHYPERTENSIVE	
	$C_{14}H_{16}N_4$	SIMTRAZENE	CYTOSTATIC	
240.14739	$C_{12}H_{20}N_2O_3$	HEXETHAL	HYPNOTIC	MS
	$C_{12}H_{20}N_2O_3$	PIRBUTEROL	BRONCHODILATOR	
	$C_{12}H_{20}N_2O_3$	TETRABARBITAL	HYPNOTIC	
240.16265	$C_{16}H_{20}N_2$	PHENIRAMINE	ANTIHIST./-ALLERG.	MS
240.18378	$C_{13}H_{24}N_2O_2$	CROPROPAMIDE	RESPIRAT.STIMULANT	MS
240.20893	$C_{15}H_{28}O_2$	MENTHYL ISOVALERATE	SEDATIVE	
240.91003	$C_6H_2NO_3CL_3$	TRICHLORONITROPHENOL	PESTICIDE	
241.06181	$C_{10}H_{12}N_3O_2CL$	TRANID	INSECTICIDE	
241.08513	$C_{13}H_{11}N_3O_2$	ACROTEBEN (TM)	TUBERCULOSTATIC	
	$C_{13}H_{11}N_3O_2$	BENQUINOX	FUNGIST./ANTIMYC.	
	$C_{13}H_{11}N_3O_2$	FLAVOTEBEN (TM)	TUBERCULOSTATIC	
	$C_{13}H_{11}N_3O_2$	SALINAZIDE	TUBERCULOSTATIC	
241.09502	$C_{11}H_{15}NO_5$	METHOCARBAMOL	MUSCLE RELAXANT	
241.11028	$C_{15}H_{15}NO_2$	MEFENAMIC ACID	ANALGESIC	
241.11749	$C_9H_{15}N_5O_3$	TETRAHYDROBIOPTERIN	DIAGNOSTIC AID	
241.13612	$C_{10}H_{19}N_5S$	PROMETRYNE	HERBICIDE	
	$C_{10}H_{19}N_5S$	TERBUTRYN	HERBICIDE	
241.95637	$C_6H_{10}O_2S_4$	DIXANTHOGEN	DESINFICIENT	
242.01916	$C_6H_{11}O_8P$	FOSCOLIC ACID	TONIC	
242.04984	$C_{15}H_{11}OCL$	CLORIDAROL	CORONARY DILATOR	
242.05641	$C_8H_{19}O_2S_2P$	ETHOPROPHOS	INSECTICIDE	
242.05705	$C_9H_{11}N_4O_2CL$	CHLOROETHYLTHEOPHYLLINE	BRONCHODILATOR	
242.05791	$C_{14}H_{10}O_4$	BENZOYLPEROXIDE	DESINFICIENT	
	$C_{14}H_{10}O_4$	SALICIL	DESINFICIENT	
242.06465	$C_8H_{18}O_4S_2$	METHYLSULFONAL	HYPNOTIC	
242.06512	$C_8H_{10}N_4O_5$	NIDROXYZONE	ANTIBIOTIC	
242.07097	$C_{12}H_{15}O_3CL$	CLOFIBRATE	ANTICHOLESTEREMIC	MS
242.08221	$C_{11}H_{15}N_2O_2CL$	ALLYLCHLORODIETHYLURACIL	------------	
	$C_{11}H_{15}N_2O_2CL$	CLORMECAINE	LOCAL ANESTHETIC	
	$C_{11}H_{15}N_2O_2CL$	IPROCLOZIDE	ANTIDEPRESSANT	
242.09027	$C_{10}H_{14}N_2O_5$	THYMIDINE	ENDOG.BIOMOLECULE	
242.09430	$C_{15}H_{14}O_3$	BENZYL MANDELATE	ANTISPASMOTIC	
	$C_{15}H_{14}O_3$	FENOPROFEN	ANALGESIC	
	$C_{15}H_{14}O_3$	GUAIACOL PHENYLACETATE	ANTITUSSIVE	
	$C_{15}H_{14}O_3$	MEXENONE	DERMATIC	
	$C_{15}H_{14}O_3$	TOLYL METHYLSALICYLATE	DESINFICIENT	
242.10151	$C_9H_{14}N_4O_4$	MOLSIDOMINE	CORONARY DILATOR	

MASS	FORMULA	NAME	CATEGORY	MS
242.10553	$C_{14}H_{14}N_2O_2$	ISONIXIN	ANTIRHEUMATIC	
	$C_{14}H_{14}N_2O_2$	METANIXIN	ANALGESIC	
242.10890	$C_{11}H_{18}N_2O_2S$	THIOPENTAL	NARCOTIC	MS
242.13068	$C_{16}H_{18}O_2$	BISPHENOL B	CHEMICAL	
	$C_{16}H_{18}O_2$	NAFCAPROIC ACID	CHOLERETIC	
242.14191	$C_{15}H_{18}N_2O$	IPRAZONE	------------	
	$C_{15}H_{18}N_2O$	SELAGINE	INSECTICIDE	
242.18820	$C_{14}H_{26}O_3$	MENGLYTATE	DESINFICIENT	
242.26097	$C_{16}H_{34}O$	CETYL ALCOHOL	PHARMACEUTICAL AID	
243.01190	$C_9H_{10}NO_3SP$	CIAFOS	INSECTICIDE	
	$C_9H_{10}NO_3SP$	CYANOX	INSECTICIDE	
243.07429	$C_{10}H_{13}NO_6$	PIRIDOXILATE	CORONARY DILATOR	
243.08552	$C_9H_{13}N_3O_5$	CYTARABINE	CYTOSTATIC	
	$C_9H_{13}N_3O_5$	CYTIDINE	ENDOG.BIOMOLECULE	
243.08686	$C_{10}H_9N_7O$	FURTERENE	DIURETIC	
243.08954	$C_{14}H_{13}NO_3$	ALONIMIDE	HYPNOTIC	
243.10480	$C_{18}H_{13}N$	CHRYSENAMINE	CHEMICAL	
243.16231	$C_{16}H_{21}NO$	NORLEVORPHANOL	ANALGESIC	MS
243.19870	$C_{17}H_{25}N$	PHENCYCLIDINE	ANALGESIC	MS
243.86524	$C_6O_2CL_4$	CHLORANIL	FUNGIST./ANTIMYC.	
244.01702	$C_{10}H_{10}N_2OCL_2$	FENMETAZOLE	ANTIDEPRESSANT	
244.03804	$C_{14}H_{12}S_2$	MESULFEN	DESINFICIENT	
244.06301	$C_8H_{12}N_4O_3S$	CARNIDAZOLE	TRICHOMONACIDE	
244.06954	$C_9H_{12}N_2O_6$	URIDINE	ENDOG.BIOMOLECULE	
244.07356	$C_{14}H_{12}O_4$	COTOIN	ANTIEPILEPTIC	
	$C_{14}H_{12}O_4$	DIOXYBENZONE	DERMATIC	
	$C_{14}H_{12}O_4$	GUAIACOL SALICYLATE	RUBEFACIENT	
244.07673	$C_{14}H_{13}N_2CL$	CLONAZOLIN	VASOCONSTRICTOR	
244.08077	$C_8H_{12}N_4O_5$	AZACITIDINE	CYTOSTATIC	
	$C_8H_{12}N_4O_5$	RIBAVIRIN	VIRUCIDE	
244.08479	$C_{13}H_{12}N_2O_3$	PHENALLYMAL	HYPNOTIC	MS
244.08817	$C_{10}H_{16}N_2O_3S$	AMIDEPHRINE	VAVO	
	$C_{10}H_{16}N_2O_3S$	BIOTIN	VITAMINE	
244.08996	$C_{15}H_{13}O_2F$	FLUPROFEN	ANALGESIC	
	$C_{15}H_{13}O_2F$	FLURBIPROFEN	ANALGESIC	MS
244.12118	$C_{14}H_{16}N_2O_2$	ETOMIDATE	HYPNOTIC	
	$C_{14}H_{16}N_2O_2$	ROLICYPRINE	ANTIDEPRESSANT	
244.14633	$C_{16}H_{20}O_2$	CYCLOHEXYLINDANECARBONIC ACID	ANTIPHLOGISTIC	
	$C_{16}H_{20}O_2$	FENESTREL	GYNECOL./OBSTRECT.	
244.15756	$C_{15}H_{20}N_2O$	FELIPYRINE	ANTIPHLOGISTIC	
244.19395	$C_{16}H_{24}N_2$	ISOAMINILE	ANTITUSSIVE	
	$C_{16}H_{24}N_2$	XYLOMETAZOLINE	VASOCONSTRICTOR	MS
244.99202	$C_6H_3N_3O_8$	STYPHNIC ACID	CHEMICAL	
245.01227	$C_9H_9N_3OCL_2$	GUANFACINE	ANTIHYPERTENSIVE	
245.04549	$C_{10}H_{12}NO_4CL$	CHLORPHENESIN CARBAMATE	ANALGESIC	
245.06479	$C_8H_{11}N_3O_6$	AZAURIDINE	CYTOSTATIC	
245.06636	$C_{11}H_{10}NO_2F_3$	FLUMETRAMIDE	MUSCLE RELAXANT	
245.11643	$C_{13}H_{15}N_3O_2$	PYROLAN	INSECTICIDE	
245.14158	$C_{15}H_{19}NO_2$	TROPACOCAINE	LOCAL ANESTHETIC	
245.15281	$C_{14}H_{19}N_3O$	ISOPYRIN	ANALGESIC	MS
	$C_{14}H_{19}N_3O$	OXOLAMINE	ANTITUSSIVE	
	$C_{14}H_{19}N_3O$	XILOBAM	MUSCLE RELAXANT	

MASS	FORMULA	NAME	CATEGORY	MS
245.17796	$C_{16}H_{23}NO$	DEZOCINE	ANALGESIC	
	$C_{16}H_{23}NO$	PYROVALERONE	STIMULANT	
	$C_{16}H_{23}NO$	TOLPERISONE	MUSCLE RELAXANT	
	$C_{16}H_{23}NO$	TOLQUINZOL	ANTIDEPRESSANT	
245.18920	$C_{15}H_{23}N_3$	IQUINDAMINE	ANTITUSSIVE	
245.21435	$C_{17}H_{27}N$	GAMFEXINE	ANTIDEPRESSANT	
245.91882	$C_5H_5N_2OCL_3S$	ETRIDIAZOL	FUNGIST./ANTIMYC.	
245.99718	$C_6H_{15}O_2S_3P$	THIOMETONE	INSECTICIDE	
246.00039	$C_8H_{11}N_2O_2BR$	ISOCIL	PESTICIDE	
246.00752	$C_8H_8N_4OCL_2$	GUANOXABENZ	ANTIHYPERTENSIVE	
246.01494	$C_6H_{15}O_4S_2P$	METHYLDEMETON-SULFOXIDE	INSECTICIDE	MS
246.02318	$C_6H_{14}O_6S_2$	BUSULFAN	CYTOSTATIC	
246.03020	$C_{10}H_{15}OS_2P$	DYFONATE	INSECTICIDE	
246.04390	$C_9H_{12}N_4CL_2$	GUANCLOFINE	ANTIHYPERTENSIVE	
246.06406	$C_{12}H_{10}N_2O_4$	NIFURPIRINOL	ANTIBIOTIC	
246.06520	$C_9H_{11}N_2O_5F$	DOXIFLURIDINE	CYTOSTATIC	
	$C_9H_{11}N_2O_5F$	FLOXURIDINE	CYTOSTATIC	
246.08652	$C_{10}H_{10}N_6O_2$	AZANIDAZOLE	TRICHOMONACIDE	
246.08921	$C_{14}H_{14}O_4$	FTALOFYNE	ANTHELMINTIC	
246.10044	$C_{13}H_{14}N_2O_3$	ACETYLTRYPTOPHANE	ENDOG.BIOMOLECULE	
	$C_{13}H_{14}N_2O_3$	METHYLPHENOBARBITAL	ANTIEPILEPTIC	MS
246.11570	$C_{17}H_{14}N_2$	ELLIPTICINE	CYTOSTATIC	
246.12560	$C_{15}H_{18}O_3$	SANTONIN	ANTHELMINTIC	
246.13683	$C_{14}H_{18}N_2O_2$	PARSALMIDE	ANALGESIC	
	$C_{14}H_{18}N_2O_2$	QUINPRENALINE	BRONCHODILATOR	
246.16198	$C_{16}H_{22}O_2$	GEROQUINOL	DERMATIC	
246.17321	$C_{15}H_{22}N_2O$	DEXIVACAINE	LOCAL ANESTHETIC	
	$C_{15}H_{22}N_2O$	MEPIVACAINE	LOCAL ANESTHETIC	MS
246.20960	$C_{16}H_{26}N_2$	PIMETINE	ANTICHOLESTEREMIC	
246.90357	$C_7H_3NO_2CLBR$	BROMCHLORENONE	DESINFICIENT	
246.94619	$C_6H_6NO_5AS$	NITARSONE	ANTIBIOTIC	
246.97868	$C_7H_5NO_7S$	NITROSULFOBENZOIC ACID	CHEMICAL	
247.02458	$C_8H_{10}NO_6P$	CODECARBOXYLASE	VITAMINE	
247.05307	$C_{11}H_{15}NOCL_2$	DICHLORISOPROTERENOL	SYMPATHOLYTIC	
247.05931	$C_{11}H_9N_3O_4$	NIFURVIDINE	ANTIBIOTIC	
247.06268	$C_8H_{13}N_3O_4S$	TINIDAZOLE	TRICHOMONACIDE	
247.10876	$C_{10}H_{18}N_3O_2CL$	SEMUSTINE	CYTOSTATIC	
247.12084	$C_{14}H_{17}NO_3$	EEDQ	ANALGESIC	
247.13208	$C_{13}H_{17}N_3O_2$	PARBENDAZOLE	ANTHELMINTIC	
247.15723	$C_{15}H_{21}NO_2$	CETOBEMIDONE	ANALGESIC	MS
	$C_{15}H_{21}NO_2$	CICLONICATE	VASODILATOR	
	$C_{15}H_{21}NO_2$	EUCAINE	LOCAL ANESTHETIC	
	$C_{15}H_{21}NO_2$	INDENOLOL	BETA-ADR.BLOCKER	
	$C_{15}H_{21}NO_2$	PETHIDINE	ANALGESIC	MS
	$C_{15}H_{21}NO_2$	PRODILIDINE	ANALGESIC	
	$C_{15}H_{21}NO_2$	TOLPRONINE	ANALGESIC	
247.19361	$C_{16}H_{25}NO$	BUTIDRINE	BETA-ADR.BLOCKER	
248.00070	$C_{10}H_{10}O_3CL_2$	DICHLOROPHENOXYBUTYRIC ACID (2.4-DB)	HERBICIDE	
248.01193	$C_9H_{10}N_2O_2CL_2$	LINURONE	HERBICIDE	
248.02964	$C_{10}H_7O_4F_3$	TRIFLUSAL	ANTICOAGULANT	
248.03845	$C_8H_{13}N_2O_3PS$	ZINOPHOS (THIONAZIN)	NEMATOCIDE	
248.04649	$C_{11}H_9N_4OCL$	NIMAZONE	ANTIPHLOGISTIC	

MASS	FORMULA	NAME	CATEGORY	MS
248.05456	$C_{10}H_8N_4O_4$	NITREFAZOLE	HYPNOTIC	
248.06195	$C_{12}H_{12}N_2O_2S$	DAPSONE	ANTIBIOTIC	
	$C_{12}H_{12}N_2O_2S$	SULFABENZ	ANTIBIOTIC	
248.08287	$C_{12}H_{13}N_4CL$	PYRIMETHAMINE	ANTIBIOTIC	
248.08373	$C_{17}H_{12}O_2$	NAPHTHYL BENZOATE	CHOLERETIC	
248.11609	$C_{13}H_{16}N_2O_3$	ACETYLPHENETURIDE	ANTIEPILEPTIC	
	$C_{13}H_{16}N_2O_3$	INDORENATE	ANTIHYPERTENSIVE	
	$C_{13}H_{16}N_2O_3$	PROFEXALONE	HYPNOTIC	
248.12733	$C_{12}H_{16}N_4O_2$	TALOXIMINE	BRONCHODILATOR	
248.14846	$C_9H_{20}N_4O_4$	NEGAMYCIN	ANTIBIOTIC	
248.15248	$C_{14}H_{20}N_2O_2$	BUNITROLOL	BETA-ADR.BLOCKER	MS
	$C_{14}H_{20}N_2O_2$	PINDOLOL	BETA-ADR.BLOCKER	MS
	$C_{14}H_{20}N_2O_2$	PIRIDOCAINE	LOCAL ANESTHETIC	
248.18886	$C_{15}H_{24}N_2O$	MORFOREX	ANOREXIC	
	$C_{15}H_{24}N_2O$	TRIMECAINE	LOCAL ANESTHETIC	
249.05720	$C_{11}H_{11}N_3O_2S$	NITRAMIZOLE	ANTHELMINTIC	
	$C_{11}H_{11}N_3O_2S$	SULFAPYRIDINE	ANTIBIOTIC	
249.07898	$C_{16}H_{11}NO_2$	BENZOXIQUINE	DESINFICIENT	
	$C_{16}H_{11}NO_2$	CINCHOPHEN	ANTIPHLOGISTIC	
249.14773	$C_{13}H_{19}N_3O_2$	AMIDANTEL	------------	
249.15175	$C_{18}H_{19}N$	BENZOCTAMINE	TRANQUILIZER	MS
249.15289	$C_{15}H_{20}NOF$	PRIMAPERONE	ANTIHYPERTENSIVE	
249.15512	$C_{15}H_{23}NS$	TENOCYCLIDINE	ANALGESIC	
249.17288	$C_{15}H_{23}NO_2$	ALPRENOLOL	BETA-ADR.BLOCKER	MS
	$C_{15}H_{23}NO_2$	BENZYLDIETHYLAMINOBUTYRIC ACID	ANTISPASMOTIC	
	$C_{15}H_{23}NO_2$	HEPTYL PHENYLAMINOACETATE	ANTISPASMOTIC	
	$C_{15}H_{23}NO_2$	PROCINOLOL	BETA-ADR.BLOCKER	
249.76283	$CHBR_3$	BROMOFORM	ANTITUSSIVE	
250.01618	$C_9H_{12}O_4CLP$	HEPTENOPHOS	INSECTICIDE	
250.01944	$C_6H_{10}N_4O_3S_2$	BUTAZOLAMIDE	DIURETIC	
	$C_6H_{10}N_4O_3S_2$	ISOBUTAMIDE	DIURETIC	
250.04415	$C_{13}H_8O_3F_2$	DIFLUNISAL	ANALGESIC	MS
250.04774	$C_{12}H_{10}O_6$	METESCULETOL	DECR.CAPILL.FRAG.	
250.05245	$C_{10}H_{10}N_4O_2S$	PIRINIDAZOLE	ANTIBIOTIC	
	$C_{10}H_{10}N_4O_2S$	SULFADIAZINE	ANTIBIOTIC	
	$C_{10}H_{10}N_4O_2S$	SULFAPYRAZINE	ANTIBIOTIC	
250.08413	$C_{13}H_{14}O_5$	ANTIMYCIN	ANTIBIOTIC	
250.09536	$C_{12}H_{14}N_2O_4$	FURFURYLISOPROPYLBARBITURIC ACID	HYPNOTIC	
250.11061	$C_{16}H_{14}N_2O$	METHAQUALONE	HYPNOTIC	MS
250.12051	$C_{14}H_{18}O_4$	CINOXATE	DERMATIC	
	$C_{14}H_{18}O_4$	METHYL DIETHYLACETYLSALICYLATE	RUBEFACIENT	
250.12815	$C_{14}H_{16}N_2F_2$	FLUCINDOL	------------	
250.13174	$C_{13}H_{18}N_2O_3$	HEPTABARBITAL	HYPNOTIC	MS
	$C_{13}H_{18}N_2O_3$	TRIMETHOXYBENZYLIMIDAZOLINE	VASOCONSTRICTOR	
250.13914	$C_{15}H_{22}OS$	TIOCTILATE	ANTIBIOTIC	
250.14298	$C_{12}H_{18}N_4O_2$	VEROFYLLINE	BRONCHODILATOR	
250.14700	$C_{17}H_{18}N_2$	AMFETAMINIL	STIMULANT	MS
250.15690	$C_{15}H_{22}O_3$	GEMFIBROZIL	ANTICHOLESTEREMIC	
250.16813	$C_{14}H_{22}N_2O_2$	AMYLCAINE	LOCAL ANESTHETIC	
	$C_{14}H_{22}N_2O_2$	TUTOCAINE	LOCAL ANESTHETIC	
251.02283	$C_8H_{11}N_3O_2CL_2$	URAMUSTINE	CYTOSTATIC	
251.07062	$C_{11}H_{10}N_3O_3F$	FLUNIDAZOLE	ANTIBIOTIC	

MASS	FORMULA	NAME	CATEGORY	MS
251.07131	$C_{13}H_{14}NO_2CL$	PIRPROFEN	ANTIRHEUMATIC	
251.09377	$C_{11}H_{14}N_5CL$	CYCLOGUANIL	ANTIBIOTIC	
251.11576	$C_{13}H_{17}NO_4$	ALIBENDAZOL	CHOLERETIC	
	$C_{13}H_{17}NO_4$	DIPROPYL ISOCINCHOMERONATE	PESTICIDE	
251.11710	$C_{14}H_{13}N_5$	PICODRALAZINE	ANTIHYPERTENSIVE	
251.13439	$C_{14}H_{21}NOS$	ESPROQUINE	CARDIOTONIC	
251.13823	$C_{11}H_{17}N_5O_2$	DIMETHAZAN	STIMULANT	
251.15214	$C_{14}H_{21}NO_3$	PIVENFRINE	SYMPATHOMIMETIC	
251.26130	$C_{17}H_{33}N$	CYVERINE	SYMPATHOMIMETIC	
252.07865	$C_{16}H_{12}O_3$	ANISINDIONE	ANTICOAGULANT	
	$C_{16}H_{12}O_3$	HYDROXYMETHYLPHENYLINDANEDIONE	ANTICOAGULANT	
252.08988	$C_{15}H_{12}N_2O_2$	DIPHENYLPYRAZOLINDIONE	ANTIRHEUMATIC	
	$C_{15}H_{12}N_2O_2$	OXCARBAZEPINE	ANTIEPILEPTIC	
	$C_{15}H_{12}N_2O_2$	PHENYTOIN	ANTIEPILEPTIC	MS
252.09390	$C_{20}H_{12}$	BENZO(A)PYRENE	CHEMICAL	
	$C_{20}H_{12}$	BENZO(E)PYRENE	CHEMICAL	
252.10294	$C_{13}H_{17}N_2OCL$	CHLORMETHYLPYRROLIDINEACETANILIDE	LOCAL ANESTHETIC	
252.11572	$C_{10}H_{16}N_6S$	CIMETIDINE	TO THERAPY ULCERS	
252.12964	$C_{13}H_{20}N_2OS$	THIOCAINE	LOCAL ANESTHETIC	
252.13616	$C_{14}H_{20}O_4$	FREQUENTIN	ANTIBIOTIC	
252.14739	$C_{13}H_{20}N_2O_3$	HYDROXYPROCAINE	LOCAL ANESTHETIC	
252.15863	$C_{12}H_{20}N_4O_2$	VELPAR	HERBICIDE	
252.20893	$C_{16}H_{28}O_2$	HYDNOCARPIC ACID	ANTIBIOTIC	
252.90424	$C_6H_6NOCL_2AS$	DICHLOROPHENARSINE	ANTIBIOTIC	
252.97384	$C_{10}H_8NO_2BR$	BROSUXIMIDE	ANTIEPILEPTIC	
252.99643	$C_{11}H_8NO_2CLS$	FENCLOZIC ACID	ANTIRHEUMATIC	
253.01573	$C_9H_7N_3O_4S$	FUROTHIAZOLE	ANTIBIOTIC	
253.01890	$C_9H_8N_5CLS$	TIZANIDINE	MUSCLE RELAXANT	
253.02146	$C_{10}H_{12}N_3BR$	GUANISOQUINE	ANTIHYPERTENSIVE	
253.04088	$C_{11}H_{11}NO_4S$	ACTINOQUINOL	------------	
253.05211	$C_{10}H_{11}N_3O_3S$	SULFAMETHOXAZOLE	ANTIBIOTIC	MS
253.07727	$C_{12}H_{15}NO_3S$	VANITIOLIDE	CHOLERETIC	
253.08111	$C_9H_{11}N_5O_4$	ERITADENINE	ANTICHOLESTEREMIC	
253.09819	$C_{12}H_{16}N_3OCL$	CARBANTEL	ANTHELMINTIC	
253.10626	$C_{11}H_{15}N_3O_4$	PYRIDINOL CARBAMATE	ANTIPHLOGISTIC	
253.10759	$C_{12}H_{11}N_7$	AMPYRIMINE	DIURETIC	
	$C_{12}H_{11}N_7$	TRIAMTERENE	DIURETIC	
253.10942	$C_{11}H_{16}N_5CL$	PROGUANIL	ANTIMALARIAL	
253.11028	$C_{16}H_{15}NO_2$	TESIMIDE	ANTIPHLOGISTIC	
253.11365	$C_{13}H_{19}NO_2S$	THANITE	INSECTICIDE	
253.12151	$C_{15}H_{15}N_3O$	ETHACRIDINE	DESINFICIENT	
	$C_{15}H_{15}N_3O$	PREMAZEPAM	TRANQUILIZER	
253.14666	$C_{17}H_{19}NO$	NEFOPAM	ANALGESIC	MS
253.18305	$C_{18}H_{23}N$	TOLPROPAMINE	ANTIHIST./-ALLERG.	
	$C_{18}H_{23}N$	TRIMETHYLDIPHENYLPROPYLAMINE	ANTISPASMOTIC	
253.20149	$C_{11}H_{23}N_7$	MELADRAZINE	ANTISPASMOTIC	
253.90109	$C_4H_3N_2OIS$	IODOTHIOURACIL	THYREOSTATIC	
253.93043	$C_8H_5O_3CL_3$	TRICHLOROPHENOXYACETIC ACID (2.4.5-T)	HERBICIDE	
254.02490	$C_{11}H_{10}O_5S$	MENADIONESULFONIC ACID	HORMONE	
254.04352	$C_{12}H_{14}O_2S_2$	DITOPHAL	ANTIBIOTIC	
254.05726	$C_7H_{14}N_2O_6S$	GLUTAURIN	DERMATIC	
254.07252	$C_{11}H_{14}N_2O_3S$	SULFADICRAMIDE	ANTIBIOTIC	

MASS	FORMULA	NAME	CATEGORY	MS
254.09430	$C_{16}H_{14}O_3$	KETOPROFEN	ANTIRHEUMATIC	MS
	$C_{16}H_{14}O_3$	METHOXYPHENYLPHENYLACRYLIC ACID	CHOLERETIC	
254.10151	$C_{10}H_{14}N_4O_4$	DIHYDROXYPROPYLTHEOBROMINE	VASODILATOR	
	$C_{10}H_{14}N_4O_4$	DIPROPHYLLINE	VASODILATOR	MS
254.10890	$C_{12}H_{18}N_2O_2S$	SPIROTHIOBARBITAL	HYPNOTIC	
	$C_{12}H_{18}N_2O_2S$	THIAMYLAL	NARCOTIC	
254.11543	$C_{13}H_{18}O_5$	MEPROPHENDIOL	ANTIEPILEPTIC	
254.11676	$C_{14}H_{14}N_4O$	PHENAMIDINE	ANTIBIOTIC	
254.11859	$C_{13}H_{19}N_2OCL$	BUTANILICAINE	LOCAL ANESTHETIC	MS
254.12666	$C_{12}H_{18}N_2O_4$	MIDODRIN	SYMPATHOMIMETIC	
254.13789	$C_{11}H_{18}N_4O_3$	IMURACETAM	------------	
254.17830	$C_{17}H_{22}N_2$	PHENBENZAMINE	ANTIHIST./-ALLERG.	
254.97724	$C_8H_5N_3O_3S_2$	TENONITRAZOLE	TRICHOMONACIDE	
254.98949	$C_{10}H_{10}NO_2BR$	BROFOXINE	TRANQUILIZER	
255.01362	$C_9H_9N_3O_2S_2$	MALEYLSULFATHIAZOLE	ANTIBIOTIC	
	$C_9H_9N_3O_2S_2$	SULFATHIAZOLE	ANTIBIOTIC	
	$C_9H_9N_3O_2S_2$	THIAZOSULFONE	ANTIBIOTIC	
255.02177	$C_{12}H_{11}NOCL_2$	PROPYZAMIDE	HERBICIDE	
255.05316	$C_{14}H_9NO_4$	ALRESTATIN	ENZYME INHIBITOR	
255.08954	$C_{15}H_{13}NO_3$	AMFENAC	ANALGESIC	
255.10078	$C_{14}H_{13}N_3O_2$	DIMETHOXYPHENYLIMIDAZOPYRIDINE	CARDIOTONIC	
255.10261	$C_{13}H_{18}NO_2CL$	ALAPROCLATE	ANTIDEPRESSANT	
	$C_{13}H_{18}NO_2CL$	CLOFOREX	ANOREXIC	
	$C_{13}H_{18}NO_2CL$	DIMETHACHLOR	HERBICIDE	
255.12930	$C_{13}H_{21}NO_2S$	DITOLAMIDE	URICOSURIC	
	$C_{13}H_{21}NO_2S$	TIPRENOLOL	BETA-ADR.BLOCKER	
255.13716	$C_{15}H_{17}N_3O$	CETOXIME	ANTIHIST./-ALLERG.	
255.13899	$C_{14}H_{22}NOCL$	CLOBUTINOL	ANTITUSSIVE	
255.16231	$C_{17}H_{21}NO$	BENZYLEPHEDRINE	SYMPATHOMIMETIC	
	$C_{17}H_{21}NO$	DIPHENHYDRAMINE	ANTIHIST./-ALLERG.	MS
	$C_{17}H_{21}NO$	OXIFENTOREX	ANOREXIC	
	$C_{17}H_{21}NO$	PHENYLTOLOXAMINE	ANTIHIST./-ALLERG.	
	$C_{17}H_{21}NO$	TOFENACIN	ANTIDEPRESSANT	
255.17355	$C_{16}H_{21}N_3$	TRIPELENNAMINE	ANTIHIST./-ALLERG.	
255.19870	$C_{18}H_{25}N$	DIMEMORFANE	ANTITUSSIVE	
	$C_{18}H_{25}N$	HEPTAVERINE	ANTISPASMOTIC	
	$C_{18}H_{25}N$	VOLAZOCINE	ANALGESIC	
255.92258	$C_4H_8O_4CL_3P$	METRIFONATE	PESTICIDE	
	$C_4H_8O_4CL_3P$	TRICHLORFON	INSECTICIDE	MS
255.98063	$C_{10}H_6N_2O_2CL_2$	PYRROLNITRIN	FUNGIST./ANTIMYC.	
255.98474	$C_7H_{14}O_3CLAS$	HEPTENECHLOROARSINIC ACID	TONIC	
255.99764	$C_9H_8N_2O_3S_2$	PHENOSULFAZOLE	ANTIBIOTIC	
256.02911	$C_{15}H_9O_2CL$	CLORINDIONE	ANTICOAGULANT	
256.07356	$C_{15}H_{12}O_4$	MONOBENZYL PHTHALATE	EXPECTORANT	
	$C_{15}H_{12}O_4$	PHENYL ACETYLSALICYLATE	ANALGESIC	
256.07673	$C_{15}H_{13}N_2CL$	CHLORMIDAZOLE	FUNGIST./ANTIMYC.	
256.08479	$C_{14}H_{12}N_2O_3$	ACETAMIDOPHENYL NICOTINATE	ANALGESIC	
256.08817	$C_{11}H_{16}N_2O_3S$	OZOLINONE	DIURETIC	
	$C_{11}H_{16}N_2O_3S$	PHENBUTAMIDE	ANTIDIABETIC	
256.10592	$C_{11}H_{16}N_2O_5$	ETHYLDESOXYURIDINE	DERMATIC	
256.12118	$C_{15}H_{16}N_2O_2$	ANCYMIDOL	PLANT GROWTH REGU.	
256.12455	$C_{12}H_{20}N_2O_2S$	THIOTETRABARBITAL	NARCOTIC	

MASS	FORMULA	NAME	CATEGORY	MS
256.13241	$C_{14}H_{16}N_4O$	ETOXAZENE	ANALGESIC	
256.16880	$C_{15}H_{20}N_4$	HETRAMINE	ANTIHIST./-ALLERG.	
256.24023	$C_{16}H_{32}O_2$	PALMITIC ACID	ORGANIC ACID	MS
256.25146	$C_{15}H_{32}N_2O$	PEMERIDE	ANTITUSSIVE	
256.92430	$C_9H_5NOCLBR$	BROMOCHLOROCHINOLINOL	FUNGIST./ANTIMYC.	
256.99454	$C_6H_{12}NO_4S_2P$	FORMOTHIONE	INSECTICIDE	
257.00104	$C_{11}H_9NO_2CL_2$	BARBAN	HERBICIDE	
257.00514	$C_{10}H_{12}NO_2BR$	BROMOSALICYLIC ISOPROPYLAMIDE	FUNGIST./ANTIMYC.	
257.03580	$C_{10}H_{11}NO_5S$	CEPHALOSPORANIC ACID	------------	
257.06228	$C_{13}H_{11}N_3OS$	TIMOPRAZOL	TO THERAPY ULCERS	
257.06881	$C_{14}H_{11}NO_4$	BENZAMIDOSALICYLIC ACID	TUBERCULOSTATIC	
257.07218	$C_{11}H_{15}NO_4S$	ETEBENECID	URICOSURIC	
257.08187	$C_{12}H_{16}NO_3CL$	MECLOFENOXATE	STIMULANT	MS
257.10117	$C_{10}H_{15}N_3O_5$	BENSERAZIDE	ENZYME INHIBITOR	
	$C_{10}H_{15}N_3O_5$	MADU	VIRUCIDE	
257.10519	$C_{15}H_{15}NO_3$	TOLMETINE	ANTIRHEUMATIC	MS
257.12159	$C_{16}H_{16}NOF$	FENISOREX	ANOREXIC	
257.14158	$C_{16}H_{19}NO_2$	MEDIFOXAMINE	ANTIDEPRESSANT	
257.17796	$C_{17}H_{23}NO$	DEXTRORPHAN	ANTITUSSIVE	MS
	$C_{17}H_{23}NO$	LEVORPHANOL	ANALGESIC	MS
	$C_{17}H_{23}NO$	PIRANDAMINE	ANTIDEPRESSANT	
	$C_{17}H_{23}NO$	RACEMORPHANE	ANALGESIC	MS
257.97524	$C_7H_7N_4O_2BR$	BROMOTHEOPHYLLINE	DIURETIC	
257.97530	$C_6H_{11}O_3I$	IODOPROPYLIDENEGLYCEROL	MUCOLYTIC	
258.00039	$C_9H_{11}N_2O_2BR$	METOBROMURON	HERBICIDE	
258.01329	$C_9H_{10}N_2O_3S_2$	ETHOXZOLAMIDE	DIURETIC	
258.03267	$C_{11}H_{12}N_2OCL_2$	LOFEXIDINE	ANTIHYPERTENSIVE	
258.03757	$C_{10}H_{10}O_8$	ACEGLATONE	ANTIPHLOGISTIC	
258.04476	$C_{15}H_{11}O_2CL$	CLORIDAROL	VASODILATOR	
258.04630	$C_{13}H_{10}N_2O_2S$	THYPHENYTOIN	ANTIEPILEPTIC	
258.05133	$C_8H_{19}O_3S_2P$	DEMETON	INSECTICIDE	
258.05283	$C_{14}H_{10}O_5$	SALSALATE	ANALGESIC	
258.05936	$C_{11}H_{15}N_2OCLS$	FOPIRTOLIN	ANALGESIC	
258.06406	$C_{13}H_{10}N_2O_4$	THALIDOMIDE	HYPNOTIC	MS
258.07866	$C_9H_{14}N_4O_3S$	SULNIDAZOLE	TRICHOMONACIDE	
258.08921	$C_{15}H_{14}O_4$	FURACRINIC ACID	DIURETIC	
	$C_{15}H_{14}O_4$	MENBUTONE	CHOLERETIC	
	$C_{15}H_{14}O_4$	PEUCEDANIN	CYTOSTATIC	
	$C_{15}H_{14}O_4$	RHAPONTIGENINE	------------	
258.10561	$C_{16}H_{15}O_2F$	FLUENETHYL	INSECTICIDE	
258.12560	$C_{16}H_{18}O_3$	FENOCINOL	ANTISPASMOTIC	
258.13683	$C_{15}H_{18}N_2O_2$	PROPOXATE	HYPNOTIC	
258.15796	$C_{12}H_{22}N_2O_4$	LORBAMATE	MUSCLE RELAXANT	
258.15929	$C_{13}H_{18}N_6$	ZOLERTINE	ANTIHYPERTENSIVE	
258.19837	$C_{18}H_{26}O$	VERSALIDE (TM)	CHEMICAL	
	$C_{18}H_{26}O$	XIBORNOL	DESINFICIENT	
258.21949	$C_{15}H_{30}O_3$	TRETHOCANIC ACID	ANTICHOLESTEREMIC	
258.87614	$C_6HNO_2CL_4$	TECNAZENE	FUNGIST./ANTIMYC.	
258.98258	$C_8H_{10}NO_4AS$	ARSACETIN	ANTIBIOTIC	
259.05461	$C_{10}H_{14}N_3OCLS$	AZINTAMIDE	CHOLERETIC	
259.06567	$C_8H_{14}N_5OSP$	AZATEPA	CYTOSTATIC	
259.08044	$C_9H_{13}N_3O_6$	PIRAZOFURIN	CYTOSTATIC	

MASS	FORMULA	NAME	CATEGORY	MS
259.08446	$C_{14}H_{13}NO_4$	DROXACIN	ANTIBIOTIC	
259.09569	$C_{13}H_{13}N_3O_3$	CICLOBENDAZOLE	ANTHELMINTIC	
259.11278	$C_{16}H_{18}NCL$	CHLOROETHYLDIBENZYLAMINE	ANTISPASMOTIC	
	$C_{16}H_{18}NCL$	CLOBENZOREX	ANOREXIC	
259.15723	$C_{16}H_{21}NO_2$	PROPRANOLOL	BETA-ADR.BLOCKER	MS
259.16846	$C_{15}H_{21}N_3O$	ETOPRINDOLE	ANTIPHLOGISTIC	
	$C_{15}H_{21}N_3O$	PRIMAQUINE	ANTIMALARIAL	
	$C_{15}H_{21}N_3O$	QUINOCIDE	ANTIMALARIAL	
259.97555	$C_9H_6N_2O_3CL_2$	METHAZOL	HERBICIDE	
259.97783	$C_7H_9N_2O_4AS$	CARBARSONE	ANTIBIOTIC	
259.98510	$C_5H_{10}O_8P_2$	PENTAERYTHRIT DIPHOSPHATE	CORONARY DILATOR	
260.01283	$C_7H_{17}O_2S_3P$	PHORATE	INSECTICIDE	
260.01604	$C_9H_{13}N_2O_2BR$	BROMACIL	HERBICIDE	MS
260.02482	$C_7H_{15}N_2O_2CL_2P$	CYCLOPHOSPHAMIDE	CYTOSTATIC	MS
	$C_7H_{15}N_2O_2CL_2P$	IFOSFAMIDE	CYTOSTATIC	
260.03546	$C_{10}H_{12}O_6S$	SULPROSAL	ANALGESIC	
260.04670	$C_9H_{12}N_2O_5S$	SULOCARBILATE	DIURETIC	
260.05072	$C_{14}H_{12}O_3S$	SUPROFEN	ANALGESIC	
	$C_{14}H_{12}O_3S$	TIAPROFENIC ACID	ANTIPHLOGISTIC	MS
260.06848	$C_{14}H_{12}O_5$	EVICROMIL	ANTIHIST./-ALLERG.	
	$C_{14}H_{12}O_5$	KHELLIN	CORONARY DILATOR	
260.11609	$C_{14}H_{16}N_2O_3$	NADOXOLOL	ANTIARRHYTHMIC	
	$C_{14}H_{16}N_2O_3$	PHETABARBITAL	ANTIEPILEPTIC	
260.12733	$C_{13}H_{16}N_4O_2$	DIAVERIDINE	COCCIDIOSTATIC	
260.13135	$C_{18}H_{16}N_2$	DIPHENYLPHENYLENEDIAMINE	ANTIOXIDANT	
260.13472	$C_{15}H_{20}N_2S$	METHAPHENILENE	ANTIHIST./-ALLERG.	
260.14125	$C_{16}H_{20}O_3$	HEXACYPRONE	CHOLERETIC	
260.15248	$C_{15}H_{20}N_2O_2$	FENSPIRIDE	BRONCHODILATOR	
260.16371	$C_{14}H_{20}N_4O$	IMOLAMINE	CORONARY DILATOR	
260.17361	$C_{12}H_{24}N_2O_4$	CARISOPRODOL	ANALGESIC	
260.17763	$C_{17}H_{24}O_2$	PHENYL UNDECYLENATE	FUNGIST./ANTIMYC.	
260.18886	$C_{16}H_{24}N_2O$	OXYMETAZOLINE	VASOCONSTRICTOR	MS
260.20010	$C_{15}H_{24}N_4$	NONAPYRIMINE	ANTIEPILEPTIC	
261.05566	$C_{14}H_{12}NO_2CL$	TOLFENAMIC ACID	ANTIPHLOGISTIC	
261.06372	$C_{13}H_{11}NO_5$	OXOLINIC ACID	ANTIBIOTIC	
261.08012	$C_{14}H_{12}NO_3F$	FLUMEQUINE	ANTIBIOTIC	
261.09204	$C_{15}H_{16}NOCL$	SETAZINDOL	ANOREXIC	
261.10011	$C_{14}H_{15}NO_4$	OXAZORONE	CHOLERETIC	
261.12997	$C_{14}H_{19}N_3S$	METHAPYRILENE	ANTIHIST./-ALLERG.	
	$C_{14}H_{19}N_3S$	THENYLDIAMINE	ANTIHIST./-ALLERG.	
261.13649	$C_{15}H_{19}NO_3$	XIMOPROFEN	ANTIRHEUMATIC	
261.15175	$C_{19}H_{19}N$	PHENINDAMINE	ANTIHIST./-ALLERG.	
261.17288	$C_{16}H_{23}NO_2$	ALPHAPRODINE	ANALGESIC	
	$C_{16}H_{23}NO_2$	BETAPRODINE	ANALGESIC	
	$C_{16}H_{23}NO_2$	BUFURALOL	BETA-ADR.BLOCKER	
	$C_{16}H_{23}NO_2$	DIETHYLAMINOPROPYL CINNAMATE	ANESTHETIC	
	$C_{16}H_{23}NO_2$	ETHOHEPTAZINE	ANALGESIC	
	$C_{16}H_{23}NO_2$	ETOXADROL	ANESTHETIC	
	$C_{16}H_{23}NO_2$	HEXYLCAINE	LOCAL ANESTHETIC	
	$C_{16}H_{23}NO_2$	MENTHYL NICOTINATE	RUBEFACIENT	
	$C_{16}H_{23}NO_2$	METHEPTAZINE	ANALGESIC	
	$C_{16}H_{23}NO_2$	PIPEROCAINE	LOCAL ANESTHETIC	

MASS	FORMULA	NAME	CATEGORY	MS
261.17288	$C_{16}H_{23}NO_2$	PROPERIDINE	ANALGESIC	
261.20926	$C_{17}H_{27}NO$	AMIXETRINE	ANALGESIC	
261.80803	C_3OCL_6	HEXACHLOROACETONE	HERBICIDE	
262.00986	$C_6H_{15}O_5S_2P$	DEMETON-S-METHYLSULFONE	INSECTICIDE	
262.01789	$C_9H_{11}N_2O_3CLS$	TIAMIZIDE	DIURETIC	
262.03882	$C_9H_{12}N_4OCL_2$	GUANOCLOR	ANTIHYPERTENSIVE	
262.05091	$C_{13}H_{11}N_2O_2CL$	CLONIXIN	ANALGESIC	
262.07021	$C_{11}H_{10}N_4O_4$	CARBADOX	ANTIBIOTIC	
262.07423	$C_{16}H_{10}N_2O_2$	INDIGO	CHEMICAL	
262.07760	$C_{13}H_{14}N_2O_2S$	BENZYLSULFAMIDE	ANTIBIOTIC	
	$C_{13}H_{14}N_2O_2S$	SULFANILYLBENZYLAMINE	ANTIBIOTIC	
262.13174	$C_{14}H_{18}N_2O_3$	LETIMIDE	ANALGESIC	
	$C_{14}H_{18}N_2O_3$	METHOHEXITAL	NARCOTIC	MS
	$C_{14}H_{18}N_2O_3$	PHYSOVENINE	NATURAL SUBSTANCE	
	$C_{14}H_{18}N_2O_3$	REPOSAL	HYPNOTIC	
262.14164	$C_{12}H_{22}O_6$	ETOGLUCID	CYTOSTATIC	
262.14700	$C_{18}H_{18}N_2$	FENHARMAN	TRANQUILIZER	
262.15690	$C_{16}H_{22}O_3$	FENCIBUTIROL	CHOLERETIC	
	$C_{16}H_{22}O_3$	HOMOSALATE	DERMATIC	
262.16813	$C_{15}H_{22}N_2O_2$	MEPINDOLOL	BETA-ADR.BLOCKER	MS
	$C_{15}H_{22}N_2O_2$	MIXIDINE	CORONARY DILATOR	
262.94111	$C_6H_6NO_6AS$	ROXARSONE	ANTIBIOTIC	
263.00173	$C_8H_{10}NO_5SP$	PARATHION-METHYL	INSECTICIDE	MS
263.00353	$C_{11}H_{12}NCL_3$	AMFECLORAL	ANOREXIC	
263.04299	$C_{12}H_9NO_6$	MILOXACIN	ANTIBIOTIC	
263.05355	$C_{14}H_{14}NSCL$	TICLOPIDINE	ANTICOAGULANT	MS
263.07131	$C_{14}H_{14}NO_2CL$	CLOPIRAC	ANTIRHEUMATIC	
263.08024	$C_{14}H_{17}NS_2$	DIMETHYLTHIAMBUTENE	ANALGESIC	
263.09061	$C_{12}H_{13}N_3O_4$	OLAQUINDOX	ANTIBIOTIC	
263.09555	$C_{12}H_{16}NSF_3$	TIFLOREX	ANOREXIC	
263.11217	$C_{15}H_{15}NOF_2$	FLUNAMINE	ANTIPARKINSONIAN	
263.11576	$C_{14}H_{17}NO_4$	MOBECARB	HEMOSTATIC	
263.12699	$C_{13}H_{17}N_3O_3$	BENZYLCARBAMYLPIPERAZINECARBOXYLATE	ANTIEPILEPTIC	
263.14408	$C_{16}H_{22}NCL$	CLOQUINOZIN	------------	
263.15214	$C_{15}H_{21}NO_3$	HYDROXYPETHIDINE	ANALGESIC	MS
263.16740	$C_{19}H_{21}N$	INDRILINE	STIMULANT	
	$C_{19}H_{21}N$	NORTRIPTYLINE	ANTIDEPRESSANT	MS
	$C_{19}H_{21}N$	PROTRIPTYLINE	ANTIDEPRESSANT	MS
	$C_{19}H_{21}N$	R-806	ANTIDEPRESSANT	
263.16854	$C_{16}H_{22}NOF$	MELPERONE	NEUROLEPTIC	MS
263.18853	$C_{16}H_{25}NO_2$	ALLYLMETHOXYPHENOXYTRIETHYLAMINE	GYNECOL./OBSTRECT.	
	$C_{16}H_{25}NO_2$	BUTACARB	INSECTICIDE	
	$C_{16}H_{25}NO_2$	BUTETAMATE	SEDATIVE	MS
	$C_{16}H_{25}NO_2$	CYCLEXANONE	ANTITUSSIVE	
	$C_{16}H_{25}NO_2$	GRAVITOL	GYNECOL./OBSTRECT.	
	$C_{16}H_{25}NO_2$	THYMYLISOAMYLCARBAMATE	ANTHELMINTIC	
	$C_{16}H_{25}NO_2$	TRAMADOL	ANALGESIC	MS
263.19976	$C_{15}H_{25}N_3O$	CAPROXAMINE	ANTIDEPRESSANT	
263.84701	C_6HOCL_5	PENTACHLOROPHENOL	DESINFICIENT	MS
263.88156	$C_8N_2CL_4$	CHLORTHALONIL	FUNGIST./ANTIMYC.	
263.97229	$C_7H_{11}O_4CL_3$	PENTHRICHLORAL	SEDATIVE	
264.00868	$C_8H_{15}O_3CL_3$	CHLORALODOL	HYPNOTIC	

MASS	FORMULA	NAME	CATEGORY	MS
264.02231	$C_{10}H_{13}O_4CLS$	CHLOROTHYMOLSULFONIC ACID	FUNGIST./ANTIMYC.	
264.03509	$C_7H_{12}N_4O_3S_2$	SULFADIAZOL	HERBICIDE	
264.04947	$C_{10}H_8N_4O_5$	F 35	ANTIBIOTIC	
264.05532	$C_{14}H_{13}O_3CL$	LONAPROFEN	ANTIRHEUMATIC	
264.06810	$C_{11}H_{12}N_4O_2S$	SULFAMERAZINE	ANTIBIOTIC	
	$C_{11}H_{12}N_4O_2S$	SULFAPERINE	ANTIBIOTIC	
264.07462	$C_{12}H_{12}N_2O_5$	TEMODOX	ANTIBIOTIC	
264.07865	$C_{17}H_{12}O_3$	NAPHTHYL SALICYLATE	ANTIRHEUMATIC	
264.07886	$C_{10}H_{20}N_2S_3$	SULFIRAME	PESTICIDE	
264.08988	$C_{16}H_{12}N_2O_2$	DIFTALONE	ANTIPHLOGISTIC	
264.09325	$C_{13}H_{16}N_2O_2S$	THIALBARBITAL	HYPNOTIC	MS
264.12224	$C_{12}H_{16}N_4O_3$	IPRAZOCHROM	ANALGESIC	
264.12626	$C_{17}H_{16}N_2O$	ETAQUALONE	SEDATIVE	
	$C_{17}H_{16}N_2O$	NICTINDOL	ANTIPHLOGISTIC	
264.13750	$C_{16}H_{16}N_4$	STILBAMIDINE	ANTIBIOTIC	
264.15863	$C_{13}H_{20}N_4O_2$	PENTIFYLLINE	VASODILATOR	MS
264.16265	$C_{18}H_{20}N_2$	AMEZEPIN	------------	
	$C_{18}H_{20}N_2$	CICLOPRAMINE	ANTIDEPRESSANT	
	$C_{18}H_{20}N_2$	MIANSERIN	ANTIDEPRESSANT	MS
264.18378	$C_{15}H_{24}N_2O_2$	DIMETHOLIZIN	ANTIHIST./-ALLERG.	
	$C_{15}H_{24}N_2O_2$	TETRACAINE	LOCAL ANESTHETIC	MS
264.22016	$C_{16}H_{28}N_2O$	DIETHYLAMINOETHYLEPHEDRINE	SYMPATHOMIMETIC	
265.03848	$C_9H_{13}N_3O_2CL_2$	DOPAN	CHEMICAL	
265.07389	$C_{16}H_{11}NO_3$	OXYCINCHOPHENE	ANALGESIC	
265.08513	$C_{15}H_{11}N_3O_2$	FURODAZOLE	ANTHELMINTIC	
265.08850	$C_{12}H_{15}N_3O_2S$	ALBENDAZOLE	ANTHELMINTIC	
265.09100	$C_8H_{15}N_3O_7$	STREPTOZOCINE	CYTOSTATIC	
265.09973	$C_{11}H_{15}N_5OS$	THIETHAZONE	TUBERCULOSTATIC	
265.11028	$C_{17}H_{15}NO_2$	INICARONE	FIBRINOLYTIC	
265.13141	$C_{14}H_{19}NO_4$	ANISOMYCIN	TRICHOMONACIDE	
265.15790	$C_{17}H_{19}N_3$	ANTAZOLINE	ANTIHIST./-ALLERG.	MS
	$C_{17}H_{19}N_3$	DELERGOTRIL	ANTIPARKINSONIAN	
265.16779	$C_{15}H_{23}NO_3$	ETHOMOXANE	TRANQUILIZER	
	$C_{15}H_{23}NO_3$	OXPRENOLOL	BETA-ADR.BLOCKER	MS
	$C_{15}H_{23}NO_3$	PARETHOXYCAINE	LOCAL ANESTHETIC	
	$C_{15}H_{23}NO_3$	TRIMOXAMINE	ANTIHYPERTENSIVE	
265.24056	$C_{17}H_{31}NO$	MYRTECAINE	ANALGESIC	
265.95786	$C_{11}H_7O_3BR$	BROMOHYDROXYNAPHTHOIC ACID	CHOLERETIC	
266.00312	$C_7H_{10}N_2O_5S_2$	MESULFAMIDE	ANTIBIOTIC	
266.02652	$C_{14}H_{12}OCL_2$	CHLORFENETHOL	PESTICIDE	
266.05705	$C_{11}H_{11}N_4O_2CL$	FENOBAM	TRANQUILIZER	
266.05791	$C_{16}H_{10}O_4$	XENYGLOXAL	ANTIBIOTIC	
266.07252	$C_{12}H_{14}N_2O_3S$	TIOXIDAZOLE	ANTHELMINTIC	
266.09027	$C_{12}H_{14}N_2O_5$	DINITROCYCLOHEXYLPHENOL	PESTICIDE	
266.09430	$C_{17}H_{14}O_3$	BENZARONE	ANTIPHLOGISTIC	
	$C_{17}H_{14}O_3$	FURAPROFEN	ANALGESIC	
	$C_{17}H_{14}O_3$	XYLOCOUMAROL	ANTICOAGULANT	
266.10151	$C_{11}H_{14}N_4O_4$	DOXOFYLLINE	BRONCHODILATOR	
	$C_{11}H_{14}N_4O_4$	TUBERCIDIN	TUBERCULOSTATIC	
266.10553	$C_{16}H_{14}N_2O_2$	MIROPROFEN	ANTIPHLOGISTIC	
266.13068	$C_{18}H_{18}O_2$	DIENESTROL	ESTROGEN	
	$C_{18}H_{18}O_2$	EQUILENIN	ESTROGEN	

MASS	FORMULA	NAME	CATEGORY	MS
266.13068	$C_{18}H_{18}O_2$	ISOPROPYLPHENYLPHENYLPROPANEDIONE	DERMATIC	
	$C_{18}H_{18}O_2$	XENYHEXENIC ACID	ANTICHOLESTEREMIC	
266.14191	$C_{17}H_{18}N_2O$	DIPHENAZOLINE	ANTIHIST./-ALLERG.	
266.15518	$C_{12}H_{26}O_4S$	DODECYLSULFURIC ACID	SOLUBILIZER ETC.	
266.16304	$C_{14}H_{22}N_2O_3$	ATENOLOL	BETA-ADR.BLOCKER	**MS**
	$C_{14}H_{22}N_2O_3$	BUCOLOME	ANTIPHLOGISTIC	
	$C_{14}H_{22}N_2O_3$	PRACTOLOL	BETA-ADR.BLOCKER	
	$C_{14}H_{22}N_2O_3$	TRIMETAZIDINE	VASODILATOR	
266.17830	$C_{18}H_{22}N_2$	CYCLIZINE	ANTIHIST./-ALLERG.	
	$C_{18}H_{22}N_2$	DESIPRAMINE	ANTIDEPRESSANT	**MS**
	$C_{18}H_{22}N_2$	MEZEPIN	ANTIDEPRESSANT	
267.05653	$C_{12}H_{13}NO_4S$	OXYCARBOXIN	FUNGIST./ANTIMYC.	
267.05816	$C_{14}H_{15}NCL_2$	CHLORNAPHAZINE	CYTOSTATIC	
267.06776	$C_{11}H_{13}N_3O_3S$	SULFAFURAZOLE	ANTIBIOTIC	
	$C_{11}H_{13}N_3O_3S$	SULFAMOXOLE	ANTIBIOTIC	
	$C_{11}H_{13}N_3O_3S$	SULFATROXAZOLE	ANTIBIOTIC	
267.09676	$C_{10}H_{13}N_5O_4$	ADENOSINE	ENDOG.BIOMOLECULE	
	$C_{10}H_{13}N_5O_4$	VIDARABINE	VIRUCIDE	
267.10817	$C_{17}H_{17}NS$	DAMOTEPIN	HYPNOTIC	
	$C_{17}H_{17}NS$	TISOQUONE	ANTICHOLESTEREMIC	
267.11384	$C_{13}H_{18}N_3OCL$	IMIDOLIN	TRANQUILIZER	
267.12593	$C_{17}H_{17}NO_2$	APOMORPHINE	EMETIC	
	$C_{17}H_{17}NO_2$	MEMOTIN	VIRUCIDE	
267.13314	$C_{11}H_{17}N_5O_3$	CAFAMINOL	VASOCONSTRICTOR	
267.14706	$C_{14}H_{21}NO_4$	AMBENOXANE	MUSCLE RELAXANT	
267.15829	$C_{13}H_{21}N_3O_3$	CARBUTEROL	BRONCHODILATOR	
267.16231	$C_{18}H_{21}NO$	AZACYCLONOL	TRANQUILIZER	
	$C_{18}H_{21}NO$	PIPRADROL	STIMULANT	
267.18344	$C_{15}H_{25}NO_3$	BUTAXAMINE	ANTICHOLESTEREMIC	
	$C_{15}H_{25}NO_3$	METOPROLOL	BETA-ADR.BLOCKER	**MS**
267.29260	$C_{18}H_{37}N$	OCTADECENYLAMINE (DECTAFLUR)	PHARMACEUTICAL AID	
267.94608	$C_9H_7O_3CL_3$	FENOPROP	HERBICIDE	**MS**
267.98803	$C_{13}H_{10}CL_2S$	CHLORBENSIDE	PESTICIDE	
268.00579	$C_{13}H_{10}O_2CL_2$	BISCHLOROPHENOXYMETHANE	PESTICIDE	
	$C_{13}H_{10}O_2CL_2$	DICHLOROPHEN	DESINFICIENT	
268.03402	$C_{11}H_{12}N_2O_2S_2$	ANTAZONIT	ANTHELMINTIC	
268.04439	$C_9H_8N_4O_6$	NIFURTOINOL	ANTIBIOTIC	
268.07356	$C_{16}H_{12}O_4$	FORMONONETIN	DIURETIC	
	$C_{16}H_{12}O_4$	FUROBUFEN	ANTIRHEUMATIC	
	$C_{16}H_{12}O_4$	ISOXEPAC	ANALGESIC	
	$C_{16}H_{12}O_4$	OXEPINAC	ANTIPHLOGISTIC	
268.08077	$C_{10}H_{12}N_4O_5$	INOSINE	PROTEC.LIVER THER.	
	$C_{10}H_{12}N_4O_5$	NIFURDAZIL	ANTIBIOTIC	
268.08479	$C_{15}H_{12}N_2O_3$	HYDROFURAMIDE	RODENTICIDE	
268.08817	$C_{12}H_{16}N_2O_3S$	TOLPYRRAMIDE	ANTIDIABETIC	
268.10994	$C_{17}H_{16}O_3$	METBUFEN	ANALGESIC	
268.11716	$C_{11}H_{16}N_4O_4$	RAZOXANE	CYTOSTATIC	
268.12118	$C_{16}H_{16}N_2O_2$	LYSERGIC ACID	HALLUCINOGEN	
	$C_{16}H_{16}N_2O_2$	RUGULOVASINE	ANTIHYPERTENSIVE	
268.13241	$C_{15}H_{16}N_4O$	RIPAZEPAM	TRANQUILIZER	
268.13578	$C_{12}H_{20}N_4OS$	ISOMETHIOZIN	HERBICIDE	
268.14633	$C_{18}H_{20}O_2$	DIETHYLSTILBESTROL	ESTROGEN	**MS**

MASS	FORMULA	NAME	CATEGORY	MS
268.14633	$C_{18}H_{20}O_2$	DIHYDROEQUILENIN	ESTROGEN	
	$C_{18}H_{20}O_2$	EQUILIN	ESTROGEN	
268.27662	$C_{18}H_{36}O$	OLEYL ALCOHOL	PHARMACEUTICAL AID	
268.31300	$C_{19}H_{40}$	PRISTANE	CHEMICAL	
268.93164	$C_7H_5NO_4CL_2S$	HALAZONE	DESINFICIENT	
269.02927	$C_{10}H_{11}N_3O_2S_2$	SULFAMETHYLTHIAZOLE	ANTIBIOTIC	
	$C_{10}H_{11}N_3O_2S_2$	SULFASOMIZOLE	ANTIBIOTIC	
269.04079	$C_{10}H_{17}NOCL_2S$	DIALLATE	HERBICIDE	
269.04865	$C_{12}H_{13}N_3CL_2$	ALINIDINE	ANTIARRHYTHMIC	
269.04953	$C_6H_{11}N_3O_9$	PROPATYLNITRATE	CORONARY DILATOR	
269.10519	$C_{16}H_{15}NO_3$	DILMEFONE	CORONARY DILATOR	
269.11241	$C_{10}H_{15}N_5O_4$	NIFURETHAZONE	ANTIBIOTIC	
269.11826	$C_{14}H_{20}NO_2CL$	ALACHLOR	HERBICIDE	
269.12145	$C_{10}H_{24}NO_3SP$	TETRAM (TM)	INSECTICIDE	
269.12766	$C_{14}H_{15}N_5O$	BENZODET	CYTOSTATIC	
	$C_{14}H_{15}N_5O$	ENDRALAZINE	ANTIHYPERTENSIVE	
269.14158	$C_{17}H_{19}NO_2$	BUTYLPHENAMIDE	FUNGIST./ANTIMYC.	
269.17796	$C_{18}H_{23}NO$	BIPHENYLYLOXYTRIETHYLAMINE	CORONARY DILATOR	
	$C_{18}H_{23}NO$	DEXTROFEMINE	GYNECOL./OBSTRECT.	
	$C_{18}H_{23}NO$	MOXASTIN	ANTIHIST./-ALLERG.	
	$C_{18}H_{23}NO$	ORPHENADRINE	ANTIHIST./-ALLERG.	MS
	$C_{18}H_{23}NO$	RACEFEMINE	GYNECOL./OBSTRECT.	
	$C_{18}H_{23}NO$	TOLADRYL	ANTIHIST./-ALLERG.	
269.23548	$C_{16}H_{31}NO_2$	HEXETYLAMINE	ANTISPASMOTIC	
269.95041	$C_6H_6O_8S_2$	PERSILIC ACID	------------	
269.95358	$C_6H_7N_2O_4CLS_2$	CLOFENAMIDE	DIURETIC	
270.01875	$C_9H_8N_6CL_2$	NEBIDRAZINE	ANTIHYPERTENSIVE	
270.02452	$C_9H_{10}N_4O_2S_2$	SULFAMETHIZOLE	ANTIBIOTIC	
270.03677	$C_{11}H_{15}N_2OBR$	BROMAMIDE	ANALGESIC	
270.05283	$C_{15}H_{10}O_5$	BAICALEIN	DESINFICIENT	
	$C_{15}H_{10}O_5$	EMODIN	LAXATIVE	
270.05599	$C_{15}H_{11}N_2OCL$	MECLOQUALONE	HYPNOTIC	
	$C_{15}H_{11}N_2OCL$	NORDAZEPAM	TRANQUILIZER	MS
270.06161	$C_{12}H_9N_2O_2F_3$	LEFLUNOMIDE	------------	
270.08921	$C_{16}H_{14}O_4$	IMPERATORIN	FLAVORING	
270.09238	$C_{16}H_{15}N_2CL$	MEDAZEPAM	TRANQUILIZER	MS
270.10044	$C_{15}H_{14}N_2O_3$	ANILAMATE	ANTIPHLOGISTIC	
270.10382	$C_{12}H_{18}N_2O_3S$	CAPROYLSULFANILAMIDE	ANTIBIOTIC	
	$C_{12}H_{18}N_2O_3S$	TOLBUTAMIDE	ANTIDIABETIC	
270.11351	$C_{13}H_{19}N_2O_2CL$	CHLOROPROCAINE	LOCAL ANESTHETIC	
270.11907	$C_{16}H_{18}N_2S$	FENETHAZINE	ANTIHIST./-ALLERG.	
270.12560	$C_{17}H_{18}O_3$	METHOXYPHENYL PHENYLBUTYRATE	EXPECTORANT	
270.13683	$C_{16}H_{18}N_2O_2$	BUTANIXIN	ANALGESIC	
	$C_{16}H_{18}N_2O_2$	ETONAM	FUNGIST./ANTIMYC.	
	$C_{16}H_{18}N_2O_2$	GLYCERGINIC ACID	SWEETENER	
	$C_{16}H_{18}N_2O_2$	PIMETREMIDE	ANTISPASMOTIC	
270.16198	$C_{18}H_{22}O_2$	DIHYDROEQUILIN	ESTROGEN	
	$C_{18}H_{22}O_2$	ESTRONE	ESTROGEN	
	$C_{18}H_{22}O_2$	HEXESTROL	ESTROGEN	
	$C_{18}H_{22}O_2$	TRENBOLONE	ANABOLIC	
270.17321	$C_{17}H_{22}N_2O$	DOXYLAMINE	ANTIHIST./-ALLERG.	MS
	$C_{17}H_{22}N_2O$	NAPHTHOCAINE	LOCAL ANESTHETIC	

MASS	FORMULA	NAME	CATEGORY	MS
270.18445	$C_{16}H_{22}N_4$	PIROGLIRID	ANTIDIABETIC	
270.25588	$C_{17}H_{34}O_2$	ISOPROPYL MYRISTATE	SOLUBILIZER ETC.	
270.29226	$C_{18}H_{38}O$	STEARYL ALCOHOL	PHARMACEUTICAL AID	
270.96665	$C_{10}H_{10}NOBRS$	BROMOPHENOXYPROPYL THIOCYANATE	DESINFICIENT	
271.02792	$C_{11}H_{11}N_3OCL_2$	MUZOLIMINE	DIURETIC	
271.04155	$C_{13}H_9N_3O_2S$	AMOSCANATE	ANTHELMINTIC	
271.04492	$C_{10}H_{13}N_3O_2S_2$	SUBATHIZONE	TUBERCULOSTATIC	
271.05307	$C_{13}H_{15}NOCL_2$	CLORGILINE	ANTIDEPRESSANT	
271.06670	$C_{15}H_{13}NO_2S$	METIAZINIC ACID	ANTIPHLOGISTIC	
271.07639	$C_{16}H_{14}NOCL$	FAMOTIN	VIRUCIDE	
271.08446	$C_{15}H_{13}NO_4$	ACETAMINOSALOL	ANALGESIC	
271.09569	$C_{14}H_{13}N_3O_3$	FTIVAZID	TUBERCULOSTATIC	
271.09906	$C_{11}H_{17}N_3O_3S$	CARBUTAMIDE	ANTIDIABETIC	
	$C_{11}H_{17}N_3O_3S$	METASULFANILYL BUTYLCARBAMIDE	ANTIDIABETIC	
271.10693	$C_{13}H_{13}N_5O_2$	PROPOXYPHENYLAZAPURINONE	ANTIHIST./-ALLERG.	
271.11682	$C_{11}H_{17}N_3O_5$	CARBUBARB	SEDATIVE	
271.12084	$C_{16}H_{17}NO_3$	NORMORPHINE	ANALGESIC	MS
271.13391	$C_{14}H_{22}NO_2CL$	BUPRANOLOL	BETA-ADR.BLOCKER	MS
271.14668	$C_{11}H_{21}N_5OS$	METHOPROTRYN	HERBICIDE	
271.15723	$C_{17}H_{21}NO_2$	APOATROPINE	ANTISPASMOTIC	
	$C_{17}H_{21}NO_2$	DESOMORPHINE	ANALGESIC	
	$C_{17}H_{21}NO_2$	NAPROPAMIDE	HERBICIDE	
	$C_{17}H_{21}NO_2$	NISOXETINE	ANTIDEPRESSANT	
271.19361	$C_{18}H_{25}NO$	CYCLAZOCINE	ANALGESIC	
	$C_{18}H_{25}NO$	DEXTROMETHORPHANE	ANTITUSSIVE	MS
	$C_{18}H_{25}NO$	LEVOMETHORPHANE	ANALGESIC	MS
	$C_{18}H_{25}NO$	RACEMETHORPHANE	ANALGESIC	MS
271.21474	$C_{15}H_{29}NO_3$	LAUROYLSARCOSINE	DESINFICIENT	
272.04670	$C_{10}H_{12}N_2O_5S$	SULFASUCCINAMIDE	ANTIBIOTIC	
272.06195	$C_{14}H_{12}N_2O_2S$	ZOLIMIDINE	TO THERAPY ULCERS	
272.07164	$C_{15}H_{13}N_2OCL$	CHLORMETHAQUALONE	HYPNOTIC	
	$C_{15}H_{13}N_2OCL$	LOFENDAZAM	TRANQUILIZER	
272.07885	$C_9H_{13}N_6O_2CL$	NIMUSTIN	CYTOSTATIC	
272.08961	$C_{12}H_{16}O_7$	ARBUTIN	DIURETIC	
272.09094	$C_{13}H_{12}N_4O_3$	VACOR	RODENTICIDE	
272.11947	$C_{12}H_{20}N_2O_3S$	SOTALOL	BETA-ADR.BLOCKER	MS
272.14125	$C_{17}H_{20}O_3$	ALLENESTROL	ESTROGEN	
272.17763	$C_{18}H_{24}O_2$	ESTRADIOL	ESTROGEN	MS
272.18886	$C_{17}H_{24}N_2O$	QUINISOCAINE	LOCAL ANESTHETIC	
272.98605	$C_{13}H_5N_3CL_2$	PRIDINITRIL	FUNGIST./ANTIMYC.	
272.99823	$C_9H_{12}NO_4AS$	METHYLARSACETIN	ANTIMALARIAL	
273.02264	$C_{11}H_{12}NO_3CLS$	CHLORMEZANONE	MUSCLE RELAXANT	MS
273.05566	$C_{15}H_{12}NO_2CL$	CARPROFEN	ANALGESIC	
273.13649	$C_{16}H_{19}NO_3$	EVADOL	ANALGESIC	
273.17288	$C_{17}H_{23}NO_2$	TILIDINE	ANALGESIC	MS
273.95798	$C_9H_5N_4CL_3$	ANILAZIN	FUNGIST./ANTIMYC.	
273.99348	$C_8H_{11}N_2O_4AS$	TRYPARSAMIDE	ANTIBIOTIC	
274.02848	$C_8H_{19}O_2S_3P$	DISULFOTON	INSECTICIDE	MS
274.03967	$C_{15}H_{11}O_3CL$	CHLORFLURENOL	PLANT GROWTH REGU.	
274.05091	$C_{14}H_{11}N_2O_2CL$	SQ 10996	ANTIDEPRESSANT	
274.06397	$C_{12}H_{16}N_2OCL_2$	FURCLOPROFEN	ANALGESIC	
	$C_{12}H_{16}N_2OCL_2$	NEBURON	HERBICIDE	

MASS	FORMULA	NAME	CATEGORY	MS
274.06414	$C_{15}H_{11}O_4F$	FLUFENISAL	ANALGESIC	
274.08097	$C_{11}H_{18}N_2O_2S_2$	THIONARCON	ANESTHETIC	
274.08413	$C_{15}H_{14}O_5$	DIHYDROXYDIMETHOXYBENZOPHENONE	DERMATIC	
	$C_{15}H_{14}O_5$	GUIACOL CARBONATE	EXPECTORANT	
	$C_{15}H_{14}O_5$	PHLORETIN	PHARMACEUTICAL AID	
274.08729	$C_{15}H_{15}N_2OCL$	NORTETRAZEPAM	TRANQUILIZER	
274.10526	$C_{12}H_{18}O_7$	DIKEGULAC	PLANT GROWTH REGU.	
	$C_{12}H_{18}O_7$	DIPROGULIC ACID	ANTICHOLESTEREMIC	
274.12368	$C_{16}H_{19}N_2CL$	CHLORPHENAMINE	ANTIHIST./-ALLERG.	MS
	$C_{16}H_{19}N_2CL$	DEXCHLORPHENIRAMINE	ANTIHIST./-ALLERG.	
274.14298	$C_{14}H_{18}N_4O_2$	ORMETOPRIM	ANTIBIOTIC	
274.15690	$C_{17}H_{22}O_3$	BORNYL SALICYLATE	RUBEFACIENT	MS
274.18926	$C_{13}H_{26}N_2O_4$	NISOBAMATE	TRANQUILIZER	
	$C_{13}H_{26}N_2O_4$	TYBAMATE	TRANQUILIZER	
274.19328	$C_{18}H_{26}O_2$	NANDROLONE	ANABOLIC	
274.20451	$C_{17}H_{26}N_2O$	PHENAMPROMIDE	ANALGESIC	
274.22967	$C_{19}H_{30}O$	HYDROXYANDROSTENE	ENDOG.BIOMOLECULE	
274.85814	$C_7H_3NOBR_2$	BROMOXYNIL	HERBICIDE	
274.97749	$C_8H_{10}NO_5AS$	ACETARSOL	ANTIBIOTIC	
275.02860	$C_{10}H_{13}NO_4S_2$	METICRANE	DIURETIC	
275.05422	$C_{12}H_9N_3O_5$	NIFUROXAZIDE	ANTIBIOTIC	
275.05588	$C_{10}H_{14}NO_6P$	PARAOXON	PARASYMP.-MIMETIC	MS
275.06545	$C_{11}H_9N_5O_4$	ACETYLFURATRIZINE	ANTIBIOTIC	
275.08024	$C_{15}H_{17}NS_2$	TIPEPIDINE	ANTITUSSIVE	
275.13822	$C_{13}H_{17}N_5O_2$	ADITEREN	------------	
275.13988	$C_{11}H_{22}N_3O_3P$	METUREDEPA	CYTOSTATIC	
275.15214	$C_{16}H_{21}NO_3$	HOMATROPINE	PARASYMPATH.-LYTIC	
275.16338	$C_{15}H_{21}N_3O_2$	MEXOLAMINE	ANALGESIC	
	$C_{15}H_{21}N_3O_2$	PHYSOSTIGMINE	PARASYMP.-MIMETIC	MS
275.16740	$C_{20}H_{21}N$	CYCLOBENZAPRINE	NEUROLEPTIC	
275.18853	$C_{17}H_{25}NO_2$	ALPHAMEPRODINE	ANALGESIC	
	$C_{17}H_{25}NO_2$	BETAMEPRODINE	ANALGESIC	
	$C_{17}H_{25}NO_2$	METETHOHEPTAZINE	ANALGESIC	
	$C_{17}H_{25}NO_2$	PROHEPTAZINE	ANALGESIC	
	$C_{17}H_{25}NO_2$	PROMEDOL	ANALGESIC	
	$C_{17}H_{25}NO_2$	PROPIPOCAINE	LOCAL ANESTHETIC	
	$C_{17}H_{25}NO_2$	TRIMEPERIDINE	ANALGESIC	
275.19976	$C_{16}H_{25}N_3O$	PROPIRAM	ANALGESIC	
275.26130	$C_{19}H_{33}N$	HEXADILIN	VASODILATOR	
276.03354	$C_{10}H_{13}N_2O_3CLS$	CHLORPROPAMIDE	ANTIDIABETIC	
276.04563	$C_{14}H_{12}O_4S$	VITAMIN K-S (II)	VITAMINE	
276.05687	$C_{13}H_{12}N_2O_3S$	SULFABENZAMIDE	ANTIBIOTIC	
276.07962	$C_{12}H_{18}N_2OCL_2$	CLENBUTEROL	BRONCHODILATOR	
276.08270	$C_8H_{16}N_6OS_2$	GLOXAZONE	ANTIBIOTIC	
276.11101	$C_{14}H_{16}N_2O_4$	TAGLUTIMIDE	HYPNOTIC	
276.11572	$C_{12}H_{16}N_6S$	ETINTIDINE	------------	
276.14739	$C_{15}H_{20}N_2O_3$	PIXIFENIDE	ANTIINFLAMMATORY	
276.16265	$C_{19}H_{20}N_2$	MEBHYDROLINE	ANTIHIST./-ALLERG.	MS
276.17254	$C_{17}H_{24}O_3$	CYCLANDELATE	VASODILATOR	
	$C_{17}H_{24}O_3$	MENTHYL SALICYLATE	RUBEFACIENT	
276.18378	$C_{16}H_{24}N_2O_2$	MOLINDONE	NEUROLEPTIC	
	$C_{16}H_{24}N_2O_2$	TETRAETHYLPHTHALIMIDE	RESPIRAT.STIMULANT	

MASS	FORMULA	NAME	CATEGORY	MS
276.20893	$C_{18}H_{28}O_2$	BOLANDIOL	ANABOLIC	
276.22016	$C_{17}H_{28}N_2O$	ETIDOCAINE	LOCAL ANESTHETIC	MS
277.01738	$C_9H_{12}NO_5SP$	FENITROTHION	INSECTICIDE	
277.02879	$C_9H_{12}N_3O_3CLS$	ALIPAMIDE	DIURETIC	
277.03820	$C_9H_7N_7O_2S$	AZATHIOPRINE	CYTOSTATIC	
277.09502	$C_{14}H_{15}NO_5$	FOLESCUTOL	ANTIHYPERTENSIVE	
277.09589	$C_{15}H_{19}NS_2$	ETHYLMETHYLTHIAMBUTENE	ANALGESIC	
277.09819	$C_{14}H_{16}N_3OCL$	METAZACHLOR	HERBICIDE	
277.11028	$C_{18}H_{15}NO_2$	ETOCRILENE	DERMATIC	
277.16779	$C_{16}H_{23}NO_3$	ESTIL	ANESTHETIC	
	$C_{16}H_{23}NO_3$	METHOXYALLYLPHENOXYDIETHYLAMIDE	NARCOTIC	
	$C_{16}H_{23}NO_3$	PARGOLOL	BETA-ADR.BLOCKER	
	$C_{16}H_{23}NO_3$	PRIBECAINE	LOCAL ANESTHETIC	
277.17903	$C_{15}H_{23}N_3O_2$	ACECAINIDE	ANTIARRHYTHMIC	
277.18305	$C_{20}H_{23}N$	AMITRIPTYLINE	ANTIDEPRESSANT	MS
	$C_{20}H_{23}N$	LITRACEN	ANTIDEPRESSANT	
	$C_{20}H_{23}N$	MAPROTILINE	ANTIDEPRESSANT	MS
277.20418	$C_{17}H_{27}NO_2$	PARDIMATE O	DERMATIC	
	$C_{17}H_{27}NO_2$	PROPIVANE	ANTISPASMOTIC	MS
277.27695	$C_{19}H_{35}N$	PERHEXILINE	CORONARY DILATOR	
277.79413	$C_3H_5BR_3$	TRIBROMOPROPANE	PESTICIDE	
277.85780	$C_7H_4O_2BR_2$	DIBROMOSALICYLALDEHYDE	DESINFICIENT	
278.01301	$C_6H_{14}O_8S_2$	TREOSULFAN	CYTOSTATIC	
278.02003	$C_{10}H_{15}O_3S_2P$	FENTHION	PESTICIDE	
278.02660	$C_9H_{15}N_2O_3BR$	ACECARBROMAL	SEDATIVE	MS
278.04266	$C_{13}H_{10}O_7$	EXIFONE	------------	
278.08375	$C_{12}H_{14}N_4O_2S$	SULFADIMIDINE	ANTIBIOTIC	
	$C_{12}H_{14}N_4O_2S$	SULFISOMIDINE	ANTIBIOTIC	
278.10553	$C_{17}H_{14}N_2O_2$	OXAPADOL	ANALGESIC	MS
278.10736	$C_{16}H_{19}O_2CL$	CLIDANAC	ANALGESIC	
278.12666	$C_{14}H_{18}N_2O_4$	MOFOXIME	ANTITUSSIVE	
278.13789	$C_{13}H_{18}N_4O_3$	LOMIFYLLINE	VASODILATOR	
	$C_{13}H_{18}N_4O_3$	PENTOXIFYLLINE	VASODILATOR	MS
278.14191	$C_{18}H_{18}N_2O$	AZANATOR	BRONCHODILATOR	
	$C_{18}H_{18}N_2O$	PROQUAZONE	ANALGESIC	MS
278.15181	$C_{16}H_{22}O_4$	BUTYLPHTHALATE	SOFTENER	MS
278.16304	$C_{15}H_{22}N_2O_3$	TOLYCAINE	LOCAL ANESTHETIC	
278.17830	$C_{19}H_{22}N_2$	METHADONE INTERMEDIATE	ANALGESIC	
	$C_{19}H_{22}N_2$	TRIPROLIDINE	ANTIHIST./-ALLERG.	
278.19943	$C_{16}H_{26}N_2O_2$	AMYDRICAINE	LOCAL ANESTHETIC	
	$C_{16}H_{26}N_2O_2$	DIMETHOCAINE	LOCAL ANESTHETIC	
278.22458	$C_{18}H_{30}O_2$	GAMOLENIC ACID	ANTICHOLESTEREMIC	
	$C_{18}H_{30}O_2$	LINOLENIC ACID	ORGANIC ACID	
279.05653	$C_{13}H_{13}NO_4S$	PROBENECIDE	URICOSURIC	
279.05990	$C_{10}H_{17}NO_4S_2$	LETOSTEINE	EXPECTORANT	
279.06776	$C_{12}H_{13}N_3O_3S$	FEXINIDAZOLE	TRICHOMONACIDE	
279.08262	$C_{15}H_{15}NOCLF$	HALONAMINE	ANTIPARKINSONIAN	
279.11067	$C_{14}H_{17}NO_5$	FENAMIFURIL	ANTIRHEUMATIC	
279.13314	$C_{12}H_{17}N_5O_3$	MORPHOLINOMETHYLTHEOPHYLLINE	DIURETIC	
279.14706	$C_{15}H_{21}NO_4$	AFUROLOL	------------	
	$C_{15}H_{21}NO_4$	METALAXYL	FUNGIST./ANTIMYC.	
279.15829	$C_{14}H_{21}N_3O_3$	KARBUTILATE	HERBICIDE	

MASS	FORMULA	NAME	CATEGORY	MS
279.15829	$C_{14}H_{21}N_3O_3$	OXAMNIQUINE	ANTIBIOTIC	
279.16231	$C_{19}H_{21}NO$	CIDOXEPIN	ANTIDEPRESSANT	
	$C_{19}H_{21}NO$	DOXEPIN	ANTIDEPRESSANT	MS
279.16953	$C_{13}H_{21}N_5O_2$	ETAMIPHYLLINE	BRONCHODILATOR	MS
279.18344	$C_{16}H_{25}NO_3$	MOXISYLYTE	SYMPATHOLYTIC	
279.19870	$C_{20}H_{25}N$	FENPIPRANE	BRONCHODILATOR	
	$C_{20}H_{25}N$	PRODIPINE	ANTIPARKINSONIAN	
279.77340	$C_2H_3OBR_3$	TRIBROMOETHANOL	NARCOTIC	
	$C_2H_3OBR_3$	TRIBROMOETHANOL	NARCOTIC	
279.87830	$C_7H_5OCL_5$	PENTACHLOROCRESOL	DESINFICIENT	
280.01705	$C_9H_{13}O_6SP$	ENDOTHIONE	INSECTICIDE	
280.06301	$C_{11}H_{12}N_4O_3S$	SULFALENE	ANTIBIOTIC	
	$C_{11}H_{12}N_4O_3S$	SULFAMETER	ANTIBIOTIC	
	$C_{11}H_{12}N_4O_3S$	SULFAMETHOXYDIAZINE	ANTIBIOTIC	MS
	$C_{11}H_{12}N_4O_3S$	SULFAMETHOXYPYRIDAZINE	ANTIBIOTIC	
	$C_{11}H_{12}N_4O_3S$	SULFAMONOMETHOXINE	ANTIBIOTIC	
280.10750	$C_{16}H_{15}OF_3$	FLUMECINOL	------------	
280.10994	$C_{18}H_{16}O_3$	IPRIFLAVONE	CORONARY DILATOR	
	$C_{18}H_{16}O_3$	PHENPROCOUMON	ANTICOAGULANT	MS
280.12118	$C_{17}H_{16}N_2O_2$	XINIDAMINE	------------	
280.12455	$C_{14}H_{20}N_2O_2S$	AZABON	STIMULANT	
280.13241	$C_{16}H_{16}N_4O$	HYDROXYSTILBAMIDINE	ANTIBIOTIC	
280.15756	$C_{18}H_{20}N_2O$	FANTRIDONE	ANTIDEPRESSANT	
280.17869	$C_{15}H_{24}N_2O_3$	CORNECAIN (tm)	LOCAL ANESTHETIC	
	$C_{15}H_{24}N_2O_3$	HYDROXYTETRACAINE	LOCAL ANESTHETIC	
	$C_{15}H_{24}N_2O_3$	MEFEXAMIDE	STIMULANT	MS
280.19395	$C_{19}H_{24}N_2$	BAMIPINE	ANTIHIST./-ALLERG.	MS
	$C_{19}H_{24}N_2$	HISTAPYRRODINE	ANTIHIST./-ALLERG.	
	$C_{19}H_{24}N_2$	IMIPRAMINE	ANTIDEPRESSANT	MS
	$C_{19}H_{24}N_2$	MONOMETACRINE	ANTIDEPRESSANT	
	$C_{19}H_{24}N_2$	PRAZEPIN	ANTIDEPRESSANT	
280.21508	$C_{16}H_{28}N_2O_2$	EPIPROPIDINE	CYTOSTATIC	
	$C_{16}H_{28}N_2O_2$	TROMANTADINE	VIRUCIDE	
280.24023	$C_{18}H_{32}O_2$	LINOLEIC ACID	ORGANIC ACID	
280.99884	$C_7H_{14}NO_4CL_3$	CHLORAL BETAINE	HYPNOTIC	
281.00104	$C_{13}H_9NO_2CL_2$	CLOFENAMIC ACID	ANTIPHLOGISTIC	
281.01701	$C_6H_{12}N_5O_2S_2P$	MENAZONE	INSECTICIDE	
281.02773	$C_{13}H_{12}NO_2CLS$	ONTIANIL	FUNGIST./ANTIMYC.	
281.06636	$C_{14}H_{10}NO_2F_3$	FLUFENAMIC ACID	ANTIRHEUMATIC	
281.08004	$C_{15}H_{11}N_3O_3$	NITRAZEPAM	HYPNOTIC	MS
281.08507	$C_{10}H_{20}NO_4SP$	PROPETAMPHOS	INSECTICIDE	
281.09293	$C_{12}H_{16}N_3O_3P$	BENZODEPA	CYTOSTATIC	
281.10519	$C_{17}H_{15}NO_3$	INDOPROFEN	ANALGESIC	
281.12382	$C_{18}H_{19}NS$	PROTHIXENE	NEUROLEPTIC	
281.12632	$C_{14}H_{19}NO_5$	TRIMETOZINE	SEDATIVE	MS
281.13756	$C_{13}H_{19}N_3O_4$	DIPROPALIN (TM)	HERBICIDE	
	$C_{13}H_{19}N_3O_4$	PENOXALINE	HERBICIDE	
281.13889	$C_{14}H_{15}N_7$	DIMINAZENE	ANTIBIOTIC	
281.14158	$C_{18}H_{19}NO_2$	APOCODEINE	EMETIC	
281.15281	$C_{17}H_{19}N_3O$	PHENTOLAMINE	VASODILATOR	
281.16271	$C_{15}H_{23}NO_4$	CYCLOHEXIMIDE	ANTIBIOTIC	
281.17796	$C_{19}H_{23}NO$	ALIMADOL	ANALGESIC	

MASS	FORMULA	NAME	CATEGORY	MS
281.17796	$C_{19}H_{23}NO$	CINNAMEDRINE	ANTISPASMOTIC	
	$C_{19}H_{23}NO$	DIPHENYLPYRALINE	ANTIHIST./-ALLERG.	MS
281.19909	$C_{16}H_{27}NO_3$	AMIFLOVERINE	ANTISPASMOTIC	
281.21435	$C_{20}H_{27}N$	ALVERINE	ANTISPASMOTIC	
	$C_{20}H_{27}N$	TERODILINE	CORONARY DILATOR	
281.27186	$C_{18}H_{35}NO$	DODEMORPH	FUNGIST./ANTIMYC.	
281.81312	C_6CL_6	HEXACHLOROBENZENE	FUNGIST./ANTIMYC.	MS
281.99628	$C_{12}H_8N_2O_2CL_2$	DICLONIXIN	ANALGESIC	
282.04967	$C_{12}H_{14}N_2O_2S_2$	BENSULDAZIC ACID	FUNGIST./ANTIMYC.	
282.05046	$C_9H_{15}O_8P$	BOMYL	INSECTICIDE	
282.06161	$C_{13}H_9N_2O_2F_3$	NIFLUMIC ACID	ANALGESIC	MS
282.10044	$C_{16}H_{14}N_2O_3$	BENDAZAC	ANTIPHLOGISTIC	
282.10382	$C_{13}H_{18}N_2O_3S$	TOLPENTAMIDE	ANTIDIABETIC	
282.12560	$C_{18}H_{18}O_3$	FLUREND	HERBICIDE	
282.13281	$C_{12}H_{18}N_4O_4$	DUPRACETAM	ANTIDEPRESSANT	
282.14673	$C_{15}H_{22}O_5$	OCTYL TRIHYDROXYBENZOATE	ANTIOXIDANT	
282.16198	$C_{19}H_{22}O_2$	MESTILBOL	ESTROGEN	
282.25588	$C_{18}H_{34}O_2$	OLEINIC ACID	ORGANIC ACID	
282.98030	$C_{12}H_7NO_3CL_2$	NITROFEN	HERBICIDE	
283.01669	$C_{13}H_{11}NO_2CL_2$	PROCYMIDONE	FUNGIST./ANTIMYC.	
283.08446	$C_{16}H_{13}NO_4$	PAPAVEROLINE	VASODILATOR	
283.09167	$C_{10}H_{13}N_5O_5$	GUANOSINE	ENDOG.BIOMOLECULE	
283.11209	$C_{16}H_{14}N_3OF$	AFLOQUALONE	MUSCLE RELAXANT	
283.13391	$C_{15}H_{22}NO_2CL$	METOLACHLOR	HERBICIDE	
283.15723	$C_{18}H_{21}NO_2$	BELOXAMIDE	ANTICHOLESTEREMIC	
	$C_{18}H_{21}NO_2$	METHYLDESORPHINE	ANALGESIC	
283.16444	$C_{12}H_{21}N_5O_3$	CADRALAZINE	ANTIHYPERTENSIVE	
283.19361	$C_{19}H_{25}NO$	BENZHYDRYLOXYETHYLDIETHYLAMINE	ANTIPARKINSONIAN	
	$C_{19}H_{25}NO$	ETOLOXAMINE	ANTIHIST./-ALLERG.	
	$C_{19}H_{25}NO$	HEXAPRADOL	STIMULANT	
	$C_{19}H_{25}NO$	LEVALLORPHAN	ANTIDOTE	MS
283.28751	$C_{18}H_{37}NO$	ALDIMORPH	FUNGIST./ANTIMYC.	
283.84322	$C_4H_2N_2O_3BR_2$	DIBROMIN	DESINFICIENT	
283.96842	$C_{11}H_9O_4BR$	BROMEBRIC ACID	CYTOSTATIC	
283.96923	$C_7H_9N_2O_4CLS_2$	DISULFAMIDE	DIURETIC	
284.01348	$C_{10}H_9N_4O_2CLS$	SULFACHLORPYRIDAZINE	ANTIBIOTIC	
	$C_{10}H_9N_4O_2CLS$	SULFACLOZIN	ANTIBIOTIC	
284.03209	$C_{15}H_8O_6$	RHEIN	NATURAL SUBSTANCE	
284.04017	$C_{10}H_{12}N_4O_2S_2$	SULFAETHIDOLE	ANTIBIOTIC	
284.05072	$C_{16}H_{12}O_3S$	TIOPINAC	ANALGESIC	
284.06043	$C_6H_{12}N_4O_9$	TROLNITRATE	CORONARY DILATOR	
284.06130	$C_7H_{16}N_4O_4S_2$	TAUROLIDINE	ANTIBIOTIC	
284.06848	$C_{16}H_{12}O_5$	RHEOCHRYSIDIN	------------	
284.07164	$C_{16}H_{13}N_2OCL$	CHLORMETHAQUALONE	------------	
	$C_{16}H_{13}N_2OCL$	DIAZEPAM	TRANQUILIZER	MS
	$C_{16}H_{13}N_2OCL$	MAZINDOL	ANOREXIC	MS
284.08308	$C_{12}H_{16}N_2O_4S$	TIAPIRINOL	VITAMINE	
284.08470	$C_{14}H_{18}N_2CL_2$	CLENPIRIN	INSECTICIDE	
284.09260	$C_{12}H_{17}N_2O_4P$	PSILOCYBIN	HALLUCINOGEN	
284.11947	$C_{13}H_{20}N_2O_3S$	CARTICAINE	LOCAL ANESTHETIC	
	$C_{13}H_{20}N_2O_3S$	DEXETOZOLIN	------------	
	$C_{13}H_{20}N_2O_3S$	ETOZOLIN	DIURETIC	

MASS	FORMULA	NAME	CATEGORY	MS
284.12916	$C_{14}H_{21}N_2O_2CL$	CLOFEXAMIDE	ANALGESIC	
	$C_{14}H_{21}N_2O_2CL$	CLOVOXAMINE	ANTIDEPRESSANT	
284.13472	$C_{17}H_{20}N_2S$	ISOPROMETHAZINE	ANTIHIST./-ALLERG.	
	$C_{17}H_{20}N_2S$	PROMAZINE	NEUROLEPTIC	MS
	$C_{17}H_{20}N_2S$	PROMETHAZINE	SEDATIVE	MS
	$C_{17}H_{20}N_2S$	TIENOPRAMINE	ANTIDEPRESSANT	
284.15248	$C_{17}H_{20}N_2O_2$	TROPICAMIDE	PARASYMPATH.-LYTIC	
284.17763	$C_{19}H_{24}O_2$	ALMESTRONE	ESTROGEN	
	$C_{19}H_{24}O_2$	METRIBOLONE	ANABOLIC	
284.18886	$C_{18}H_{24}N_2O$	AZAPROCIN	ANALGESIC	
284.20010	$C_{17}H_{24}N_4$	TOLPIPRAZOL	TRANQUILIZER	
284.21402	$C_{20}H_{28}O$	CINGESTROL	GESTAGEN	
	$C_{20}H_{28}O$	DELANTERONE	ANTIANDROGEN	
	$C_{20}H_{28}O$	LYNESTRENOL	GYNECOL./OBSTRECT.	
	$C_{20}H_{28}O$	RETINAL	ENDOG.BIOMOLECULE	
	$C_{20}H_{28}O$	TIGESTOL	GESTAGEN	
284.22525	$C_{19}H_{28}N_2$	IPRINDOLE	ANTIDEPRESSANT	
284.23515	$C_{17}H_{32}O_3$	PALMOXIRIC ACID	ANTICHOLESTEREMIC	
284.27153	$C_{18}H_{36}O_2$	HEXYL DODECANOATE	DERMATIC	
	$C_{18}H_{36}O_2$	STEARIC ACID	ORGANIC ACID	MS
284.96448	$C_6H_8N_3O_4CLS_2$	CHLORAMINOPHENAMIDE	DIURETIC	
284.98780	$C_9H_7N_3O_4S_2$	NITROSULFATHIAZOLE	ANTIBIOTIC	
284.99595	$C_{12}H_9NO_3CL_2$	VINCLOZOLIN	FUNGIST./ANTIMYC.	
285.04194	$C_{10}H_{11}N_3O_5S$	NIFURATEL	TRICHOMONACIDE	
285.06223	$C_9H_{20}NO_3S_2P$	PROTHOATE	INSECTICIDE	
285.10348	$C_{13}H_{19}NO_4S$	PROBENECID	URICOSURIC	
285.11134	$C_{15}H_{15}N_3O_3$	VERAZIDE	TUBERCULOSTATIC	
285.11471	$C_{12}H_{19}N_3O_3S$	SULFANILAMIDODIETHYLACETAMIDE	ANTIBIOTIC	
285.12997	$C_{16}H_{19}N_3S$	ISOTHIPENDYL	ANTIHIST./-ALLERG.	MS
	$C_{16}H_{19}N_3S$	PROTHIPENDYL	NEUROLEPTIC	MS
285.13649	$C_{17}H_{19}NO_3$	CHAVICINE	NATURAL SUBSTANCE	MS
	$C_{17}H_{19}NO_3$	HYDROMORPHONE	ANALGESIC	MS
	$C_{17}H_{19}NO_3$	MORPHINE	ANALGESIC	MS
	$C_{17}H_{19}NO_3$	NORCODEINE	ANALGESIC	MS
285.15175	$C_{21}H_{19}N$	INTRIPTYLINE	ANTIDEPRESSANT	
285.17288	$C_{18}H_{23}NO_2$	KETAZOCINE	ANALGESIC	
	$C_{18}H_{23}NO_2$	MEDRYLAMINE	ANTIHIST./-ALLERG.	
285.17625	$C_{15}H_{27}NO_2S$	LETHANE (TM)	INSECTICIDE	
285.18411	$C_{17}H_{23}N_3O$	MEPYRAMINE	ANTIHIST./-ALLERG.	
	$C_{17}H_{23}N_3O$	PIPERYLON	ANALGESIC	
285.20926	$C_{19}H_{27}NO$	PENTAZOCINE	ANALGESIC	MS
285.94695	$C_8H_8O_5CL_2S$	DICHLOROPHENOXYETHYL HYDROGENSULFATE	HERBICIDE	
285.96221	$C_{12}H_8O_2CL_2S$	FENTICLOR	FUNGIST./ANTIMYC.	
285.99530	$C_{10}H_{11}N_2O_3BR$	BRALLOBARBITAL	HYPNOTIC	MS
286.01276	$C_{14}H_{10}CL_2F_2$	DFDD	INSECTICIDE	
286.01944	$C_9H_{10}N_4O_3S_2$	SULFAMETROL	ANTIBIOTIC	
286.04861	$C_{16}H_{14}OS_2$	TENYLIDONE	PROTEC.LIVER THER.	
286.05091	$C_{15}H_{11}N_2O_2CL$	DEMOXEPAM	TRANQUILIZER	
	$C_{15}H_{11}N_2O_2CL$	OXAZEPAM	TRANQUILIZER	MS
286.05274	$C_{14}H_{16}O_2CL_2$	FENCLORAC	ANTIPHLOGISTIC	
286.07760	$C_{15}H_{14}N_2O_2S$	SULFACINNAMINE	ANTIBIOTIC	
286.08413	$C_{16}H_{14}O_5$	GUACETISAL	EXPECTORANT	

MASS	FORMULA	NAME	CATEGORY	MS
286.08750	$C_{13}H_{18}O_5S$	ETHOFUMESATE	HERBICIDE	
286.09873	$C_{12}H_{18}N_2O_4S$	ANISYLBUTAMIDE	ANTIDIABETIC	
286.11782	$C_{13}H_{14}N_6O_2$	METAZIDE	TUBERCULOSTATIC	
286.12051	$C_{17}H_{18}O_4$	PROCROMIL	ANTIHIST./-ALLERG.	
286.12299	$C_{15}H_{15}N_4OF$	ZOLAZEPAM	TRANQUILIZER	
286.15037	$C_{17}H_{22}N_2S$	THENALIDINE	ANTIHIST./-ALLERG.	
286.15690	$C_{18}H_{22}O_3$	METHALLENESTRIL	ESTROGEN	
286.16813	$C_{17}H_{22}N_2O_2$	FENPIPALONE	ANTIRHEUMATIC	
286.17936	$C_{16}H_{22}N_4O$	THONZYLAMINE	ANTIHIST./-ALLERG.	
286.19328	$C_{19}H_{26}O_2$	BOLDENONE	ANABOLIC	
	$C_{19}H_{26}O_2$	METHYLESTRADIOL	ESTROGEN	
286.20451	$C_{18}H_{26}N_2O$	BUPIVACAINE	LOCAL ANESTHETIC	MS
286.22967	$C_{20}H_{30}O$	DESOGESTREL	GESTAGEN	
	$C_{20}H_{30}O$	RETINOL	VITAMINE	
286.95746	$C_{11}H_7NO_2CL_2S$	CLANTIFEN	ANALGESIC	
287.04149	$C_8H_{18}NO_4S_2P$	VAMIDOTHIONE	INSECTICIDE	
287.05759	$C_{10}H_{13}N_3O_5S$	NIFURTIMOX	ANTIBIOTIC	
287.07045	$C_{11}H_{15}N_5CL_2$	CHLORPROGUANIL	ANTIMALARIAL	
287.07285	$C_{14}H_{13}N_3O_2S$	SULMAZOL	------------	
287.08254	$C_{15}H_{14}N_3OCL$	DAZADROL	ANTIDEPRESSANT	
287.15214	$C_{17}H_{21}NO_3$	DIHYDROMORPHINE	ANALGESIC	MS
	$C_{17}H_{21}NO_3$	ETODOLAC	ANTIPHLOGISTIC	
	$C_{17}H_{21}NO_3$	GALANTAMINE	PARASYMP.-MIMETIC	
	$C_{17}H_{21}NO_3$	RITODRINE	GYNECOL./OBSTRECT.	
287.16740	$C_{21}H_{21}N$	CYPROHEPTADINE	ANTIHIST./-ALLERG.	MS
287.18853	$C_{18}H_{25}NO_2$	ALLYLPRODINE	ANALGESIC	
	$C_{18}H_{25}NO_2$	MOXAZOCINE	ANALGESIC	
287.19976	$C_{17}H_{25}N_3O$	PROXAZOLE	ANALGESIC	
	$C_{17}H_{25}N_3O$	RHODOQUINE	ANTIMALARIAL	
287.20966	$C_{15}H_{29}NO_4$	DIOXAMATE	ANTIPARKINSONIAN	
287.22491	$C_{19}H_{29}NO$	CYCRIMINE	PARASYMPATH.-LYTIC	
	$C_{19}H_{29}NO$	PROCYCLIDINE	ANTIPARKINSONIAN	MS
287.86007	$C_6H_6CL_6$	LINDANE	PESTICIDE	MS
287.95116	$C_{12}H_7O_2CL_3$	TRICLOSANE	DESINFICIENT	MS
288.01095	$C_{10}H_{13}N_2O_3BR$	PROPALLYLONAL	HYPNOTIC	MS
288.04413	$C_9H_{21}O_2S_3P$	TERBUFOS	INSECTICIDE	
288.04900	$C_{12}H_{16}O_4S_2$	MALOTILATE	PROTEC.LIVER THER.	
288.06339	$C_{15}H_{12}O_6$	ERIODICTYOL	EXPECTORANT	
288.06676	$C_{12}H_{16}O_6S$	PROTIOFATE	FUNGIST./ANTIMYC.	
288.08988	$C_{18}H_{12}N_2O_2$	XANTOCILLINE	ANTIBIOTIC	
288.09662	$C_{12}H_{20}N_2O_2S_2$	METHITURAL	NARCOTIC	MS
288.09977	$C_{16}H_{16}O_5$	ALKANNIN	DESINFICIENT	
288.10294	$C_{16}H_{17}N_2OCL$	TETRAZEPAM	MUSCLE RELAXANT	MS
288.11438	$C_{12}H_{20}N_2O_4S$	SOTERENOL	BRONCHODILATOR	
288.12224	$C_{14}H_{16}N_4O_3$	PIROMIDIC ACID	ANTIBIOTIC	
288.14739	$C_{16}H_{20}N_2O_3$	MORSUXIMIDE	ANTIEPILEPTIC	
288.17254	$C_{18}H_{24}O_3$	EPIESTRIOL	ESTROGEN	
	$C_{18}H_{24}O_3$	ESTRIOL	ESTROGEN	MS
288.18378	$C_{17}H_{24}N_2O_2$	PHENGLUTARIMIDE	ANTIPARKINSONIAN	MS
288.20893	$C_{19}H_{28}O_2$	BENORTERONE	ANTIANDROGEN	
	$C_{19}H_{28}O_2$	METHYLESTRENOLONE	GESTAGEN	
	$C_{19}H_{28}O_2$	PRASTERONE	ANABOLIC	

MASS	FORMULA	NAME	CATEGORY	MS
288.20893	$C_{19}H_{28}O_2$	TESTOSTERONE	ANDROGEN	MS
	$C_{19}H_{28}O_2$	TRESTOLONE	ANDROGEN	
288.22016	$C_{18}H_{28}N_2O$	BUMECAINE	LOCAL ANESTHETIC	
	$C_{18}H_{28}N_2O$	BUPIVACAINE	LOCAL ANESTHETIC	MS
288.24531	$C_{20}H_{32}O$	BOLENOL	ANABOLIC	
	$C_{20}H_{32}O$	ETHYLESTRENOL	ANABOLIC	
289.02879	$C_{10}H_{12}N_3O_3CLS$	QUINETHAZONE	DIURETIC	
289.04809	$C_8H_{11}N_5O_5S$	SATRANIDAZOLE	------------	
289.06538	$C_8H_{19}NO_6S_2$	IMPROSULFANE	CYTOSTATIC	
289.07727	$C_{15}H_{15}NO_3S$	ADRAFINIL	SYMPATHOMIMETIC	
289.08696	$C_{16}H_{16}NO_2CL$	NICOCLONATE	ANTICHOLESTEREMIC	
289.11028	$C_{19}H_{15}NO_2$	ALLYLPHENYL CINCHONINATE	URICOSURIC	
289.12334	$C_{17}H_{20}NOCL$	CLEMEPROL	ANTIDEPRESSANT	
	$C_{17}H_{20}NOCL$	CLOFEDANOL	ANTITUSSIVE	
289.12488	$C_{15}H_{19}N_3OS$	BUTAMISOL	ANTHELMINTIC	
289.13458	$C_{16}H_{20}N_3CL$	CHLOROPYRAMINE	ANTIHIST./-ALLERG.	MS
289.15388	$C_{14}H_{19}N_5O_2$	ETAZOLATE	TRANQUILIZER	
289.16779	$C_{17}H_{23}NO_3$	ATROPINE	PARASYMPATH.-LYTIC	MS
	$C_{17}H_{23}NO_3$	HYOSCYAMINE	PARASYMPATH.-LYTIC	MS
289.18037	$C_{18}H_{25}O_3$	OXABOLONE	ANABOLIC	
289.18305	$C_{21}H_{23}N$	TACLAMINE	TRANQUILIZER	
289.20418	$C_{18}H_{27}NO_2$	ALIFEDRIN	------------	
	$C_{18}H_{27}NO_2$	AMINOHEXAN	ANALGESIC	
	$C_{18}H_{27}NO_2$	BUTAVERINE	ANTISPASMOTIC	
	$C_{18}H_{27}NO_2$	CARAMIPHEN	PARASYMPATH.-LYTIC	
	$C_{18}H_{27}NO_2$	DYCLONINE	LOCAL ANESTHETIC	
	$C_{18}H_{27}NO_2$	PENTAPIPERIDE	ANTISPASMOTIC	
289.24056	$C_{19}H_{31}NO$	BENCYCLANE	VASODILATOR	MS
289.91885	$C_7H_3N_2O_3I$	NITROXINIL	PESTICIDE	
289.97001	$C_8H_{13}O_3CL_2SP$	DICHLOFENTHIONE	NEMATOCIDE	
290.03950	$C_{10}H_{14}N_2O_4S_2$	SULTIAME	ANTIEPILEPTIC	
290.05546	$C_{16}H_9O_2F_3$	FLUINDAROL	ANTICOAGULANT	
290.07904	$C_{15}H_{14}O_6$	CIANIDANOL	PROTEC.LIVER THER.	
290.08221	$C_{15}H_{15}N_2O_2CL$	CHLOROXURONE	HERBICIDE	
290.10553	$C_{18}H_{14}N_2O_2$	PHENANTHRYLMETHYLHYDANTOIN	ANTIEPILEPTIC	
290.11859	$C_{16}H_{19}N_2OCL$	CARBINOXAMINE	ANTIHIST./-ALLERG.	
	$C_{16}H_{19}N_2OCL$	ROTOXAMINE	ANTIHIST./-ALLERG.	
290.13789	$C_{14}H_{18}N_4O_3$	BENOMYL	FUNGIST./ANTIMYC.	
	$C_{14}H_{18}N_4O_3$	TRIMETHOPRIM	ANTIBIOTIC	MS
290.16304	$C_{16}H_{22}N_2O_3$	PROCATEROL	BRONCHODILATOR	
290.17428	$C_{15}H_{22}N_4O_2$	CARTAZOLATE	ANTIDEPRESSANT	
290.17830	$C_{20}H_{22}N_2$	AZATADINE	ANTIHIST./-ALLERG.	MS
290.17944	$C_{17}H_{23}N_2OF$	AZABUPERONE	NEUROLEPTIC	
290.18820	$C_{18}H_{26}O_3$	HYDROXYNORTESTOSTERONE	ANABOLIC	
	$C_{18}H_{26}O_3$	IBUVERINE	ANTISPASMOTIC	
290.19943	$C_{17}H_{26}N_2O_2$	PARIDOCAINE	LOCAL ANESTHETIC	
290.22458	$C_{19}H_{30}O_2$	ANDROSTANOLONE	ANABOLIC	
	$C_{19}H_{30}O_2$	ANDROSTENEDIOL	ANABOLIC	
291.02984	$C_{14}H_{10}NO_4CL$	LOBENZARIT	ANALGESIC	
291.03303	$C_{10}H_{14}NO_5SP$	PARATHION-ETHYL	INSECTICIDE	MS
291.06622	$C_{15}H_{14}NO_3CL$	ZOMEPIRAC	ANALGESIC	MS
291.06776	$C_{13}H_{13}N_3O_3S$	AMIDAPSONE	ANTIBIOTIC	

MASS	FORMULA	NAME	CATEGORY	MS
291.07900	$C_{12}H_{13}N_5O_2S$	SULFAMIDOCHRYSOIDINE	ANTIBIOTIC	
291.07911	$C_{12}H_{19}NO_3CLP$	CRUFOMATE	INSECTICIDE	
291.07929	$C_{13}H_{19}NO_2CL_2$	CLORANOLOL	BETA-ADR.BLOCKER	
291.08954	$C_{18}H_{13}NO_3$	NAPTALAM	HERBICIDE	
291.09676	$C_{12}H_{13}N_5O_4$	CARPRAZIDIL	ANTIHYPERTENSIVE	
291.11154	$C_{16}H_{21}NS_2$	DIETHYLTHIAMBUTENE	ANALGESIC	
291.12593	$C_{19}H_{17}NO_2$	METHOXYPHENYLPYRIDYLCRESOL	LAXATIVE	
	$C_{19}H_{17}NO_2$	NEOCINCHOPHEN	ANALGESIC	
291.14053	$C_{15}H_{21}N_3OS$	ZOLAMINE	ANTIHIST./-ALLERG.	
291.15829	$C_{15}H_{21}N_3O_3$	GENESERINE	PARASYMP.-MIMETIC	
291.16231	$C_{20}H_{21}NO$	BUTINOLIN	ANTISPASMOTIC	
	$C_{20}H_{21}NO$	COTRIPTYLINE	ANTIDEPRESSANT	
	$C_{20}H_{21}NO$	DANITRACENE	ANTIHIST./-ALLERG.	
291.17355	$C_{19}H_{21}N_3$	PERLAPINE	HYPNOTIC	
291.18344	$C_{17}H_{25}NO_3$	CYCLOPENTOLATE	ANTICHOLINERGIC	
	$C_{17}H_{25}NO_3$	EUCATROPINE	PARASYMPATH.-LYTIC	
	$C_{17}H_{25}NO_3$	LEVOBUNOLOL	BETA-ADR.BLOCKER	MS
	$C_{17}H_{25}NO_3$	PECILOCIN	ANTIBIOTIC	
291.19870	$C_{21}H_{25}N$	MELITRACENE	ANTIDEPRESSANT	MS
	$C_{21}H_{25}N$	PYROPHENDAN	ANTISPASMOTIC	
291.21983	$C_{18}H_{29}NO_2$	DIETHYLAMINOETHYLMETHYLPHENYLVALERATE	ANTISPASMOTIC	
	$C_{18}H_{29}NO_2$	EXAPROLOL	BETA-ADR.BLOCKER	
	$C_{18}H_{29}NO_2$	KETOCAINE	LOCAL ANESTHETIC	
	$C_{18}H_{29}NO_2$	LOTUCAINE	LOCAL ANESTHETIC	
	$C_{18}H_{29}NO_2$	PENBUTOLOL	BETA-ADR.BLOCKER	MS
291.97493	$C_5H_{10}O_{10}P_2$	DIPHOSPHONOPROPANEDICARBONIC ACID	DIAGNOSTIC AID	
292.04217	$C_{16}H_{14}OCL_2$	PROCLONOL	FUNGIST./ANTIMYC.	
292.04909	$C_9H_8N_8O_2S$	TIAMIPRINE	CYTOSTATIC	
292.06467	$C_{10}H_{17}N_2O_4SP$	ETIMPHOS	INSECTICIDE	
292.08816	$C_{14}H_{16}N_2O_3S$	SULFANILYLANILINOETHANOL	ANTIBIOTIC	
292.09067	$C_{10}H_{16}N_2O_8$	EDETIC ACID (EDTA)	ANTIDOTE	
292.09469	$C_{15}H_{16}O_6$	PICROTOXINE	RESPIRAT.STIMULANT	
292.09786	$C_{15}H_{17}N_2O_2CL$	CLIMBAZOLE	FUNGIST./ANTIMYC.	
292.10994	$C_{19}H_{16}O_3$	CUMATETRALYL	RODENTICIDE	MS
292.12749	$C_{17}H_{18}O_2F_2$	BIFLURANOL	------------	
292.16746	$C_{17}H_{24}O_4$	TRICHODERMIN	CYTOSTATIC	
292.17869	$C_{16}H_{24}N_2O_3$	CARTEOLOL	BETA-ADR.BLOCKER	MS
292.19395	$C_{20}H_{24}N_2$	DIMETINDENE	ANTIHIST./-ALLERG.	MS
	$C_{20}H_{24}N_2$	ELANTRINE	ANTIPARKINSONIAN	
	$C_{20}H_{24}N_2$	ENPRAZEPIN	ANTIDEPRESSANT	
292.21508	$C_{17}H_{28}N_2O_2$	AMBUCETAMIDE	ANTISPASMOTIC	
	$C_{17}H_{28}N_2O_2$	ENDOMIDE	RESPIRAT.STIMULANT	
	$C_{17}H_{28}N_2O_2$	LEUCINOCAINE	LOCAL ANESTHETIC	
292.83717	$C_6NO_2CL_5$	QUINTOZENE	FUNGIST./ANTIMYC.	
292.86870	$C_7H_5NO_2BR_2$	DIBROMOSALICYLAMIDE	DESINFICIENT	
293.04868	$C_{10}H_{16}NO_5SP$	WARBEX VET (TM)	ANTHELMINTIC	
293.09310	$C_{14}H_{16}N_3O_2CL$	AMIPIZONE	------------	
	$C_{14}H_{16}N_3O_2CL$	TRIADIMEFON	FUNGIST./ANTIMYC.	MS
293.10519	$C_{18}H_{15}NO_3$	OXAPROZINE	ANTIPHLOGISTIC	
293.12382	$C_{19}H_{19}NS$	PIMETHIXENE	ANTIHIST./-ALLERG.	
293.15618	$C_{15}H_{23}N_3OS$	DIMAZOLE	FUNGIST./ANTIMYC.	
293.16271	$C_{16}H_{23}NO_4$	PROMOLATE	ANTITUSSIVE	

MASS	FORMULA	NAME	CATEGORY	MS
293.17796	$C_{20}H_{23}NO$	AMITRIPTYLINOXIDE	ANTIDEPRESSANT	MS
293.18920	$C_{19}H_{23}N_3$	AMITRAZ	PESTICIDE	
	$C_{19}H_{23}N_3$	BINODALINE	ANTIDEPRESSANT	
293.19909	$C_{17}H_{27}NO_3$	BUTOXYCAINE	LOCAL ANESTHETIC	
	$C_{17}H_{27}NO_3$	EMBUTRAMIDE	NARCOTIC	
	$C_{17}H_{27}NO_3$	PRAMOCAINE	LOCAL ANESTHETIC	
	$C_{17}H_{27}NO_3$	STADACAINE	LOCAL ANESTHETIC	
	$C_{17}H_{27}NO_3$	N-VANILLYLNONANAMIDE	RUBEFACIENT	
293.21435	$C_{21}H_{27}N$	BUDIPINE	ANTIPARKINSONIAN	
	$C_{21}H_{27}N$	BUTRIPTYLINE	ANTIDEPRESSANT	
	$C_{21}H_{27}N$	PRAMIVERINE	ANTISPASMOTIC	
	$C_{21}H_{27}N$	PROZAPINE	ANTISPASMOTIC	
293.23548	$C_{18}H_{31}NO_2$	KETOCAINOL	ANTIARRHYTHMIC	
293.85272	$C_7H_4O_3BR_2$	DIBROMOSALICYLIC ACID	DESINFICIENT	
294.01175	$C_{14}H_{11}O_3CLS$	CLIPROFEN	ANTIPHLOGISTIC	
294.06004	$C_{11}H_{10}N_4O_6$	NIFURMAZOLE	ANTIBIOTIC	
294.06722	$C_{16}H_{11}N_4CL$	ESTAZOLAM	HYPNOTIC	
294.07866	$C_{12}H_{14}N_4O_3S$	SULFACITINE	ANTIBIOTIC	
	$C_{12}H_{14}N_4O_3S$	SULFAETHOXYPYRIDAZINE	ANTIBIOTIC	
	$C_{12}H_{14}N_4O_3S$	SULFAMETOMIDINE	ANTIBIOTIC	
294.08032	$C_{10}H_{19}N_2O_4SP$	CYANTHOATE	INSECTICIDE	
294.08921	$C_{18}H_{14}O_4$	HYDROXYNAPHTHYLMETHYLSALICYLIC ACID	ORGANIC ACID	
294.09392	$C_{16}H_{14}N_4S$	PHENYL(PHENYLTHIAZOLYL)GUANIDINE	VIRUCIDE	
294.10044	$C_{17}H_{14}N_2O_3$	ROSOXACIN	ANTIBIOTIC	
294.10227	$C_{16}H_{19}O_3CL$	BUCLOXIC ACID	ANTIRHEUMATIC	
294.11034	$C_{15}H_{18}O_6$	CEDRIN	ANTIMALARIAL	
294.12157	$C_{14}H_{18}N_2O_5$	ASPARTAME	SWEETENER	
294.13580	$C_{12}H_{19}N_6OP$	TRIAMPHOS	FUNGIST./ANTIMYC.	MS
294.16198	$C_{20}H_{22}O_2$	NORGESTRIENONE	GESTAGEN	
294.16872	$C_{14}H_{30}O_2S_2$	TIADENOL	ANTICHOLESTEREMIC	
294.17321	$C_{19}H_{22}N_2O$	AMEDALINE	ANTIDEPRESSANT	
	$C_{19}H_{22}N_2O$	BENANSERIN	SEROTONINE ANTAG.	
	$C_{19}H_{22}N_2O$	CINCHONIDINE	TONIC	MS
	$C_{19}H_{22}N_2O$	CINCHONINE	TONIC	MS
	$C_{19}H_{22}N_2O$	KETIMIPRAMINE	ANTIDEPRESSANT	
	$C_{19}H_{22}N_2O$	NOXIPTYLINE	ANTIDEPRESSANT	MS
294.18311	$C_{17}H_{26}O_4$	EMBELIN	ANTHELMINTIC	
294.19434	$C_{16}H_{26}N_2O_3$	PROPOXYCAINE	LOCAL ANESTHETIC	
	$C_{16}H_{26}N_2O_3$	PROXYMETACAINE	LOCAL ANESTHETIC	
294.19837	$C_{21}H_{26}O$	ALDRENOGEST	GESTAGEN	
294.20960	$C_{20}H_{26}N_2$	DIBENZYLAMINOETHYLPYRROLIDINE	ANTIHIST./-ALLERG.	
	$C_{20}H_{26}N_2$	DIMETACRINE	ANTIDEPRESSANT	MS
	$C_{20}H_{26}N_2$	HISTAPIPERIDINE	ANTIHIST./-ALLERG.	
	$C_{20}H_{26}N_2$	MIMBANE	ANALGESIC	
	$C_{20}H_{26}N_2$	TRIMIPRAMINE	ANTIDEPRESSANT	MS
294.90284	$C_9H_4NO_2CL_3S$	FOLPET	FUNGIST./ANTIMYC.	
294.94883	$C_7H_6N_3O_4CLS_2$	CHLOROTHIAZIDE	DIURETIC	
295.01669	$C_{14}H_{11}NO_2CL_2$	DICLOFENAC	ANTIRHEUMATIC	MS
	$C_{14}H_{11}NO_2CL_2$	MECLOFENAMIC ACID	ANTIRHEUMATIC	
295.08044	$C_{12}H_{13}N_3O_6$	GLYCONIAZIDE	TUBERCULOSTATIC	
295.09100	$C_{14}H_{18}N_3CLS$	CHLOROPYRILENE	ANTIHIST./-ALLERG.	
295.09167	$C_{11}H_{13}N_5O_5$	AZIDAMFENICOL	ANTIBIOTIC	

MASS	FORMULA	NAME	CATEGORY	MS
295.09569	$C_{16}H_{13}N_3O_3$	MEBENDAZOLE	ANTHELMINTIC	
	$C_{16}H_{13}N_3O_3$	NIMETAZEPAM	TRANQUILIZER	MS
295.10559	$C_{14}H_{17}NO_6$	NITROTHAL-ISOPROPYL	FUNGIST./ANTIMYC.	
295.10876	$C_{14}H_{18}N_3O_2CL$	TRIADIMENOL	FUNGIST./ANTIMYC.	
295.12084	$C_{18}H_{17}NO_3$	INDOBUFEN	ANTICOAGULANT	
295.12806	$C_{12}H_{17}N_5O_4$	NIFURPIPONE	ANTIBIOTIC	
295.13947	$C_{19}H_{21}NS$	DOSULEPIN	ANTIDEPRESSANT	
	$C_{19}H_{21}NS$	PIZOTIFENE	SEROTONINE ANTAG.	MS
295.15723	$C_{19}H_{21}NO_2$	DIMEPROZANE	TRANQUILIZER	
	$C_{19}H_{21}NO_2$	OXITRIPTYLINE	ANTIEPILEPTIC	
295.16846	$C_{18}H_{21}N_3O$	DIBENZEPIN	ANTIDEPRESSANT	MS
	$C_{18}H_{21}N_3O$	ETOFURADINE	ANTITUSSIVE	
	$C_{18}H_{21}N_3O$	OXADIMEDINE	ANTIHIST./-ALLERG.	
295.17836	$C_{16}H_{25}NO_4$	FLOREDIL	CORONARY DILATOR	
295.19361	$C_{20}H_{25}NO$	DIFEMETOREX	ANOREXIC	
	$C_{20}H_{25}NO$	DIPHEPANOL	ANTITUSSIVE	
	$C_{20}H_{25}NO$	NORMETHADONE	ANTITUSSIVE	MS
	$C_{20}H_{25}NO$	PERASTINE	ANTIHIST./-ALLERG.	
	$C_{20}H_{25}NO$	PRIDINOL	ANTIPARKINSONIAN	MS
	$C_{20}H_{25}NO$	TALOPRAM	ANTIDEPRESSANT	
295.20485	$C_{19}H_{25}N_3$	PICOPERINE	ANTITUSSIVE	
295.23000	$C_{21}H_{29}N$	DIISOPROMINE	CHOLERETIC	
295.94482	$C_6H_9N_2O_5SAS$	SULFARSIDE	ANTIBIOTIC	
295.97142	$C_{14}H_4N_2O_2S_2$	DITHIANONE	FUNGIST./ANTIMYC.	
295.97738	$C_{11}H_{11}O_3CL_3$	TRICHLOROISOBUTYL SALICYLATE	ANALGESIC	
296.00070	$C_{14}H_{10}O_3CL_2$	FENCLOFENAC	ANTIPHLOGISTIC	
296.00379	$C_{10}H_8N_4O_3S_2$	NITRODAN	ANTHELMINTIC	
296.04425	$C_{10}H_{11}N_2O_3F_3S$	FLUORIDAMID	PESTICIDE	
296.04832	$C_{14}H_{14}N_2OCL_2$	ENILCONAZOLE	FUNGIST./ANTIMYC.	
296.05094	$C_{10}H_{20}N_2S_4$	DISULFIRAM	ENZYME INHIBITOR	MS
296.06201	$C_{10}H_{11}N_2O_5F_3$	TRIFLURIDINE	VIRUCIDE	
296.07726	$C_{14}H_{11}N_2O_2F_3$	FLUNIXIN	ANALGESIC	
296.09833	$C_{17}H_{16}N_2OS$	BENTAZEPAM	TRANQUILIZER	
296.10486	$C_{18}H_{16}O_4$	BENZYL FUMARATE	CHEMICAL	
296.11947	$C_{14}H_{20}N_2O_3S$	GLYCYCLAMIDE	ANTIDIABETIC	
296.13135	$C_{21}H_{16}N_2$	PARANYLINE	ANTIINFLAMMATORY	
296.13472	$C_{18}H_{20}N_2S$	METHDILAZINE	ANTIHIST./-ALLERG.	
	$C_{18}H_{20}N_2S$	PARATHIAZINE	ANTIHIST./-ALLERG.	
296.13856	$C_{15}H_{16}N_6O$	AMICARBALIDE	ANTIBIOTIC	
296.15248	$C_{18}H_{20}N_2O_2$	VINTENATE	------------	
296.16238	$C_{16}H_{24}O_5$	EXIPROBEN	CHOLERETIC	
296.16371	$C_{17}H_{20}N_4O$	PROPIZEPINE	ANTIDEPRESSANT	
296.17763	$C_{20}H_{24}O_2$	ETHINYLESTRADIOL	ESTROGEN	
	$C_{20}H_{24}O_2$	METHESTROL	ESTROGEN	
296.18886	$C_{19}H_{24}N_2O$	DIMEVAMIDE	ANTICHOLINERGIC	
	$C_{19}H_{24}N_2O$	IMIPRAMINOXIDE	ANTIDEPRESSANT	
	$C_{19}H_{24}N_2O$	PHENYLHEPTYLNICOTINAMIDE	ANTISPASMOTIC	
296.30792	$C_{20}H_{40}O$	ISOPHYTOL	CHEMICAL	
296.96276	$C_8H_9NO_5CLSP$	CHLORTHION	INSECTICIDE	
	$C_8H_9NO_5CLSP$	DICAPTHON	INSECTICIDE	
296.96448	$C_7H_8N_3O_4CLS_2$	HYDROCHLOROTHIAZIDE	DIURETIC	
296.97263	$C_{10}H_{10}NO_3CL_3$	CLORACETADOL	ANALGESIC	

MASS	FORMULA	NAME	CATEGORY	MS
296.98946	$C_8H_{12}NO_5S_2P$	CYTHIOATE	PESTICIDE	
297.06057	$C_{12}H_{15}N_3O_2S_2$	GLYBUZOLE	ANTIDIABETIC	
297.07833	$C_{12}H_{15}N_3O_4S$	SULFAMIDOPYRIN	ANALGESIC	
297.10348	$C_{14}H_{19}NO_4S$	TRITIOZIN	TO THERAPY ULCERS	
297.10732	$C_{11}H_{15}N_5O_5$	PSICOFURANINE	CYTOSTATIC	
297.11874	$C_{18}H_{19}NOS$	TOLINDATE	FUNGIST./ANTIMYC.	
297.12843	$C_{19}H_{20}NCL$	LOSINDOL	ANTIDEPRESSANT	
297.13649	$C_{18}H_{19}NO_3$	GLAZIOVIN	ANTIDEPRESSANT	
297.17288	$C_{19}H_{23}NO_2$	BENZHYDROLOXYETHYLMORPHOLINE	ANTIHIST./-ALLERG.	
	$C_{19}H_{23}NO_2$	ELUCAINE	LOCAL ANESTHETIC	
	$C_{19}H_{23}NO_2$	TREPIPAM	NEUROLEPTIC	
297.18411	$C_{18}H_{23}N_3O$	ACETERGAMINE	------------	
	$C_{18}H_{23}N_3O$	ATOLIDE	ANTIEPILEPTIC	
297.19401	$C_{16}H_{27}NO_4$	GUAFECAINOL	LOCAL ANESTHETIC	
	$C_{16}H_{27}NO_4$	VALPERINOL	SEDATIVE	
297.20926	$C_{20}H_{27}NO$	CYCLORPHAN	ANTIDOTE	
	$C_{20}H_{27}NO$	TREPTILAMINE	ANTISPASMOTIC	
297.30316	$C_{19}H_{39}NO$	TRIDEMORPH	FUNGIST./ANTIMYC.	
297.33955	$C_{20}H_{43}N$	DIMANTINE	ANTHELMINTIC	
298.05410	$C_{12}H_{15}N_2O_3SP$	DIETHQUINALPHIONE	INSECTICIDE	
	$C_{12}H_{15}N_2O_3SP$	PHOXIM	INSECTICIDE	
298.05582	$C_{11}H_{14}N_4O_2S_2$	GLYPROTHIAZOL	ANTIDIABETIC	
298.08413	$C_{17}H_{14}O_5$	COUMAFURYL	RODENTICIDE	
	$C_{17}H_{14}O_5$	XANOXIC ACID	ANTIHIST./-ALLERG.	
298.10842	$C_{14}H_{19}N_2O_3CL$	CLOXIMATE	ANALGESIC	
298.12051	$C_{18}H_{18}O_4$	METOCHALCONE	CHOLERETIC	
298.12368	$C_{18}H_{19}N_2CL$	CYCLIRAMINE	ANTIHIST./-ALLERG.	
298.13174	$C_{17}H_{18}N_2O_3$	DIPHOXAZIDE	TRANQUILIZER	
298.13512	$C_{14}H_{22}N_2O_3S$	PIPROZOLINE	CHOLERETIC	
298.14164	$C_{15}H_{22}O_6$	SESAMEX	PESTICIDE	
298.14298	$C_{16}H_{18}N_4O_2$	NIALAMIDE	ANTIDEPRESSANT	
	$C_{16}H_{18}N_4O_2$	PIRIBEDIL	VASODILATOR	
298.15037	$C_{18}H_{22}N_2S$	ALIMEMAZINE	NEUROLEPTIC	MS
	$C_{18}H_{22}N_2S$	DIETHAZINE	ANTIPARKINSONIAN	
298.16813	$C_{18}H_{22}N_2O_2$	CARAZOLOL	BETA-ADR.BLOCKER	MS
	$C_{18}H_{22}N_2O_2$	PHENACAINE	LOCAL ANESTHETIC	
298.17936	$C_{17}H_{22}N_4O$	MINAPRINE	ANTIDEPRESSANT	
298.19328	$C_{20}H_{26}O_2$	BENZESTROL	ESTROGEN	
	$C_{20}H_{26}O_2$	NORETHISTERONE	GESTAGEN	MS
	$C_{20}H_{26}O_2$	NORETYNODREL	GESTAGEN	
	$C_{20}H_{26}O_2$	PROMETHESTROL	ESTROGEN	
298.20049	$C_{14}H_{26}N_4O_3$	PAREPTIDE	ANTIPARKINSONIAN	
298.20451	$C_{19}H_{26}N_2O$	NAFTYPRAMIDE	ANTIPHLOGISTIC	
298.25080	$C_{18}H_{34}O_3$	RICINOLEIC ACID	ORGANIC ACID	
298.28718	$C_{19}H_{38}O_2$	ISOPROPYL PALMITATE	DERMATIC	
	$C_{19}H_{38}O_2$	METHYL STEARATE	PHARMACEUTICAL AID	MS
298.32357	$C_{20}H_{42}O$	OCTYLDODECANOL	PHARMACEUTICAL AID	
298.93414	$C_9H_8NO_2CL_3S$	CAPTAN	FUNGIST./ANTIMYC.	
299.03812	$C_{12}H_{14}NO_4SP$	PLONDREL	FUNGIST./ANTIMYC.	
299.05209	$C_{13}H_{18}NO_2BR$	BROMOISOVALERYLPHENETIDINE	SEDATIVE	
299.06883	$C_{10}H_{13}N_5O_4S$	THIOGUANOSINE	CYTOSTATIC	
299.06894	$C_{10}H_{19}NO_5CLP$	PHOSPHAMIDONE	INSECTICIDE	

MASS	FORMULA	NAME	CATEGORY	MS
299.07285	$C_{15}H_{13}N_3O_2S$	FENBENDAZOLE	ANTHELMINTIC	
299.08254	$C_{16}H_{14}N_3OCL$	CHLORDIAZEPOXIDE	TRANQUILIZER	MS
299.09061	$C_{15}H_{13}N_3O_4$	ACONIAZIDE	TUBERCULOSTATIC	
299.10923	$C_{16}H_{17}N_3OS$	BEPIASTINE	ANTIHIST./-ALLERG.	
299.11893	$C_{17}H_{18}N_3CL$	LERGOTRIL	GYNECOL./OBSTRECT.	
299.12699	$C_{16}H_{17}N_3O_3$	MENITRAZEPAM	TRANQUILIZER	
299.14006	$C_{14}H_{22}N_3O_2CL$	METOCLOPRAMIDE	ANTISPASMOTIC	MS
299.15214	$C_{18}H_{21}NO_3$	CODEINE	ANTITUSSIVE	MS
	$C_{18}H_{21}NO_3$	DIMETHYLAMINOETHYL BENZILATE	ANTISPASMOTIC	
	$C_{18}H_{21}NO_3$	HYDROCODONE	ANTITUSSIVE	MS
	$C_{18}H_{21}NO_3$	METOPON	ANALGESIC	
299.16338	$C_{17}H_{21}N_3O_2$	MEMPP	ANALGESIC	
	$C_{17}H_{21}N_3O_2$	NICOGRELATE	------------	
299.18853	$C_{19}H_{25}NO_2$	BUPHENINE	VASODILATOR	MS
	$C_{19}H_{25}NO_2$	PROPINETIDINE	ANTITUSSIVE	
299.22491	$C_{20}H_{29}NO$	GEMAZOCINE	ANTIDOTE	
	$C_{20}H_{29}NO$	IBAZOCINE	ANALGESIC	
299.28243	$C_{18}H_{37}NO_2$	PALMIDROL	ANTIPHLOGISTIC	
299.97859	$C_{15}H_9O_2BR$	BROMINDIONE	ANTICOAGULANT	
	$C_{15}H_9O_2BR$	ISOBROMINDIONE	URICOSURIC	
300.03509	$C_{10}H_{12}N_4O_3S_2$	SULFATROZOLE	ANTIBIOTIC	
300.03824	$C_{14}H_8N_2O_6$	NIFUROQUINE	ANTIBIOTIC	
300.04880	$C_{16}H_{13}N_2CLS$	SULAZEPAM	TRANQUILIZER	
300.05284	$C_{10}H_{12}N_4O_5S$	CARBAZOCHROME SULFONIC ACID	HEMOSTATIC	
300.05532	$C_{17}H_{13}O_3CL$	ITANOXONE	ANTICHOLESTEREMIC	
300.06339	$C_{16}H_{12}O_6$	ACETYLSALICYLSALICYLIC ACID	ANALGESIC	
	$C_{16}H_{12}O_6$	DIOSMETIN	NATURAL SUBSTANCE	
	$C_{16}H_{12}O_6$	HEMATEIN	CHEMICAL	
	$C_{16}H_{12}O_6$	HYDROXYETHOXYOXOXANTHENECARBONIC ACID	ANTIHIST./-ALLERG.	
	$C_{16}H_{12}O_6$	PRATENSEIN	NATURAL SUBSTANCE	
	$C_{16}H_{12}O_6$	TECTORIGENIN	NATURAL SUBSTANCE	
300.06656	$C_{16}H_{13}N_2O_2CL$	CLOBAZAM	TRANQUILIZER	MS
	$C_{16}H_{13}N_2O_2CL$	TEMAZEPAM	TRANQUILIZER	MS
	$C_{16}H_{13}N_2O_2CL$	TOLNIDAMINE	------------	
300.06810	$C_{14}H_{12}N_4O_2S$	SULFAQUINOXALINE	ANTIBIOTIC	
300.10294	$C_{17}H_{17}N_2OCL$	ETIFOXINE	TRANQUILIZER	
300.11101	$C_{16}H_{16}N_2O_4$	DESMEDIPHAM	HERBICIDE	
	$C_{16}H_{16}N_2O_4$	PHENMEDIPHAM	HERBICIDE	
300.13214	$C_{13}H_{20}N_2O_6$	ACTINOBOLIN	ANTIBIOTIC	
300.13933	$C_{18}H_{21}N_2CL$	CHLORCYCLIZINE	ANTIHIST./-ALLERG.	MS
	$C_{18}H_{21}N_2CL$	CLOMACRANE	TRANQUILIZER	
	$C_{18}H_{21}N_2CL$	CLOSIRAMINE	ANTIHIST./-ALLERG.	
300.15863	$C_{16}H_{20}N_4O_2$	AZAPROPAZONE	ANTIRHEUMATIC	
300.17254	$C_{19}H_{24}O_3$	PIRNABINE	------------	
	$C_{19}H_{24}O_3$	TESTOLACTONE	CYTOSTATIC	
300.20893	$C_{20}H_{28}O_2$	ETHYNIDIOL	GESTAGEN	
	$C_{20}H_{28}O_2$	ISOTRETINOIN	DERMATIC	
	$C_{20}H_{28}O_2$	METANDIENONE	ANABOLIC	
	$C_{20}H_{28}O_2$	NORDINONE	ANTIANDROGEN	
	$C_{20}H_{28}O_2$	NORGESTERONE	GESTAGEN	
	$C_{20}H_{28}O_2$	NORVINISTERONE	GESTAGEN	
	$C_{20}H_{28}O_2$	TRETINOIN	DERMATIC	

MASS	FORMULA	NAME	CATEGORY	MS
300.24531	$C_{21}H_{32}O$	ALLYLESTRENOL	GESTAGEN	MS
300.87379	$C_9H_5NOBR_2$	BROXYQUINOLINE	DESINFICIENT	
301.05057	$C_{16}H_{12}NO_3CL$	BENOXAPROFEN	ANALGESIC	MS
301.09589	$C_{17}H_{19}NS_2$	DITHIADEN (TM)	ANTIDEPRESSANT	
301.12334	$C_{18}H_{20}NOCL$	PYROXAMINE	ANTIHIST./-ALLERG.	
301.13141	$C_{17}H_{19}NO_4$	FURALAXYL	FUNGIST./ANTIMYC.	
	$C_{17}H_{19}NO_4$	MORPHINE-N-OXIDE	ANALGESIC	
	$C_{17}H_{19}NO_4$	OXYMORPHONE	ANALGESIC	
301.13478	$C_{14}H_{23}NO_4S$	SULFONTEROL	BRONCHODILATOR	
301.14264	$C_{16}H_{19}N_3O_3$	FEBRIFUGINE	COCCIDIOSTATIC	
	$C_{16}H_{19}N_3O_3$	PRAZITONE	ANTIDEPRESSANT	
301.14666	$C_{21}H_{19}NO$	CYPROLIDOL	ANTIDEPRESSANT	
301.15725	$C_{12}H_{23}N_5O_2S$	LAMBAST (TM)	HERBICIDE	
301.15790	$C_{20}H_{19}N_3$	ROSANILINE	FUNGIST./ANTIMYC.	
301.16779	$C_{18}H_{23}NO_3$	BUTOPAMINE	CARDIOTONIC	
	$C_{18}H_{23}NO_3$	DIHYDROCODEINE	ANTITUSSIVE	MS
	$C_{18}H_{23}NO_3$	DOBUTAMINE	CARDIOTONIC	
	$C_{18}H_{23}NO_3$	ISOXSUPRINE	VASODILATOR	
	$C_{18}H_{23}NO_3$	METHYLDIHYDROMORPHINE	ANALGESIC	
301.21541	$C_{18}H_{27}N_3O$	PENTAQUINE	ANTIMALARIAL	
301.24056	$C_{20}H_{31}NO$	TRIHEXYPHENIDYL	ANTIPARKINSONIAN	MS
301.95712	$C_{12}H_8O_3CL_2S$	CHLORFENSONE	PESTICIDE	
	$C_{12}H_8O_3CL_2S$	GENITE (TM)	PESTICIDE	
301.96186	$C_6H_{11}N_2O_4S_3P$	METHIDATHIONE	INSECTICIDE	
301.99823	$C_4H_6N_4O_{12}$	ERITRITYL NITRATE	CORONARY DILATOR	
302.00627	$C_{14}H_6O_8$	ELLAGIC ACID	HEMOSTATIC	
302.01127	$C_{13}H_{12}O_4CL_2$	ETACRINIC ACID	DIURETIC	
302.02490	$C_{15}H_{10}O_5S$	TIXANOX	ANTIHIST./-ALLERG.	
302.02660	$C_{11}H_{15}N_2O_3BR$	BUTALLYLONAL	HYPNOTIC	
	$C_{11}H_{15}N_2O_3BR$	NARCOBARBITAL	NARCOTIC	MS
302.04266	$C_{15}H_{10}O_7$	MORIN	CHEMICAL	
	$C_{15}H_{10}O_7$	QUERCETIN	NATURAL SUBSTANCE	
302.06222	$C_{16}H_{12}N_2OCLF$	FLUDIAZEPAM	TRANQUILIZER	
302.06445	$C_{16}H_{15}N_2CLS$	ETASULIN	------------	
302.06512	$C_{13}H_{10}N_4O_5$	NICARBAZIN	COCCIDIOSTATIC	
302.07904	$C_{16}H_{14}O_6$	HEMATOXYLIN	CHEMICAL	
302.08375	$C_{14}H_{14}N_4O_2S$	CAMBENDAZOLE	ANTHELMINTIC	
302.09430	$C_{20}H_{14}O_3$	FLORANTYRONE	CHOLERETIC	
302.10151	$C_{14}H_{14}N_4O_4$	TERIZIDONE	ANTIBIOTIC	
302.11140	$C_{12}H_{18}N_2O_7$	BICOZAMYCIN	ANTIBIOTIC	
302.14191	$C_{20}H_{18}N_2O$	DIPHENYLETHYL NICOTINAMIDE	ANTISPASMOTIC	
302.17428	$C_{16}H_{22}N_4O_2$	AMINOPROPYLON	ANALGESIC	
302.18167	$C_{18}H_{26}N_2S$	TANDAMINE	ANTIDEPRESSANT	
302.18820	$C_{19}H_{26}O_3$	ALLETHRIN I	INSECTICIDE	
	$C_{19}H_{26}O_3$	EPIMESTROL	ESTROGEN	
302.22458	$C_{20}H_{30}O_2$	METENOLONE	ANABOLIC	
	$C_{20}H_{30}O_2$	METHYLTESTOSTERONE	ANDROGEN	
303.00182	$C_{10}H_{16}NOCL_3S$	TRIALLATE	HERBICIDE	
303.04444	$C_{11}H_{14}N_3O_3CLS$	GLYCLOPYRAMIDE	ANTIDIABETIC	
303.04829	$C_{15}H_{14}NO_2SP$	CYANOPHENPHOS	INSECTICIDE	
303.07929	$C_{14}H_{19}NO_2CL_2$	CHLORAMBUCIL	CYTOSTATIC	MS
303.08718	$C_{12}H_{18}NO_6P$	MIOTICOL	PARASYMP.-MIMETIC	

MASS	FORMULA	NAME	CATEGORY	MS
303.10580	$C_{13}H_{22}NO_3SP$	PHENAMIPHOS	NEMATOCIDE	
303.12191	$C_{15}H_{17}N_3O_4$	PIDYLON	ANTIRHEUMATIC	
303.13314	$C_{14}H_{17}N_5O_3$	PIPEMIDIC ACID	ANTIBIOTIC	
303.13899	$C_{18}H_{22}NOCL$	CHLORPHENOXAMINE	ANTIHIST./-ALLERG.	MS
	$C_{18}H_{22}NOCL$	PHENOXYBENZAMINE	VASODILATOR	
303.14706	$C_{17}H_{21}NO_4$	COCAINE	LOCAL ANESTHETIC	MS
	$C_{17}H_{21}NO_4$	FENOTEROL	BRONCHODILATOR	
	$C_{17}H_{21}NO_4$	HYDROMORPHINOL	ANALGESIC	
	$C_{17}H_{21}NO_4$	PSEUDOCOCAINE	LOCAL ANESTHETIC	
	$C_{17}H_{21}NO_4$	SCOPOLAMINE	PARASYMPATH.-LYTIC	MS
303.16953	$C_{15}H_{21}N_5O_2$	ADITOPRIM	------------	
303.18344	$C_{18}H_{25}NO_3$	ATROMEPINE	ANTISPASMOTIC	
303.19870	$C_{22}H_{25}N$	PIROHEPTIN	ANTIPARKINSONIAN	
303.21983	$C_{19}H_{29}NO_2$	NEXERIDIN	ANALGESIC	
303.25621	$C_{20}H_{33}NO$	FENPROPEMORPH	FUNGIST./ANTIMYC.	
303.91461	$C_6H_6N_2O_4CL_2S_2$	DICLOFENAMIDE	ENZYME INHIBITOR	
304.01702	$C_{15}H_{10}N_2OCL_2$	DECLORAZEPAM	TRANQUILIZER	
304.05178	$C_{14}H_{12}N_2O_4S$	TIOXACIN	ANTIBIOTIC	
304.05831	$C_{15}H_{12}O_7$	KHELLINOCARBONIC ACID	VASODILATOR	
304.07453	$C_{13}H_{18}N_2O_2CL_2$	MEDPHALAN	CYTOSTATIC	
	$C_{13}H_{18}N_2O_2CL_2$	MELPHALAN	CYTOSTATIC	
	$C_{13}H_{18}N_2O_2CL_2$	MERPHALAN	CYTOSTATIC	
	$C_{13}H_{18}N_2O_2CL_2$	METAMELFALAN	CYTOSTATIC	
304.08010	$C_{16}H_{17}N_2CLS$	CHLORPHENETAZINE	TRANQUILIZER	
304.08479	$C_{18}H_{12}N_2O_3$	XANTHOCILLIN Y1	ANTIBIOTIC	
304.08816	$C_{15}H_{16}N_2O_3S$	SULFAMETOYL	ANTIBIOTIC	
304.09566	$C_{10}H_{22}N_2O_4CL_2$	MANNOMUSTINE	CYTOSTATIC	
304.10105	$C_{12}H_{21}N_2O_3SP$	DIMPYLATE	INSECTICIDE	MS
304.11582	$C_{13}H_{20}O_8$	PENTAERYTHRITOL TETRAACETATE	ANTICHOLESTEREMIC	
304.12455	$C_{16}H_{20}N_2O_2S$	TIPINDOL	ANTIHIST./-ALLERG.	
304.13108	$C_{17}H_{20}O_5$	ACETYLHELENALIN	NATURAL SUBSTANCE	
	$C_{17}H_{20}O_5$	MATRICARIN	NATURAL SUBSTANCE	
304.13355	$C_{15}H_{17}N_4O_2F$	FLUPIRTIN	ANALGESIC	
304.13986	$C_{14}H_{19}N_2O_2F_3$	FLUBANILATE	ANTIDEPRESSANT	
304.14231	$C_{16}H_{20}N_2O_4$	DIARBARONE	ANTICOAGULANT	
304.14547	$C_{16}H_{21}N_4CL$	ENPIPRAZOLE	TRANQUILIZER	
	$C_{16}H_{21}N_4CL$	MEPIPRAZOLE	STIMULANT	
304.17869	$C_{17}H_{24}N_2O_3$	CARPERIDINE	ANALGESIC	
304.22631	$C_{17}H_{28}N_4O$	PIPERAMIDE	PESTICIDE	
304.24023	$C_{20}H_{32}O_2$	ARACHIDONIC ACID	ORGANIC ACID	
	$C_{20}H_{32}O_2$	DROSTANOLONE	ANABOLIC	
	$C_{20}H_{32}O_2$	MESTANOLONE	ANABOLIC	
	$C_{20}H_{32}O_2$	MESTEROLONE	ANDROGEN	
	$C_{20}H_{32}O_2$	METHANDRIOL	ANABOLIC	
304.91044	C_9H_5NOCLI	CLIOQUINOL	DESINFICIENT	
304.91783	$C_7H_7NO_4CL_3P$	FOSPIRATE	ANTHELMINTIC	
304.95490	$C_9H_8NO_3I$	IODOHIPPURIC ACID	DIAGNOSTIC AID	
305.04703	$C_{13}H_{11}N_3O_4S$	SULFONIAZIDE	TUBERCULOSTATIC	
305.07198	$C_{18}H_{12}N_3CL$	CLIMIQUALIN	ANTICHOLESTEREMIC	
305.08187	$C_{16}H_{16}NO_3CL$	NICOFIBRATE	ANTICHOLESTEREMIC	
305.09630	$C_{11}H_{20}N_3O_3SP$	PIRIMIPHOS-METHYL	INSECTICIDE	
	$C_{11}H_{20}N_3O_3SP$	PYRIMITATE	INSECTICIDE	

MASS	FORMULA	NAME	CATEGORY	MS
305.13756	$C_{15}H_{19}N_3O_4$	TROPABAZATE	------------	
305.14072	$C_{15}H_{20}N_5CL$	SPIRAZIN	ANTHELMINTIC	
305.16271	$C_{17}H_{23}NO_4$	ATROPINE-N-OXIDE	PARASYMPATH.-LYTIC	
	$C_{17}H_{23}NO_4$	BUCUMOLOL	BETA-ADR.BLOCKER	
	$C_{17}H_{23}NO_4$	CETRAXATE	TO THERAPY ULCERS	
305.19909	$C_{18}H_{27}NO_3$	CAPSAICIN	RUBEFACIENT	
	$C_{18}H_{27}NO_3$	DROXYPROPIN	ANTITUSSIVE	
	$C_{18}H_{27}NO_3$	MINEPENTATE	ANTIPARKINSONIAN	
305.23548	$C_{19}H_{31}NO_2$	AMAFOLONE	ANTIARRHYTHMIC	
305.91023	$C_6H_{12}O_4BR_2$	MITOBRONITOL	CYTOSTATIC	
	$C_6H_{12}O_4BR_2$	MITOLACTOL	CYTOSTATIC	
305.93239	$C_8H_7N_2OIS$	IODOPROPINYLOXYMETHYLTHIOPYRIMIDIN	FUNGIST./ANTIMYC.	
305.98513	$C_9H_{11}N_2O_5BR$	BROXURIDIN	------------	
306.04559	$C_8H_{20}O_6SP_2$	PHOSARBIN	PARASYMP.-MIMETIC	
306.06743	$C_{14}H_{14}N_2O_4S$	ACEDIASULFONIC ACID	ANTIBIOTIC	
306.07395	$C_{15}H_{14}O_7$	LEUCOCIANIDOL	VITAMINE	
306.07866	$C_{13}H_{14}N_4O_3S$	FORMYLSULFISOMIDINE	ANTIBIOTIC	
306.09421	$C_{18}H_{20}CL_2$	PERTHANE	INSECTICIDE	
306.12560	$C_{20}H_{18}O_3$	PHENOLPHTHALOL	LAXATIVE	
306.12878	$C_9H_{18}N_6O_6$	HEXAMETHYLOLMELAMINE	CYTOSTATIC	
306.14673	$C_{17}H_{22}O_5$	PYRETHROSIN	NATURAL SUBSTANCE	
306.15796	$C_{16}H_{22}N_2O_4$	INPROQUONE	CYTOSTATIC	
306.18311	$C_{18}H_{26}O_4$	ISOAMYL PHTHALATE	SOFTENER	
306.19434	$C_{17}H_{26}N_2O_3$	DIBUSADOL	ANALGESIC	
	$C_{17}H_{26}N_2O_3$	SOQUINOLOL	BETA-ADR.BLOCKER	
306.20174	$C_{19}H_{30}OS$	EPITIOSTANOL	CYTOSTATIC	
306.21950	$C_{19}H_{30}O_3$	ANDROSTANEDIOLONE	ENDOG.BIOMOLECULE	
	$C_{19}H_{30}O_3$	OXANDROLONE	ANABOLIC	
306.23073	$C_{18}H_{30}N_2O_2$	BUTACAINE	LOCAL ANESTHETIC	
306.98367	$C_{11}H_{11}NO_3CL_2S$	DICHLORMEZANONE	MUSCLE RELAXANT	
306.98441	$C_{13}H_{10}NO_3BR$	RESORANTEL	ANTHELMINTIC	
307.02629	$C_{12}H_9N_3O_5S$	ACETOXYNITROTHIAZOLYLBENZAMIDE	ANTHELMINTIC	
307.08381	$C_{10}H_{17}N_3O_6S$	GLUTATHIONE	ENDOG.BIOMOLECULE	
307.09167	$C_{12}H_{13}N_5O_5$	NIFURIZONE	ANTIBIOTIC	
307.10309	$C_{19}H_{17}NOS$	TOLNAFTATE	FUNGIST./ANTIMYC.	
307.11030	$C_{13}H_{17}N_5O_2S$	SULFASYMAZINE	ANTIBIOTIC	
307.14514	$C_{16}H_{22}N_3OCL$	CLETOQUINE	ANTIPHLOGISTIC	
	$C_{16}H_{22}N_3OCL$	ZETIDOLIN	------------	
307.15723	$C_{20}H_{21}NO_2$	MOXAVERINE	ANTISPASMOTIC	MS
307.16060	$C_{17}H_{25}NO_2S$	NEOTROPINE	PARASYMPATH.-LYTIC	
307.16846	$C_{19}H_{21}N_3O$	TALASTINE	ANTIHIST./-ALLERG.	
307.17836	$C_{17}H_{25}NO_4$	BUFLOMEDIL	VASODILATOR	
	$C_{17}H_{25}NO_4$	IBOPAMINE	DIURETIC	
	$C_{17}H_{25}NO_4$	TROCIMINE	ANTIDEPRESSANT	
307.19361	$C_{21}H_{25}NO$	BENZATROPINE	PARASYMPATH.-LYTIC	MS
	$C_{21}H_{25}NO$	HEPZIDIN	ANTIDEPRESSANT	
307.21474	$C_{18}H_{29}NO_3$	AMPROTROPINE	PARASYMPATH.-LYTIC	
	$C_{18}H_{29}NO_3$	BETOXOLOL	BETA-ADR.BLOCKER	
	$C_{18}H_{29}NO_3$	BUTAMIRATE	ANTITUSSIVE	
	$C_{18}H_{29}NO_3$	TOPICAINE	LOCAL ANESTHETIC	
307.22598	$C_{17}H_{29}N_3O_2$	AMOXECAINE	LOCAL ANESTHETIC	
307.80470	$C_4H_7OBR_3$	TRIBROMOBUTANOL	CHEMICAL	

MASS	FORMULA	NAME	CATEGORY	MS
307.96212	$C_8H_{11}O_6CL_3$	CHLORALOSE	HYPNOTIC	
307.99255	$C_{12}H_8N_2O_4S_2$	NITROPHENIDE	COCCIDIOSTATIC	
308.03059	$C_{11}H_{17}O_4S_2P$	FENSULFOTHION	NEMATOCIDE	MS
308.03546	$C_{14}H_{12}O_6S$	SULISOBENZONE	DERMATIC	
308.04332	$C_{16}H_8N_2O_5$	CATALIN	OPHTALMIC	
308.04670	$C_{13}H_{12}N_2O_5S$	NIMESULIDE	ANTIPHLOGISTIC	
	$C_{13}H_{12}N_2O_5S$	SULFANILAMIDOSALICYLIC ACID	ANTIBIOTIC	
308.07164	$C_{18}H_{13}N_2OCL$	PINAZEPAM	TRANQUILIZER	
308.08287	$C_{17}H_{13}N_4CL$	ALPRAZOLAM	TRANQUILIZER	
308.09431	$C_{13}H_{16}N_4O_3S$	CYCOTIAMINE	VITAMINE	
308.10486	$C_{19}H_{16}O_4$	WARFARIN	ANTICOAGULANT	MS
308.11609	$C_{18}H_{16}N_2O_3$	AMFONELIC ACID	STIMULANT	
308.12733	$C_{17}H_{16}N_4O_2$	NIFENAZONE	ANALGESIC	MS
308.13722	$C_{15}H_{20}N_2O_5$	TRIMETHPHENCARBAMOYLMETHIMINODIAC.	DIAGNOSTIC AID	
308.14125	$C_{20}H_{20}O_3$	EQUILENIN ACETATE	ESTROGEN	
308.15248	$C_{19}H_{20}N_2O_2$	PHENYLBUTAZONE	ANALGESIC	MS
308.15431	$C_{18}H_{25}O_2CL$	NORCLOSTEBOL	ANABOLIC	
308.18886	$C_{20}H_{24}N_2O$	INDECAINIDE	------------	
308.20999	$C_{17}H_{28}N_2O_3$	AMBUCAINE	LOCAL ANESTHETIC	
	$C_{17}H_{28}N_2O_3$	BETHOXYCAINE	LOCAL ANESTHETIC	
	$C_{17}H_{28}N_2O_3$	BRONCHOCAINE	LOCAL ANESTHETIC	
	$C_{17}H_{28}N_2O_3$	METABUTOXYCAINE	LOCAL ANESTHETIC	
	$C_{17}H_{28}N_2O_3$	OXYBUPROCAINE	LOCAL ANESTHETIC	
308.27153	$C_{20}H_{36}O_2$	ETHYL LINOLEATE	CHEMICAL	
308.31915	$C_{20}H_{40}N_2$	GLYODIN	FUNGIST./ANTIMYC.	
309.03234	$C_{15}H_{13}NO_2CL_2$	NITROBISCHLOROPHENYLPROPANE	INSECTICIDE	
309.06372	$C_{17}H_{11}NO_5$	CARBOXYHYDROXYCINCHOPHEN	ANTIARRHYTHMIC	
309.07833	$C_{13}H_{15}N_3O_4S$	ACETYL SULFISOXAZOLE	ANTIBIOTIC	
	$C_{13}H_{15}N_3O_4S$	GLYMIDINE	ANTIDIABETIC	
309.08956	$C_{12}H_{15}N_5O_3S$	SULFAGUANOL	ANTIBIOTIC	
309.10011	$C_{18}H_{15}NO_4$	AMINAFTONE	HEMOSTATIC	
309.10348	$C_{15}H_{19}NO_4S$	BENCISTEINE	MUCOLYTIC	
309.11874	$C_{19}H_{19}NOS$	KETOTIFEN	ANTIHIST./-ALLERG.	MS
309.12124	$C_{15}H_{19}NO_6$	ESCULAMINE	HEMOSTATIC	
309.12258	$C_{16}H_{15}N_5O_2$	TRIZOXIME	ANTIDEPRESSANT	
309.13405	$C_{17}H_{18}NOF_3$	FLUOXETIN	ANTIDEPRESSANT	
309.13649	$C_{19}H_{19}NO_3$	DIMETHYLAMINOETHOXYFLAVONE	CORONARY DILATOR	
309.14371	$C_{13}H_{19}N_5O_4$	DIMETHAMINOETHYLTHEOPHYLL. ACET.	BRONCHODILATOR	
309.14773	$C_{18}H_{19}N_3O_2$	DIACETAZOTOL	DERMATIC	
309.15512	$C_{20}H_{23}NS$	METIXENE	PARASYMPATH.-LYTIC	MS
309.17288	$C_{20}H_{23}NO_2$	AMOLANONE	LOCAL ANESTHETIC	
	$C_{20}H_{23}NO_2$	CIHEPTOLAN	ANALGESIC	
	$C_{20}H_{23}NO_2$	DEXOXADROL	ANALGESIC	
	$C_{20}H_{23}NO_2$	DIOXADROL	ANTIDEPRESSANT	
	$C_{20}H_{23}NO_2$	LEVOXADROL	ANTIDEPRESSANT	
	$C_{20}H_{23}NO_2$	PAVATRINE	PARASYMPATH.-LYTIC	
309.18411	$C_{19}H_{23}N_3O$	BENZYDAMINE	ANALGESIC	MS
309.18594	$C_{18}H_{28}NOCL$	CLOFENCICLAN	STIMULANT	
309.19401	$C_{17}H_{27}NO_4$	METIPRANOLOL	BETA-ADR.BLOCKER	MS
	$C_{17}H_{27}NO_4$	NADOLOL	BETA-ADR.BLOCKER	MS
309.20926	$C_{21}H_{27}NO$	BENPROPERINE	ANTITUSSIVE	
	$C_{21}H_{27}NO$	DIFENIDOL	ANTIHIST./-ALLERG.	

MASS	FORMULA	NAME	CATEGORY	MS
309.20926	$C_{21}H_{27}NO$	ISOMETHADONE	ANALGESIC	
	$C_{21}H_{27}NO$	LEVOMETHADONE	ANALGESIC	MS
	$C_{21}H_{27}NO$	METHADONE	ANALGESIC	MS
309.26678	$C_{19}H_{35}NO_2$	DICYCLOVERINE	ANTISPASMOTIC	MS
309.84442	$C_8H_4CL_6$	BISTRICHLOROMETHYLBENZENE	ANTHELMINTIC	
309.91373	$C_9H_5N_2O_2CL_3S$	CLOTIOXONE	FUNGIST./ANTIMYC.	
309.99530	$C_{12}H_{11}N_2O_3BR$	bROPHEBARBITAL	HYPNOTIC	
310.01635	$C_{15}H_{12}O_3CL_2$	SESIN	HERBICIDE	
310.02511	$C_{14}H_{15}O_2S_2P$	EDIPHENPHOS	FUNGIST./ANTIMYC.	
310.03206	$C_{14}H_9N_2O_2CLF_2$	DIFLUBENZURONE	INSECTICIDE	
310.05984	$C_{17}H_{14}N_2S_2$	FEZATIONE	FUNGIST./ANTIMYC.	
310.05990	$C_{11}H_{13}N_2O_3F_3S$	MEFLUIDIDE	PLANT GROWTH REGU.	
310.07358	$C_{12}H_{14}N_4O_4S$	SULFADIMETHOXINE	ANTIBIOTIC	
	$C_{12}H_{14}N_4O_4S$	SULFADOXINE	ANTIBIOTIC	
310.08729	$C_{18}H_{15}N_2OCL$	SL-512	ANALGESIC	
310.10526	$C_{15}H_{18}O_7$	PICROTIN	NATURAL SUBSTANCE	
310.10863	$C_{12}H_{22}O_7S$	DIISOBUTYL SULFOSUCCINIC ACID	HERBICIDE	
310.11806	$C_{17}H_{17}O_2F_3$	TERFLURANOL	CYTOSTATIC	
310.13512	$C_{15}H_{22}N_2O_3S$	HEPTOLAMIDE	ANTIDIABETIC	
310.14164	$C_{16}H_{22}O_6$	TREPIBUTONE	CHOLERETIC	
310.14481	$C_{16}H_{23}N_2O_2CL$	ALLOCLAMIDE	ANTITUSSIVE	
310.14700	$C_{22}H_{18}N_2$	BIFONAZOLE	FUNGIST./ANTIMYC.	
310.15037	$C_{19}H_{22}N_2S$	DIMELAZINE	SEDATIVE	
	$C_{19}H_{22}N_2S$	PECAZINE	NEUROLEPTIC	MS
310.15690	$C_{20}H_{22}O_3$	NAFENOPIN	ANTICHOLESTEREMIC	
310.16813	$C_{19}H_{22}N_2O_2$	HYDROXINDASOL	STIMULANT	
	$C_{19}H_{22}N_2O_2$	RAUPIN	ANTIHYPERTENSIVE	
310.18926	$C_{16}H_{26}N_2O_4$	PAMATOLOL	BETA-ADR.BLOCKER	
310.19328	$C_{21}H_{26}O_2$	CANNABINOL	NATURAL SUBSTANCE	MS
	$C_{21}H_{26}O_2$	MESTRANOL	ESTROGEN	
310.20451	$C_{20}H_{26}N_2O$	ANILOPAM	ANALGESIC	
	$C_{20}H_{26}N_2O$	IBOGAINE	ANTIDEPRESSANT	
	$C_{20}H_{26}N_2O$	TABERNANTHINE	ANALGESIC	
310.25080	$C_{19}H_{34}O_3$	METHOPRENE	INSECTICIDE	
310.28718	$C_{20}H_{38}O_2$	PROSTANOIC ACID	ORGANIC ACID	
310.93487	$C_{12}H_7NO_2CLBR$	HALACRINATE	FUNGIST./ANTIMYC.	
310.94448	$C_7H_{10}NO_6SAS$	PHENARSONE SULFOXYLATE	ANTIBIOTIC	
310.96156	$C_{12}H_{10}NO_2BRS$	BROFEZIL	ANTIPHLOGISTIC	
310.98828	$C_{11}H_{12}NO_3CL_3$	CHLORALSALICYLAMIDE	SEDATIVE	
310.99452	$C_{11}H_6N_3O_6CL$	LODOXAMIDE	ANTIHIST./-ALLERG.	
311.02279	$C_{14}H_8NO_2F_3S$	FLUTIAZINE	ANTIPHLOGISTIC	
311.04277	$C_{14}H_{11}NO_3F_2S$	DIFLUMIDONE	ANTIPHLOGISTIC	
311.06883	$C_{11}H_{13}N_5O_4S$	SULFATRIAZINE	ANTIBIOTIC	
311.08437	$C_{16}H_{19}NOCL_2$	MITOCLOMINE	CYTOSTATIC	
311.09061	$C_{16}H_{13}N_3O_4$	NITROMETHAQUALONE	HYPNOTIC	
311.09398	$C_{13}H_{17}N_3O_4S$	METAMIZOL	ANALGESIC	MS
311.10769	$C_{19}H_{18}NOCL$	CLOPIPAZANE	TRANQUILIZER	
311.12971	$C_{17}H_{17}NF_4$	MK-251	ANTIARRHYTHMIC	
311.13036	$C_{14}H_{21}N_3O_3S$	METAHEXAMIDE	ANTIDIABETIC	
	$C_{14}H_{21}N_3O_3S$	TOLAZAMIDE	ANTIDIABETIC	
311.14408	$C_{20}H_{22}NCL$	PYRROBUTAMINE	ANTIHIST./-ALLERG.	
311.15214	$C_{19}H_{21}NO_3$	NALORPHINE	ANTIDOTE	

MASS	FORMULA	NAME	CATEGORY	MS
311.15214	$C_{19}H_{21}NO_3$	THEBAINE	NATURAL SUBSTANCE	MS
311.15936	$C_{13}H_{21}N_5O_4$	XANTHINOL	VASODILATOR	
311.17077	$C_{20}H_{25}NS$	TALSUPRAM	ANTIDEPRESSANT	
311.17644	$C_{16}H_{26}N_3OCL$	CLODACAINE	LOCAL ANESTHETIC	
311.18853	$C_{20}H_{25}NO_2$	ADIPHENINE	ANTISPASMOTIC	MS
	$C_{20}H_{25}NO_2$	BENZOBUTAMINE	ANTITUSSIVE	
	$C_{20}H_{25}NO_2$	ESTRAZINOL	ESTROGEN	
	$C_{20}H_{25}NO_2$	FEMOXETIN	ANTIDEPRESSANT	
	$C_{20}H_{25}NO_2$	FOMOCAINE	LOCAL ANESTHETIC	
	$C_{20}H_{25}NO_2$	PROPANOCAINE	LOCAL ANESTHETIC	
311.18967	$C_{17}H_{26}NO_3F$	BUTOFILOLOL	BETA-ADR.BLOCKER	
311.19976	$C_{19}H_{25}N_3O$	TAPRILIDIN	VASODILATOR	
311.22491	$C_{21}H_{29}NO$	ALPHAMETHADOL	ANALGESIC	
	$C_{21}H_{29}NO$	BETAMETHADOL	ANALGESIC	
	$C_{21}H_{29}NO$	BIPERIDEN	ANTIPARKINSONIAN	MS
	$C_{21}H_{29}NO$	BUFENADRIN	ANTIHIST./-ALLERG.	
	$C_{21}H_{29}NO$	DIMEPHETANOL	ANALGESIC	
	$C_{21}H_{29}NO$	TRIPERIDEN	ANTIPARKINSONIAN	
311.85082	$C_3H_6OI_2$	DIIODOPROPANOL	RUBEFACIENT	
311.97299	$C_{11}H_{15}CL_2S_2P$	CHLORTHIOPHOS	INSECTICIDE	
312.04478	$C_{12}H_{13}N_4O_2CLS$	SULFACLOMIDE	ANTIBIOTIC	
312.06339	$C_{17}H_{12}O_6$	AFLATOXIN B1	NATURAL SUBSTANCE	
	$C_{17}H_{12}O_6$	TALOSALATE	ANALGESIC	
312.06656	$C_{17}H_{13}N_2O_2CL$	LONAZOLAC	ANALGESIC	MS
312.07147	$C_{12}H_{16}N_4O_2S_2$	GLYBUTHIAZOLE	ANTIDIABETIC	
312.09709	$C_{14}H_{12}N_6O_3$	PTEROIC ACID	ORGANIC ACID	
312.10294	$C_{18}H_{17}N_2OCL$	CLAZOLAM	TRANQUILIZER	
312.11438	$C_{14}H_{20}N_2O_4S$	PENTENYLPENICILLIN	NATURAL SUBSTANCE	
312.12224	$C_{16}H_{16}N_4O_3$	MATUBEN (TM)	CYTOSTATIC	
312.12390	$C_{14}H_{21}N_2O_4P$	PSILOCYBIN-ETH	HALLUCINOGEN	
312.15863	$C_{17}H_{20}N_4O_2$	PROPAMIDINE	ANTIBIOTIC	
312.16265	$C_{22}H_{20}N_2$	BENZINDOPYRINE	TRANQUILIZER	
312.16602	$C_{19}H_{24}N_2S$	PROFENAMINE	ANTIPARKINSONIAN	MS
312.17255	$C_{20}H_{24}O_3$	ESTRONE ACETATE	ESTROGEN	
	$C_{20}H_{24}O_3$	TRENBOLONE ACETATE	ANABOLIC	
312.18378	$C_{19}H_{24}N_2O_2$	DICARFEN	ANTIPARKINSONIAN	
	$C_{19}H_{24}N_2O_2$	PRAZIQUANTEL	ANTHELMINTIC	
	$C_{19}H_{24}N_2O_2$	SALVERINE	ANTISPASMOTIC	
312.20893	$C_{21}H_{28}O_2$	DEMEGESTONE	GESTAGEN	
	$C_{21}H_{28}O_2$	DYDROGESTERONE	GESTAGEN	
	$C_{21}H_{28}O_2$	ETHISTERONE	GESTAGEN	
	$C_{21}H_{28}O_2$	LEVONORGESTREL	GESTAGEN	
	$C_{21}H_{28}O_2$	NORGESTREL	GESTAGEN	
	$C_{21}H_{28}O_2$	TIBOLONE	ANABOLIC	
312.22016	$C_{20}H_{28}N_2O$	PYTAMINE	DIURETIC	
312.23006	$C_{18}H_{32}O_4$	ETHYLDIOXOPENTADECANE CARBOXYLATE	------------	
312.30283	$C_{20}H_{40}O_2$	ARACHIDIC ACID	NATURAL SUBSTANCE	
312.98600	$C_{10}H_{14}NO_2CL_2SP$	ZYTRON (DMPA)	HERBICIDE	
313.06500	$C_{12}H_{16}N_3O_3SP$	TRIAZOPHOS	INSECTICIDE	
313.08627	$C_{16}H_{12}N_3O_3F$	FLUBENDAZOLE	ANTHELMINTIC	
	$C_{16}H_{12}N_3O_3F$	FLUNITRAZEPAM	HYPNOTIC	MS
313.09502	$C_{17}H_{15}NO_5$	BENORILATE	ANALGESIC	

MASS	FORMULA	NAME	CATEGORY	MS
313.09819	$C_{17}H_{16}N_3OCL$	AMOXAPINE	ANTIDEPRESSANT	
313.15388	$C_{16}H_{19}N_5O_2$	DIMABEFYLLINE	BRONCHODILATOR	
313.16779	$C_{19}H_{23}NO_3$	DIMETHYLAMINOMETHYLETHYL BENZILATE	ANTISPASMOTIC	
	$C_{19}H_{23}NO_3$	ETHYLMORPHINE	ANTITUSSIVE	MS
	$C_{19}H_{23}NO_3$	OXYFEDRINE	CORONARY DILATOR	
	$C_{19}H_{23}NO_3$	XENYSALATE	DERMATIC	
313.18086	$C_{17}H_{28}NO_2CL$	PROPIVANE	ANTISPASMOTIC	
313.20418	$C_{20}H_{27}NO_2$	BICYCLOPHENAMINE	ANTISPASMOTIC	
	$C_{20}H_{27}NO_2$	FENALCOMINE	CORONARY DILATOR	
	$C_{20}H_{27}NO_2$	TROPENTANE	PARASYMPATH.-LYTIC	
	$C_{20}H_{27}NO_2$	VETRABUTINE	ANTISPASMOTIC	
313.24056	$C_{21}H_{31}NO$	COGAZOCINE	ANALGESIC	
313.97001	$C_{10}H_{13}O_3CL_2SP$	DICHLOFENTHION	INSECTICIDE	
313.97805	$C_{13}H_9N_2OCL_3$	TRICLOCARBAN	DESINFICIENT	
313.98475	$C_{13}H_9N_2CL_2FS$	FLUORDICHLOROTHIOCARBANILIDE	FUNGIST./ANTIMYC.	
313.99162	$C_{11}H_{11}N_2OI$	IODPHENAZONE	ANALGESIC	
314.04582	$C_{16}H_{11}N_2O_3CL$	TESICAM	ANTIPHLOGISTIC	
314.06043	$C_{12}H_{15}N_4O_2CLS$	DU 717	ANTIHYPERTENSIVE	
314.06222	$C_{17}H_{12}N_2OCLF$	NUARIMOL	FUNGIST./ANTIMYC.	
314.06512	$C_{14}H_{10}N_4O_5$	DANTROLENE	MUSCLE RELAXANT	
314.07904	$C_{17}H_{14}O_6$	AFLATOXIN B2	NATURAL SUBSTANCE	
314.08375	$C_{15}H_{14}N_4O_2S$	SULFAPHENAZOLE	ANTIBIOTIC	
314.09114	$C_{17}H_{18}N_2S_2$	SULBENTIN	FUNGIST./ANTIMYC.	
314.09193	$C_{14}H_{19}O_6P$	CIODRIN	INSECTICIDE	
314.09527	$C_{15}H_{20}N_2OCL_2$	CLIBUCAINE	LOCAL ANESTHETIC	
314.10017	$C_{14}H_{18}O_8$	GLUCOVANILLIN	FLAVORING	
314.11676	$C_{19}H_{14}N_4O$	DIQUINOLYLUREA	ANTIBIOTIC	
314.13003	$C_{14}H_{22}N_2O_4S$	AMYLPENICILLIN	ANTIBIOTIC	
314.14126	$C_{13}H_{22}N_4O_3S$	RANITIDINE	TO THERAPY ULCERS	
314.14529	$C_{18}H_{22}N_2OS$	METHOPROMAZINE	NEUROLEPTIC	
314.14912	$C_{15}H_{18}N_6O_2$	PIMEFYLLINE	CORONARY DILATOR	
314.15498	$C_{19}H_{23}N_2CL$	CLOMIPRAMINE	ANTIDEPRESSANT	MS
	$C_{19}H_{23}N_2CL$	HOMOCHLORCYCLIZINE	ANTIHIST./-ALLERG.	
314.18820	$C_{20}H_{26}O_3$	ESTRADIOL ACETATE	ESTROGEN	
	$C_{20}H_{26}O_3$	GESTADIENOL	GESTAGEN	
	$C_{20}H_{26}O_3$	TAXODIONE	CYTOSTATIC	
314.22458	$C_{21}H_{30}O_2$	CANNABIDIOL	NATURAL SUBSTANCE	MS
	$C_{21}H_{30}O_2$	METYNODIOL	GESTAGEN	
	$C_{21}H_{30}O_2$	PROGESTERONE	GESTAGEN	
	$C_{21}H_{30}O_2$	TETRAHYDROCANNABINOL	HALLUCINOGEN	MS
	$C_{21}H_{30}O_2$	URUSHIOL IV + V	CHEMICAL	
314.28210	$C_{19}H_{38}O_3$	CETYL LACTATE	PHARMACEUTICAL AID	
314.88944	$C_{10}H_7NOBR_2$	BROQUINALDOL	FUNGIST./ANTIMYC.	
314.96206	$C_{13}H_8NO_2CL_3$	TRICHLOROPHENYLCARBANILATE	FUNGIST./ANTIMYC.	
	$C_{13}H_8NO_2CL_3$	TRICHLOROSALICYLANILIDE	FUNGIST./ANTIMYC.	
315.00072	$C_{14}H_{10}N_3OBR$	BROMAZEPAM	TRANQUILIZER	MS
315.04107	$C_{15}H_{10}N_3O_3CL$	CLONAZEPAM	ANTIEPILEPTIC	MS
315.06537	$C_{12}H_{15}N_5OCL_2$	CLOCIGUANIL	ANTIMALARIAL	
315.08485	$C_{18}H_{18}NCLS$	CHLORPROTHIXENE	NEUROLEPTIC	MS
315.09292	$C_{17}H_{17}NO_3S$	PROTIZIC ACID	ORGANIC ACID	
315.11384	$C_{17}H_{18}N_3OCL$	CLOBENZEPAM	ANTIHIST./-ALLERG.	
315.12191	$C_{16}H_{17}N_3O_4$	ANTRAMYCIN	CYTOSTATIC	

MASS	FORMULA	NAME	CATEGORY	MS
315.12845	$C_{13}H_{22}N_5CLS$	IPROZILAMINE	MUSCLE RELAXANT	
315.14706	$C_{18}H_{21}NO_4$	CODEINE-N-OXIDE	ANTITUSSIVE	
	$C_{18}H_{21}NO_4$	OXYCODONE	ANALGESIC	MS
315.16953	$C_{16}H_{21}N_5O_2$	ALIZAPRIDE	ANTIHIST./-ALLERG.	
315.18344	$C_{19}H_{25}NO_3$	NALTROPINE	PARASYMPATH.-LYTIC	
	$C_{19}H_{25}NO_3$	TETRAHYDROTHEBAINE	------------	
315.19870	$C_{23}H_{25}N$	FENDILINE	CORONARY DILATOR	MS
315.21983	$C_{20}H_{29}NO_2$	BREMAZOCINE	ANALGESIC	
315.23106	$C_{19}H_{29}N_3O$	PAMAQUINE	ANTIMALARIAL	
315.25354	$C_{18}H_{35}O_4$	DIHYDROXYSTEARIC ACID	CHEMICAL	
315.98401	$C_{12}H_{10}N_2O_2CL_2S$	PAZOXIDE	ANTIHYPERTENSIVE	
316.01388	$C_5H_8N_4O_{12}$	PENTAERYTHRITOL TETRANITRATE	CORONARY DILATOR	
316.04225	$C_{12}H_{17}N_2O_3BR$	BROMALLYLMETHYLBUTYLBARBITURIC ACID	HYPNOTIC	
316.05751	$C_{16}H_{17}N_2BR$	ZIMELIDINE	ANTIDEPRESSANT	MS
316.10379	$C_{15}H_{25}O_2BR$	BORNYL BROMOISOVALERATE	SEDATIVE	
316.12210	$C_{15}H_{19}N_2F_3S$	TICARBODIN	ANTHELMINTIC	
316.12455	$C_{17}H_{20}N_2O_2S$	DIOXOPROTHAZINE	ANTIHIST./-ALLERG.	
	$C_{17}H_{20}N_2O_2S$	ETOCARLIDE	TUBERCULOSTATIC	
	$C_{17}H_{20}N_2O_2S$	TINORIDINE	ANTIPHLOGISTIC	
316.15691	$C_{13}H_{24}N_4O_3S$	BUPIRIMATE	FUNGIST./ANTIMYC.	
	$C_{13}H_{24}N_4O_3S$	TIMOLOL	BETA-ADR.BLOCKER	MS
316.16094	$C_{18}H_{24}N_2OS$	SULOXIFEN	BRONCHODILATOR	
316.17869	$C_{18}H_{24}N_2O_3$	AMQUINATE	ANTIMALARIAL	
316.20385	$C_{20}H_{28}O_3$	CAFESTOL	ANTIINFLAMMATORY	
	$C_{20}H_{28}O_3$	CINERIN I	INSECTICIDE	
	$C_{20}H_{28}O_3$	ENESTEBOL	ANABOLIC	
	$C_{20}H_{28}O_3$	GESTONORONE	GESTAGEN	
	$C_{20}H_{28}O_3$	MYTATRIENEDIOL	ESTROGEN	
316.22631	$C_{18}H_{28}N_4O$	BUTALAMINE	VASODILATOR	
316.24023	$C_{21}H_{32}O_2$	BOLASTERONE	ANABOLIC	
	$C_{21}H_{32}O_2$	CALUSTERONE	GYNECOL./OBSTRECT.	
	$C_{21}H_{32}O_2$	CYCLOPREGNOL	CORTICOID	
	$C_{21}H_{32}O_2$	METHYL ABIETATE	SOLVENT	
	$C_{21}H_{32}O_2$	NORBOLETONE	ANABOLIC	
	$C_{21}H_{32}O_2$	PREGNENOLONE	GESTAGEN	
	$C_{21}H_{32}O_2$	URISHOL III	CHEMICAL	
316.26136	$C_{18}H_{36}O_4$	DIHYDROXYSTEARIC ACID	DERMATIC	
316.94133	$C_{12}H_6NO_3CL_3$	QUINOAMIDE	HERBICIDE	
316.99454	$C_{11}H_{12}NO_4S_2P$	IMIDAN	INSECTICIDE	
317.00577	$C_{10}H_{12}N_3O_3S_2P$	AZINPHOS-METHYL	INSECTICIDE	MS
317.10519	$C_{20}H_{15}NO_3$	OXYPHENISATINE	LAXATIVE	
317.15464	$C_{19}H_{24}NOCL$	MECLOXAMINE	PARASYMPATH.-LYTIC	MS
317.16271	$C_{18}H_{23}NO_4$	COCAETHYLENE	LOCAL ANESTHETIC	
317.19909	$C_{19}H_{27}NO_3$	TETRABENAZINE	NEUROLEPTIC	MS
317.23548	$C_{20}H_{31}NO_2$	DROFENINE	ANTISPASMOTIC	MS
	$C_{20}H_{31}NO_2$	METCARAPHEN	ANTISPASMOTIC	
317.86564	$C_8H_2O_5CL_4$	MUCOCHLORIC ANHYDRIDE	FUNGIST./ANTIMYC.	
317.95366	$C_{14}H_{10}CL_4$	MITOTANE	CYTOSTATIC	
	$C_{14}H_{10}CL_4$	TDE (DDD)	INSECTICIDE	
318.03267	$C_{16}H_{12}N_2OCL_2$	CLOROQUALONE	ANTITUSSIVE	
318.05936	$C_{16}H_{15}N_2OCLS$	CLOTIAZEPAM	TRANQUILIZER	MS
318.07316	$C_{16}H_{19}N_2BR$	BROMPHENIRAMINE	ANTIHIST./-ALLERG.	MS

MASS	FORMULA	NAME	CATEGORY	MS
318.08921	$C_{20}H_{14}O_4$	PHENOLPHTHALEIN	LAXATIVE	
	$C_{20}H_{14}O_4$	PHENYL PHTHALATE	SOFTENER	
318.09018	$C_{14}H_{20}N_2O_2CL_2$	DICLOMETIDE	------------	
318.09575	$C_{17}H_{19}N_2CLS$	CHLORPROMAZINE	NEUROLEPTIC	MS
318.13866	$C_{19}H_{23}O_2CL$	CHLOROESTRONE METHYL ETHER	ANTICHOLESTEREMIC	
318.14673	$C_{18}H_{22}O_5$	ZEARALENONE	ANABOLIC	
318.21950	$C_{20}H_{30}O_3$	OXYMESTERONE	ANABOLIC	
318.23073	$C_{19}H_{30}N_2O_2$	BENRIXATE	ANTIARRHYTHMIC	
	$C_{19}H_{30}N_2O_2$	BIETHAMIVERINE	ANTISPASMOTIC	
	$C_{19}H_{30}N_2O_2$	CAMIVERINE	ANTISPASMOTIC	
318.25588	$C_{21}H_{34}O_2$	DIMETHYLANDROSTANOLONE	ANABOLIC	
	$C_{21}H_{34}O_2$	URUSHIOL II	CHEMICAL	
319.03782	$C_{13}H_{15}NO_4CL_2$	CETOFENICOL	ANTIBIOTIC	
319.14197	$C_{17}H_{21}NO_5$	PROQUINOLATE	COCCIDIOSTATIC	
319.15723	$C_{21}H_{21}NO_2$	OXETORONE	ANTIHIST./-ALLERG.	
319.18153	$C_{18}H_{26}N_3CL$	CHLOROQUINE	ANTIRHEUMATIC	MS
319.21474	$C_{19}H_{29}NO_3$	BUTOPIPRINE	ANTITUSSIVE	
	$C_{19}H_{29}NO_3$	CYCLODRINE	PARASYMPATH.-LYTIC	
319.89654	$C_{12}H_4O_2CL_4$	2.3.7.8-TCDD (DIOXIN)	CHEMICAL	MS
319.89974	$C_8H_8O_3CL_3SP$	FENCLOFOS	PESTICIDE	
319.96606	$C_{10}H_8O_8S_2$	CHROMOTROPIC ACID	CHEMICAL	
319.97077	$C_8H_8N_4O_4S_3$	BENZOLAMIDE	ENZYME INHIBITOR	
319.97379	$C_{14}H_9CL_3F_2$	DFDT	INSECTICIDE	
320.01193	$C_{15}H_{10}N_2O_2CL_2$	LORAZEPAM	TRANQUILIZER	MS
320.03059	$C_{12}H_{17}O_4S_2P$	PHENTHOATE	INSECTICIDE	
320.03626	$C_8H_{18}N_2O_5CLSP$	SUFOSFAMIDE	CYTOSTATIC	
320.07971	$C_{18}H_{12}N_2O_4$	XANTHOCILLIN Y2	ANTIBIOTIC	
320.10486	$C_{20}H_{16}O_4$	PHENOLPHTHALEIN	LAXATIVE	
320.11609	$C_{19}H_{16}N_2O_3$	FANTAN	ANTIARRHYTHMIC	
320.12599	$C_{17}H_{20}O_6$	MYCOPHENOLIC ACID	CYTOSTATIC	
320.13722	$C_{16}H_{20}N_2O_5$	ETEROBARB	ANTIEPILEPTIC	
320.14462	$C_{18}H_{24}O_3S$	DIBUTYLNAPHTHALENE SULFONATE	ANTITUSSIVE	
320.15248	$C_{20}H_{20}N_2O_2$	BEFURALIN	ANTIDEPRESSANT	
	$C_{20}H_{20}N_2O_2$	FEPRAZONE	ANALGESIC	
	$C_{20}H_{20}N_2O_2$	PRENAZONE	ANTIINFLAMMATORY	
320.16554	$C_{18}H_{25}N_2OCL$	RODACAINE	LOCAL ANESTHETIC	
320.19876	$C_{19}H_{28}O_4$	ATRACTYLIGENIN	NATURAL SUBSTANCE	
320.22525	$C_{22}H_{28}N_2$	CARBAZOCINE	ANALGESIC	
320.24638	$C_{19}H_{32}N_2O_2$	CAMYLOFINE	ANTISPASMOTIC	MS
320.27153	$C_{21}H_{36}O_2$	ALLOPREGNANEDIOL	ENDOG.BIOMOLECULE	
	$C_{21}H_{36}O_2$	PENTADECYLCATECHOL	DIAGNOSTIC AID	
	$C_{21}H_{36}O_2$	URUSHIOL I	CHEMICAL	
321.04194	$C_{13}H_{11}N_3O_5S$	SALAZOSULFAMIDE	ANTIBIOTIC	
321.06872	$C_{17}H_{17}NOCL_2$	MOXIFENSINE	ANTIPARKINSONIAN	
321.10011	$C_{19}H_{15}NO_4$	SYNTAVERINE	MUSCLE RELAXANT	
321.12211	$C_{17}H_{23}NOS_2$	THIHEXINOL	PARASYMPATH.-LYTIC	
321.13247	$C_{15}H_{19}N_3O_5$	CARBOQUONE	CYTOSTATIC	
321.13649	$C_{20}H_{19}NO_3$	ACRONINE	CYTOSTATIC	
	$C_{20}H_{19}NO_3$	OXAZIDIONE	ANTICOAGULANT	
321.14956	$C_{18}H_{24}NO_2CL$	CLOCANFAMIDE	TO THERAPY ULCERS	
321.15360	$C_{12}H_{23}N_3O_7$	TRISAMINOETHYL CITRATE	FIBRINOLYTIC	
321.16079	$C_{17}H_{24}N_3OCL$	CLAMOXYQUINE	ANTIBIOTIC	

MASS	FORMULA	NAME	CATEGORY	MS
321.16886	$C_{16}H_{23}N_3O_4$	GABEXATE	ENZYME INHIBITOR	
321.17288	$C_{21}H_{23}NO_2$	FLAVAMINE	ANTISPASMOTIC	
	$C_{21}H_{23}NO_2$	NORLOBELANINE	NATURAL SUBSTANCE	
321.17357	$C_{14}H_{23}N_7S$	IMPROMIDINE	TO THERAPY ULCERS	
321.19401	$C_{18}H_{27}NO_4$	ETOXERIDINE	ANALGESIC	
321.20926	$C_{22}H_{27}NO$	ETYBENZATROPINE	PARASYMPATH.-LYTIC	
	$C_{22}H_{27}NO$	PHENAZOCINE	ANALGESIC	
321.26678	$C_{20}H_{35}NO_2$	DIHEXYVERINE	ANTISPASMOTIC	
321.82916	$C_5H_4O_3CL_6$	CLORETATE	HYPNOTIC	
321.86555	$C_6H_8O_2CL_6$	CHLORALACETONECHLOROFORM	CHEMICAL	
321.89443	$C_{12}H_6CL_4S$	TETRASUL	PESTICIDE	
322.01233	$C_{11}H_{12}N_2O_5CL_2$	CHLORAMPHENICOL	ANTIBIOTIC	MS
322.01635	$C_{16}H_{12}O_3CL_2$	CLOFENOXYDE	FUNGIST./ANTIMYC.	
322.01715	$C_9H_{18}N_2O_2CL_3P$	TROFOSFAMIDE	CYTOSTATIC	
322.02275	$C_8H_{20}O_5S_2P_2$	SULFOTEP	INSECTICIDE	
322.02848	$C_{12}H_{19}O_2S_3P$	SULPROFOS	INSECTICIDE	
322.03249	$C_{14}H_{10}O_9$	DIGALLIC ACID	NATURAL SUBSTANCE	
322.07358	$C_{13}H_{14}N_4O_4S$	ACETYL SULFAMETHOXYPYRIDAZINE	ANTIBIOTIC	
322.11649	$C_{15}H_{18}N_2O_6$	BINAPACRYL	PESTICIDE	
322.12051	$C_{20}H_{18}O_4$	CYCLOCOUMAROL	ANTICOAGULANT	
	$C_{20}H_{18}O_4$	HYDROXYOXOPHENYLPENTYLCUMARIN	ANTICOAGULANT	
	$C_{20}H_{18}O_4$	PHASEOLIN	NATURAL SUBSTANCE	
	$C_{20}H_{18}O_4$	PYRANOCUMARIN	RODENTICIDE	
322.13174	$C_{19}H_{18}N_2O_3$	KEBUZONE	ANTIRHEUMATIC	
322.13512	$C_{16}H_{22}N_2O_3S$	GLYHEXAMIDE	ANTIDIABETIC	
322.14298	$C_{18}H_{18}N_4O_2$	MESOCARB	STIMULANT	
322.15037	$C_{20}H_{22}N_2S$	MEQUITAZINE	ANTIHIST./-ALLERG.	MS
322.15287	$C_{16}H_{22}N_2O_5$	BUTILFENIN	DIAGNOSTIC AID	
	$C_{16}H_{22}N_2O_5$	ETIFENIN	DIAGNOSTIC AID	
322.16813	$C_{20}H_{22}N_2O_2$	AKUAMMICINE	NATURAL SUBSTANCE	
	$C_{20}H_{22}N_2O_2$	DIOCAINE	LOCAL ANESTHETIC	
	$C_{20}H_{22}N_2O_2$	GELSEMINE	NATURAL SUBSTANCE	
322.16996	$C_{19}H_{27}O_2CL$	CLOSTEBOL	ANABOLIC	
322.17803	$C_{18}H_{26}O_5$	TALERANOL	------------	
	$C_{18}H_{26}O_5$	ZERANOL	ESTROGEN	
322.20451	$C_{21}H_{26}N_2O$	FENPIPRAMIDE	ANTISPASMOTIC	MS
322.24090	$C_{22}H_{30}N_2$	APRINDINE	ANTIARRHYTHMIC	MS
322.98072	$C_{13}H_{10}NOI$	BENODANIL	FUNGIST./ANTIMYC.	
323.03812	$C_{14}H_{14}NO_4SP$	EPN	INSECTICIDE	
323.04799	$C_{16}H_{15}NO_2CL_2$	BULAN	INSECTICIDE	
323.05186	$C_9H_{14}N_3O_8P$	CYTIDINE PHOSPHATE	ENDOG.BIOMOLECULE	
323.11576	$C_{19}H_{17}NO_4$	STYLOPINE	NATURAL SUBSTANCE	
323.12699	$C_{18}H_{17}N_3O_3$	SALICYLAMIDOPHENAZONE	ANALGESIC	
323.13036	$C_{15}H_{21}N_3O_3S$	GLICLAZIDE	ANTIDIABETIC	
323.13439	$C_{20}H_{21}NOS$	TOLCICLATE	FUNGIST./ANTIMYC.	
323.14562	$C_{19}H_{21}N_3S$	CYAMEMAZINE	NEUROLEPTIC	
	$C_{19}H_{21}N_3S$	METIAPINE	NEUROLEPTIC	
323.15214	$C_{20}H_{21}NO_3$	DIMEFLINE	RESPIRAT.STIMULANT	
	$C_{20}H_{21}NO_3$	GALIPINE	FLAVORING	
323.17327	$C_{17}H_{25}NO_5$	ALLOXYDIM	HERBICIDE	
	$C_{17}H_{25}O_5N$	ANTHALLAN	ANTIHIST./-ALLERG.	
323.18853	$C_{21}H_{25}NO_2$	CINNAMAVERINE	ANTITUSSIVE	

MASS	FORMULA	NAME	CATEGORY	MS
323.18853	$C_{21}H_{25}NO_2$	MYFADOL	ANALGESIC	
	$C_{21}H_{25}NO_2$	PIPERIDOLATE	ANALGESIC	
323.19976	$C_{20}H_{25}N_3O$	LYSERGIDE (LSD)	HALLUCINOGEN	MS
	$C_{20}H_{25}N_3O$	PRODIGIOSIN	FUNGIST./ANTIMYC.	
323.20966	$C_{18}H_{29}NO_4$	BUFETOLOL	BETA-ADR.BLOCKER	
	$C_{18}H_{29}NO_4$	GUAIAPATE	ANTITUSSIVE	
	$C_{18}H_{29}NO_4$	IPROXAMINE	VASODILATOR	
323.97366	$C_9H_{10}N_2O_5CLSP$	AZAMETHIPHOS	INSECTICIDE	
324.03200	$C_{16}H_{14}O_3CL_2$	CHLOROBENZILATE	PESTICIDE	
324.03587	$C_9H_{13}N_2O_9P$	URIDINE MONOPHOSPHATE	ENDOG.BIOMOLECULE	
324.09977	$C_{19}H_{16}O_5$	EFLOXATE	VASODILATOR	
	$C_{19}H_{16}O_5$	ISOCROMIL	------------	
324.10294	$C_{19}H_{17}N_2OCL$	PRAZEPAM	TRANQUILIZER	MS
324.10565	$C_{12}H_{20}O_{10}$	THROMBO-HOLZINGER	ANTICOAGULANT	
324.10699	$C_{13}H_{16}N_4O_6$	FURALTADONE	ANTIBIOTIC	
	$C_{13}H_{16}N_4O_6$	LEVOFURALTADONE	ANTIBIOTIC	
324.11101	$C_{18}H_{16}N_2O_4$	NIOMETACIN	ANALGESIC	
324.11438	$C_{15}H_{20}N_2O_4S$	ACETOHEXAMIDE	ANTIDIABETIC	
324.13616	$C_{20}H_{20}O_4$	OTOBAIN	NATURAL SUBSTANCE	
324.14204	$C_{13}H_{24}O_9$	STROPHANTHOBIOSE	SUGAR	
324.14739	$C_{19}H_{20}N_2O_3$	AMPHOTALIDE	FUNGIST./ANTIMYC.	
	$C_{19}H_{20}N_2O_3$	DITAZOL	ANALGESIC	MS
	$C_{19}H_{20}N_2O_3$	OXYPHENBUTAZONE	ANTIPHLOGISTIC	MS
324.15076	$C_{16}H_{24}N_2O_3S$	GLYOCTAMIDE	ANTIDIABETIC	
324.15863	$C_{18}H_{20}N_4O_2$	NITRACRIN	CYTOSTATIC	
324.16852	$C_{16}H_{24}N_2O_5$	TRIMETHOBENZGLYCINE	SEDATIVE	
324.17592	$C_{18}H_{28}O_3S$	SULFOXIDE	PESTICIDE	
324.18378	$C_{20}H_{24}N_2O_2$	QUINIDINE	ANTIARRHYTHMIC	MS
	$C_{20}H_{24}N_2O_2$	QUININE	ANTIMALARIAL	MS
	$C_{20}H_{24}N_2O_2$	VIQUIDIL	VASODILATOR	
324.20893	$C_{22}H_{28}O_2$	ETYNODIOL	GESTAGEN	
324.22016	$C_{21}H_{28}N_2O$	ARPENAL	PARASYMPATH.-LYTIC	
	$C_{21}H_{28}N_2O$	DIAMPROMIDE	ANALGESIC	
324.24531	$C_{23}H_{32}O$	DIBUTYLDIMETHYLBENZYLPHENOL	INSECTICIDE	
324.95052	$C_{13}H_9NO_2CLBR$	BROMOCHLOROSALICYLANILIDE	DESINFICIENT	
324.99578	$C_9H_{12}N_3O_4CLS_2$	ETHIAZIDE	DIURETIC	
325.02076	$C_{10}H_{16}NO_5S_2P$	FAMOPHOS	INSECTICIDE	
325.08448	$C_{12}H_{15}N_5O_4S$	SIGUMID	ANTIBIOTIC	
325.10626	$C_{17}H_{15}N_3O_4$	MOTRAZEPAM	TRANQUILIZER	
325.12334	$C_{20}H_{20}NOCL$	BENZAPRINOXIDE	ANTIDEPRESSANT	
325.13141	$C_{19}H_{19}NO_4$	BULBOCAPNINE	NATURAL SUBSTANCE	
	$C_{19}H_{19}NO_4$	DOMESTICINE	NATURAL SUBSTANCE	
	$C_{19}H_{19}NO_4$	NANDININE	NATURAL SUBSTANCE	
325.13458	$C_{19}H_{20}N_3CL$	CLEMIZOLE	ANTIHIST./-ALLERG.	
325.14601	$C_{15}H_{23}N_3O_3S$	MECILLINAM	ANTIBIOTIC	
325.15254	$C_{16}H_{23}NO_6$	CAPOBENIC ACID	CORONARY DILATOR	
	$C_{16}H_{23}NO_6$	MOFLOVERINE	ANTISPASMOTIC	
	$C_{16}H_{23}NO_6$	MONOCROTALINE	NATURAL SUBSTANCE	
325.16779	$C_{20}H_{23}NO_3$	POLDIN METILSULFATE	PARASYMPATH.-LYTIC	
	$C_{20}H_{23}NO_3$	TRICLAZATE	PARASYMPATH.-LYTIC	
325.17903	$C_{19}H_{23}N_3O_2$	ERGOMETRINE	GYNECOL./OBSTRECT	MS
325.20418	$C_{21}H_{27}NO_2$	APROFEN	ANTISPASMOTIC	

MASS	FORMULA	NAME	CATEGORY	MS
325.20418	$C_{21}H_{27}NO_2$	DIETIFEN	FUNGIST./ANTIMYC.	
	$C_{21}H_{27}NO_2$	ETAFENONE	CORONARY DILATOR	
	$C_{21}H_{27}NO_2$	IFENPRODIL	VASODILATOR	
	$C_{21}H_{27}NO_2$	SPASMADRYL	PARASYMPATH.-LYTIC	
325.24056	$C_{22}H_{31}NO$	ETHOXYPHENYLDIETHYLAMINOPHENYLBUTANE	ANTISPASMOTIC	
325.96445	$C_8H_{14}O_5CL_3P$	BUTONATE	INSECTICIDE	
325.98611	$C_{13}H_8N_2O_4CL_2$	NICLOSAMIDE	ANTHELMINTIC	
326.03950	$C_{13}H_{14}N_2O_4S_2$	DIPHENYLMETHANEDISULFONAMIDE	DIURETIC	
	$C_{13}H_{14}N_2O_4S_2$	GLIOTOXIN	ANTIBIOTIC	
326.07904	$C_{18}H_{14}O_6$	CINFENOAC	ANTIPHLOGISTIC	
326.10017	$C_{15}H_{18}O_8$	MELILOTOSIDE	NATURAL SUBSTANCE	
326.11140	$C_{14}H_{18}N_2O_7$	DINOBUTON	PESTICIDE	
326.12130	$C_{12}H_{22}O_{10}$	RUTINOSE	SUGAR	
	$C_{12}H_{22}O_{10}$	SCILLABIOSE	SUGAR	
326.12982	$C_{18}H_{19}N_4CL$	CLOZAPINE	NEUROLEPTIC	MS
326.14126	$C_{14}H_{22}N_4O_3S$	DELFANTRIN	ANALGESIC	
326.14529	$C_{19}H_{22}N_2OS$	ACEPROMAZINE	SEDATIVE	MS
	$C_{19}H_{22}N_2OS$	ACEPROMETHAZINE	SEDATIVE	MS
	$C_{19}H_{22}N_2OS$	TIAZESIM	ANTIDEPRESSANT	
326.16304	$C_{19}H_{22}N_2O_3$	BUMADIZON	ANTIRHEUMATIC	
326.18167	$C_{20}H_{26}N_2S$	ETYMEMAZINE	TRANQUILIZER	
326.18820	$C_{21}H_{26}O_3$	ESTRONE PROPIONATE	ESTROGEN	
	$C_{21}H_{26}O_3$	MOXESTROL	ESTROGEN	
	$C_{21}H_{26}O_3$	OCTABENZONE	DERMATIC	
	$C_{21}H_{26}O_3$	THYMOL CARBONATE	ANTHELMINTIC	
326.19157	$C_{18}H_{30}O_3S$	DODECYLBENZENESULFONIC ACID	SOLUBILIZER ETC.	
326.19943	$C_{20}H_{26}N_2O_2$	AJMALINE	ANTIARRHYTHMIC	
	$C_{20}H_{26}N_2O_2$	DIHYDROQUINIDINE	ANTIARRHYTHMIC	
	$C_{20}H_{26}N_2O_2$	HYDROQUININE	DERMATIC	
	$C_{20}H_{26}N_2O_2$	VERADOLIN	ANALGESIC	
	$C_{20}H_{26}N_2O_2$	VERILOPAM	ANALGESIC	
326.22458	$C_{22}H_{30}O_2$	PROMEGESTONE	GESTAGEN	
326.23581	$C_{21}H_{30}N_2O$	BUNAFTINE	ANTIARRHYTHMIC	
	$C_{21}H_{30}N_2O$	HYDROXYSTENOZOL	ANABOLIC	
326.78938	$C_6H_4NBR_3$	TRIBROMOANILINE	CHEMICAL	
326.93874	$C_{11}H_9NO_2CL_4$	CLOPONONE	DESINFICIENT	
327.00652	$C_{14}H_{11}NO_4CL_2$	DICLOFURAZOLE	ANTIBIOTIC	
327.03475	$C_{12}H_{13}N_3O_4S_2$	SULFANILYLSULFANILAMIDE	ANTIBIOTIC	
327.07114	$C_{13}H_{17}N_3O_3S_2$	GLYSOBUZOLE	ANTIDIABETIC	
327.11384	$C_{18}H_{18}N_3OCL$	LOXAPINE	NEUROLEPTIC	MS
327.12374	$C_{16}H_{22}NO_4CL$	CLOFIBRIDE	ANTICHOLESTEREMIC	
327.12528	$C_{14}H_{21}N_3O_4S$	SULMEPRIDE	ANTIDEPRESSANT	
327.12593	$C_{22}H_{17}NO_2$	CHINOLYLMETHYLENEDIPHENOL	LAXATIVE	
327.14706	$C_{19}H_{21}NO_4$	BOLDINE	CHOLERETIC	
	$C_{19}H_{21}NO_4$	CORYTUBERINE	NATURAL SUBSTANCE	
	$C_{19}H_{21}NO_4$	NALOXONE	ANTIDOTE	MS
327.16569	$C_{20}H_{25}NOS$	TIFENAMIL	ANTISPASMOTIC	
327.17469	$C_{19}H_{22}N_3OF$	AZAPERONE	NEUROLEPTIC	
327.17692	$C_{19}H_{25}N_3S$	AMINOPROMAZINE	ANTISPASMOTIC	
327.18344	$C_{20}H_{25}NO_3$	BENACTYZINE	SEDATIVE	MS
	$C_{20}H_{25}NO_3$	DIFEMERINE	ANTISPASMOTIC	
	$C_{20}H_{25}NO_3$	DIMENOXADOL	ANALGESIC	

MASS	FORMULA	NAME	CATEGORY	MS
327.18682	$C_{17}H_{29}NO_3S$	SETHOXYDIM	HERBICIDE	
327.21983	$C_{21}H_{29}NO_2$	BUTORPHANOL	ANALGESIC	
327.77340	$C_6H_3OBR_3$	TRIBROMOPHENOL	CHEMICAL	
328.05178	$C_{16}H_{12}N_2O_4S$	ORANGE I + II	CHEMICAL	
328.05344	$C_{14}H_{17}O_5SP$	POTASAN (E838)	INSECTICIDE	
328.05831	$C_{17}H_{12}O_7$	AFLATOXIN G1 + M1	NATURAL SUBSTANCE	
328.06484	$C_{14}H_{17}N_2O_3CLS$	CLOREXOLONE	DIURETIC	
328.07944	$C_{14}H_{16}O_9$	BERGENIN	NATURAL SUBSTANCE	
328.09154	$C_{14}H_{20}N_2O_3S_2$	THIOHEXAMIDE	ANTIDIABETIC	
328.09786	$C_{18}H_{17}N_2O_2CL$	OXAZOLAM	TRANQUILIZER	MS
328.09940	$C_{16}H_{16}N_4O_2S$	SULFAPYRAZOLE	ANTIBIOTIC	
328.10995	$C_{22}H_{16}O_3$	ETHYL BISCOUMACETATE	ANTICOAGULANT	
328.13108	$C_{19}H_{20}O_5$	DIPHEBYL (TM)	CHOLERETIC	
328.14547	$C_{18}H_{21}N_4CL$	MIDAMALINE	LOCAL ANESTHETIC	
328.14568	$C_{15}H_{24}N_2O_4S$	TIAPRIDE	ANTIPARKINSONIAN	MS
328.16094	$C_{19}H_{24}N_2OS$	FENCARBAMIDE	ANTISPASMOTIC	MS
	$C_{19}H_{24}N_2OS$	LEVOMEPROMAZINE	NEUROLEPTIC	MS
328.17869	$C_{19}H_{24}N_2O_3$	LABETALOL	ANTIHYPERTENSIVE	MS
328.20385	$C_{21}H_{28}O_3$	BOLDENONE ACETATE	ANABOLIC	
	$C_{21}H_{28}O_3$	ESTRADIOL PROPIONATE	ESTROGEN	
	$C_{21}H_{28}O_3$	PYRETHRIN I	INSECTICIDE	
328.24023	$C_{22}H_{32}O_2$	PROMESTRIENE	CORTICOID	
	$C_{22}H_{32}O_2$	SYNHEXYL	HALLUCINOGEN	
328.25146	$C_{21}H_{32}N_2O$	STANOZOLOL	ANABOLIC	
328.95439	$C_{11}H_{11}NO_2CL_4$	CHLORBETAMIDE	ANTIBIOTIC	
328.97519	$C_8H_6N_3O_4F_3S_2$	FLUMETHIAZIDE	DIURETIC	
329.02773	$C_{17}H_{12}NO_2CLS$	FENTIAZAC	ANALGESIC	
329.03340	$C_{13}H_{13}N_3O_3CL_2$	IPRODIONE	FUNGIST./ANTIMYC.	
329.04886	$C_{14}H_{16}NO_4CLS$	TIMOFIBRATE	ANTICHOLESTEREMIC	
329.05252	$C_{10}H_{12}N_5O_6P$	CYCLIC AMP	ENDOG.BIOMOLECULE	
329.05672	$C_{16}H_{12}N_3O_3CL$	METHYLCLONAZEPAM	TRANQUILIZER	MS
329.06394	$C_{17}H_{16}NO_2SP$	QUINTIOFOS	INSECTICIDE	
329.09310	$C_{17}H_{16}N_3O_2CL$	CARBURAZEPAM	TRANQUILIZER	
329.10117	$C_{16}H_{15}N_3O_5$	OPINIAZIDE	TUBERCULOSTATIC	
	$C_{16}H_{15}N_3O_5$	PIROLATE	ANTIHIST./-ALLERG.	
329.11241	$C_{15}H_{15}N_5O_4$	ETOFYLLINE NICOTINATE	VASODILATOR	
329.12949	$C_{18}H_{20}N_3OCL$	CLODAZONE	ANTIDEPRESSANT	
329.14158	$C_{22}H_{19}NO_2$	INDOXOLE	ANTIPHLOGISTIC	
329.14272	$C_{19}H_{20}NO_3F$	PAROXETIN	ANTIDEPRESSANT	
329.14495	$C_{19}H_{23}NO_2S$	MEPROTHIXOL	ANTITUSSIVE	
329.15464	$C_{20}H_{24}NOCL$	CLOPERASTINE	ANTITUSSIVE	
329.16271	$C_{19}H_{23}NO_4$	CINNAMOYLCOCAINE	NATURAL SUBSTANCE	
329.17796	$C_{23}H_{23}NO$	TRIPHENYLMETHYLMORPHOLINE	PESTICIDE	
329.18517	$C_{17}H_{23}N_5O_2$	QUINAZOSIN	ANTIHYPERTENSIVE	
329.19909	$C_{20}H_{27}NO_3$	NAMOXYRATE	ANALGESIC	
	$C_{20}H_{27}NO_3$	TRILOSTANE	DIURETIC	
329.21435	$C_{24}H_{27}N$	PRENYLAMINE	CORONARY DILATOR	MS
329.23548	$C_{21}H_{31}NO_2$	ANDROISOXAZOLE	ANABOLIC	
	$C_{21}H_{31}NO_2$	BORNAPRINE	ANTIPARKINSONIAN	MS
329.28310	$C_{21}H_{35}N_3$	BUCAINIDE	ANTIARRHYTHMIC	
329.30423	$C_{18}H_{39}N_3O_2$	DODICIN	DESINFICIENT	
329.81970	$C_6H_4O_4BR_2S$	DIBROMOPHENOL SULFONIC ACID	DESINFICIENT	

MASS	FORMULA	NAME	CATEGORY	MS
329.90202	$C_{10}H_6O_4CL_4$	CHLORTHAL-METHYL (DCPA)	HERBICIDE	
329.95204	$C_{13}H_8O_4CL_2S$	TIENILIC ACID	DIURETIC	
330.00772	$C_{12}H_{11}N_2O_5CLS$	FUROSEMIDE	DIURETIC	
330.03267	$C_{17}H_{12}N_2OCL_2$	FENARIMOL	FUNGIST./ANTIMYC.	
330.03607	$C_{10}H_{19}O_6S_2P$	MALATHION	INSECTICIDE	MS
330.04807	$C_{14}H_{19}OI$	CICLIOMENOL	DESINFICIENT	
330.05713	$C_{17}H_{12}N_2O_2CLF$	PIRAZOLAC	ANTIRHEUMATIC	
330.07080	$C_{13}H_{18}N_2O_4S_2$	ALMECILLINE	ANTIBIOTIC	
330.07395	$C_{17}H_{14}O_7$	AFLATOXIN G2 + M2	NATURAL SUBSTANCE	
330.10227	$C_{19}H_{19}O_3CL$	CAPROCHLORONE	VIRUCIDE	
330.12560	$C_{22}H_{18}O_3$	ANISACRIL	ANOREXIC	
330.13866	$C_{20}H_{23}O_2CL$	ETHYNERONE	GESTAGEN	
330.14020	$C_{18}H_{22}N_2O_2S$	OXOMEMAZINE	ANTIHIST./-ALLERG.	
330.17321	$C_{22}H_{22}N_2O$	CYCINCHOPHEN	ANTIRHEUMATIC	
330.19434	$C_{19}H_{26}N_2O_3$	ISOXAPROLOL	BETA-ADR.BLOCKER	
330.21950	$C_{21}H_{30}O_3$	DESOXYCORTONE	CORTICOID	
	$C_{21}H_{30}O_3$	HYDROXYPROGESTERONE	GESTAGEN	
	$C_{21}H_{30}O_3$	JASMOLIN I	INSECTICIDE	
	$C_{21}H_{30}O_3$	NANDROLONE PROPIONATE	ANABOLIC	
	$C_{21}H_{30}O_3$	TESTOSTERONE ACETATE	ANDROGEN	
330.23073	$C_{20}H_{30}N_2O_2$	DIPIPROVERINE	ANTISPASMOTIC	
	$C_{20}H_{30}N_2O_2$	FURAZABOL	ANABOLIC	
330.25588	$C_{22}H_{34}O_2$	ANAGESTONE	GESTAGEN	
330.97971	$C_{13}H_{15}NCLBRS$	MITOTENAMINE	CYTOSTATIC	
330.99083	$C_8H_8N_3O_4F_3S_2$	HYDROFLUMETHIAZIDE	DIURETIC	
331.02160	$C_{12}H_{14}N_3O_2CLS_2$	BUTADIAZAMIDE	ANTIDIABETIC	
331.06268	$C_{15}H_{13}N_3O_4S$	PIROXICAM	ANTIPHLOGISTIC	
331.06451	$C_{14}H_{18}NO_4CLS$	TIBRIC ACID	ANTICHOLESTEREMIC	
331.07574	$C_{13}H_{18}N_3O_3CLS$	GLYPINAMIDE	ANTIDIABETIC	
331.07976	$C_{18}H_{18}NOCLS$	ZOTEPIN	NEUROLEPTIC	
331.13391	$C_{19}H_{22}NO_2CL$	CHLORDIMORIN	ANALGESIC	
	$C_{19}H_{22}NO_2CL$	DIFENCLOXAZINE	TRANQUILIZER	
331.13839	$C_{19}H_{19}NO_2F_2$	FLAZALONE	ANTIPHLOGISTIC	
331.14197	$C_{18}H_{21}NO_5$	PROTOKYLOL	SYMPATHOMIMETIC	
331.15321	$C_{17}H_{21}N_3O_4$	TRIMETAMIDE	ANTIHYPERTENSIVE	
331.17029	$C_{20}H_{26}NOCL$	CLOFENETAMINE	ANTIPARKINSONIAN	
331.17836	$C_{19}H_{25}NO_4$	PSICAINE-NEU (TM)	LOCAL ANESTHETIC	
	$C_{19}H_{25}NO_4$	SALMEFAMOL	BRONCHODILATOR	
	$C_{19}H_{25}NO_4$	TETRAMETRIN	INSECTICIDE	
331.18959	$C_{18}H_{25}N_3O_3$	DIETHYLAMINOETHYLPHENOBARBITAL	NARCOTIC	
	$C_{18}H_{25}N_3O_3$	POLINAL (TM)	ANALGESIC	
331.19361	$C_{23}H_{25}NO$	DECITROPINE	PARASYMPATH.-LYTIC	
331.20083	$C_{17}H_{25}N_5O_2$	PRIZIDILOL	BETA-ADR.BLOCKER	
331.21474	$C_{20}H_{29}NO_3$	DITRAN (TM)	ANTIDEPRESSANT	
	$C_{20}H_{29}NO_3$	IPRAGRATIN	PARASYMPATH.-LYTIC	
	$C_{20}H_{29}NO_3$	OXYCLIPIN	PARASYMPATH.-LYTIC	
	$C_{20}H_{29}NO_3$	PROMANDELINE	PARASYMPATH.-LYTIC	
331.22598	$C_{19}H_{29}N_3O_2$	AMINDOCATE	ANTIHIST./-ALLERG.	
331.93612	$C_{10}H_{12}O_2CL_3SP$	TRICHLORONATE	INSECTICIDE	
331.96231	$C_9H_{11}N_2O_2CL_2FS_2$	DICHLOFLUANIDE	FUNGIST./ANTIMYC.	
332.05639	$C_{16}H_{13}N_2O_4CL$	CLORAZEPATE	TRANQUILIZER	MS
332.06848	$C_{20}H_{12}O_5$	FLUORESCEIN	DIAGNOSTIC AID	

MASS	FORMULA	NAME	CATEGORY	MS
332.08308	$C_{16}H_{16}N_2O_4S$	ACEDAPSONE	ANTIMALARIAL	
332.11947	$C_{17}H_{20}N_2O_3S$	TOSIFEN	CORONARY DILATOR	
332.15835	$C_{14}H_{24}N_2O_7$	SPECTINOMYCIN	ANTIBIOTIC	
332.18886	$C_{22}H_{24}N_2O$	TROPIRIN	PARASYMPATH.-LYTIC	
332.22525	$C_{23}H_{28}N_2$	INDOPIN	ANALGESIC	
332.23515	$C_{21}H_{32}O_3$	ALFAXALONE	NARCOTIC	
	$C_{21}H_{32}O_3$	ANDROSTENEDIOL ACETATE	ANABOLIC	
	$C_{21}H_{32}O_3$	HYDROXYDIONE	NARCOTIC	
	$C_{21}H_{32}O_3$	OXYMETHOLONE	ANABOLIC	
333.04357	$C_{16}H_{13}N_3OCL_2$	BENCLONIDINE	ANTIHYPERTENSIVE	
333.05480	$C_{15}H_{13}N_5CL_2$	ROBENIDINE	COCCIDIOSTATIC	
333.07282	$C_{17}H_{20}NOBR$	BROMAZINE	ANTIHIST./-ALLERG.	
	$C_{17}H_{20}NOBR$	BROMODIPHENHYDRAMINE	ANTIHIST./-ALLERG.	
333.08406	$C_{16}H_{20}N_3BR$	BROMOPYRAMINE	ANTIHIST./-ALLERG.	
333.10011	$C_{20}H_{15}NO_4$	BISOXATIN	LAXATIVE	
333.15512	$C_{22}H_{23}NS$	TROPATEPIN	PARASYMPATH.-LYTIC	
333.16886	$C_{17}H_{23}N_3O_4$	PRIMIDOLOL	BETA-ADR.BLOCKER	
333.17288	$C_{22}H_{23}NO_2$	ENPROMATE	CYTOSTATIC	
333.19401	$C_{19}H_{27}NO_4$	DROTEBANOL	ANTITUSSIVE	
333.19718	$C_{19}H_{28}N_3CL$	SONTOQUINE	ANTIMALARIAL	
333.20926	$C_{23}H_{27}NO$	DEPTROPINE	BRONCHODILATOR	
333.23039	$C_{20}H_{31}NO_3$	CARBETAPENTANE	ANTITUSSIVE	
333.88887	$C_{10}H_7O_2CL_5$	PLIFERATE	INSECTICIDE	
333.90010	$C_9H_7N_2OCL_5$	CHLORANIFORMETHANE	FUNGIST./ANTIMYC.	
334.02758	$C_{16}H_{12}N_2O_2CL_2$	LORMETAZEPAM	TRANQUILIZER	MS
334.03571	$C_{20}H_{15}BR$	TRIPHENYLBROMETHYLENE	ESTROGEN	
334.06397	$C_{17}H_{16}N_2OCL_2$	TUCLAZEPAM	------------	
334.08348	$C_{12}H_{18}N_2O_7S$	GLUCOSYLSULFANILAMIDE	ANTIBIOTIC	
334.08413	$C_{20}H_{14}O_5$	FLUORESCIN	DIAGNOSTIC AID	
334.09291	$C_{17}H_{13}N_2O_2F_3$	TRIFLUBAZAM	TRANQUILIZER	
334.09873	$C_{16}H_{18}N_2O_4S$	PENICILLINE G	ANTIBIOTIC	
	$C_{16}H_{18}N_2O_4S$	SULFAPROXYLINE	ANTIBIOTIC	
334.10056	$C_{15}H_{23}O_4CLS$	ARAMITE	PESTICIDE	
334.12772	$C_{15}H_{18}N_4O_5$	MITOMYCIN C	CYTOSTATIC	
334.13174	$C_{20}H_{18}N_2O_3$	CINNOFURADIONE	ANALGESIC	
334.16411	$C_{16}H_{22}N_4O_4$	TETROXOPRIM	ANTIBIOTIC	
334.16813	$C_{21}H_{22}N_2O_2$	BUFEZOLAC	ANTIPHLOGISTIC	
	$C_{21}H_{22}N_2O_2$	STRYCHNINE	TONIC	MS
334.17936	$C_{20}H_{22}N_4O$	DIFENAMIZOLE	ANALGESIC	
334.18926	$C_{18}H_{26}N_2O_4$	PROGLUMIDE	TO THERAPY ULCERS	
334.22564	$C_{19}H_{30}N_2O_3$	FENALAMIDE	ANTISPASMOTIC	
335.01651	$C_{11}H_{14}N_3O_3CLS_2$	TIZOLEMIDE	DIURETIC	
335.05759	$C_{14}H_{13}N_3O_5S$	ISOXICAM	ANALGESIC	
	$C_{14}H_{13}N_3O_5S$	SULFANITRAN	ANTIBIOTIC	
335.06883	$C_{13}H_{13}N_5O_4S$	SULFACHRYSOIDINE	ANTIBIOTIC	
335.07245	$C_{17}H_{15}NO_3CLF$	FLAMPROP-METHYL	HERBICIDE	
335.09244	$C_{17}H_{18}NO_4CL$	PIRIFIBRATE	ANTICHOLESTEREMIC	
335.10929	$C_{13}H_{16}N_3O_4F_3$	TRIFLURALIN	HERBICIDE	
335.14970	$C_{19}H_{20}NOF_3$	BOXIDINE	ANTICHOLESTEREMIC	
335.15936	$C_{15}H_{21}N_5O_4$	RIBOPRIN	CYTOSTATIC	
335.17644	$C_{18}H_{26}N_3OCL$	HYDROXYCHLOROQUINE	ANTIMALARIAL	
335.18853	$C_{22}H_{25}NO_2$	TROPACINE	PARASYMPATH.-LYTIC	

MASS	FORMULA	NAME	CATEGORY	MS
335.22491	$C_{23}H_{29}NO$	DIPHENYLMETHOXYISOPROPYL NORTROPANE	ANTIHIST./-ALLERG.	
	$C_{23}H_{29}NO$	NORPIPANONE	ANALGESIC	
335.24604	$C_{20}H_{33}NO_3$	GANGLEFEN	VASODILATOR	
	$C_{20}H_{33}NO_3$	OXELADIN	ANTITUSSIVE	**MS**
335.26130	$C_{24}H_{33}N$	DROPRENILAMINE	CORONARY DILATOR	
336.01646	$C_{12}H_8N_4O_6S$	NIFURZIDE	ANTIBIOTIC	
336.06339	$C_{19}H_{12}O_6$	DICOUMAROL	ANTICOAGULANT	
336.08769	$C_{16}H_{17}N_2O_4CL$	CLONIXERIL	ANALGESIC	
336.11101	$C_{19}H_{16}N_2O_4$	BENZOBARBITAL	ANTIEPILEPTIC	
336.11284	$C_{18}H_{21}O_4CL$	BARTHRIN	INSECTICIDE	
336.20491	$C_{18}H_{28}N_2O_4$	ACEBUTOLOL	BETA-ADR.BLOCKER	**MS**
336.21007	$C_{20}H_{29}O_3F$	FLUOXYMESTERONE	ANDROGEN	
336.22016	$C_{22}H_{28}N_2O$	DIPHENYLHEXAMETHYLENEIMINOBUTYRAMIDE	PARASYMPATH.-LYTIC	
	$C_{22}H_{28}N_2O$	FENTANYL	ANALGESIC	**MS**
336.24129	$C_{19}H_{32}N_2O_3$	GYNODAL (TM)	LOCAL ANESTHETIC	
336.89492	$C_9H_9NO_3BR_2$	DIBROMOTYROSINE	THYREOSTATIC	
337.00210	$C_{14}H_9N_3O_3CL_2$	CLODANOLEN	MUSCLE RELAXANT	
337.01910	$C_{13}H_{11}N_3O_4S_2$	SUDOXICAM	ANTIPHLOGISTIC	
	$C_{13}H_{11}N_3O_4S_2$	TENOXICAM	ANTIPHLOGISTIC	
337.02879	$C_{14}H_{12}N_3O_3CLS$	FENQUIZONE	DIURETIC	
337.07304	$C_{17}H_{12}N_5OCL$	INTRAZOLE	ANTIPHLOGISTIC	
337.10224	$C_{13}H_{15}N_5O_6$	NIFURFOLIN	ANTIBIOTIC	
337.14601	$C_{16}H_{23}N_3O_3S$	GLIDAZAMIDE	ANTIDIABETIC	
337.16779	$C_{21}H_{23}NO_3$	PARGEVERINE	PARASYMPATH.-LYTIC	
337.17903	$C_{20}H_{23}N_3O_2$	BITERTANOL	FUNGIST./ANTIMYC.	
337.18892	$C_{18}H_{27}NO_5$	PLATYPHYLLINE	ANTISPASMOTIC	
	$C_{18}H_{27}NO_5$	PROPANIDID	NARCOTIC	
337.20418	$C_{22}H_{27}NO_2$	AMINEPTINE	ANTIDEPRESSANT	
	$C_{22}H_{27}NO_2$	DANAZOL	HORMONE	
	$C_{22}H_{27}NO_2$	LOBELINE	RESPIRAT.STIMULANT	**MS**
	$C_{22}H_{27}NO_2$	PHENERIDIN	ANALGESIC	
337.22531	$C_{19}H_{31}NO_4$	DECIMEMID	ANTIEPILEPTIC	
337.23654	$C_{18}H_{31}N_3O_3$	PAFENOLOL	BETA-ADR.BLOCKER	
337.24394	$C_{20}H_{35}NOS$	SULOCTIDIL	VASODILATOR	
338.01127	$C_{16}H_{12}O_4CL_2$	TRELOXINATE	ANTICHOLESTEREMIC	
338.01281	$C_{14}H_{11}N_2O_4CLS$	CHLORTALIDONE	DIURETIC	
338.02306	$C_8H_8O_2HG$	PHENYLMERCURIC ACETATE	DESINFICIENT	**MS**
338.03784	$C_{13}H_{15}N_4O_2BR$	BRODIMOPRIM	ANTIBIOTIC	
338.08783	$C_{16}H_{13}N_2O_3F_3$	COLFENAMATE	ANALGESIC	
338.12715	$C_{16}H_{21}N_3O_3CL$	MECLONAZEPAM	ANTHELMINTIC	
338.13387	$C_{13}H_{18}N_6O_5$	MOXNIDAZOLE	TRICHOMONACIDE	
338.13993	$C_{14}H_{26}O_7S$	DIAMYL SULFOSUCCINIC ACID	SOLUBILIZER ETC.	
338.14779	$C_{16}H_{22}N_2O_6$	BAYER E 39	CYTOSTATIC	
338.16304	$C_{20}H_{22}N_2O_3$	PERIVINE	CYTOSTATIC	
338.18820	$C_{22}H_{26}O_3$	ETHINYLESTRADIOL ACETATE	ESTROGEN	
	$C_{22}H_{26}O_3$	RESMETHRIN	INSECTICIDE	
338.20933	$C_{19}H_{30}O_5$	PIPERONYL BUTOXIDE	PESTICIDE	
338.21066	$C_{20}H_{26}N_4O$	LISURIDE	ANTIHIST./-ALLERG.	
338.23581	$C_{22}H_{30}N_2O$	PIRMENOL	ANTIARRHYTHMIC	
339.00652	$C_{15}H_{11}NO_4CL_2$	CLAMIDOXIC ACID	ANTIPHLOGISTIC	
339.03321	$C_{15}H_{14}NO_4CLS$	ACLANTATE	ANTIPHLOGISTIC	
339.05251	$C_{13}H_{13}N_3O_6S$	CEFACETRILE	ANTIBIOTIC	

MASS	FORMULA	NAME	CATEGORY	MS
339.08889	$C_{14}H_{17}N_3O_5S$	SULFACECOL	ANTIBIOTIC	
339.12528	$C_{15}H_{21}N_3O_4S$	CROTONYLSULFANILYLBUTYLUREA	ANTIDIABETIC	
	$C_{15}H_{21}N_3O_4S$	GLICLAZIDE	ANTIDIABETIC	
339.13716	$C_{22}H_{17}N_3O$	PIRIQUALONE	------------	
339.14706	$C_{20}H_{21}NO_4$	PAPAVERINE	ANTISPASMOTIC	MS
339.15023	$C_{20}H_{22}N_3CL$	DORASTIN	ANTIHIST./-ALLERG.	
339.17692	$C_{20}H_{25}N_3S$	PERAZINE	NEUROLEPTIC	MS
339.18344	$C_{21}H_{25}NO_3$	MORAMIDE INTERMEDIATE	ANALGESIC	
	$C_{21}H_{25}NO_3$	PIPETHANATE	PARASYMPATH.-LYTIC	
339.19468	$C_{20}H_{25}N_3O_2$	METHYLERGOMETRINE	GYNECOL./OBSTRECT.	
	$C_{20}H_{25}N_3O_2$	PROPISERGIDE	SYMPATHOLYTIC	
339.21983	$C_{22}H_{29}NO_2$	DEXTROPROPOXYPHEN	ANALGESIC	MS
	$C_{22}H_{29}NO_2$	LEVOPROPOXYPHENE	ANTITUSSIVE	
	$C_{22}H_{29}NO_2$	NORACYMETHADOL	ANALGESIC	
339.23106	$C_{21}H_{29}N_3O$	DISOPYRAMIDE	ANTIARRHYTHMIC	MS
339.27734	$C_{20}H_{37}NO_3$	ROCIVERINE	ANTISPASMOTIC	
339.36135	$C_{21}H_{45}N_3$	HEXETIDINE	DESINFICIENT	
339.99606	$C_6H_{14}O_{12}P_2$	FRUCTOSE DIPHOSPHATE	ENDOG.BIOMOLECULE	
340.02692	$C_{16}H_{14}O_4CL_2$	DICLOFOP-METHYL	HERBICIDE	
340.02772	$C_9H_{20}N_2O_3CL_3P$	DEFOSFAMIDE	CYTOSTATIC	
340.07944	$C_{15}H_{16}O_9$	ESCULIN	NATURAL SUBSTANCE	
340.10995	$C_{23}H_{16}O_3$	DIPHACINONE	RODENTICIDE	
	$C_{23}H_{16}O_3$	DIPHENADIONE	ANTICOAGULANT	
340.16094	$C_{20}H_{24}N_2OS$	BOTIACRINE	ANTIPARKINSONIAN	
	$C_{20}H_{24}N_2OS$	CINASERINE	CYTOSTATIC	
	$C_{20}H_{24}N_2OS$	LUCANTHONE	ANTHELMINTIC	
	$C_{20}H_{24}N_2OS$	PROPIOMAZINE	SEDATIVE	
	$C_{20}H_{24}N_2OS$	PROPIONYLPROMAZINE	TRANQUILIZER	
340.16344	$C_{16}H_{24}N_2O_6$	PYRISUCCIDEANOL	STIMULANT	
340.17869	$C_{20}H_{24}N_2O_3$	LOCHNERIDINE	NATURAL SUBSTANCE	
	$C_{20}H_{24}N_2O_3$	MEPHEMORPHOLINOETHOXYBENZAMIDE	ANALGESIC	
	$C_{20}H_{24}N_2O_3$	YOHIMBIC ACID	ANTISPASMOTIC	
340.18993	$C_{19}H_{24}N_4O_2$	PENTAMIDINE	ANTIBIOTIC	
340.19395	$C_{24}H_{24}N_2$	ACRIDOREX	ANOREXIC	
340.20385	$C_{22}H_{28}O_3$	CANRENONE	DIURETIC	
	$C_{22}H_{28}O_3$	HYDROXYMETHYLENEPROGESTERONE	GESTAGEN	
	$C_{22}H_{28}O_3$	NORETHINDRONE ACETATE	GESTAGEN	
	$C_{22}H_{28}O_3$	SANTALYL SALICYLATE	DESINFICIENT	
340.21508	$C_{21}H_{28}N_2O_2$	DECLOXIZINE	BRONCHODILATOR	
	$C_{21}H_{28}N_2O_2$	ETHYLHYDROCUPREINE	DESINFICIENT	
340.24023	$C_{23}H_{32}O_2$	DIMETHISTERONE	GESTAGEN	
	$C_{23}H_{32}O_2$	MEDROGESTONE	GESTAGEN	
	$C_{23}H_{32}O_2$	MEDROGESTONE	GESTAGEN	
340.33413	$C_{22}H_{44}O_2$	BUTYL STEARATE	SOFTENER	
341.05040	$C_{13}H_{15}N_3O_4S_2$	SULFABENZENESULFONEMETHYLAMIDE	ANTIBIOTIC	
341.05355	$C_{17}H_{11}NO_7$	ARISTOLOCHIC ACID	NATURAL SUBSTANCE	
341.06978	$C_{15}H_{17}N_3O_2CL_2$	PROPICONAZOLE	FUNGIST./ANTIMYC.	
341.14093	$C_{15}H_{23}N_3O_4S$	CICLACILLIN	ANTIBIOTIC	
	$C_{15}H_{23}N_3O_4S$	ISOSULPIRIDE	ANTIHIST./-ALLERG.	
	$C_{15}H_{23}N_3O_4S$	SULPIRIDE	ANTIDEPRESSANT	
341.15464	$C_{21}H_{24}NOCL$	CLOBENZTROPINE	ANTIHIST./-ALLERG.	
341.16271	$C_{20}H_{23}NO_4$	ACETYLDIPHEMIN	ANTIRHEUMATIC	

MASS	FORMULA	NAME	CATEGORY	MS
341.16271	$C_{20}H_{23}NO_4$	DIHYDROPROPAVERINE	ANTISPASMOTIC	
	$C_{20}H_{23}NO_4$	ISOCORYDINE	SYMPATHOLYTIC	
	$C_{20}H_{23}NO_4$	THEBACONE	ANTITUSSIVE	MS
341.17394	$C_{19}H_{23}N_3O_3$	NICOTINOYLPROCAINE	LOCAL ANESTHETIC	
341.18518	$C_{18}H_{23}N_5O_2$	FENETYLLINE	STIMULANT	MS
341.19909	$C_{21}H_{27}NO_3$	BENAPRIZINE	ANTIPARKINSONIAN	
	$C_{21}H_{27}NO_3$	DIMETHAMINOMETHYLETHYLETHYLBENZILATE	ANALGESIC	
	$C_{21}H_{27}NO_3$	PROPAFENONE	ANTIARRHYTHMIC	MS
341.78905	$C_7H_5OBR_3$	TRIBROMOCRESOL	FUNGIST./ANTIMYC.	
341.97386	$C_{11}H_{16}O_2CLS_3P$	CARBOFENOTIONE	INSECTICIDE	
342.04565	$C_{12}H_{14}N_4O_4S_2$	THIOPHANATE-METHYL	FUNGIST./ANTIMYC.	
342.06589	$C_{19}H_{15}O_4CL$	COUMACHLOR	RODENTICIDE	
342.07060	$C_{17}H_{15}N_4CLS$	ETIZOLAM	TRANQUILIZER	
342.11622	$C_{12}H_{22}O_{11}$	CELLOBIOSE	SUGAR	
	$C_{12}H_{22}O_{11}$	GENTIOBIOSE	SUGAR	
	$C_{12}H_{22}O_{11}$	ISOMALTOSE	SUGAR	
	$C_{12}H_{22}O_{11}$	LACTOSE	SUGAR	
	$C_{12}H_{22}O_{11}$	LACTULOSE	SUGAR	
	$C_{12}H_{22}O_{11}$	MALTOSE	SUGAR	
	$C_{12}H_{22}O_{11}$	MELIBIOSE	SUGAR	
	$C_{12}H_{22}O_{11}$	SACCHAROSE	SUGAR	
	$C_{12}H_{22}O_{11}$	SOPHOROSE	SUGAR	
	$C_{12}H_{22}O_{11}$	TREHALOSE	SUGAR	
	$C_{12}H_{22}O_{11}$	TURANOSE	SUGAR	
342.21950	$C_{22}H_{30}O_3$	ENDRISONE	CORTICOID	
	$C_{22}H_{30}O_3$	MEGESTROL	ESTROGEN	
	$C_{22}H_{30}O_3$	SICCANIN	FUNGIST./ANTIMYC.	
343.08954	$C_{14}H_{22}N_3O_2BR$	BROMOPRIDE	STOMACHIC	MS
343.09100	$C_{18}H_{18}N_3CLS$	CLOTIAPINE	NEUROLEPTIC	
343.11548	$C_{15}H_{15}N_6O_4$	ETOFYLLINE NICOTINATE	VASODILATOR	
343.17029	$C_{21}H_{26}NOCL$	CLEMASTINE	ANTIHIST./-ALLERG.	MS
343.17183	$C_{19}H_{25}N_3OS$	THIAMBUTOSINE	ANTIBIOTIC	
343.17836	$C_{20}H_{25}NO_4$	ACETYLDIHYDROCODEINE	ANALGESIC	MS
343.22598	$C_{20}H_{29}N_3O_2$	CINCHOCAINE	LOCAL ANESTHETIC	
343.25113	$C_{22}H_{33}NO_2$	ATISINE	ANTIINFLAMMATORY	
343.96029	$C_{12}H_6N_2O_6CL_2$	NICLOFOLAN	ANTHELMINTIC	
343.96282	$C_{11}H_{15}O_2CL_2S_2P$	PROTHIOFOS	INSECTICIDE	
344.00245	$C_{13}H_{12}O_7S_2$	SULTOSILIC ACID	ANTICHOLESTEREMIC	
344.01376	$C_{16}H_{15}O_2CL_3$	METHOXYCHLOR	INSECTICIDE	MS
344.05322	$C_{17}H_{12}O_8$	PROBICROMIL	ANTIHIST./-ALLERG.	
344.06945	$C_{15}H_{18}N_2O_3CL_2$	OXADIAZONE	HERBICIDE	
344.08961	$C_{18}H_{16}O_7$	EUPATORIN	EMETIC	
	$C_{18}H_{16}O_7$	USNIC ACID	DESINFICIENT	
344.09277	$C_{18}H_{17}N_2O_3CL$	ARFENDAZAM	------------	
344.10803	$C_{22}H_{17}N_2CL$	CLOTRIMAZOLE	FUNGIST./ANTIMYC.	
	$C_{22}H_{17}N_2CL$	LOMBAZOLE	ANTIBIOTIC	
344.11140	$C_{19}H_{21}N_2CLS$	CLOROTEPIN	NEUROLEPTIC	
344.11207	$C_{16}H_{16}N_4O_5$	NIFURQUINAZOL	ANTIBIOTIC	
344.13809	$C_{19}H_{24}N_2S_2$	METHIOMEPRAZINE	NEUROLEPTIC	
344.15431	$C_{21}H_{25}O_2CL$	TRENGESTONE	GESTAGEN	
344.16238	$C_{20}H_{24}O_5$	TERBUFIBROL	ANTICHOLESTEREMIC	
344.17116	$C_{17}H_{23}N_2O_2F_3$	FLUALAMIDE	ANTITUSSIVE	

MASS	FORMULA	NAME	CATEGORY	MS
344.17361	$C_{19}H_{24}N_2O_4$	PIPRATECOL	VASODILATOR	
	$C_{19}H_{24}N_2O_4$	TOLAMOLOL	BETA-ADR.BLOCKER	
344.19876	$C_{21}H_{28}O_4$	DEHYDROCORTICOSTERONE	CORTICOID	
	$C_{21}H_{28}O_4$	DEPRODONE	CORTICOID	
	$C_{21}H_{28}O_4$	FORMEBOLONE	ANABOLIC	
344.20999	$C_{20}H_{28}N_2O_3$	OXYPHENCYCLIMINE	PARASYMPATH.-LYTIC	
344.23515	$C_{22}H_{32}O_3$	MEDROXYPROGESTERONE	GESTAGEN	
	$C_{22}H_{32}O_3$	MEDRYSONE	CORTICOID	
	$C_{22}H_{32}O_3$	METHENOLONE ACETATE	ANABOLIC	
	$C_{22}H_{32}O_3$	STENBOLONE ACETATE	ANABOLIC	
	$C_{22}H_{32}O_3$	TESTOSTERONE PROPIONATE	ANDROGEN	
344.27153	$C_{23}H_{36}O_2$	DIMEPREGNENE	GYNECOL./OBSTRECT.	
344.32905	$C_{21}H_{44}O_3$	BATILOL	DERMATIC	
345.03707	$C_{12}H_{16}N_3O_3S_2P$	AZINPHOS-ETHYL	INSECTICIDE	MS
345.04744	$C_{10}H_{12}N_5O_7P$	CYCLIC GMP	ENDOG.BIOMOLECULE	
345.09139	$C_{14}H_{20}N_3O_3CLS$	CLOPAMIDE	DIURETIC	
345.09946	$C_{13}H_{19}N_3O_6S$	NITRALINE	HERBICIDE	
345.11637	$C_{15}H_{24}NO_4SP$	ISOFENPHOS	INSECTICIDE	
345.14956	$C_{20}H_{24}NO_2CL$	DIAPHEN	ANTIHIST./-ALLERG.	
	$C_{20}H_{24}NO_2CL$	METOFOLINE	ANALGESIC	
345.15110	$C_{18}H_{23}N_3O_2S$	PODILFEN	ANTIHYPERTENSIVE	
345.15762	$C_{19}H_{23}NO_5$	TRETOQUINOL	BRONCHODILATOR	
345.15896	$C_{20}H_{19}N_5O$	ACODAZOLE	------------	
345.19401	$C_{20}H_{27}NO_4$	BEVANTOLOL	BETA-ADR.BLOCKER	
345.26678	$C_{22}H_{35}NO_2$	SECOVERINE	ANTISPASMOTIC	
345.97796	$C_{10}H_{13}N_2O_2CL_2FS_2$	TOLYLFLUANIDE	FUNGIST./ANTIMYC.	
346.00763	$C_{11}H_{17}N_2O_2CL_3S$	CLODANTOIN	FUNGIST./ANTIMYC.	
346.03731	$C_{14}H_{16}O_6CLP$	COROXON	PARASYMP.-MIMETIC	
346.09471	$C_{12}H_{18}N_4O_6S$	ORYZALIN	HERBICIDE	
346.09922	$C_{17}H_{15}O_2F_5$	PENTAFLURANOL	------------	
346.11649	$C_{17}H_{18}N_2O_6$	NIFEDIPINE	CORONARY DILATOR	
346.12051	$C_{22}H_{18}O_4$	BENZYL PHTHALATE	CHEMICAL	
	$C_{22}H_{18}O_4$	CRESOLPHTHALEIN	CHEMICAL	
346.12705	$C_{19}H_{23}N_2CLS$	CHLORPROETHAZINE	NEUROLEPTIC	
346.13103	$C_{12}H_{28}O_7P_2$	TETRAISOPROPYL PYROPHOSPHATE	PARASYMP.-MIMETIC	
346.13357	$C_{20}H_{23}O_3CL$	BECLOBRATE	ANTICHOLESTEREMIC	
346.14164	$C_{19}H_{22}O_6$	GIBBERELLIC ACID	NATURAL SUBSTANCE	
346.14360	$C_{12}H_{24}N_6O_2P_2$	DIPIN	CYTOSTATIC	
346.16813	$C_{22}H_{22}N_2O_2$	CINNOPENTAZONE	ANALGESIC	
346.16927	$C_{19}H_{23}N_2O_3F$	ROXOPERONE	NEUROLEPTIC	
346.17803	$C_{20}H_{26}O_5$	ALLETHRIN II	INSECTICIDE	
346.21441	$C_{21}H_{30}O_4$	ALGESTONE	GESTAGEN	
	$C_{21}H_{30}O_4$	CORTICOSTERONE	CORTICOID	
	$C_{21}H_{30}O_4$	CORTODOXONE	ANTIPHLOGISTIC	
	$C_{21}H_{30}O_4$	DESOXYHYDROXYCORTICOSTERONE	CORTICOID	
346.22564	$C_{20}H_{30}N_2O_3$	MORPHERIDINE	ANALGESIC	
346.23554	$C_{18}H_{34}O_6$	SORBITANE LAURATE	SOLUBILIZER ETC.	
346.25080	$C_{22}H_{34}O_3$	MESTEROLONE ACETATE	ANDROGEN	
346.77360	CHO_3I_2S	DIMETHIODAL	DIAGNOSTIC AID	
346.83042	$C_5H_3NOI_2$	IOPYDONE	DIAGNOSTIC AID	
346.91081	$C_{10}H_9NO_2CL_4S$	CAPTAFOL	FUNGIST./ANTIMYC.	
346.96311	$C_{11}H_{14}NO_3S_2AS$	ARSTHINOL	ANTIBIOTIC	

MASS	FORMULA	NAME	CATEGORY	MS
347.06309	$C_{10}H_{14}N_5O_7P$	ADENOSINE PHOSPHATE	CORONARY DILATOR	
347.06883	$C_{14}H_{13}N_5O_4S$	NIFURALIDE	ANTIBIOTIC	
347.08848	$C_{18}H_{22}NOBR$	EMBRAMINE	ANTIHIST./-ALLERG.	
347.09244	$C_{18}H_{18}NO_4CL$	CLANOBUTIN	CHOLERETIC	
347.09398	$C_{16}H_{17}N_3O_4S$	CEFALEXIN	ANTIBIOTIC	
347.09971	$C_{17}H_{22}N_3BR$	ADEPTOLON (TM)	ANTIHIST./-ALLERG.	MS
347.10704	$C_{14}H_{22}N_3O_3CLS$	LORAPRIDE	------------	
347.13689	$C_{18}H_{21}NO_6$	IPROCROLOL	BETA-ADR.BLOCKER	
347.14562	$C_{21}H_{21}N_3S$	TIOMERGIN	ANTIDEPRESSANT	
347.18608	$C_{21}H_{24}NF_3$	FLUOTRACENE	NEUROLEPTIC	
347.19976	$C_{22}H_{25}N_3O$	BENZPIPERYLON	ANTIRHEUMATIC	
	$C_{22}H_{25}N_3O$	INDORAMINE	ANTIHYPERTENSIVE	
347.20966	$C_{20}H_{29}NO_4$	FEDRILATE	ANTITUSSIVE	
347.22491	$C_{24}H_{29}NO$	DEXCLAMOL	NEUROLEPTIC	
	$C_{24}H_{29}NO$	PHENOMORPHAN	ANALGESIC	
347.22540	$C_{21}H_{32}N_2CL$	VIMINOL	ANALGESIC	MS
347.78142	$CH_2O_3I_2S$	DIMETHIODAL	DIAGNOSTIC AID	
347.90435	$C_{10}H_9O_3CL_4P$	DIETREEN-T	INSECTICIDE	
348.00440	$C_{14}H_9N_2OCL_2F_3$	HALOCARBANE	DESINFICIENT	
348.04323	$C_{17}H_{14}N_2O_2CL_2$	CLOXAZOLAM	TRANQUILIZER	
348.06770	$C_{17}H_{14}N_2O_3CLF$	DOXEFAZEPAM	TRANQUILIZER	
348.07800	$C_{16}H_{16}N_2O_5S$	SUCCISULFONE	ANTIBIOTIC	
348.10856	$C_{18}H_{15}N_2O_2F_3$	FLUMIZOL	ANTIPHLOGISTIC	
348.11101	$C_{20}H_{16}N_2O_4$	CAMPTOTHECIN	CYTOSTATIC	
348.11284	$C_{19}H_{21}O_4CL$	CLOFOP-ISOBUTYL	HERBICIDE	
348.12561	$C_{16}H_{20}N_4O_3S$	TORASEMIDE	DIURETIC	
348.14337	$C_{16}H_{20}N_4O_5$	PORFIROMYCIN	ANTIBIOTIC	
348.14739	$C_{21}H_{20}N_2O_3$	SERPENTINE	NATURAL SUBSTANCE	
348.14922	$C_{20}H_{25}O_3CL$	AMADINONE	GESTAGEN	
348.16986	$C_{19}H_{20}N_6O$	IMIDOCARB	PESTICIDE	
348.17592	$C_{20}H_{28}O_3S$	ETHYL DIBUNATE	ANTITUSSIVE	
348.20491	$C_{19}H_{28}N_2O_4$	CARPINDOLOL	BETA-ADR.BLOCKER	
348.22016	$C_{23}H_{28}N_2O$	LEIOPYRROLE	ANTISPASMOTIC	
348.23006	$C_{21}H_{32}O_4$	ALFADOLONE	NARCOTIC	
348.25655	$C_{24}H_{32}N_2$	CYCLOHEXYLDIPHENYLETHYLPIPERAZINE	ANALGESIC	
348.92309	$C_{13}H_7NO_2CL_4$	TETRACHLOROSALICYLANILIDE	PRESERVATIVE	
348.92629	$C_9H_{11}NO_3CL_3SP$	CHLORPYRIFOS	INSECTICIDE	MS
349.07153	$C_{16}H_{16}NO_6P$	NAFTALOFOS	ANTHELMINTIC	
349.10963	$C_{16}H_{19}N_3O_4S$	AMPICILLIN	ANTIBIOTIC	MS
	$C_{16}H_{19}N_3O_4S$	CEFRADINE	ANTIBIOTIC	
349.12896	$C_{19}H_{18}NO_2F_3$	PREFENAMATE	ANALGESIC	
349.13141	$C_{21}H_{19}NO_4$	CINMETACIN	ANTIPHLOGISTIC	
	$C_{21}H_{19}NO_4$	OXARBAZOL	------------	
349.20418	$C_{23}H_{27}NO_2$	PITUXATE	ANTITUSSIVE	
349.20755	$C_{20}H_{31}NO_2S$	CETIEDIL	VASODILATOR	
349.24056	$C_{24}H_{31}NO$	DIPIPANONE	ANALGESIC	
	$C_{24}H_{31}NO$	PIPIDONE	ANALGESIC	
349.90058	$C_{12}H_6N_2CL_4S$	CHLORFENSULFIDE	PESTICIDE	
349.94503	$C_{12}H_9N_2O_2CL_3S$	LOTIFAZOL	------------	
350.07904	$C_{20}H_{14}O_6$	ETHYLIDENEBISHYDROXYCOUMARIN	ANTICOAGULANT	
350.09365	$C_{16}H_{18}N_2O_5S$	PHENOXYMETHYLPENICILLIN	ANTIBIOTIC	MS
350.15181	$C_{22}H_{22}O_4$	DIENESTROL DIACETATE	ESTROGEN	

MASS	FORMULA	NAME	CATEGORY	MS
350.15181	$C_{22}H_{22}O_4$	INDENESTROL DIACETATE	ESTROGEN	
350.16304	$C_{21}H_{22}N_2O_3$	STRYCHNINE-N-OXIDE	TONIC	
350.19943	$C_{22}H_{26}N_2O_2$	INDOCAT	ANTIHIST./-ALLERG.	
	$C_{22}H_{26}N_2O_2$	VINPOCETIN	VASODILATOR	
350.20057	$C_{19}H_{27}N_2O_3F$	CARPERONE	NEUROLEPTIC	
350.32971	$C_{22}H_{42}N_2O$	HEPTADECENYLIMIDAZOLINEETHANOL	SOLUBILIZER ETC.	
350.90623	$C_9H_6NO_4IS$	CHINIOFON	DESINFICIENT	
351.11384	$CC_{19}H_{18}N_3OCL$	CYPRAZEPAM	TRANQUILIZER	
351.12507	$C_{19}H_{18}N_5CL$	ADINAZOLAM	TRANQUILIZER	
351.12528	$C_{16}H_{21}N_3O_4S$	EPICILLIN	ANTIBIOTIC	
351.14461	$C_{19}H_{20}NO_2F_3$	BENFLUOREX	ANTICHOLESTEREMIC	
351.15829	$C_{20}H_{21}N_3O_3$	MOQUIZONE	CHOLERETIC	
351.16953	$C_{19}H_{21}N_5O_2$	PIRENZEPIN	TO THERAPY ULCERS	MS
351.18344	$C_{22}H_{25}NO_3$	PIPOXOLAN	ANTISPASMOTIC	
	$C_{22}H_{25}NO_3$	TROPINE BENZILATE	ANTISPASMOTIC	
351.20457	$C_{19}H_{29}NO_5$	BURODILIN	ANTISPASMOTIC	
	$C_{19}H_{29}NO_5$	DIPIVEFRINE	SYMPATHOMIMETIC	
351.21983	$C_{23}H_{29}NO_2$	PHENADOXONE	ANALGESIC	
	$C_{23}H_{29}NO_2$	PINOLCAINE	LOCAL ANESTHETIC	
	$C_{23}H_{29}NO_2$	PYRROLIFEN	ANALGESIC	
351.36135	$C_{22}H_{45}N_3$	HEXEDINE	DESINFICIENT	
351.85096	$C_5H_6N_2O_3CL_6$	DICHLORALUREA (DCU)	HERBICIDE	
351.91469	$C_{14}H_9CL_5$	CLOFENOTANE (DDT)	INSECTICIDE	
351.95589	$C_{10}H_8O_{10}S_2$	SULMARIN	HEMOSTATIC	
352.05678	$C_{17}H_{18}N_2CL_2S$	DICHLORPROMAZINE	TRANQUILIZER	
352.05903	$C_{17}H_{12}N_2OCLF_3$	HALAZEPAM	TRANQUILIZER	
352.07137	$C_{17}H_{17}O_6CL$	GRISEOFULVIN	FUNGIST./ANTIMYC.	
352.09469	$C_{20}H_{16}O_6$	TRIACETOXYANTHRACENE	DERMATIC	
352.12210	$C_{18}H_{19}N_2F_3S$	TRIFLUPROMAZINE	NEUROLEPTIC	MS
352.14231	$C_{20}H_{20}N_2O_4$	LENIQUINSIN	ANTIHYPERTENSIVE	
352.16746	$C_{22}H_{24}O_4$	DIETHYLSTILBESTROL DIACETATE	ESTROGEN	
352.17869	$C_{21}H_{24}N_2O_3$	HYDROXINDASATE	DIURETIC	
	$C_{21}H_{24}N_2O_3$	RAUBASIN	ANTIHYPERTENSIVE	
	$C_{21}H_{24}N_2O_3$	STRYCHNINIC ACID	TONIC	
352.21508	$C_{22}H_{28}N_2O_2$	ANILERIDINE	ANALGESIC	
	$C_{22}H_{28}N_2O_2$	ENCAINIDE	ANTIARRHYTHMIC	
352.22498	$C_{20}H_{32}O_5$	DINOPROSTONE	GYNECOL./OBSTRECT.	
352.23621	$C_{19}H_{32}N_2O_4$	BETOXYCAINE	LOCAL ANESTHETIC	
352.24023	$C_{24}H_{32}O_2$	QUINBOLONE	ANABOLIC	
352.25146	$C_{23}H_{32}N_2O$	MOXAPRINDIN	ANTIARRHYTHMIC	
352.26136	$C_{21}H_{36}O_4$	DOXAPROST	BRONCHODILATOR	
352.98726	$C_9H_{12}N_3O_4I$	IODODESOXYCYTIDINE	DERMATIC	
352.99758	$C_7H_5NO_3HG$	NITROMERSOL	DESINFICIENT	
353.01402	$C_{13}H_{11}N_3O_5S_2$	MALEYLSULFATHIAZOL	ANTIBIOTIC	
353.02708	$C_{11}H_{16}N_3O_4CLS_2$	BUTIZIDE	DIURETIC	
353.05855	$C_{17}H_{17}NO_3CL_2$	TEROFENAMATE	ANTIPHLOGISTIC	
353.06009	$C_{15}H_{16}N_3O_3CLS$	GLYPARAMIDE	ANTIDIABETIC	
353.08994	$C_{19}H_{15}NO_6$	ACENOCOUMAROL	ANTICOAGULANT	MS
353.10050	$C_{21}H_{20}NCLS$	NUCLOTIXENE	ANTIDEPRESSANT	
353.12632	$C_{20}H_{19}NO_5$	BERBERIN	DESINFICIENT	
	$C_{20}H_{19}NO_5$	DUOMETACINE	ANALGESIC	
353.12949	$C_{20}H_{20}N_3OCL$	AMOPYROQUINE	ANTIBIOTIC	

MASS	FORMULA	NAME	CATEGORY	MS
353.14093	$C_{16}H_{23}N_3O_4S$	DIBUPYRONE	ANALGESIC	
353.15618	$C_{20}H_{23}N_3OS$	SOPITAZINE	PARASYMPATH.-LYTIC	
353.18384	$C_{18}H_{27}NO_6$	TRIXOLAN	CHOLERETIC	
353.19909	$C_{22}H_{27}NO_3$	DIOXAPHETYL BUTYRATE	ANALGESIC	
	$C_{22}H_{27}NO_3$	OXPHENERIDINE	ANALGESIC	
	$C_{22}H_{27}NO_3$	ZOCAINONE	------------	
353.21033	$C_{21}H_{27}N_3O_2$	METHYSERGIDE	SEROTONINE ANTAG.	
353.23548	$C_{23}H_{31}NO_2$	ACETYLMETHADOL	ANALGESIC	
	$C_{23}H_{31}NO_2$	ALPHACETYLMETHADOL	ANALGESIC	
	$C_{23}H_{31}NO_2$	BETACETYLMETHADOL	ANALGESIC	
	$C_{23}H_{31}NO_2$	LEVACETYLMETHADOL	ANALGESIC	
	$C_{23}H_{31}NO_2$	MOTRETINIDE	DERMATIC	
	$C_{23}H_{31}NO_2$	PROADIFEN	ENZYME INHIBITOR	
353.87262	$C_4H_8N_2OI_2$	DIIODOPROPYLUREA	RUBEFACIENT	
353.88426	$C_{12}H_6O_2CL_4S$	BITHIONOL	DESINFICIENT	
	$C_{12}H_6O_2CL_4S$	TETRADIFON	PESTICIDE	
353.95785	$C_{10}H_{16}N_2O_2BR_2$	PIPOBROMAN	CYTOSTATIC	
353.97128	$C_9H_{11}N_2O_5I$	IODOXURIDINE	VIRUCIDE	
354.01741	$C_{15}H_{12}N_2O_4CL_2$	UREFIBRATE	ANTICHOLESTEREMIC	
354.04411	$C_{15}H_{15}N_2O_4CLS$	XIPAMIDE	DIURETIC	
354.05620	$C_{19}H_{14}O_5S$	PHENOLSULFOPHTHALEIN	DIAGNOSTIC AID	
354.11842	$C_{15}H_{22}N_4O_2S_2$	ALLITHIAMINE	VITAMINE	
354.13683	$C_{23}H_{18}N_2O_2$	ISOFEZOLAC	ANTIPHLOGISTIC	
354.16133	$C_{17}H_{26}N_2O_4S$	SULTOPRIDE	NEUROLEPTIC	
354.17659	$C_{21}H_{26}N_2OS$	OXYRIDAZINE	NEUROLEPTIC	
354.19434	$C_{21}H_{26}N_2O_3$	VINCAMINE	VASODILATOR	
	$C_{21}H_{26}N_2O_3$	YOHIMBINE	SYMPATHOLYTIC	
354.20558	$C_{20}H_{26}N_4O_2$	HEXAMIDINE	ANTIBIOTIC	
354.21950	$C_{23}H_{30}O_3$	ETRETINATE	DERMATIC	
	$C_{23}H_{30}O_3$	MELENGESTROL	GESTAGEN	
354.23073	$C_{22}H_{30}N_2O_2$	ASPIDOSPERMINE	RESPIRAT.STIMULANT	
	$C_{22}H_{30}N_2O_2$	EPROZINOL	BRONCHODILATOR	
354.24063	$C_{20}H_{34}O_5$	ALPROSTADIL	VASODILATOR	
	$C_{20}H_{34}O_5$	DINOPROST	GYNECOL./OBSTRECT.	
355.00480	$C_{12}H_{15}NO_5CL_2S$	RACEFENICOL	ANTIBIOTIC	
	$C_{12}H_{15}NO_5CL_2S$	THIAMPHENICOL	ANTIBIOTIC	
355.02967	$C_{13}H_{13}N_3O_5S_2$	SUCCINYLSULFATHIAZOLE	ANTIBIOTIC	
355.05467	$C_{12}H_{13}N_3O_4CLF_3$	FLUCHLORALIN	HERBICIDE	
355.06605	$C_{14}H_{17}N_3O_4S_2$	DIMETHYLSULFAMOYLSULFANILANILIDE	ANTIBIOTIC	
355.07574	$C_{15}H_{18}N_3O_3CLS$	TIARAMIDE	ANALGESIC	
355.10646	$C_{20}H_{21}NOS_2$	TINOFEDRIN	VASODILATOR	
355.12989	$C_{16}H_{22}N_3O_4CL$	PLAFIBRIDE	ANTICHOLESTEREMIC	
355.14514	$C_{20}H_{22}N_3OCL$	AMODIAQUIN	ANTIBIOTIC	
355.17836	$C_{21}H_{25}NO_4$	GLAUCINE	ANTITUSSIVE	
	$C_{21}H_{25}NO_4$	NALMEXONE	ANALGESIC	
355.19476	$C_{22}H_{26}NO_2F$	MOPERONE	NEUROLEPTIC	MS
355.19699	$C_{22}H_{29}NOS$	DIPROFEN	ANTISPASMOTIC	
	$C_{22}H_{29}NOS$	XENTHIORATE	ANTICHOLESTEREMIC	
355.21474	$C_{22}H_{29}NO_3$	ANISOHYDROCINNAMOL	ANTISPASMOTIC	
355.25113	$C_{23}H_{33}NO_2$	XIPRANOLOL	BETA-ADR.BLOCKER	
	$C_{23}H_{33}NO_2$	XYLOXEMIN	ANTITUSSIVE	
355.34234	$C_{18}H_{41}N_7$	GUAZATINE	FUNGIST./ANTIMYC.	

MASS	FORMULA	NAME	CATEGORY	MS
355.99426	$C_{12}H_{13}N_4O_2BRS$	SULFABROMOMETHAZINE	ANTIBIOTIC	
356.07034	$C_{17}H_{13}N_2CLF_4$	FLETAZEPAM	TRANQUILIZER	
356.08825	$C_{20}H_{17}O_3FS$	SULINDAC	ANALGESIC	MS
356.10084	$C_{18}H_{16}N_2O_6$	BUFROLIN	ANTIHIST./-ALLERG.	
356.11074	$C_{16}H_{20}O_9$	GENTIOPICRIN	ANTIMALARIAL	
356.12599	$C_{20}H_{20}O_6$	CUBEBIN	DESINFICIENT	
356.12916	$C_{20}H_{21}N_2O_2CL$	DINAZAFONE	------------	
356.13407	$C_{15}H_{24}N_4O_2S_2$	PROSULTIAMINE	VITAMINE	
356.15585	$C_{20}H_{24}N_2O_2S$	HYCANTHONE	ANTHELMINTIC	
356.19001	$C_{21}H_{25}N_2O_2F$	FLUANISONE	NEUROLEPTIC	MS
356.19876	$C_{22}H_{28}O_4$	ESTRADIOL DIACETATE	ESTROGEN	
356.20124	$C_{20}H_{25}N_4OF$	NIAPRAZINE	ANTIHIST./-ALLERG.	
356.23515	$C_{23}H_{32}O_3$	ESTRADIOL VALERATE	ESTROGEN	
	$C_{23}H_{32}O_3$	QUINESTRADIOL	ESTROGEN	
356.31915	$C_{24}H_{40}N_2$	CONESSINE	ANTIBIOTIC	
357.01353	$C_7H_3N_3F_{12}$	MIDAFLUR	NEUROLEPTIC	
357.07679	$C_{19}H_{16}NO_4CL$	CLOMETACIN	ANALGESIC	
	$C_{19}H_{16}NO_4CL$	INDOMETACIN	ANALGESIC	MS
357.14956	$C_{21}H_{24}NO_2CL$	QUILLIFOLIN	ANALGESIC	
357.15762	$C_{20}H_{23}NO_5$	CIPROQUINATE	COCCIDIOSTATIC	
357.18009	$C_{18}H_{23}N_5O_3$	CAFEDRINE	STIMULANT	MS
357.18526	$C_{20}H_{24}N_3O_2F$	FLUPRANONE	ANTIHYPERTENSIVE	
357.18594	$C_{22}H_{28}NOCL$	SETASTIN	ANTIHIST./-ALLERG.	
357.19401	$C_{21}H_{27}NO_4$	DESPASMIN (TM)	ANTISPASMOTIC	
	$C_{21}H_{27}NO_4$	NALBUPHIN	ANALGESIC	
357.20926	$C_{25}H_{27}NO$	CINFENINE	ANTIDEPRESSANT	
357.23039	$C_{22}H_{31}NO_3$	AMICIBONE	ANTITUSSIVE	
	$C_{22}H_{31}NO_3$	OXYBUTYNIN	ANTISPASMOTIC	
357.96953	$C_{12}H_{14}O_4CL_3P$	CHLORFENVINFOS	INSECTICIDE	
357.97594	$C_{13}H_8N_2O_6CL_2$	NITROCLOFEN	------------	
358.10526	$C_{19}H_{18}O_7$	BENFURODIL HEMISUCCINATE	VASODILATOR	
	$C_{19}H_{18}O_7$	CARBONYLBISETHYLSALICYLATE	ANALGESIC	
358.10996	$C_{17}H_{18}N_4O_3S$	ENVIROXIME	------------	
358.13512	$C_{19}H_{22}N_2O_3S$	DIMETHOXANATE	ANTITUSSIVE	
358.17803	$C_{21}H_{26}O_5$	PREDNISONE	CORTICOID	
358.20451	$C_{24}H_{26}N_2O$	BELARIZINE	VASODILATOR	
358.20566	$C_{21}H_{27}N_2O_2F$	ANISOPIROL	NEUROLEPTIC	
358.21441	$C_{22}H_{30}O_4$	CANRENOIC ACID	DIURETIC	
358.25080	$C_{23}H_{34}O_3$	PREGNENOLONE ACETATE	CORTICOID	
	$C_{23}H_{34}O_3$	TESTOSTERONE ISOBUTYRATE	ANDROGEN	
358.33480	$C_{24}H_{42}N_2$	FECLEMINE	ANTISPASMOTIC	
358.95681	$C_9H_{11}N_3O_4CL_2S_2$	METHYCLOTHIAZIDE	DIURETIC	
359.04953	$C_{17}H_{14}N_3O_2CLS$	TIAZURIL	COCCIDIOSTATIC	
359.05922	$C_{18}H_{15}N_3OCL_2$	ULDAZEPAM	TRANQUILIZER	
359.11511	$C_{14}H_{21}N_3O_6S$	ADICILLIN	ANTIBIOTIC	
359.17077	$C_{24}H_{25}NS$	TIXADIL	SEDATIVE	
359.17327	$C_{20}H_{25}NO_5$	POSKINE	PARASYMPATH.-LYTIC	
359.17414	$C_{21}H_{29}NS_2$	CAPTODIAME	SEDATIVE	
359.24604	$C_{22}H_{33}NO_3$	AJACONINE	PESTICIDE	
	$C_{22}H_{33}NO_3$	CYCLOMETHYCAINE	LOCAL ANESTHETIC	
359.83725	$C_9H_4OCL_3I$	HALOPROGIN	FUNGIST./ANTIMYC.	
360.06770	$C_{18}H_{14}N_2O_3CLF$	ETHYLLOFLAZATE	TRANQUILIZER	

MASS	FORMULA	NAME	CATEGORY	MS
360.07944	$C_{18}H_{18}N_2O_2CLP$	FOSAZEPAM	TRANQUILIZER	
360.08183	$C_{14}H_{12}N_6O_6$	NITROVIN	DESINFICIENT	
360.10631	$C_{19}H_{21}N_2OCLS$	CHLORACYZINE	ANTISPASMOTIC	
	$C_{19}H_{21}N_2OCLS$	HALETAZOLE	ANTIBIOTIC	
360.11284	$C_{20}H_{21}O_4CL$	FENOFIBRATE	ANTICHOLESTEREMIC	
360.13214	$C_{18}H_{20}N_2O_6$	NITRENDIPINE	ANTIHYPERTENSIVE	
360.14922	$C_{21}H_{25}O_3CL$	DELMADINONE	GESTAGEN	
360.16046	$C_{20}H_{25}N_2O_2CL$	MEFECLORAZINE	NEUROLEPTIC	
360.17976	$C_{18}H_{24}N_4O_4$	CARBAZERAN	TONIC	
360.19368	$C_{21}H_{28}O_5$	ALDOSTERONE	ENDOG.BIOMOLECULE	
	$C_{21}H_{28}O_5$	CINERIN II	INSECTICIDE	
	$C_{21}H_{28}O_5$	CORTISONE	CORTICOID	
	$C_{21}H_{28}O_5$	PREDNISOLONE	CORTICOID	MS
360.21481	$C_{18}H_{32}O_7$	BUTYL CITRATE	SOFTENER	
360.22131	$C_{21}H_{29}N_2O_2F$	FLUCIPRAZINE	NEUROLEPTIC	
360.23006	$C_{22}H_{32}O_4$	ILOPROST	VASODILATOR	
360.26645	$C_{23}H_{36}O_3$	DROMOSTANOLONE PROPIONATE	CYTOSTATIC	
	$C_{23}H_{36}O_3$	PROPETANDROL	ANABOLIC	
361.10809	$C_{19}H_{20}NO_4CL$	BEZAFIBRATE	ANTICHOLESTEREMIC	
361.10963	$C_{17}H_{19}N_3O_4S$	METAMPICILLIN	ANTIBIOTIC	
361.11536	$C_{18}H_{24}N_3BR$	BROMBENZDIETHYLPYRIDETHYLENEDIAMINE	ANTIHIST./-ALLERG.	
361.13141	$C_{22}H_{19}NO_4$	BISACODYL	LAXATIVE	MS
361.15120	$C_{17}H_{21}N_4O_5$	THEODRENALINE	STIMULANT	
361.15254	$C_{19}H_{23}NO_6$	BUTOCROLOL	BETA-ADR.BLOCKER	
361.17903	$C_{22}H_{23}N_3O_2$	PIR 353	ANALGESIC	
361.18642	$C_{24}H_{27}NS$	TIOPROPAMINE	TO THERAPY ULCERS	
361.18892	$C_{20}H_{27}NO_5$	BUQUINOLATE	COCCIDIOSTATIC	
	$C_{20}H_{27}NO_5$	CARBOCROMENE	CORONARY DILATOR	
361.20418	$C_{24}H_{27}NO_2$	CYHEPTROPINE	ANTIARRHYTHMIC	
	$C_{24}H_{27}NO_2$	LEVOPHENACYLMORPHAN	ANALGESIC	
361.21541	$C_{23}H_{27}N_3O$	LIBEXIN	ANTITUSSIVE	
	$C_{23}H_{27}N_3O$	PRENOXDIAZINE	ANTITUSSIVE	
361.22531	$C_{21}H_{31}NO_4$	FURETHIDINE	ANALGESIC	
361.24056	$C_{25}H_{31}NO$	BUTACLAMOL	TRANQUILIZER	
	$C_{25}H_{31}NO$	ISAMFAZONE	ANTIRHEUMATIC	
361.29808	$C_{23}H_{39}NO_2$	CETABEN	ANTICHOLESTEREMIC	
361.33446	$C_{24}H_{43}NO$	CLINOLAMIDE	ANTICHOLESTEREMIC	
361.87572	$C_{12}H_8CL_6$	ALDRIN	INSECTICIDE	MS
	$C_{12}H_8CL_6$	ISODRIN	INSECTICIDE	
362.01443	$C_{18}H_{13}N_2CL_3$	ALICONAZOLE	FUNGIST./ANTIMYC.	
362.01446	$C_{14}H_{16}O_5CLSP$	COUMAFOS	PESTICIDE	
362.05726	$C_{16}H_{14}N_2O_6S$	PHTHALYLSULFACETAMIDE	ANTIBIOTIC	
362.06043	$C_{16}H_{15}N_4O_2CLS$	SULFACLORAZOL	ANTIBIOTIC	
362.06701	$C_{22}H_{19}BR$	BROPARESTROL	ESTROGEN	
362.08335	$C_{18}H_{16}N_2O_3CLF$	PROFLAZEPAM	TRANQUILIZER	
362.09365	$C_{17}H_{18}N_2O_5S$	PIRETANIDE	DIURETIC	
362.13003	$C_{18}H_{22}N_2O_4S$	BESUNIDE	DIURETIC	
362.16487	$C_{21}H_{27}O_3CL$	CHLORMADINONE	GESTAGEN	
	$C_{21}H_{27}O_3CL$	CISMADINONE	GESTAGEN	
362.17025	$C_{16}H_{22}N_6O_4$	PROTIRELIN	DIAGNOSTIC AID	
362.17765	$C_{18}H_{26}N_4O_2S$	MESULERGIN	------------	
362.19943	$C_{23}H_{26}N_2O_2$	BENZETIMIDE	ANTICHOLINERGIC	

MASS	FORMULA	NAME	CATEGORY	MS
362.19943	$C_{23}H_{26}N_2O_2$	DEXETIMIDE	PARASYMPATH.-LYTIC	
362.20126	$C_{22}H_{31}O_2CL$	CLOMETERONE	GYNECOL./OBSTRECT.	
362.20933	$C_{21}H_{30}O_5$	HUMULON	SEDATIVE	
	$C_{21}H_{30}O_5$	HYDROCORTISONE	CORTICOID	
362.21249	$C_{21}H_{31}N_2OCL$	VIMINOL	ANALGESIC	MS
363.05800	$C_{10}H_{14}N_5O_8P$	GMP	ENDOG.BIOMOLECULE	
363.06947	$C_{15}H_{18}N_5OBR$	BROPERAMOL	ANTIPHLOGISTIC	
363.08735	$C_{18}H_{18}NO_5CL$	ETOFIBRATE	ANTICHOLESTEREMIC	
363.08889	$C_{16}H_{17}N_3O_5S$	CEFADROXIL	ANTIBIOTIC	
363.10375	$C_{19}H_{19}NO_3CLF$	FLAMPROP-ISOPROPYL	HERBICIDE	
363.16012	$C_{20}H_{26}NO_3CL$	ADAFENOXATE	------------	
363.17942	$C_{18}H_{25}N_3O_5$	CAROCAINIDE	------------	
363.19468	$C_{22}H_{25}N_3O_2$	BUCINDOLOL	BETA-ADR.BLOCKER	
363.23106	$C_{23}H_{29}N_3O$	OPIPRAMOL	NEUROLEPTIC	MS
	$C_{23}H_{29}N_3O$	PIROLAZAMIDE	ANTIARRHYTHMIC	
363.25219	$C_{20}H_{33}N_3O_3$	TALINOLOL	BETA-ADR.BLOCKER	
363.84922	$C_8H_8O_3CL_2BRSP$	BROMOPHOS	INSECTICIDE	MS
363.89926	$C_{10}H_9O_4CL_4P$	TETRACHLORVINFOS	INSECTICIDE	
363.89944	$C_{11}H_9O_3CL_5$	ERBON	HERBICIDE	
364.02692	$C_{18}H_{14}O_4CL_2$	INDACRIC ACID	DIURETIC	
364.02846	$C_{16}H_{13}N_2O_4CLS$	SUCLOFENIDE	ANTIEPILEPTIC	
364.09741	$C_{10}H_{24}N_2O_8S_2$	RITROSULFAN	CYTOSTATIC	
364.10930	$C_{17}H_{20}N_2O_5S$	BUMETANIDE	DIURETIC	
	$C_{17}H_{20}N_2O_5S$	PHENETICILLIN	ANTIBIOTIC	
364.11716	$C_{19}H_{16}N_4O_4$	ZIDOMETACIN	ANTIPHLOGISTIC	
364.16344	$C_{18}H_{24}N_2O_6$	CINEPAZIC ACID	CORONARY DILATOR	
	$C_{18}H_{24}N_2O_6$	DINOCAP	FUNGIST./ANTIMYC.	
364.16746	$C_{23}H_{24}O_4$	CYCLOFENIL	GYNECOL./OBSTRECT.	
364.17063	$C_{23}H_{25}N_2CL$	MALACHITE GREEN	DESINFICIENT	
364.17869	$C_{22}H_{24}N_2O_3$	TRIBUZONE	ANALGESIC	
364.18052	$C_{21}H_{29}O_3CL$	CLOGESTONE	GESTAGEN	
	$C_{21}H_{29}O_3CL$	HYDROMADINONE	GESTAGEN	
364.20499	$C_{21}H_{29}O_4F$	FLUGESTONE	GESTAGEN	
364.24023	$C_{25}H_{32}O_2$	QUINESTROL	ESTROGEN	MS
365.02438	$C_{12}H_7N_5O_9$	NIFURSOL	ANTIBIOTIC	
365.05855	$C_{18}H_{17}NO_3CL_2$	BENZOYLPROP-ETHYL	HERBICIDE	
365.06009	$C_{16}H_{16}N_3O_3CLS$	INDAPAMIDE	DIURETIC	
	$C_{16}H_{16}N_3O_3CLS$	METOLAZONE	DIURETIC	
365.10454	$C_{16}H_{19}N_3O_5S$	AMOXICILLIN	ANTIBIOTIC	
	$C_{16}H_{19}N_3O_5S$	CEFROXADIN	ANTIBIOTIC	
365.10857	$C_{21}H_{19}NO_3S$	ALKOFANONE	ANTIDIARRHOEAL	
365.15618	$C_{21}H_{23}N_3OS$	PERICIAZINE	NEUROLEPTIC	MS
365.16271	$C_{22}H_{23}NO_4$	NEQUINATE	COCCIDIOSTATIC	
365.19909	$C_{23}H_{27}NO_3$	ETABENZARONE	ANTIPHLOGISTIC	
365.21033	$C_{22}H_{27}N_3O_2$	CAROVERINE	ANTISPASMOTIC	
365.22022	$C_{20}H_{31}NO_5$	IBUTEROL	SYMPATHOMIMETIC	
365.93307	$C_{12}H_{12}N_2O_2AS_2$	ARSPHENAMINE	ANTIBIOTIC	
366.05380	$C_{17}H_{16}N_2O_3CL_2$	PARCONAZOLE	FUNGIST./ANTIMYC.	
366.07080	$C_{16}H_{18}N_2O_4S_2$	TIFENCILLINE	ANTIBIOTIC	
366.09173	$C_{16}H_{19}N_4O_2CLS$	PIRINIXIL	ANTICHOLESTEREMIC	
366.13618	$C_{16}H_{22}N_4O_4S$	ACETIAMINE	VITAMINE	
366.14673	$C_{22}H_{22}O_5$	CYCLOVALONE	CHOLERETIC	

MASS	FORMULA	NAME	CATEGORY	MS
366.14989	$C_{22}H_{23}N_2OCL$	CHLORTETRACYCLINE	ANTIBIOTIC	
366.16133	$C_{18}H_{26}N_2O_4S$	GLIBORNURIDE	ANTIDIABETIC	
366.20960	$C_{26}H_{26}N_2$	AZIPRAMINE	ANTIDEPRESSANT	
366.23073	$C_{23}H_{30}N_2O_2$	PIMINODINE	ANALGESIC	
366.24063	$C_{21}H_{34}O_5$	ARBAPROSTIL	TO THERAPY ULCERS	
	$C_{21}H_{34}O_5$	TETRAHYDROCORTISOL	CORTICOID	
366.25588	$C_{25}H_{34}O_2$	QUINGESTANOL	GESTAGEN	
366.26711	$C_{24}H_{34}N_2O$	BEPRIDIL	CORONARY DILATOR	
366.98687	$C_{12}H_{15}NO_4CLS_2P$	PHOSALONE	INSECTICIDE	
367.03936	$C_{15}H_{14}N_3O_4CLS$	CEFACLOR	ANTIBIOTIC	
367.15321	$C_{20}H_{21}N_3O_4$	PHENYTOIN-NORVALINE	ANTIEPILEPTIC	
367.17836	$C_{22}H_{25}NO_4$	DIMOXYLINE	ANTISPASMOTIC	
	$C_{22}H_{25}NO_4$	PITOFENONE	ANTISPASMOTIC	
367.21474	$C_{23}H_{29}NO_3$	BENZETHIDINE	ANALGESIC	
	$C_{23}H_{29}NO_3$	FENBUTRAZATE	STIMULANT	MS
367.90961	$C_{14}H_9OCL_5$	DICOFOL	PESTICIDE	
368.02154	$C_5H_{11}N_2O_2CLHG$	CHLORMERODRIN	DIURETIC	
368.02675	$C_{12}H_{17}N_2O_5CLS_2$	UK 12130	VASODILATOR	
368.08474	$C_{17}H_{21}O_5SP$	COUMITHOATE	INSECTICIDE	
368.08645	$C_{16}H_{20}N_2O_4S_2$	PYRITINOL	DYNAMIC	MS
368.09277	$C_{20}H_{17}N_2O_3CL$	KETAZOLAM	TRANQUILIZER	MS
368.12599	$C_{21}H_{20}O_6$	CURCUMIN	CHOLERETIC	
368.12916	$C_{21}H_{21}N_2O_2CL$	ICLAZEPAM	TRANQUILIZER	
368.17361	$C_{21}H_{24}N_2O_4$	CYCLARBAMATE	TRANQUILIZER	
368.20999	$C_{22}H_{28}N_2O_3$	ETHYLYOHIMBATE	ANTISPASMOTIC	
368.22525	$C_{26}H_{28}N_2$	CINNARIZINE	ANTIHIST./-ALLERG.	
368.23515	$C_{24}H_{32}O_3$	MENOCTONE	ANTIMALARIAL	
368.25628	$C_{21}H_{36}O_5$	CARBOPROST	GYNECOL./OBSTRECT.	
368.34028	$C_{22}H_{44}N_2O_2$	GLYODIN	FUNGIST./ANTIMYC.	
368.90000	$C_{13}H_9NO_2BR_2$	DIBROMSALAN	DESINFICIENT	
	$C_{13}H_9NO_2BR_2$	METABROMSALAN	DESINFICIENT	
368.98561	$C_{10}H_{12}N_3O_6CLS_2$	CARMETIZIDE	DIURETIC	
369.04532	$C_{14}H_{15}N_3O_5S_2$	SULFADIASULFONE	ANTIBIOTIC	
369.09139	$C_{16}H_{20}N_3O_3CLS$	TRIPAMIDE	ANTIHYPERTENSIVE	
369.11879	$C_{18}H_{18}NO_4F_3$	ETOFENAMATE	ANTIPHLOGISTIC	
369.15762	$C_{21}H_{23}NO_5$	HEROIN	ANALGESIC	MS
369.17223	$C_{17}H_{27}N_3O_4S$	AMISULPRIDE	------------	
369.20524	$C_{21}H_{27}N_3O_3$	AMIDOXIME	ANALGESIC	
369.23039	$C_{23}H_{31}NO_3$	NORGESTIMATE	GESTAGEN	
369.82110	$C_{10}H_5CL_7$	HEPTACHLOR	INSECTICIDE	
370.00024	$C_{11}H_{13}N_4O_4CL_3$	TRICLOFYLLINE	BRONCHODILATOR	
370.00735	$C_{12}H_{11}N_6O_2CLS_2$	AZOSEMIDE	DIURETIC	
370.06887	$C_{19}H_{14}O_8$	FLAVODIC ACID	------------	
370.07695	$C_{14}H_{18}N_4O_4S_2$	THIOPHANATE	FUNGIST./ANTIMYC.	
370.10525	$C_{20}H_{18}O_7$	SESAMOLIN	NATURAL SUBSTANCE	
370.10842	$C_{20}H_{19}N_2O_3CL$	PIVOXAZEPAM	TRANQUILIZER	
370.15374	$C_{21}H_{26}N_2S_2$	THIORIDAZINE	NEUROLEPTIC	MS
370.16996	$C_{23}H_{27}O_2CL$	GESTACLONE	GESTAGEN	
370.17803	$C_{22}H_{26}O_5$	HYDROXYESTRONE DIACETATE	ESTROGEN	
370.18119	$C_{22}H_{27}N_2OCL$	LORCAINIDE	ANTIARRHYTHMIC	MS
370.18273	$C_{20}H_{26}N_4OS$	OXYPENDYL	ANTIHIST./-ALLERG.	
370.21575	$C_{24}H_{26}N_4$	ROPIZINE	ANTIEPILEPTIC	

MASS	FORMULA	NAME	CATEGORY	MS
370.25080	$C_{24}H_{34}O_3$	RIMEXOLONE	CORTICOID	
370.28718	$C_{25}H_{38}O_2$	PENMESTEROL	ANABOLIC	
370.83042	$C_7H_3NOI_2$	IOXYNIL	HERBICIDE	
371.09648	$C_{14}H_{17}N_3O_9$	AZARIBINE	CYTOSTATIC	
371.10367	$C_{19}H_{18}N_3O_3CL$	CAMAZEPAM	TRANQUILIZER	MS
371.14812	$C_{19}H_{21}N_3O_5$	BISAZIRANYLMETHYLNAPHTHOCHINONE-MEC	CYTOSTATIC	
371.15129	$C_{19}H_{22}N_5OCL$	TRAZODONE	ANTIDEPRESSANT	MS
371.15149	$C_{16}H_{25}N_3O_5S$	SULVERAPRIDE	------------	
371.15936	$C_{18}H_{21}N_5O_4$	METRIFUDIL	CORONARY DILATOR	
371.16969	$C_{22}H_{23}NO_2F_2$	LENPERONE	TRANQUILIZER	
371.17327	$C_{21}H_{25}NO_5$	DEMECOLCINE	CYTOSTATIC	
371.22491	$C_{26}H_{29}NO$	TAMOXIFEN	GYNECOL./OBSTRECT.	
372.08769	$C_{19}H_{17}N_2O_4CL$	GLAFENINE	ANALGESIC	
	$C_{19}H_{17}N_2O_4CL$	OXAMETACIN	ANALGESIC	
372.16852	$C_{20}H_{24}N_2O_5$	CODOXIME	ANTITUSSIVE	
	$C_{20}H_{24}N_2O_5$	DIAMFENETIDE	ANTHELMINTIC	
	$C_{20}H_{24}N_2O_5$	MEDROXALOL	ANTIHYPERTENSIVE	
372.16986	$C_{21}H_{20}N_6O$	bIS(AMINOQUINALDYL)UREA	DESINFICIENT	
372.19368	$C_{22}H_{28}O_5$	ISOPREDNIDENE	------------	
	$C_{22}H_{28}O_5$	MEPREDNISONE	CORTICOID	
	$C_{22}H_{28}O_5$	PREDNYLIDENE	CORTICOID	
	$C_{22}H_{28}O_5$	PYRETHRIN II	INSECTICIDE	
372.23006	$C_{23}H_{32}O_4$	DEOXYCORTICOSTERONE ACETATE	CORTICOID	
	$C_{23}H_{32}O_4$	HYDROXYPROGESTERONE ACETATE	GESTAGEN	
	$C_{23}H_{32}O_4$	NORGESTOMET	GESTAGEN	
	$C_{23}H_{32}O_4$	PRORENOATE	DIURETIC	
372.24129	$C_{22}H_{32}N_2O_3$	MOCIPRAZINE	ANTIHIST./-ALLERG.	
372.26645	$C_{24}H_{36}O_3$	ANAGESTONE ACETATE	GESTAGEN	
373.07080	$C_{15}H_{14}N_3O_3F_3S$	GALOSEMIDE	ANTIPHLOGISTIC	
373.08613	$C_{14}H_{20}N_3O_5SP$	PYRAZOPHOS	FUNGIST./ANTIMYC.	
373.13478	$C_{20}H_{23}NO_4S$	DESACETYLTHIOCOLCHICINE	CYTOSTATIC	
373.13795	$C_{20}H_{24}N_3CLS$	PROCHLORPERAZINE	NEUROLEPTIC	MS
373.15571	$C_{20}H_{24}N_3O_2CL$	CLEBOPRIDE	ANTIHIST./-ALLERG.	
373.79269	$C_6H_6OCL_8$	OCTACHLORODIPROPYLETHER	PESTICIDE	
373.92655	$C_{12}H_{12}N_2O_2BR_2$	METHYLDIBROMOPHENYLETHYLHYDANTOIN	ANTIEPILEPTIC	
373.98367	$C_{15}H_7N_2O_2CL_2F_3$	FENAZAFLOR	PESTICIDE	
373.99932	$C_{14}H_{20}N_2BR_2$	BROMHEXINE	EXPECTORANT	MS
374.07097	$C_{23}H_{15}O_3CL$	CHLORPHACINONE	RODENTICIDE	
374.10017	$C_{19}H_{18}O_8$	ATRANORIN	ANTIBIOTIC	
374.16487	$C_{22}H_{27}O_3CL$	CYPROTERONE	ANTIANDROGEN	MS
374.17428	$C_{22}H_{22}N_4O_2$	FORBISEN	------------	
374.17611	$C_{21}H_{27}N_2O_2CL$	HYDROXYZINE	TRANQUILIZER	MS
374.19541	$C_{19}H_{26}N_4O_4$	PIQUIZIL	BRONCHODILATOR	
374.20933	$C_{22}H_{30}O_5$	JASMOLIN II	INSECTICIDE	
	$C_{22}H_{30}O_5$	METHYLPREDNISOLONE	CORTICOID	
374.24571	$C_{23}H_{34}O_4$	ACETOXYPREGNENOLONE	ANTIRHEUMATIC	
	$C_{23}H_{34}O_4$	ANDROSTENEDIOL DIACETATE	ANABOLIC	
	$C_{23}H_{34}O_4$	DIGITOXIGENINE	NATURAL SUBSTANCE	
	$C_{23}H_{34}O_4$	UZARIGENIN	NATURAL SUBSTANCE	
374.28210	$C_{24}H_{38}O_3$	CANBISOL	ANTIHYPERTENSIVE	
	$C_{24}H_{38}O_3$	STANOLONE VALERATE	ANDROGEN	
375.10013	$C_{16}H_{17}N_5O_4S$	AZIDOCILLIN	ANTIBIOTIC	

MASS	FORMULA	NAME	CATEGORY	MS
375.14014	$C_{21}H_{23}NO_2CLF$	HALOPERIDOL	NEUROLEPTIC	MS
375.14706	$C_{23}H_{21}NO_4$	XENAZOIC ACID	ANTIBIOTIC	
375.17136	$C_{20}H_{26}N_3O_2CL$	PICLOPASTINE	ANTIHIST./-ALLERG.	
375.18344	$C_{24}H_{25}NO_3$	BENZYLMORPHINE	ANTITUSSIVE	
375.21983	$C_{25}H_{29}NO_2$	PRENOVERINE	ANTISPASMOTIC	
375.23221	$C_{21}H_{30}N_3O_2F$	PIPAMPERONE	NEUROLEPTIC	MS
375.93489	$C_{11}H_{15}O_2CL_2S_3P$	PHENKAPTON (TM)	PESTICIDE	
375.97859	$C_{13}H_{18}N_2OBR_2$	AMBROXOL	EXPECTORANT	MS
376.02227	$C_{17}H_{14}N_2O_2BRF$	HALOXAZOLAM	HYPNOTIC	
376.03815	$C_{18}H_{14}N_2O_3CL_2$	ETHYLDIRAZEPATE	TRANQUILIZER	
376.09469	$C_{22}H_{16}O_6$	RESISTOMYCIN	ANTIBIOTIC	
376.13829	$C_{17}H_{20}N_4O_6$	RIBOFLAVIN	VITAMINE	
376.14568	$C_{19}H_{24}N_2O_4S$	MESUDIPIN	CORONARY DILATOR	
376.18052	$C_{22}H_{29}O_3CL$	CLOMEGESTONE	GESTAGEN	
376.20385	$C_{25}H_{28}O_3$	ESTRADIOL BENZOATE	ESTROGEN	
376.20499	$C_{22}H_{29}O_4F$	DESOXIMETASONE	CORTICOID	
	$C_{22}H_{29}O_4F$	DOXIBETASOL	CORTICOID	
	$C_{22}H_{29}O_4F$	FLUOCORTOLONE	CORTICOID	
	$C_{22}H_{29}O_4F$	FLUOROMETHOLONE	CORTICOID	
376.21508	$C_{24}H_{28}N_2O_2$	MELETIMIDE	PARASYMPATH.-LYTIC	
376.27259	$C_{22}H_{36}N_2O_3$	FENETRADIL	CORONARY DILATOR	
376.29506	$C_{20}H_{36}N_6O$	LAUROGUADINE	DESINFICIENT	
376.92622	$C_{12}H_{13}NO_3BR_2$	FURSALAN	DESINFICIENT	
376.93729	$C_{11}H_{12}NO_5S_2AS$	THIACETARSAMIDE	ANTIBIOTIC	
377.08635	$C_{22}H_{13}NO_3F_2$	PHENYLDIFLUOROQUINOLYLOXY BENZOATE	DESINFICIENT	
377.15618	$C_{22}H_{23}N_3OS$	THIOCARBANIDIN	TUBERCULOSTATIC	
377.18518	$C_{21}H_{23}N_5O_2$	DIMORPHOLINOPHENYLPYRIDOPYRIDAZINE	DIURETIC	
377.19824	$C_{19}H_{28}N_5OCL$	ETOPERIDONE	ANTIDEPRESSANT	
377.21033	$C_{23}H_{27}N_3O_2$	MORAZONE	ANALGESIC	MS
377.22156	$C_{22}H_{27}N_5O$	METOQUIZIN	TO THERAPY ULCERS	
377.24671	$C_{24}H_{31}N_3O$	FAMPROFAZONE	ANALGESIC	
	$C_{24}H_{31}N_3O$	HOMOPIPRAMOL	DESINFICIENT	
377.78258	$C_4H_7O_4BR_2CL_2P$	NALED	INSECTICIDE	
377.87063	$C_{12}H_8OCL_6$	DIELDRIN	INSECTICIDE	
	$C_{12}H_8OCL_6$	ENDRIN	INSECTICIDE	
378.08856	$C_{17}H_{18}N_2O_6S$	CARBENICILLIN	ANTIBIOTIC	
378.11668	$C_{17}H_{16}N_2OF_6$	MEFLOQUINE	ANTIMALARIAL	
378.11688	$C_{19}H_{23}N_2O_2CLS$	PYRIDATE	HERBICIDE	
378.12495	$C_{18}H_{22}N_2O_5S$	ISOPROPICILLIN	ANTIBIOTIC	
	$C_{18}H_{22}N_2O_5S$	LEVOPROPICILLIN	ANTIBIOTIC	
	$C_{18}H_{22}N_2O_5S$	PROPICILLIN	ANTIBIOTIC	
378.16133	$C_{19}H_{26}N_2O_4S$	ZINTEROL	BRONCHODILATOR	
378.18311	$C_{24}H_{26}O_4$	ESTROFURATE	ESTROGEN	
378.18425	$C_{21}H_{27}O_5F$	DESCINOLONE	CORTICOID	
	$C_{21}H_{27}O_5F$	FLUPREDNISOLONE	CORTICOID	
	$C_{21}H_{27}O_5F$	ISOFLUPREDONE	ANTIPHLOGISTIC	
378.18648	$C_{21}H_{30}O_4S$	TIXOCORTOL	CORTICOID	
378.21950	$C_{25}H_{30}O_3$	NANDROLONE BENZOATE	ANABOLIC	
378.23073	$C_{24}H_{30}N_2O_2$	DESMETHYLMORAMIDE	ANALGESIC	
	$C_{24}H_{30}N_2O_2$	DOXAPRAM	STIMULANT	
378.24063	$C_{22}H_{34}O_5$	PLEUROMULIN	ANTIBIOTIC	
378.27701	$C_{23}H_{38}O_4$	METENEPROST	GYNECOL./OBSTRECT.	

MASS	FORMULA	NAME	CATEGORY	MS
378.90219	$C_8H_8N_3O_4CL_3S_2$	TRICHLORMETHIAZIDE	DIURETIC	
379.01599	$C_{14}H_{12}NO_4F_3S_2$	PERFLUIDONE	HERBICIDE	
379.04273	$C_{13}H_{18}N_3O_4CLS_2$	CYCLOPENTHIAZIDE	DIURETIC	
379.16961	$C_{22}H_{22}N_3O_2F$	DROPERIDOL	NEUROLEPTIC	MS
379.18173	$C_{20}H_{29}NO_4S$	CAMPHAMEDRINE	RESPIRAT.STIMULANT	
379.18959	$C_{22}H_{25}N_3O_3$	SOLYPERTINE	SYMPATHOLYTIC	
	$C_{22}H_{25}N_3O_3$	SPIROXATRINE	NEUROLEPTIC	
379.20083	$C_{21}H_{25}N_5O_2$	NIPROFAZONE	ANALGESIC	
379.22598	$C_{23}H_{29}N_3O_2$	ETOMIDOLINE	ANTISPASMOTIC	
	$C_{23}H_{29}N_3O_2$	OXYPERTINE	NEUROLEPTIC	MS
379.24711	$C_{20}H_{33}N_3O_4$	CELIPROLOL	BETA-ADR.BLOCKER	
380.02500	$C_{18}H_{15}N_2OCL_3$	ECONAZOLE	FUNGIST./ANTIMYC.	
	$C_{18}H_{15}N_2OCL_3$	ORCONAZOLE	FUNGIST./ANTIMYC.	
380.08961	$C_{21}H_{16}O_7$	COUMETAROL	ANTICOAGULANT	
380.10421	$C_{17}H_{20}N_2O_6S$	METHICILLIN	ANTIBIOTIC	
380.11792	$C_{23}H_{21}O_3CL$	CHLOROTRIANISENE	ESTROGEN	
380.13099	$C_{21}H_{26}O_2CL_2$	BICLOTYMOL	DESINFICIENT	
380.19876	$C_{24}H_{28}O_4$	DIETHYLSTILBESTROL DIPROPIONATE	ESTROGEN	
380.19990	$C_{21}H_{29}O_5F$	FLUDROCORTISONE	CORTICOID	
380.20999	$C_{23}H_{28}N_2O_3$	ACOXATRINE	VASODILATOR	
	$C_{23}H_{28}N_2O_3$	BOPINDOLOL	BETA-ADR.BLOCKER	
380.23515	$C_{25}H_{32}O_3$	NILESTRIOL	ESTROGEN	
380.24638	$C_{24}H_{32}N_2O_2$	EPRAZINONE	BRONCHODILATOR	
381.05838	$C_{13}H_{20}N_3O_4CLS_2$	MEBUTIZIDE	DIURETIC	
381.13649	$C_{25}H_{19}NO_3$	FENDOSAL	ANALGESIC	
381.16079	$C_{22}H_{24}N_3OCL$	AZELASTINE	ANTIHIST./-ALLERG.	
381.18526	$C_{22}H_{24}N_3O_2F$	BENPERIDOL	NEUROLEPTIC	MS
	$C_{22}H_{24}N_3O_2F$	DECLENPERONE	SEDATIVE	
381.19401	$C_{23}H_{27}NO_4$	TROPENZILE	ANTISPASMOTIC	
381.23039	$C_{24}H_{31}NO_3$	PIPOXIZINE	BRONCHODILATOR	
381.87420	$C_{10}H_5N_4CL_3S_3$	SUBENDAZOLE	ANTHELMINTIC	
382.04240	$C_{13}H_{19}N_2O_5CLS_2$	MEFRUSIDE	DIURETIC	
382.18926	$C_{22}H_{26}N_2O_4$	TOFISOPAM	TRANQUILIZER	
382.21441	$C_{24}H_{30}O_4$	ACETOXYMETHYLENEPROGESTERONE	GESTAGEN	
	$C_{24}H_{30}O_4$	PROMETHESTROL DIACETATE	ESTROGEN	
382.22564	$C_{23}H_{30}N_2O_3$	VINPOLINE	VASODILATOR	
382.26203	$C_{24}H_{34}N_2O_2$	EUPROCIN	DESINFICIENT	
382.28718	$C_{26}H_{38}O_2$	QUINGESTRONE	GESTAGEN	
382.29841	$C_{25}H_{38}N_2O$	BUNAMIDINE	ANTHELMINTIC	
382.98350	$C_{11}H_{14}N_3O_4CLS_3$	ALTIZIDE	DIURETIC	
383.03581	$C_{13}H_{13}N_5O_5S_2$	CEFTIZOXIME	ANTIBIOTIC	
383.06912	$C_{18}H_{19}NO_4CL_2$	FELODIPIN	------------	
383.13689	$C_{21}H_{21}NO_6$	HYDRASTIN	HEMOSTATIC	
383.15149	$C_{17}H_{25}N_3O_5S$	VERALIPRIDE	------------	
383.15936	$C_{19}H_{21}N_5O_4$	PRAZOSIN	ANTIHYPERTENSIVE	
383.20091	$C_{22}H_{26}N_3O_2F$	SPIRAMIDE	NEUROLEPTIC	
383.24604	$C_{24}H_{33}NO_3$	NAFTIDROFURYL	VASODILATOR	
383.31881	$C_{26}H_{41}NO$	MELINAMIDE	ANTICHOLESTEREMIC	
383.98762	$C_9H_{22}O_4S_4P_2$	ETHIONE	PESTICIDE	
384.01078	$C_9H_{10}O_2SHG$	THIOMERSAL	DESINFICIENT	
384.01991	$C_{17}H_{15}N_2O_2CL_3$	TRICLODAZOL	TRANQUILIZER	
384.04498	$C_{15}H_{16}N_2O_6S_2$	TICARCILLIN	ANTIBIOTIC	

MASS	FORMULA	NAME	CATEGORY	MS
384.10075	$C_{18}H_{22}N_2O_3CL_2$	DICLOFURIM	CORONARY DILATOR	
384.18715	$C_{22}H_{28}N_2O_2S$	BECANTONE	ANTHELMINTIC	
	$C_{22}H_{28}N_2O_2S$	PERIMETAZINE	NEUROLEPTIC	
384.22737	$C_{20}H_{28}N_6O_2$	FENCAMINE	ANTIDEPRESSANT	
384.23006	$C_{24}H_{32}O_4$	BUFOGENIN	STIMULANT	
	$C_{24}H_{32}O_4$	ESTRADIOL BUTYRYLACETATE	ESTROGEN	
	$C_{24}H_{32}O_4$	ESTRADIOL DIPROPIONATE	ESTROGEN	
	$C_{24}H_{32}O_4$	MEGESTROL ACETATE	CYTOSTATIC	
	$C_{24}H_{32}O_4$	SCILLARENIN	NATURAL SUBSTANCE	
384.24129	$C_{23}H_{32}N_2O_3$	ZIPEPROL	ANTITUSSIVE	
384.26645	$C_{25}H_{36}O_3$	ESTRADIOL HEPTANOATE	ESTROGEN	
384.33922	$C_{27}H_{44}O$	COLECALCIFEROL	VITAMINE	
384.95298	$C_{12}H_{14}NO_3CL_2S_2P$	BENOXAFOS	PESTICIDE	
385.15254	$C_{21}H_{23}NO_6$	COLCHICEINE	URICOSURIC	
385.17501	$C_{19}H_{23}N_5O_4$	METHYLPHENETHYLADENOSINE	------------	
385.21139	$C_{20}H_{27}N_5O_3$	BAMIFYLLINE	VASODILATOR	
385.23654	$C_{22}H_{31}N_3O_3$	TAZIPRINONE	ANTITUSSIVE	
385.24778	$C_{21}H_{31}N_5O_2$	BUSPIRONE	TRANQUILIZER	
385.98142	$C_{16}H_{13}N_2OCL_3S$	TIOCONAZOLE	FUNGIST./ANTIMYC.	
386.03613	$C_{10}H_{13}OCLHG$	MERCUROBUTOL	DESINFICIENT	
386.08176	$C_{12}H_{22}N_2O_8S_2$	PIPOSULFAN	CYTOSTATIC	
386.14866	$C_{21}H_{26}N_2OS_2$	MESORIDAZINE	TRANQUILIZER	
386.15095	$C_{20}H_{23}N_4O_2CL$	CLONITAZENE	ANALGESIC	
386.19943	$C_{25}H_{26}N_2O_2$	MEDIBAZINE	CORONARY DILATOR	
386.20280	$C_{22}H_{30}N_2O_2S$	SUFENTANIL	ANALGESIC	
386.24571	$C_{24}H_{34}O_4$	MEDROXYPROGESTERONE ACETATE	GESTAGEN	
	$C_{24}H_{34}O_4$	PROLIGESTONE	GESTAGEN	
386.28210	$C_{25}H_{38}O_3$	ANAGESTONE PROPIONATE	GESTAGEN	
	$C_{25}H_{38}O_3$	TESTOSTERONE ISOCAPRONATE	ANDROGEN	
386.35487	$C_{27}H_{46}O$	CHOLESTEROL	ENDOG.BIOMOLECULE	**MS**
387.01143	$C_{14}H_{14}N_3O_4CLS_2$	BENZYLHYDROCHLOROTHIAZIDE	DIURETIC	
387.13676	$C_{12}H_{24}N_9P_3$	APHOLATE	PESTICIDE	
387.14014	$C_{22}H_{23}NO_2CLF$	CLOROPERONE	TRANQUILIZER	
387.15137	$C_{21}H_{23}N_3OCLF$	FLURAZEPAM	HYPNOTIC	**MS**
387.17136	$C_{21}H_{26}N_3O_2CL$	ACRANIL (TM)	ANTHELMINTIC	
387.20457	$C_{22}H_{29}NO_5$	TRIMEBUTINE	ANTISPASMOTIC	
387.22704	$C_{20}H_{29}N_5O_3$	BUQUINERAN	------------	
	$C_{20}H_{29}N_5O_3$	URAPIDIL	ANTIHYPERTENSIVE	
387.23106	$C_{25}H_{29}N_3O$	NUFENOXOL	ANTIBIOTIC	
388.09469	$C_{23}H_{16}O_6$	PAMOIC ACID	------------	
388.10507	$C_{17}H_{17}N_6O_3CL$	ZOPICLONE	HYPNOTIC	
388.11899	$C_{20}H_{21}N_2O_4CL$	FIPEXIDE	STIMULANT	
388.15221	$C_{21}H_{24}O_7$	VISNADIN	CARDIOTONIC	
388.16344	$C_{20}H_{24}N_2O_6$	NISOLDIPINE	CORONARY DILATOR	
388.19982	$C_{21}H_{28}N_2O_5$	TRIMETHOBENZAMIDE	ANTIHIST./-ALLERG.	
388.21508	$C_{25}H_{28}N_2O_2$	CINPERENE	TRANQUILIZER	
388.22498	$C_{23}H_{32}O_5$	CANNOGENINE	NATURAL SUBSTANCE	
	$C_{23}H_{32}O_5$	CORTICOSTERONE ACETATE	CORTICOID	
388.25261	$C_{23}H_{33}N_2O_2F$	PROPYPERONE	NEUROLEPTIC	
388.26136	$C_{24}H_{36}O_4$	BOLANDIOL DIPROPIONATE	ANABOLIC	
	$C_{24}H_{36}O_4$	DEHYDROCHOLIC ACID	CHOLERETIC	
	$C_{24}H_{36}O_4$	METHANDRIOL DIACETATE	ANABOLIC	

MASS	FORMULA	NAME	CATEGORY	MS
388.33413	$C_{26}H_{44}O_2$	THYMOL PALMITATE	ANTHELMINTIC	
	$C_{26}H_{44}O_2$	TOCOL	ANTIOXIDANT	
388.34536	$C_{25}H_{44}N_2O$	AZACOSTEROL	ANTICHOLESTEREMIC	
388.37052	$C_{27}H_{48}O$	CHOLESTANOL	ANTIPHLOGISTIC	
389.02708	$C_{14}H_{16}N_3O_4CLS_2$	CYCLOTHIAZIDE	DIURETIC	
389.14093	$C_{19}H_{23}N_3O_4S$	HETACILLIN	ANTIBIOTIC	
389.16992	$C_{18}H_{23}N_5O_5$	REPROTEROL	BRONCHODILATOR	
389.20631	$C_{19}H_{27}N_5O_4$	ALFUZOSIN	------------	
389.77058	$C_8H_5CL_6BR$	BROMOCICLEN	INSECTICIDE	
390.07895	$C_{21}H_{20}O_3CL_2$	PERMETHRINE	INSECTICIDE	
390.08856	$C_{18}H_{18}N_2O_6S$	CEFALORAM	ANTIBIOTIC	
390.18425	$C_{22}H_{27}O_5F$	FLUOCORTIN	CORTICOID	
	$C_{22}H_{27}O_5F$	FLUPREDNIDENE	CORTICOID	
390.18628	$C_{25}H_{27}N_2CL$	MECLOZINE	ANTIHIST./-ALLERG.	**MS**
390.19032	$C_{19}H_{26}N_4O_5$	HOQUIZIL	BRONCHODILATOR	
390.22064	$C_{23}H_{31}O_4F$	DIMESONE	CORTICOID	
390.24063	$C_{23}H_{34}O_5$	DIGOXIGENIN	NATURAL SUBSTANCE	
	$C_{23}H_{34}O_5$	GITOXIGENIN	NATURAL SUBSTANCE	
390.25186	$C_{22}H_{34}N_2O_4$	OXAMARIN	HEMOSTATIC	
390.27701	$C_{24}H_{38}O_4$	BISETHYLHEXYL PHTHALATE	CHEMICAL	
390.30350	$C_{27}H_{38}N_2$	FENOCTIMINE	------------	
390.82025	$C_6H_3NO_3I_2$	DIIODONITROPHENOL	ANTHELMINTIC	
391.07420	$C_{20}H_{19}NO_3CL_2$	BENZMALECENE	ANTIHIST./-ALLERG.	
391.13882	$C_{19}H_{25}N_3O_2S_2$	DIMETOTIAZINE	SEROTONINE ANTAG.	
391.17836	$C_{24}H_{25}NO_4$	FLAVOXATE	ANTISPASMOTIC	
391.18959	$C_{23}H_{25}N_3O_3$	PHENODIANISYL	LOCAL ANESTHETIC	
391.19949	$C_{21}H_{29}NO_6$	ISOPRENALINGUAIACOLGLYCEROLETHER	BRONCHODILATOR	
391.23721	$C_{23}H_{29}N_5O$	TOQUIZINE	TO THERAPY ULCERS	
391.88052	$C_{10}H_{12}O_3CL_2BRSP$	BROMOPHOS-ETHYL	INSECTICIDE	
391.94819	$C_{11}H_{13}N_2O_5S_2AS$	THIOCARBASONE	ANTIBIOTIC	
391.94981	$C_{15}H_{10}N_4CLBRS$	BROTIZOLAM	TRANQUILIZER	**MS**
392.13905	$C_{21}H_{25}O_5CL$	CHLOROPREDNISONE	CORTICOID	
	$C_{21}H_{25}O_5CL$	CLOPREDNOL	CORTICOID	
392.19474	$C_{20}H_{28}N_2O_6$	CINEPAZET	CORONARY DILATOR	
392.19990	$C_{22}H_{29}O_5F$	BETAMETHASONE	CORTICOID	
	$C_{22}H_{29}O_5F$	DEXAMETHASONE	CORTICOID	
	$C_{22}H_{29}O_5F$	FLUPEROLONE	CORTICOID	
	$C_{22}H_{29}O_5F$	PARAMETHASONE	CORTICOID	
392.24638	$C_{25}H_{32}N_2O_2$	DEXTROMORAMIDE	ANALGESIC	**MS**
	$C_{25}H_{32}N_2O_2$	LEVOMORAMIDE	ANALGESIC	
392.29266	$C_{24}H_{40}O_4$	CHENODESOXYCHOLIC ACID	------------	
	$C_{24}H_{40}O_4$	DESOXYCHOLIC ACID	CHOLERETIC	
	$C_{24}H_{40}O_4$	URSODESOXYCHOLIC ACID	------------	
392.99390	$C_{14}H_{21}NO_2BR_2$	SPASMOLYTOL	ANTISPASMOTIC	
392.99932	$C_{18}H_{13}NO_3CL_2S$	TIOXAPROFEN	ANTIPHLOGISTIC	
393.00252	$C_{14}H_{17}NO_4CLS_2P$	DIALIFOR	INSECTICIDE	
393.02199	$C_{13}H_{16}N_3O_5CLS_2$	AMBUSIDE	DIURETIC	
393.06124	$C_6H_{13}N_3O_4HG$	MERBIURELIDIN	DIURETIC	
393.06307	$C_{16}H_{15}N_3O_7S$	SULFALOXIC ACID	ANTIBIOTIC	
393.11471	$C_{21}H_{19}N_3O_3S$	AMSACRINE	CYTOSTATIC	
393.13835	$C_{14}H_{23}N_3O_{10}$	PENTETIC ACID	ANTIDOTE	
393.17223	$C_{19}H_{27}N_3O_4S$	AMANTOCILLINE	ANTIBIOTIC	

MASS	FORMULA	NAME	CATEGORY	MS
393.18526	$C_{23}H_{24}N_3O_2F$	PIRENPERONE	------------	
393.19401	$C_{24}H_{27}NO_4$	TYLOCREBINE	CYTOSTATIC	
393.22164	$C_{24}H_{28}N_3OF$	SPIRILENE	NEUROLEPTIC	
393.23039	$C_{25}H_{31}NO_3$	METINDIZATE	ANTISPASMOTIC	
	$C_{25}H_{31}NO_3$	TESTOSTERONE NICOTINATE	ANABOLIC	
393.72126	CHI_3	IODOFORM	DESINFICIENT	
393.79777	$C_9H_6CL_8$	ALODAN	PESTICIDE	
394.10525	$C_{22}H_{18}O_7$	JUSTICIDIN A	CHEMICAL	
394.13267	$C_{20}H_{21}N_2OF_3S$	FLUACIZINE	ANTIDEPRESSANT	
394.14164	$C_{23}H_{22}O_6$	DEGUELIN	INSECTICIDE	
	$C_{23}H_{22}O_6$	ROTENONE	INSECTICIDE	
394.15043	$C_{20}H_{21}N_2O_3F_3$	FLUCETOREX	ANOREXIC	
394.15625	$C_{19}H_{26}N_2O_5S$	MESUPRIN	VASODILATOR	
394.17917	$C_{21}H_{27}O_6F$	TRIAMCINOLONE	CORTICOID	
394.18657	$C_{19}H_{22}N_8O_2$	WY-3654	DIURETIC	
394.18926	$C_{23}H_{26}N_2O_4$	BRUCINE	NATURAL SUBSTANCE	**MS**
394.19557	$C_{22}H_{28}O_4F_2$	DIFLUCORTOLONE	CORTICOID	
394.21441	$C_{25}H_{30}O_4$	BIXIN	CHEMICAL	
394.27193	$C_{23}H_{38}O_5$	GEMEPROST	GYNECOL./OBSTRECT.	
395.14568	$C_{19}H_{20}N_3O_3F_3$	MORNIFLUMATE	ANALGESIC	
395.17327	$C_{23}H_{25}NO_5$	DIACETYLNALORPHINE	ANTIDOTE	
395.20091	$C_{23}H_{26}N_3O_2F$	SPIPERONE	NEUROLEPTIC	
395.20966	$C_{24}H_{29}NO_4$	ETHAVERINE	ANTISPASMOTIC	**MS**
395.29366	$C_{25}H_{37}N_3O$	DIAMOCAINE	LOCAL ANESTHETIC	
396.00215	$C_{18}H_{15}N_2CL_3S$	SULCONAZOLE	FUNGIST./ANTIMYC.	
396.04498	$C_{16}H_{16}N_2O_6S_2$	CEFALOTIN	ANTIBIOTIC	
396.11438	$C_{21}H_{20}N_2O_4S$	BIPHENYLYLPENICILLIN	ANTIBIOTIC	
396.13953	$C_{23}H_{24}O_4S$	KADETHRINE	INSECTICIDE	
396.16066	$C_{20}H_{28}O_6S$	TIAPROST	GYNECOL./OBSTRECT.	
396.20491	$C_{23}H_{28}N_2O_4$	CRINOLOL	ANTIHYPERTENSIVE	
	$C_{23}H_{28}N_2O_4$	QUININE ETHYLCARBONATE	ANTIMALARIAL	
396.21614	$C_{22}H_{28}N_4O_3$	ETONITAZENE	ANALGESIC	
396.22131	$C_{24}H_{29}N_2O_2F$	ACEPERONE	VASODILATOR	
396.23006	$C_{25}H_{32}O_4$	MELENGESTROL ACETATE	GESTAGEN	
	$C_{25}H_{32}O_4$	NANDROLONE FURYLPROPIONATE	ANABOLIC	
396.26645	$C_{26}H_{36}O_3$	ESTRADIOL CYPIONATE	ESTROGEN	
396.33922	$C_{28}H_{44}O$	ERGOCALCIFEROL	VITAMINE	
	$C_{28}H_{44}O$	ERGOSTEROL	VITAMINE	
396.84607	$C_9H_5NOI_2$	DIIODOHYDROXYQUINOLINE	ANTIBIOTIC	
396.99915	$C_{12}H_{16}N_3O_4CLS_3$	METHALTHIAZIDE	DIURETIC	
397.06051	$C_{14}H_{24}NO_4S_3P$	BENSULIDE	HERBICIDE	
397.10523	$C_{18}H_{22}O_8P$	FOSFESTROL	ESTROGEN	
397.16241	$C_{22}H_{24}N_3OFS$	TIMIPERONE	NEUROLEPTIC	
397.18017	$C_{22}H_{24}N_3O_3F$	ZOLOPERONE	NEUROLEPTIC	
397.18892	$C_{23}H_{27}NO_5$	OCTAVERINE	ANTISPASMOTIC	
397.20016	$C_{22}H_{27}N_3O_4$	DIPERODON	LOCAL ANESTHETIC	
397.22531	$C_{24}H_{31}NO_4$	DROTAVERINE	ANTISPASMOTIC	
	$C_{24}H_{31}NO_4$	FENAFTIC ACID	CHOLERETIC	
397.87893	$C_{14}H_8O_4BR_2$	DIBROMODIHYDROXYBENZIL	DESINFICIENT	
397.98437	$C_{12}H_{11}N_4O_7AS$	NPA ACID	COCCIDIOSTATIC	
397.99647	$C_{12}H_{15}N_6OS_2AS$	MELARSOPROL	ANTIBIOTIC	
398.04363	$C_{17}H_{16}N_2O_5CL_2$	CLEFAMIDE	ANTIBIOTIC	

MASS	FORMULA	NAME	CATEGORY	MS
398.06849	$C_{18}H_{14}N_4O_5S$	SALAZOSULFAPYRIDINE	ANTIBIOTIC	
398.08578	$C_{18}H_{22}O_6S_2$	BISSULFOPHENYLHEXANE	ESTROGEN	
398.10017	$C_{21}H_{18}O_8$	DAUNOMYCINONE	CYTOSTATIC	
398.14464	$C_{17}H_{26}N_4O_3S_2$	FURSULTIAMINE	VITAMINE	
398.15095	$C_{21}H_{23}N_4O_2CL$	CLOPERIDONE	TRANQUILIZER	
398.16642	$C_{22}H_{26}N_2O_3S$	ZEPASTINE	ANTIHIST./-ALLERG.	
398.20688	$C_{22}H_{29}O_3F_3$	FLUMEDROXONE	GYNECOL./OBSTRECT.	
398.22056	$C_{23}H_{30}N_2O_4$	PHOLCODIN	ANTITUSSIVE	
398.28210	$C_{26}H_{38}O_3$	TESTOSTERONE HEXAHYDROBENZOATE	ANDROGEN	
398.28931	$C_{20}H_{38}N_4O_4$	DIMORPHOLAMINE	RESPIRAT.STIMULANT	
398.35084	$C_{23}H_{46}N_2O_3$	PENDECAMAINE	PHARMACEUTICAL AID	
398.35487	$C_{28}H_{46}O$	DIHYDROTACHYSTEROL	------------	
	$C_{28}H_{46}O$	VITAMIN D4	VITAMINE	
398.87903	$C_{13}H_6NO_3CL_5$	OXYCLOZANIDE	ANTIBIOTIC	
399.14507	$C_{15}H_{23}N_6O_5S$	ADENOSYLMETHIONIN	PROTEC.LIVER THER.	
399.16166	$C_{21}H_{25}N_3O_3S$	PIPAZETATE	ANTITUSSIVE	
399.16819	$C_{22}H_{25}NO_6$	COLCHICINE	CYTOSTATIC	
399.18029	$C_{22}H_{29}N_3S_2$	THIETHYLPERAZINE	ANTIHIST./-ALLERG.	
399.20774	$C_{23}H_{30}N_3OCL$	MEPACRIN	ANTIMALARIAL	
400.10143	$C_{18}H_{24}O_6S_2$	DIBUTYLNAPHTALENEDISULFONIC ACID	------------	
400.13761	$C_{22}H_{25}N_2OCLS$	CLOPENTHIXOL	NEUROLEPTIC	MS
400.18859	$C_{23}H_{28}O_6$	PREDNISONE ACETATE	CORTICOID	
400.20385	$C_{27}H_{28}O_3$	ETHINYLESTRADIOL BENZOATE	ESTROGEN	
400.21845	$C_{23}H_{32}N_2O_2S$	TIOCARLIDE	TUBERCULOSTATIC	
400.26250	$C_{22}H_{37}O_5F$	FLUOCORTOLONE PIVALATE	CORTICOID	
400.29775	$C_{26}H_{40}O_3$	MESABOLONE	ANABOLIC	
	$C_{26}H_{40}O_3$	TESTOSTERONE HEPTANOATE	ANDROGEN	
400.33413	$C_{27}H_{44}O_2$	ALFACALCIDOL	VITAMINE	
	$C_{27}H_{44}O_2$	CALCIFEDIOL	VITAMINE	
	$C_{27}H_{44}O_2$	GEFARNATE	TO THERAPY ULCERS	
	$C_{27}H_{44}O_2$	HYDROXYCHOLECALCIFEROL	VITAMINE	
401.02708	$C_{15}H_{16}N_3O_4CLS_2$	BEMETIZIDE	DIURETIC	
401.05448	$C_{17}H_{14}NO_5F_3S$	TRIFLUMIDATE	ANTIPHLOGISTIC	
401.06909	$C_{13}H_{18}N_3O_4F_3S_2$	PENFLUTIZIDE	DIURETIC	
401.10454	$C_{19}H_{19}N_3O_5S$	OXACILLIN	ANTIBIOTIC	
401.11027	$C_{20}H_{24}N_3OBR$	BROMOLYSERGIC ACID DIETHYLAMIDE	SEROTONINE ANTAG.	
401.12632	$C_{24}H_{19}NO_5$	DIPHESATINE	LAXATIVE	
401.12970	$C_{21}H_{23}NO_5S$	SUDEXANOX	ANTIHIST./-ALLERG.	
401.13063	$C_{21}H_{21}N_3O_2CLF$	ALOZAFONE	SEDATIVE	
401.13286	$C_{21}H_{24}N_3OCLS$	PIPAMAZINE	ANTIHIST./-ALLERG.	
401.15062	$C_{21}H_{24}N_3O_3CL$	FOMINOBEN	RESPIRAT.STIMULANT	
401.18384	$C_{22}H_{27}NO_6$	NISBUTEROL	BRONCHODILATOR	
401.19507	$C_{21}H_{27}N_3O_5$	MOROCROMEN	VASODILATOR	
401.22787	$C_{23}H_{29}N_3OF_2$	AMPEROXIDE	------------	
402.09508	$C_{20}H_{18}O_9$	FRANGULIN B	LAXATIVE	
402.11034	$C_{24}H_{18}O_6$	BISACETOXYPHENYLPHTHALIDE	LAXATIVE	
402.14357	$C_{21}H_{26}N_2O_2S_2$	SULFORIDAZINE	NEUROLEPTIC	MS
402.15979	$C_{23}H_{27}O_4CL$	DELMADIONE ACETATE	GESTAGEN	
402.16785	$C_{22}H_{26}O_7$	ZEARALEONE DIACETATE	ANABOLIC	
402.18628	$C_{26}H_{27}N_2CL$	CLOCINIZINE	ANTIHIST./-ALLERG.	
402.20424	$C_{23}H_{30}O_6$	ALDOSTERONE ACETATE	CORTICOID	
	$C_{23}H_{30}O_6$	CORTISONE ACETATE	CORTICOID	

MASS	FORMULA	NAME	CATEGORY	MS
402.20424	$C_{23}H_{30}O_6$	FENPROSTALENE	GYNECOL./OBSTRECT.	
	$C_{23}H_{30}O_6$	PREDNISOLONE ACETATE	CORTICOID	
402.20761	$C_{20}H_{34}O_6S$	ENTSUFONE	PHARMACEUTICAL AID	
402.22287	$C_{24}H_{34}O_3S$	SPIROXASONE	DIURETIC	
402.22671	$C_{21}H_{30}N_4O_4$	CINITAPRIDE	------------	
402.24063	$C_{24}H_{34}O_5$	DEHYDROCHOLIC ACID	CHOLERETIC	
402.27701	$C_{25}H_{38}O_4$	ANDROSTENEDIOL DIPROPIONATE	ANABOLIC	
402.29814	$C_{22}H_{42}O_6$	SORBITANE PALMITATE	PHARMACEUTICAL AID	
403.02967	$C_{17}H_{13}N_3O_5S_2$	PHTHALYLSULFATHIAZOLE	ANTIBIOTIC	
403.08227	$C_{20}H_{18}NO_6CL$	OCHRATOXIN A	NATURAL SUBSTANCE	
403.14851	$C_{21}H_{26}N_3OCLS$	PERPHENAZINE	NEUROLEPTIC	**MS**
403.20266	$C_{22}H_{30}N_3O_2CL$	ALEPRIDE	------------	
403.21474	$C_{26}H_{29}NO_3$	AMINOXYTRIPHENE	CORONARY DILATOR	
	$C_{26}H_{29}NO_3$	DOXAMINOL	CARDIOTONIC	
403.22598	$C_{25}H_{29}N_3O_2$	METERGOLINE	SEROTONINE ANTAG.	
403.81689	$C_9H_6O_3CL_6S$	ENDOSULFAN	INSECTICIDE	
403.84990	$C_{13}H_6O_2CL_6$	HEXACHLOROPHENE	DESINFICIENT	
404.01705	$C_{14}H_{16}N_2O_6S_3$	ALDESULFONE	ANTIBIOTIC	
404.02492	$C_{16}H_{12}N_4O_5S_2$	SALAZOSULFATHIAZOLE	ANTIBIOTIC	
404.11947	$C_{23}H_{20}N_2O_3S$	SULFINPYRAZONE	ANTIRHEUMATIC	**MS**
404.13722	$C_{23}H_{20}N_2O_5$	BENTIROMIDE	DIAGNOSTIC AID	
404.14376	$C_{20}H_{25}N_4OCLS$	CLOXYPENDYL	NEUROLEPTIC	
404.17361	$C_{24}H_{24}N_2O_4$	NICOCODINE	ANTITUSSIVE	
404.17544	$C_{23}H_{29}O_4CL$	CHLORMADINONE ACETATE	GESTAGEN	
404.20640	$C_{26}H_{26}N_2F_2$	FLUNARIZINE	VASODILATOR	**MS**
404.21989	$C_{23}H_{32}O_6$	HYDROCORTISONE ACETATE	CORTICOID	
404.23112	$C_{22}H_{32}N_2O_5$	BENZQUINAMIDE	NEUROLEPTIC	
404.23515	$C_{27}H_{32}O_3$	ESTRADIOL PHENYLPROPIONATE	ESTROGEN	
404.27490	$C_{25}H_{40}O_2S$	MEPITIOSTANE	CYTOSTATIC	
404.83590	$C_7H_5NO_3I_2$	DIIODOPYRIDONEACETIC ACID	DIAGNOSTIC AID	
405.00201	$C_{14}H_{13}N_3O_4CLFS_2$	PARAFLUTIZIDE	DIURETIC	
405.09946	$C_{18}H_{19}N_3O_6S$	CEFALOGLYCINE	ANTIBIOTIC	
405.13430	$C_{21}H_{24}NO_5CL$	MORCLOFONE	ANTITUSSIVE	
405.13584	$C_{19}H_{23}N_3O_5S$	OXETACILLIN	ANTIBIOTIC	
405.18594	$C_{26}H_{28}NOCL$	CLOMIFENE	GYNECOL./OBSTRECT.	
	$C_{26}H_{28}NOCL$	ZUCLOMIFENE	GYNECOL./OBSTRECT.	
405.18999	$C_{20}H_{27}N_3O_6$	ADAMANTOYLCYTARABIN	IMMUN SUPPRESSOR	
	$C_{20}H_{27}N_3O_6$	FEBARBAMATE	HYPNOTIC	
405.22637	$C_{21}H_{31}N_3O_5$	CINPROPAZIDE	CORONARY DILATOR	
405.25874	$C_{17}H_{35}N_5O_6$	ASTROMICINE	ANTIBIOTIC	
405.28791	$C_{24}H_{39}NO_4$	CASSAINE	CARDIOTONIC	
405.32429	$C_{25}H_{43}NO_3$	MINAXOLONE	ANESTHETIC	
405.79777	$C_{10}H_6CL_8$	CHLORDAN	INSECTICIDE	
406.11404	$C_{20}H_{17}N_2O_4F_3$	FLOCTAFENINE	ANALGESIC	
406.11436	$C_{21}H_{27}O_3BR$	BROMOOXOPROGESTERONE	HORMONE	
406.11986	$C_{19}H_{22}N_2O_6S$	PENAMECILLIN	ANTIBIOTIC	
406.18926	$C_{24}H_{26}N_2O_4$	NICODICODINE	ANTITUSSIVE	
406.21039	$C_{21}H_{30}N_2O_6$	PHENYLBUTAZONE TRIMETHOXYBENZOATE	ANTIPHLOGISTIC	
406.21376	$C_{18}H_{34}N_2O_6S$	LINCOMYCIN	ANTIBIOTIC	
406.21555	$C_{23}H_{31}O_5F$	FLUROGESTONE ACETATE	GESTAGEN	
406.23554	$C_{23}H_{34}O_6$	DIGINATIGENIN	NATURAL SUBSTANCE	
	$C_{23}H_{34}O_6$	DIHYDROSTROPHANTHIDIN	NATURAL SUBSTANCE	

MASS	FORMULA	NAME	CATEGORY	MS
406.25080	$C_{27}H_{34}O_3$	NANDROLONE PHENPROPIONATE	ANABOLIC	
	$C_{27}H_{34}O_3$	TESTOSTERONE PHENYLACETATE	ANDROGEN	
406.27193	$C_{24}H_{38}O_5$	ALFAPROSTOL	GYNECOL./OBSTRECT.	
407.16430	$C_{21}H_{24}N_3F_3S$	TRIFLUOPERAZINE	NEUROLEPTIC	MS
407.30356	$C_{24}H_{41}NO_4$	CASSAIDINE	CARDIOTONIC	
407.77704	$C_9H_4OCL_8$	TELODRIN	INSECTICIDE	
407.99651	$C_{12}H_{13}N_4O_6CLS_2$	SUMETIZIDE	DIURETIC	
408.08452	$C_{22}H_{16}O_8$	ETHYLBISCOUMACETATE	ANTICOAGULANT	
408.10565	$C_{19}H_{20}O_{10}$	KHELLOSIDE	CORONARY DILATOR	
408.15037	$C_{22}H_{26}O_4CLF$	CLOBETASONE	CORTICOID	
408.17035	$C_{22}H_{29}O_5CL$	ALCLOMETASONE	CORTICOID	
	$C_{22}H_{29}O_5CL$	BECLOMETASONE	CORTICOID	
408.18248	$C_{22}H_{24}N_2OF_4$	TEFLUDAZINE	------------	
408.21480	$C_{22}H_{32}O_7$	CASCARILLIN	NATURAL SUBSTANCE	
408.22131	$C_{25}H_{29}N_2O_2F$	MINDOPERONE	TRANQUILIZER	
408.24129	$C_{25}H_{32}N_2O_3$	LOFENTANIL	ANALGESIC	
408.26645	$C_{27}H_{36}O_3$	ORESTRATE	ESTROGEN	
408.28758	$C_{24}H_{40}O_5$	CHOLIC ACID	CHOLERETIC	
409.08477	$C_{20}H_{21}NO_4CL_2$	BICLOFIBRATE	ANTICHOLESTEREMIC	
	$C_{20}H_{21}NO_4CL_2$	LIFIBRATE	ANTICHOLESTEREMIC	
409.14447	$C_{24}H_{24}NO_3CL$	ENICLOFIBRATE	ANTICHOLESTEREMIC	
409.16649	$C_{22}H_{23}NO_2F_4$	TRIFLUPERIDOL	NEUROLEPTIC	MS
409.21878	$C_{24}H_{31}N_3OS$	BUTAPERAZINE	NEUROLEPTIC	MS
409.22531	$C_{25}H_{31}NO_4$	FENPERATE	ANTIHYPERTENSIVE	
409.23654	$C_{24}H_{31}N_3O_3$	MILIPERTINE	TRANQUILIZER	
409.29808	$C_{27}H_{39}NO_2$	VERATRAMINE	NATURAL SUBSTANCE	
409.82907	$C_{10}H_{10}CL_8$	TOXAPHEN	INSECTICIDE	MS
410.01780	$C_{19}H_{17}N_2CL_3S$	BUTOCONAZOLE	FUNGIST./ANTIMYC.	
410.08241	$C_{22}H_{18}O_6S$	THIOPORAN	ANTICOAGULANT	
410.12567	$C_{21}H_{28}O_2BRF$	HALOPROGESTERONE	GESTAGEN	
410.16602	$C_{22}H_{28}O_4CLF$	CLOBETASOL	CORTICOID	
	$C_{22}H_{28}O_4CLF$	CLOCORTOLONE	CORTICOID	
410.19048	$C_{22}H_{28}O_5F_2$	DIFLORASONE	ANTIPHLOGISTIC	
	$C_{22}H_{28}O_5F_2$	FLUMETASONE	CORTICOID	
410.20280	$C_{24}H_{30}N_2O_2S$	PIPERACETAZINE	NEUROLEPTIC	
410.24571	$C_{26}H_{34}O_4$	PROMETHESTROL DIPROPIONATE	ESTROGEN	
410.25694	$C_{25}H_{34}N_2O_3$	TILORONE	VIRUCIDE	
410.39125	$C_{30}H_{50}$	SQUALENE	DESINFICIENT	MS
410.44877	$C_{28}H_{58}O$	OCTACOSANOL	CHEMICAL	
411.13180	$C_{22}H_{21}NO_7$	CETOCYCLINE	ANTIBIOTIC	
411.19805	$C_{23}H_{29}N_3O_2S$	ACETOPHENAZINE	NEUROLEPTIC	
411.24096	$C_{25}H_{33}NO_4$	ETORPHINE	ANALGESIC	
411.83536	$C_8H_8O_3CL_2ISP$	IODFENPHOS	INSECTICIDE	
412.12082	$C_{21}H_{26}O_4CL_2$	DICHLORISONE	ANTIPHLOGISTIC	
412.15691	$C_{21}H_{24}N_4O_3S$	VINTIAMOL	VITAMINE	
412.16168	$C_{22}H_{27}O_3CLF_2$	HALOCORTOLONE	CORTICOID	
412.19982	$C_{23}H_{28}N_2O_5$	RESERPILINE	ANTIHYPERTENSIVE	
412.24611	$C_{22}H_{36}O_7$	ACETYLANDROMEDOL	ANTIHYPERTENSIVE	
412.29775	$C_{27}H_{40}O_3$	TESTOSTERONE CIPIONATE	ANDROGEN	
412.86321	$C_8H_7N_3O_4CL_4S_2$	TECLOTHIAZIDE	DIURETIC	
413.01418	$C_{16}H_{17}N_3O_3CLBR$	HALOFUGINONE	COCCIDIOSTATIC	
413.13286	$C_{22}H_{24}N_3OCLS$	AZACLORZINE	VASODILATOR	

MASS	FORMULA	NAME	CATEGORY	MS
413.14745	$C_{22}H_{23}NO_7$	NOSCAPINE	ANTITUSSIVE	MS
413.32938	$C_{27}H_{43}NO_2$	RUBIJERVINE	FUNGIST./ANTIMYC.	
413.95936	$C_{14}H_{14}O_6CL_3P$	HALOXON	ANTHELMINTIC	
413.98603	$C_{18}H_{14}N_2OCL_4$	ISOCONAZOLE	FUNGIST./ANTIMYC.	
	$C_{18}H_{14}N_2OCL_4$	MICONAZOLE	FUNGIST./ANTIMYC.	MS
414.05555	$C_{16}H_{18}N_2O_7S_2$	SULBENICILLIN	ANTIBIOTIC	
	$C_{16}H_{18}N_2O_7S_2$	TEMOCILLIN	ANTIBIOTIC	
414.08274	$C_{21}H_{13}N_2O_4F_3$	TALNIFLUMATE	ANALGESIC	
414.09508	$C_{21}H_{18}O_9$	ADRIAMYCINONE	CYTOSTATIC	
414.12495	$C_{21}H_{22}N_2O_5S$	NAFCILLIN	ANTIBIOTIC	
414.13147	$C_{22}H_{22}O_8$	PODOPHYLLOTOXIN	CYTOSTATIC	
414.13618	$C_{20}H_{22}N_4O_4S$	CEFROTIL	ANTIBIOTIC	
414.13781	$C_{17}H_{20}N_2O_3F_6$	FLECAINIDE	ANTIARRHYTHMIC	MS
414.14270	$C_{21}H_{22}N_2O_7$	SANCYCLINE	ANTIBIOTIC	
414.16133	$C_{22}H_{26}N_2O_4S$	DILTIAZEM	CORONARY DILATOR	
414.18246	$C_{19}H_{30}N_2O_6S$	TISOCROMIDE	ANTIDEPRESSANT	
414.20424	$C_{24}H_{30}O_6$	ESTRIOL TRIACETATE	ESTROGEN	
	$C_{24}H_{30}O_6$	MEPREDNISONE ACETATE	CORTICOID	
414.21547	$C_{23}H_{30}N_2O_5$	FEPROMIDE	ANTIARRHYTHMIC	
414.21864	$C_{23}H_{31}N_4OCL$	AMINOACRICHIN (TM)	ANTIMALARIAL	
414.21950	$C_{28}H_{30}O_3$	METHYLHEPTYLBENZOYLBIPHENYLCARBOXYLATE	DERMATIC	
414.27701	$C_{26}H_{38}O_4$	GESTONORONE CAPROATE	GESTAGEN	
	$C_{26}H_{38}O_4$	LUPULON	ANTIBIOTIC	
414.29948	$C_{24}H_{38}N_4O_2$	MOXIPRAQUINE	ANTIBIOTIC	
414.31340	$C_{27}H_{42}O_3$	METHENOLONE ENANTHATE	ANABOLIC	
414.38617	$C_{29}H_{50}O$	SITOSTEROL	ANTICHOLESTEREMIC	
415.06605	$C_{19}H_{17}N_3O_4S_2$	CEFALORIDINE	ANTIBIOTIC	
415.07420	$C_{22}H_{19}NO_3CL_2$	CYPERMETHRIN	INSECTICIDE	
415.07982	$C_{19}H_{17}NO_4CLF_3$	HALOFENATE	ANTICHOLESTEREMIC	
415.08227	$C_{21}H_{18}NO_6CL$	ACEMETACIN	ANTIRHEUMATIC	MS
415.10494	$C_{16}H_{21}N_3O_8S$	CEPHALOSPORIN C	ANTIBIOTIC	
415.14535	$C_{22}H_{25}NO_5S$	THIOCOLCHICINE	MUSCLE RELAXANT	
415.14628	$C_{22}H_{23}N_3O_2CLF$	MILENPERONE	NEUROLEPTIC	
416.07906	$C_{18}H_{16}N_4O_6S$	QUINACILLIN	ANTIBIOTIC	
416.10249	$C_{21}H_{21}O_7P$	GUAIACOL PHOSPHATE	EXPECTORANT	
416.11074	$C_{21}H_{20}O_9$	FRANGULIN A	LAXATIVE	
416.12123	$C_{19}H_{29}O_2I$	IOFENDYLATE	DIAGNOSTIC AID	
416.16371	$C_{27}H_{20}N_4O$	PYRINOLINE	ANTIARRHYTHMIC	
416.16891	$C_{23}H_{29}N_2OCLS$	XANTHIOL	NEUROLEPTIC	
416.17544	$C_{24}H_{29}O_4CL$	CHLORSUPERLUTINE	GESTAGEN	
	$C_{24}H_{29}O_4CL$	CYPROTERONE ACETATE	ANTIANDROGEN	
416.20213	$C_{24}H_{32}O_4S$	SPIRONOLACTONE	DIURETIC	
416.21989	$C_{24}H_{32}O_6$	DESONIDE	CORTICOID	
	$C_{24}H_{32}O_6$	METHYLPREDNISOLONE ACETATE	CORTICOID	
416.25359	$C_{21}H_{32}N_6O_3$	ALFETANIL	ANALGESIC	
416.27740	$C_{22}H_{40}O_7$	AGARICIC ACID	ORGANIC ACID	
416.29266	$C_{26}H_{40}O_4$	METHANDRIOL DIPROPIONATE	ANABOLIC	
416.32905	$C_{27}H_{44}O_3$	CALCITRIOL	VITAMINE	
417.08916	$C_{20}H_{17}N_3O_4CLF$	ETHYLCARFLUZEPATE	TRANQUILIZER	
417.12124	$C_{24}H_{19}NO_6$	BISOXATIN ACETATE	LAXATIVE	
417.22637	$C_{22}H_{31}N_3O_5$	CINEPAZIDE	VASODILATOR	
417.23039	$C_{27}H_{31}NO_3$	ASOCAINOL	------------	

MASS	FORMULA	NAME	CATEGORY	MS
417.25152	$C_{24}H_{35}NO_5$	DECOQUINATE	COCCIDIOSTATIC	
418.04057	$C_{17}H_{14}N_4O_5S_2$	PHTHALYLSULFAMETHIAZOL	ANTIBIOTIC	
418.08693	$C_{20}H_{25}O_3CL_3$	CLOXESTRADIOL	ESTROGEN	
418.12051	$C_{28}H_{18}O_4$	NAPHTHOLPHTHALEIN	CHEMICAL	
418.12639	$C_{21}H_{22}O_9$	ALOIN	NATURAL SUBSTANCE	
418.17400	$C_{21}H_{26}N_2O_7$	NIMODIPINE	VASODILATOR	
418.18119	$C_{26}H_{27}N_2OCL$	LOFEPRAMINE	ANTIDEPRESSANT	**MS**
418.20232	$C_{23}H_{31}N_2O_3CL$	ETODROXIZINE	SEDATIVE	**MS**
418.21039	$C_{22}H_{30}N_2O_6$	MOXICOUMONE	ANTICOAGULANT	
418.21555	$C_{24}H_{31}O_5F$	FLUOCORTOLONE ACETATE	CORTICOID	
418.23554	$C_{24}H_{34}O_6$	MEXRENOATE	DIURETIC	
418.91565	$C_{17}H_{11}NO_2BR_2$	BROXALDINE	DESINFICIENT	
419.08962	$C_{21}H_{23}NO_2BRF$	BROMPERIDOL	NEUROLEPTIC	**MS**
419.12882	$C_{25}H_{22}NO_3CL$	FENVALERATE	INSECTICIDE	
419.22089	$C_{25}H_{29}N_3O_3$	ADIMOLOL	------------	
419.24604	$C_{27}H_{33}NO_3$	ETHAMOXYTRIPHETOL	GYNECOL./OBSTRECT.	
419.69956	$C_7H_4OBR_4$	TETRABROMOCRESOL	DESINFICIENT	
419.97777	$C_8H_{10}O_3S_2HG$	TIMERFONE	DESINFICIENT	
420.12005	$C_{19}H_{21}N_4O_5CL$	ETOFYLLINECLOFIBRATE	ANTICHOLESTEREMIC	
420.14337	$C_{22}H_{20}N_4O_5$	TALMETOPRIM	ANTIBIOTIC	
420.19482	$C_{23}H_{29}O_6F$	FLUPREDNISOLONE ACETATE	CORTICOID	
420.22604	$C_{22}H_{32}N_2O_6$	HEXOPRENALINE	BRONCHODILATOR	
420.23727	$C_{21}H_{32}N_4O_5$	PIREPOLOL	------------	
420.25253	$C_{25}H_{32}N_4O_2$	PIPEBUZONE	ANALGESIC	
420.26645	$C_{28}H_{36}O_3$	TESTOSTERONE PHENYLPROPIONATE	ANDROGEN	
420.86720	$C_8H_9NO_3I_2$	IOPYDOL	DIAGNOSTIC AID	
421.03779	$C_{15}H_{14}N_3O_4F_3S_2$	BENDROFLUMETHIAZIDE	DIURETIC	
421.14357	$C_{21}H_{22}N_3OF_3S$	FTORMETAZINE	ANTIDEPRESSANT	
421.14716	$C_{20}H_{24}N_3O_4FS$	FLUBEPRIDE	ANTIDEPRESSANT	
421.24375	$C_{19}H_{31}N_7O_4$	MOPIDAMOL	ANTICOAGULANT	
421.28282	$C_{24}H_{39}NO_5$	ERYTHROPHLEINE	CARDIOTONIC	
421.91532	$C_{17}H_{12}O_3BR_2$	BENZBROMARONE	URICOSURIC	**MS**
422.13003	$C_{23}H_{22}N_2O_4S$	OSMODIZONE	URICOSURIC	
422.19407	$C_{22}H_{30}O_8$	VALTRATE	TRANQUILIZER	
422.20262	$C_{17}H_{26}N_8O_5$	BLASTICIDIN S	ANTIBIOTIC	
422.21047	$C_{23}H_{31}O_6F$	FLUDROCORTISONE ACETATE	CORTICOID	
422.23383	$C_{20}H_{38}O_7S$	DIOCTYL SULFOSUCCINIC ACID	LAXATIVE	
	$C_{20}H_{38}O_7S$	DOCUSATE	SOLUBILIZER ETC.	
422.48515	$C_{30}H_{62}$	SQUALANE	CHEMICAL	
423.05588	$C_{17}H_{17}N_3O_6S_2$	CEFAPIRIN	ANTIBIOTIC	
423.07364	$C_{17}H_{17}N_3O_8S$	CEFURACETIME	ANTIBIOTIC	
423.24096	$C_{26}H_{33}NO_4$	CYPRENORPHINE	ANTIDOTE	
423.26209	$C_{23}H_{37}NO_6$	TOCAMPHYL	CHOLERETIC	
423.82681	$C_{13}H_8O_2CL_2BR_2$	BROMCHLOROPHEN	DESINFICIENT	
424.06889	$C_{16}H_{16}N_4O_8S$	CEFUROXIME	ANTIBIOTIC	
424.13043	$C_{19}H_{24}N_2O_7S$	FURBICILLIN	ANTIBIOTIC	
424.16527	$C_{22}H_{29}O_6CL$	CLOPROSTENOL	------------	
424.17987	$C_{18}H_{33}N_2O_5CLS$	CLINDAMYCIN	ANTIBIOTIC	
424.20320	$C_{21}H_{32}N_2O_5S$	CAMPHOTAMIDE	RESPIRAT.STIMULANT	
424.20972	$C_{22}H_{32}O_8$	DIDROVALTRATE	SEDATIVE	
424.21508	$C_{28}H_{28}N_2O_2$	DIFENOXIN	ANTIDIARRHOEAL	
424.30898	$C_{27}H_{40}N_2O_2$	ISOOCTYLHYDROCUPREINE	DESINFICIENT	

MASS	FORMULA	NAME	CATEGORY	MS
424.33011	$C_{24}H_{44}N_2O_4$	SUXEMERIDE	ANTITUSSIVE	
424.95524	$C_{10}H_{11}N_3O_4CLF_3S_3$	EPITIZIDE	DIURETIC	
425.00095	$C_{10}H_9NO_3SHG$	CIALIT (TM)	DESINFICIENT	
425.18384	$C_{24}H_{27}NO_6$	MECINARONE	VASODILATOR	
425.21370	$C_{24}H_{31}N_3O_2S$	CARFENAZINE	NEUROLEPTIC	
425.23548	$C_{29}H_{31}NO_2$	NAFOXIDIN	------------	
425.24135	$C_{22}H_{35}NO_7$	AMOPROXAN	CORONARY DILATOR	
425.25661	$C_{26}H_{35}NO_4$	DIPRENORPHINE	ANTIDOTE	
425.79199	$C_6H_4O_4I_2S$	DIIODOHYDROXYBENZOLSULFONIC ACID	DESINFICIENT	
425.94662	$C_{17}H_{16}O_3BR_2$	ISOPROPYL DIBROMOBENZILATE	PESTICIDE	
426.07493	$C_{19}H_{20}N_2O_5CL_2$	ETOFAMIDE	ANTIBIOTIC	
426.12495	$C_{22}H_{22}N_2O_5S$	FENBENCILLIN	ANTIBIOTIC	
426.13647	$C_{22}H_{28}O_4CL_2$	MECLORISONE	CORTICOID	
426.15731	$C_{18}H_{26}N_4O_6S$	CETOTIAMINE	VITAMINE	
426.20424	$C_{25}H_{30}O_6$	FLUAZACORT	CORTICOID	
426.24196	$C_{27}H_{30}N_4O$	OXATOMIDE	ANTIHIST./-ALLERG.	
426.25186	$C_{25}H_{34}N_2O_4$	FEXICAINE	LOCAL ANESTHETIC	
426.27701	$C_{27}H_{38}O_4$	AZAFRIN	NATURAL SUBSTANCE	
426.37091	$C_{26}H_{50}O_4$	BISETHYLHEXYL SEBACATE	CHEMICAL	
	$C_{26}H_{50}O_4$	GLYCOL DILAURATE	CHEMICAL	
426.98127	$C_{18}H_{13}N_3OCL_4$	OXICONAZOLE	FUNGIST./ANTIMYC.	
427.02942	$C_{10}H_{15}N_5O_{10}P_2$	ADENOSINE DIPHOSPHATE	ENDOG.BIOMOLECULE	
427.05080	$C_{16}H_{17}N_3O_7S_2$	CEFOXITIN	ANTIBIOTIC	
427.09504	$C_{19}H_{17}N_5O_5S$	SALAZOSULFADIMIDINE	ANTIBIOTIC	
427.15658	$C_{22}H_{25}N_3O_4S$	MORACIZINE	ANTIARRHYTHMIC	
427.22935	$C_{24}H_{33}N_3O_2S$	DIXYRAZINE	NEUROLEPTIC	MS
428.03883	$C_{21}H_{16}O_6S_2$	METHARGEN	DESINFICIENT	
428.07900	$C_{18}H_{22}O_8P_2$	FOSFESTROL	ESTROGEN	
428.08405	$C_{18}H_{22}N_4O_2CL_2S$	ASAZOL	CYTOSTATIC	
428.10766	$C_{22}H_{27}O_2CL_3$	TRICHLORODITHYMOLETHANE	DESINFICIENT	
428.18106	$C_{22}H_{27}O_5F_3$	CORMETASONE	CORTICOID	
428.20597	$C_{22}H_{28}N_4O_5$	NITRACRIDINE	ANTIBIOTIC	
428.23112	$C_{24}H_{32}N_2O_5$	METOSERPATE	ANTIDEPRESSANT	
428.29266	$C_{27}H_{40}O_4$	HYDROXYPROGESTERONE CAPROATE	GESTAGEN	
	$C_{27}H_{40}O_4$	LONTANYL	ANDROGEN	
428.31379	$C_{24}H_{44}O_6$	SORBITANE OLEATE	SOLUBILIZER ETC.	
428.32905	$C_{28}H_{44}O_3$	ANAGESTONE HEXANAOTE	GESTAGEN	
	$C_{28}H_{44}O_3$	NANDROLONE DECANOATE	ANABOLIC	
429.06645	$C_{16}H_{19}N_3O_7S_2$	SUNCILLIN	ANTIBIOTIC	
429.07431	$C_{18}H_{15}N_5O_6S$	SALANTEL	ANTHELMINTIC	
	$C_{18}H_{15}N_5O_6S$	SALAZODIN	ANTIBIOTIC	
429.15360	$C_{21}H_{23}N_3O_7$	AMICYCLINE	ANTIBIOTIC	
429.18594	$C_{28}H_{28}NOCL$	ENCLOMIFEN	GYNECOL./OBSTRECT.	
429.25152	$C_{25}H_{35}NO_5$	MEBEVERINE	ANTISPASMOTIC	
430.02531	$C_{14}H_{14}N_4O_8S_2$	DINSED	COCCIDIOSTATIC	
430.09465	$C_{18}H_{24}O_8P_2$	HEXESTROL DIPHOSPHATE	CYTOSTATIC	
430.13762	$C_{21}H_{22}N_2O_8$	DEMECYCLINE	ANTIBIOTIC	
430.18233	$C_{24}H_{28}N_2O_2CLF$	AMIPERONE	NEUROLEPTIC	
430.21441	$C_{28}H_{30}O_4$	THYMOLPHTHALEIN	CHEMICAL	
430.21894	$C_{18}H_{26}N_{10}O_3$	CONGOCIDINE	ANTIBIOTIC	
430.23554	$C_{25}H_{34}O_6$	BUDESONIDE	CORTICOID	
430.26203	$C_{28}H_{34}N_2O_2$	BENDERIZINE	------------	

MASS	FORMULA	NAME	CATEGORY	MS
430.26203	$C_{28}H_{34}N_2O_2$	CARBIFENE	ANALGESIC	
430.27193	$C_{26}H_{38}O_5$	EDOGESTRONE	GESTAGEN	
430.27326	$C_{27}H_{34}N_4O$	PIRITRAMIDE	ANALGESIC	MS
430.30831	$C_{27}H_{42}O_4$	RUSCOGENINE	ENDOG.BIOMOLECULE	
430.32944	$C_{24}H_{46}O_6$	SORBITANE STEARATE	SOLUBILIZER ETC.	
430.38108	$C_{29}H_{50}O_2$	TOCOPHEROL	VITAMINE	
430.98350	$C_{15}H_{14}N_3O_4CLS_3$	BENZTHIAZIDE	DIURETIC	
431.13758	$C_{18}H_{21}N_7O_4S$	TIODAZOSIN	ANTIHYPERTENSIVE	
431.23213	$C_{25}H_{29}N_5O_2$	BISFENAZONE	ANALGESIC	
431.92479	$C_{10}H_{14}N_4O_2CL_6$	TRIFORINE	FUNGIST./ANTIMYC.	
432.03135	$C_{17}H_{18}N_2O_5CL_2S$	CLOMETOCILLIN	ANTIBIOTIC	
432.10485	$C_{21}H_{25}N_2O_3BR$	BROVINCAMINE	VASODILATOR	
432.19482	$C_{24}H_{29}O_6F$	ACROCIONIDE	CORTICOID	
	$C_{24}H_{29}O_6F$	FLUPREDNIDENE ACETATE	CORTICOID	
432.22604	$C_{23}H_{32}N_2O_6$	ENCIPRAZINE	------------	
432.23323	$C_{28}H_{33}N_2CL$	BUCLIZINE	ANTIHIST./-ALLERG.	
432.25119	$C_{25}H_{36}O_6$	HYDROXYDIONE SUCCINATE	NARCOTIC	
432.30283	$C_{30}H_{40}O_2$	CITRAURIN	NATURAL SUBSTANCE	
432.32396	$C_{27}H_{44}O_4$	CHLOROGENIN	NATURAL SUBSTANCE	
	$C_{27}H_{44}O_4$	DIGALOGENIN	NATURAL SUBSTANCE	
	$C_{27}H_{44}O_4$	GITOGENIN	NATURAL SUBSTANCE	
432.86720	$C_9H_9NO_3I_2$	DIIODOTYROSINE	THYREOSTATIC	
432.99915	$C_{15}H_{16}N_3O_4CLS_3$	HYDROBENTIZIDE	DIURETIC	
433.16714	$C_{21}H_{27}N_3O_5S$	SARPICILLIN	ANTIBIOTIC	
433.17995	$C_{23}H_{26}N_3F_3S$	CICLOFENAZINE	NEUROLEPTIC	
433.20353	$C_{22}H_{31}N_3O_4S$	PENETHRACILLIN	ANTIBIOTIC	
433.22531	$C_{27}H_{31}NO_4$	ESTRAPRONICATE	------------	
434.11823	$C_{21}H_{29}O_3CL_3$	CLOXOTESTOSTERONE	ANDROGEN	
434.11977	$C_{19}H_{28}N_2O_3CL_2S$	PHENAMET	CYTOSTATIC	
434.13724	$C_{18}H_{22}N_6O_5S$	BL-P 1654	ANTIBIOTIC	
434.14962	$C_{23}H_{27}O_6CL$	CHLOROPREDNISONE ACETATE	CORTICOID	
434.16397	$C_{23}H_{25}N_2OF_3S$	FLUPENTIXOL	NEUROLEPTIC	MS
434.21047	$C_{24}H_{31}O_6F$	BETAMETHASONE ACETATE	CORTICOID	
	$C_{24}H_{31}O_6F$	DEXAMETHASONE ACETATE	CORTICOID	
	$C_{24}H_{31}O_6F$	FLUNISOLIDE	CORTICOID	
	$C_{24}H_{31}O_6F$	FLUPEROLONE ACETATE	CORTICOID	
	$C_{24}H_{31}O_6F$	PARAMETHASONE ACETATE	CORTICOID	
	$C_{24}H_{31}O_6F$	TRIAMCINOLONE ACETONIDE	CORTICOID	
434.21249	$C_{27}H_{31}N_2OCL$	CHLORBENZOXAMINE	PARASYMPATH.-LYTIC	
434.29333	$C_{28}H_{38}N_2O_2$	BUTOPROZINE	ANTIARRHYTHMIC	
435.05344	$C_{16}H_{16}N_3O_4F_3S_2$	PHENYLETHYLHYDROFLUMETHIAZIDE	DIURETIC	
435.06557	$C_{19}H_{18}N_3O_5CLS$	CLOXACILLIN	ANTIBIOTIC	
435.09166	$C_{21}H_{20}N_3O_2CL_2F$	LODIPERONE	------------	
435.21179	$C_{20}H_{29}N_5O_6$	TRIMAZOSINE	ANTIHYPERTENSIVE	
435.26209	$C_{24}H_{37}NO_6$	LAUROYLPYRIDOXOL DIACETATE	VITAMINE	
436.06118	$C_{14}H_{10}N_4HG$	BARBAK	HERBICIDE	
436.12236	$C_{21}H_{25}N_2O_4CLS$	TIANEPTINE	------------	
436.13695	$C_{21}H_{24}O_{10}$	PHLORIZIN	ANTIMALARIAL	
436.16527	$C_{23}H_{29}O_6CL$	DELPROSTENATE	------------	
436.22612	$C_{24}H_{33}O_6F$	FLUDROXYCORTIDE	CORTICOID	
436.26136	$C_{28}H_{36}O_4$	OXYMETHOLONE ENOL BENZOATE	ANABOLIC	
436.27597	$C_{24}H_{40}N_2O_3S$	OLEOYLSULFANILAMIDE	ANTIBIOTIC	

MASS	FORMULA	NAME	CATEGORY	MS
436.27847	$C_{20}H_{40}N_2O_8$	PANGAMIC ACID	VITAMINE	
436.29775	$C_{29}H_{40}O_3$	BOLMANTALATE	ANABOLIC	
436.30898	$C_{28}H_{40}N_2O_2$	BIALAMICOL	ANTIBIOTIC	
436.77202	$C_{11}H_6NOBR_3S$	TIBROFAN	DESINFICIENT	
436.88739	$C_{14}H_8NO_2BR_2F_3$	FLUSALAN	DESINFICIENT	
437.02391	$C_{18}H_{15}NO_8S_2$	PICOSULFURIC ACID	LAXATIVE	
437.02862	$C_{16}H_{15}N_5O_4S_3$	CEFETRIZOLE	------------	
437.17487	$C_{22}H_{26}N_3OF_3S$	FLUPHENAZINE	NEUROLEPTIC	MS
437.21216	$C_{27}H_{32}NO_2CL$	TRIPARANOL	ANTICHOLESTEREMIC	
437.23146	$C_{25}H_{31}N_3O_4$	ALPERTINE	TRANQUILIZER	
437.25661	$C_{27}H_{35}NO_4$	ALLETORPHINE	ANALGESIC	
438.17909	$C_{24}H_{26}N_2O_6$	SUXIBUZONE	ANTIPHLOGISTIC	
438.18899	$C_{22}H_{30}O_9$	SIMARUBIN	NATURAL SUBSTANCE	
438.19552	$C_{19}H_{35}N_2O_5CLS$	MIRINCAMYCIN	ANTIBIOTIC	
438.19948	$C_{20}H_{39}O_2I$	ETHYLIODOSTEARATE	DIAGNOSTIC AID	
438.20424	$C_{26}H_{30}O_6$	DIMETHYLMANGOSTIN	NATURAL SUBSTANCE	
438.24177	$C_{24}H_{35}O_6F$	DROCINONIDE	CORTICOID	
438.27701	$C_{28}H_{38}O_4$	PROMETHESTROL DIBUTYRATE	ESTROGEN	
438.29162	$C_{24}H_{42}N_2O_3S$	STEARYLSULFAMIDE	ANTIBIOTIC	
438.31340	$C_{29}H_{42}O_3$	ESTRADIOL UNDECENOATE	ESTROGEN	
438.34978	$C_{30}H_{46}O_2$	ERGOSTEROL ACETATE	VITAMINE	
438.97089	$C_{11}H_{13}N_3O_4CLF_3S_3$	POLYTHIAZIDE	DIURETIC	
438.99962	$C_{12}H_5O_{12}N_7$	DIPICRYLAMINE	CHEMICAL	
439.16810	$C_{23}H_{31}NO_3CL_2$	ESTRAMUSTINE	CYTOSTATIC	
439.21409	$C_{21}H_{33}N_3O_5S$	PIVMECILLINAM	ANTIBIOTIC	
440.01437	$C_{13}H_{12}N_8O_4S_3$	CEFTEZOL	ANTIBIOTIC	
440.08243	$C_{17}H_{20}N_4O_6S_2$	CEFSUMIDE	ANTIBIOTIC	
440.15567	$C_{19}H_{20}N_8O_5$	AMINOPTERIN	CYTOSTATIC	
440.20463	$C_{22}H_{32}O_9$	SIMARUBIDIN	NATURAL SUBSTANCE	
440.21744	$C_{24}H_{31}O_4F_3$	FLUMEDROXONE ACETATE	GYNECOL./OBSTRECT.	
440.26751	$C_{26}H_{36}N_2O_4$	BISOBRIN	FIBRINOLYTIC	
440.29266	$C_{28}H_{40}O_4$	PENTAGESTRONE ACETATE	GESTAGEN	
440.32905	$C_{29}H_{44}O_3$	ESTRADIOL UNDECANOATE	ESTROGEN	
440.36543	$C_{30}H_{48}O_2$	MENTHOL ABIETATE	CHOLERETIC	
441.13968	$C_{19}H_{19}N_7O_6$	FOLIC ACID	VITAMINE	
441.16416	$C_{24}H_{28}N_3OCLS$	CLOTIXAMIDE	TRANQUILIZER	
441.18999	$C_{23}H_{27}N_3O_6$	ERGONOVINE MALEATE	GYNECOL./OBSTRECT.	
441.21514	$C_{25}H_{31}NO_6$	DEFLAZACORT	CORTICOID	
442.09536	$C_{28}H_{14}N_2O_4$	INDANTHRENE	CHEMICAL	
442.13762	$C_{22}H_{22}N_2O_8$	METACYCLINE	ANTIBIOTIC	
442.19916	$C_{25}H_{30}O_7$	PICROLICHENIC ACID	NATURAL SUBSTANCE	
442.28316	$C_{26}H_{38}N_2O_4$	DEPERSOLON	CORTICOID	
	$C_{26}H_{38}N_2O_4$	MAZIPREDONE	CORTICOID	
442.34470	$C_{29}H_{46}O_3$	TESTOSTERONE CAPRINATE	ANDROGEN	
442.38108	$C_{30}H_{50}O_2$	BETULIN	NATURAL SUBSTANCE	
443.11511	$C_{21}H_{21}N_3O_6S$	FUROXICILLIN	ANTIBIOTIC	
443.12752	$C_{22}H_{22}NO_2CLF_4$	CLOFLUPEROL	NEUROLEPTIC	
443.13689	$C_{26}H_{21}NO_6$	TRIACETYLDIPHENOLISATIN	LAXATIVE	
443.17012	$C_{23}H_{29}N_3O_2S_2$	TIOTIXENE	NEUROLEPTIC	MS
443.17646	$C_{16}H_{25}N_7O_8$	GOUGEROTIN	CYTOSTATIC	
443.91062	$C_{13}H_{14}N_2O_4SAS_2$	NEOARSPHENAMINE	ANTIBIOTIC	
444.06927	$C_{21}H_{16}O_{11}$	CITRODISALYL	ANALGESIC	

MASS	FORMULA	NAME	CATEGORY	MS
444.13734	$C_{21}H_{29}O_6CLS$	LUPROSTIOL	------------	
444.15327	$C_{22}H_{24}N_2O_8$	DOXYCYCLINE	ANTIBIOTIC	
	$C_{22}H_{24}N_2O_8$	TETRACYCLINE	ANTIBIOTIC	
444.17255	$C_{31}H_{24}O_3$	DIFENACOUM	RODENTICIDE	
444.25119	$C_{26}H_{36}O_6$	PREDNISOLONE TRIMETHYLACETATE	CORTICOID	
444.30283	$C_{31}H_{40}O_2$	MENATETRENONE	HEMOSTATIC	
445.10493	$C_{22}H_{24}N_3OCLS_2$	SPICLOMAZINE	TRANQUILIZER	
445.14939	$C_{22}H_{27}N_3O_3S_2$	METOPIMAZINE	ANTIHIST./-ALLERG.	
445.15908	$C_{23}H_{28}N_3O_2CLS$	THIOPROPAZATE	NEUROLEPTIC	MS
445.16714	$C_{22}H_{27}N_3O_5S$	GLIPENTIDE	ANTIDIABETIC	
445.17367	$C_{23}H_{27}NO_8$	NARCEINE	ANTITUSSIVE	
445.17838	$C_{21}H_{27}N_5O_4S$	GLIPIZIDE	ANTIDIABETIC	
446.01464	$C_{22}H_{16}O_4CL_2S$	TIOCLOMAROL	ANTICOAGULANT	
446.06651	$C_{13}H_{22}N_2O_{11}S_2$	GLUCOSULFAMIDE	ANTIBIOTIC	
446.11457	$C_{24}H_{19}N_4O_3CL$	NICAFENINE	ANALGESIC	
446.12601	$C_{20}H_{22}N_4O_6S$	FEBANTEL	ANTHELMINTIC	
446.18102	$C_{22}H_{30}N_4O_2S_2$	THIOPROPERAZINE	NEUROLEPTIC	MS
446.19407	$C_{24}H_{30}O_8$	DESASPIDIN	ANTHELMINTIC	
	$C_{24}H_{30}O_8$	FLAVASPIDIC ACID	NATURAL SUBSTANCE	
446.30456	$C_{28}H_{38}N_4O$	CARPIPRAMINE	ANTIDEPRESSANT	
446.37600	$C_{29}H_{50}O_3$	TOCOPHEROLQUINONE	ANTIHYPERTENSIVE	
446.81051	$C_{13}H_8NO_2BR_3$	TRIBROMSALAN	DESINFICIENT	
446.88285	$C_{10}H_{11}NO_3I_2$	PROPYLIODONE	DIAGNOSTIC AID	
447.15922	$C_{23}H_{24}N_3OF_3S$	AZAFTOZINE	CORONARY DILATOR	
447.26343	$C_{26}H_{33}N_5O_2$	NILPRAZOLE	TO THERAPY ULCERS	
447.26930	$C_{19}H_{37}N_5O_7$	SISOMICIN	ANTIBIOTIC	
448.10057	$C_{21}H_{20}O_{11}$	ASTRAGALIN	CARDIOTONIC	
448.26136	$C_{29}H_{36}O_4$	ALGESTONE ACETOPHENIDE	GESTAGEN	
448.31888	$C_{27}H_{44}O_5$	DIGITOGENIN	NATURAL SUBSTANCE	
448.82573	$C_8H_5NO_5I_2$	IODOXYL	DIAGNOSTIC AID	
449.17329	$C_{20}H_{27}N_5O_5S$	GLISOXEPID	ANTIDIABETIC	
449.21370	$C_{26}H_{31}N_3O_2S$	PRETIADIL	CORONARY DILATOR	
449.26425	$C_{28}H_{33}N_3F_2$	DIFLUANAZINE	STIMULANT	
449.28495	$C_{19}H_{39}N_5O_7$	GENTAMYCIN C1A	ANTIBIOTIC	
449.97386	$C_6H_6N_6O_{18}$	INOSITOL HEXANITRATE	CORONARY DILATOR	
450.02253	$C_{15}H_{18}N_2O_8S_3$	NOPRYLSULFAMIDE	ANTIBIOTIC	
450.04667	$C_{24}H_{19}O_4BR$	BROMOSTYRYLIDENEDIPHENOL DIACETATE	ESTROGEN	
450.18965	$C_{27}H_{31}N_2CLS$	BENTIPIMINE	ANTICHOLINERGIC	
450.18985	$C_{24}H_{34}O_4S_2$	TIOMESTERONE	ANABOLIC	
450.26176	$C_{25}H_{38}O_7$	LASERPITIN	NATURAL SUBSTANCE	
450.34978	$C_{31}H_{46}O_2$	PHYTOMENADIONE	HEMOSTATIC	
451.06622	$C_{20}H_{23}N_3O_2CLBR$	BROCLEPRIDE	TRANQUILIZER	
451.15413	$C_{22}H_{24}N_3O_2F_3S$	FTORPROPAZINE	ANTIDEPRESSANT	
451.15930	$C_{24}H_{25}NOF_4S$	PIFLUTIXOL	NEUROLEPTIC	
451.18557	$C_{23}H_{25}N_5O_5$	DOXAZOSIN	ANTIHYPERTENSIVE	
451.19052	$C_{23}H_{28}N_3OF_3S$	HOMOFENAZINE	NEUROLEPTIC	MS
451.26421	$C_{18}H_{37}N_5O_8$	DIBEKACIN	ANTIBIOTIC	
451.27226	$C_{28}H_{37}NO_4$	HOMOPRENORPHINE	ANALGESIC	
451.98951	$C_6H_8N_6O_{18}$	MANNITOL HEXANITRATE	CORONARY DILATOR	
452.17453	$C_{23}H_{27}N_2O_2F_3S$	FLUPIMAZINE	NEUROLEPTIC	
452.17658	$C_{24}H_{30}O_5CLF$	CLOCORTOLONE ACETATE	CORTICOID	
452.20105	$C_{24}H_{30}O_6F_2$	FLUMETHASONE ACETATE	CORTICOID	

MASS	FORMULA	NAME	CATEGORY	MS
452.20105	$C_{24}H_{30}O_6F_2$	FLUOCINOLONE ACETONIDE	CORTICOID	
452.22460	$C_{25}H_{32}N_4O_2S$	TIOPERIDONE	TRANQUILIZER	
452.24638	$C_{30}H_{32}N_2O_2$	DIPHENOXYLATE	ANTIDIARRHOEAL	MS
452.32905	$C_{30}H_{44}O_3$	BOLDENONE UNDECENOATE	ANABOLIC	
452.36543	$C_{31}H_{48}O_2$	DIHYDROVITAMIN K1	HEMOSTATIC	
453.05615	$C_{19}H_{17}N_3O_5CLFS$	FLUCLOXACILLIN	ANTIBIOTIC	
453.23039	$C_{30}H_{31}NO_3$	TRIOXIFEN	GYNECOL./OBSTRECT.	
453.25152	$C_{27}H_{35}NO_5$	ACETORPHINE	NARCOTIC	
453.93332	$C_{20}H_{10}O_4CL_4$	PHENOLTETRACHLOROPHTHALEIN	LAXATIVE	
454.03002	$C_{14}H_{14}N_8O_4S_3$	CEFAZOLIN	ANTIBIOTIC	
454.06734	$C_{24}H_{20}N_2OCL_2S$	FENTICONAZOLE	------------	
454.11986	$C_{23}H_{22}N_2O_6S$	CARFECILLIN	ANTIBIOTIC	
454.13138	$C_{23}H_{28}O_5CL_2$	DICHLORISONE ACETATE	CORTICOID	
454.17020	$C_{23}H_{26}N_2OF_4S$	TEFLUTIXOL	NEUROLEPTIC	
454.17132	$C_{20}H_{22}N_8O_5$	A-NINOPTERIN	CYTOSTATIC	
	$C_{20}H_{22}N_8O_5$	METHOTREXATE	CYTOSTATIC	
454.19223	$C_{24}H_{32}O_5CLF$	HALCINONIDE	CORTICOID	
454.22750	$C_{17}H_{34}N_4O_{10}$	RIBOSTAMYCIN	ANTIBIOTIC	
454.23688	$C_{28}H_{30}N_4O_2$	FUPRAZOL	BRONCHODILATOR	
454.26609	$C_{20}H_{38}N_8S_2$	BITIPAZONE	COCCIDIOSTATIC	
454.28316	$C_{27}H_{38}N_2O_4$	VERAPAMIL	CORONARY DILATOR	MS
454.30965	$C_{30}H_{38}N_4$	QUINDECAMINE	DESINFICIENT	
454.34470	$C_{30}H_{46}O_3$	ANAGESTONE CYCLOPENTYLPROPIONATE	GESTAGEN	
455.05694	$C_{16}H_{17}N_5O_7S_2$	CEFOTAXIME	ANTIBIOTIC	
455.15533	$C_{20}H_{21}N_7O_6$	NINOPTERIN	CYTOSTATIC	
455.18950	$C_{26}H_{31}N_3CL_2$	AMINOQUINOL	ANTIBIOTIC	
455.23079	$C_{26}H_{33}NO_6$	PIPROFUROL	VASODILATOR	
455.63503	ASI_3	ARSENIC TRIIODIDE	------------	
456.00875	$C_{12}H_{26}O_6S_4P_2$	DIOXATION	INSECTICIDE	
456.15729	$C_{28}H_{24}O_6$	FUROSTILBESTROL	ESTROGEN	
456.23861	$C_{26}H_{34}NO_6$	CHOLYLGLYCINE	CHOLERETIC	
456.27232	$C_{24}H_{40}O_8$	TROPITAL (TM)	PESTICIDE	
456.29074	$C_{28}H_{41}N_2OCL$	TEROXALEN	ANTIBIOTIC	
456.32396	$C_{29}H_{44}O_4$	LAPINONE	ANTIMALARIAL	
456.36035	$C_{30}H_{48}O_3$	NANDROLONE DODECANOATE	ANABOLIC	
457.15841	$C_{20}H_{27}NO_{11}$	AMYGDALIN	NATURAL SUBSTANCE	
457.18490	$C_{23}H_{27}N_3O_7$	MINOCYCLINE	ANTIBIOTIC	
458.14309	$C_{24}H_{27}N_2O_3CLS$	FUROMAZINE	NEUROLEPTIC	
458.23045	$C_{26}H_{34}O_7$	FUMAGILLIN	ANTIBIOTIC	
458.24819	$C_{28}H_{31}N_4OF$	ASTEMIZOLE	ANTIHIST./-ALLERG.	
458.26684	$C_{27}H_{38}O_6$	PREDNISOLONE TEBUTATE	CORTICOID	
458.37600	$C_{30}H_{50}O_3$	PRIMULAIC ACID	EXPECTORANT	
	$C_{30}H_{50}O_3$	TOCOPHEROL ACETATE	VITAMINE	
458.87016	$C_{13}H_7N_3O_6BR_2$	BROMFENOXIME	HERBICIDE	
459.12778	$C_{21}H_{21}N_3O_9$	NITROCYCLINE	ANTIBIOTIC	
459.15214	$C_{23}H_{30}N_3O_2BR$	BRAZERGOLIN	VASODILATOR	
459.16166	$C_{26}H_{25}N_3O_3S$	FENOVERINE	ANTISPASMOTIC	
459.95968	$C_{14}H_{18}N_2O_6AS_2$	DIFETARSONE	ANTIBIOTIC	
460.14818	$C_{22}H_{24}N_2O_9$	OXYTETRACYCLINE	ANTIBIOTIC	
460.20972	$C_{25}H_{32}O_8$	ASPIDIN	NATURAL SUBSTANCE	
	$C_{25}H_{32}O_8$	PREDNISOLONE SUCCINATE	CORTICOID	
460.21289	$C_{25}H_{33}N_2O_4CL$	NISTERIM	ANDROGEN	

MASS	FORMULA	NAME	CATEGORY	MS
460.28249	$C_{27}H_{40}O_{6}$	HYDROCORTISONE TEBUTATE	CORTICOID	
460.82616	$C_{14}H_{10}NO_{2}BR_{3}$	BENSALAN	DESINFICIENT	
460.84875	$C_{15}H_{10}NO_{2}CLBR_{2}S$	BROTIANIDE	ANTHELMINTIC	
461.02012	$C_{18}H_{25}NO_{3}BR_{2}$	OXABREXIN	------------	
461.13691	$C_{20}H_{23}N_{5}O_{6}S$	AZLOCILLIN	ANTIBIOTIC	
461.16206	$C_{22}H_{27}N_{3}O_{6}S$	PIVCEFALEXIN	ANTIBIOTIC	
461.22022	$C_{28}H_{31}NO_{5}$	TOBUTEROL	------------	
461.22787	$C_{28}H_{29}N_{3}OF_{2}$	PIMOZIDE	NEUROLEPTIC	MS
462.05555	$C_{20}H_{18}N_{2}O_{7}S_{2}$	ARANOTIN	VIRUCIDE	
462.07801	$C_{18}H_{18}N_{6}O_{5}S_{2}$	CEFAMANDOL	ANTIBIOTIC	
	$C_{18}H_{18}N_{6}O_{5}S_{2}$	CEFATRIZIN	ANTIBIOTIC	
462.22537	$C_{25}H_{34}O_{8}$	HYDROCORTISONE SUCCINATE	CORTICOID	
462.24177	$C_{26}H_{35}O_{6}F$	AMCINAFAL	CORTICOID	
462.26309	$C_{27}H_{34}N_{4}O_{3}$	TRICHOMONAZID (TM)	TRICHOMONACIDE	
462.78767	$C_{13}H_{8}NOSBR_{3}$	TIOSALAN	DESINFICIENT	
463.17771	$C_{22}H_{29}N_{3}O_{6}S$	PIVAMPICILLIN	ANTIBIOTIC	
463.23587	$C_{28}H_{33}NO_{5}$	MEPRAMIDIL	CORONARY DILATOR	
463.30060	$C_{20}H_{41}N_{5}O_{7}$	GENTAMYCIN C2	ANTIBIOTIC	
464.09548	$C_{21}H_{20}O_{12}$	ISOQUERCITRIN	CARDIOTONIC	
464.09865	$C_{21}H_{21}N_{2}O_{8}CL$	DEMECLOCYCLINE	ANTIBIOTIC	
464.14443	$C_{22}H_{20}N_{6}O_{6}$	DINIPROFYLLINE	VASODILATOR	
464.26751	$C_{28}H_{36}N_{2}O_{4}$	PSYCHOTRINE	NATURAL SUBSTANCE	
465.15697	$C_{21}H_{27}N_{3}O_{7}S$	BACAMPICILLIN	ANTIBIOTIC	
465.18213	$C_{23}H_{31}NO_{7}S$	SULPROSTONE	GYNECOL./OBSTRECT.	
465.98973	$C_{16}H_{20}O_{6}S_{3}P_{2}$	TEMEFOS	PESTICIDE	
466.10760	$C_{19}H_{23}N_{4}O_{6}SP$	BENFOTIAMINE	VITAMINE	
466.14318	$C_{16}H_{24}O_{3}HG$	ACETOMEROCTOL	DESINFICIENT	
466.18140	$C_{27}H_{30}O_{5}S$	THYMOL BLUE	CHEMICAL	
466.19223	$C_{25}H_{32}O_{5}CLF$	CLOBETASOL PROPIONATE	CORTICOID	
466.28316	$C_{28}H_{38}N_{2}O_{4}$	CEPHAELINE	EMETIC	
	$C_{28}H_{38}N_{2}O_{4}$	FEBUVERINE	ANTISPASMOTIC	
466.30965	$C_{31}H_{38}N_{4}$	BUTERIZIN	VASODILATOR	
467.13786	$C_{22}H_{27}N_{3}O_{4}CL_{2}$	CLOXACEPRIDE	------------	
467.25913	$C_{18}H_{37}N_{5}O_{9}$	TOBRAMYCIN	ANTIBIOTIC	
467.30356	$C_{29}H_{41}NO_{4}$	BUPRENORPHINE	ANALGESIC	MS
467.31479	$C_{28}H_{41}N_{3}O_{3}$	OXETACAINE	LOCAL ANESTHETIC	
	$C_{28}H_{41}N_{3}O_{3}$	TIROPRAMIDE	ANALGESIC	
467.87195	$C_{13}H_{10}O_{3}I_{2}$	FURIDARONE	CORONARY DILATOR	
467.97965	$C_{17}H_{18}N_{4}O_{2}BR_{2}$	DIBROMOPROPAMIDINE	ANTIBIOTIC	
468.04118	$C_{20}H_{26}N_{2}OBR_{2}$	ADAMEXIN	EXPECTORANT	
468.04258	$C_{19}H_{18}N_{4}O_{4}CL_{2}S$	PRAZOCILLIN	ANTIBIOTIC	
468.06927	$C_{23}H_{16}O_{11}$	CROMOGLICIC ACID	ANTIHIST./-ALLERG.	
468.11065	$C_{23}H_{26}O_{6}CL_{2}$	SIMFIBRATE	ANTICHOLESTEREMIC	
468.18697	$C_{21}H_{24}N_{8}O_{5}$	A-DENOPTERIN	CYTOSTATIC	
468.24315	$C_{18}H_{36}N_{4}O_{10}$	GENTAMYCIN A	ANTIBIOTIC	
468.25119	$C_{28}H_{36}O_{6}$	CLINOFIBRATE	ANTICHOLESTEREMIC	
468.32396	$C_{30}H_{44}O_{4}$	TERBUFICIN	ANTIDIABETIC	
468.37158	$C_{30}H_{48}N_{2}O_{2}$	HEXESTROL BISDIETHYLAMINOETHYL ETHER	CORONARY DILATOR	
	$C_{30}H_{48}N_{2}O_{2}$	SYMETIN	ANTIBIOTIC	
469.02660	$C_{19}H_{17}N_{3}O_{5}CL_{2}S$	DICLOXACILLIN	ANTIBIOTIC	
469.17098	$C_{21}H_{23}N_{7}O_{6}$	DENOPTERIN	CYTOSTATIC	
469.25767	$C_{26}H_{35}N_{3}O_{5}$	PARATENSIOL	ANTIHYPERTENSIVE	

MASS	FORMULA	NAME	CATEGORY	MS
469.30395	$C_{25}H_{43}NO_7$	METHYMYCIN	ANTIBIOTIC	
469.68853	$C_{10}CL_{10}$	DIENOCHLOR	PESTICIDE	
470.01125	$C_{13}H_{13}N_6O_4F_3S_3$	CEFAZAFLUR	ANTIBIOTIC	
470.26684	$C_{28}H_{38}O_6$	WITHAFERIN A	CYTOSTATIC	
470.33961	$C_{30}H_{46}O_4$	ENOXOLONE	TO THERAPY ULCERS	
471.04533	$C_{15}H_{17}N_7O_5S_3$	CEFMETAZOL	ANTIBIOTIC	
471.05186	$C_{16}H_{17}N_5O_8S_2$	CEFTIOXIDE	ANTIBIOTIC	
471.06057	$C_{12}H_{15}NO_6HG$	MERCUDERAMIDE	DIURETIC	
471.22302	$C_{22}H_{29}N_7O_5$	PUROMYCIN	ANTIBIOTIC	
471.31373	$C_{32}H_{41}NO_2$	TERFENADINE	ANTIHIST./-ALLERG.	
472.09971	$C_{18}H_{21}N_4O_9CL$	BOFUMUSTIN	CYTOSTATIC	
472.12215	$C_{27}H_{22}N_4CL_2$	CLOFAZIMINE	ANTIBIOTIC	
472.22095	$C_{25}H_{32}N_2O_7$	BOMETOLOL	BETA-ADR.BLOCKER	
472.39165	$C_{31}H_{52}O_3$	TOCOPHEROL ACETATE	VITAMINE	
473.16590	$C_{20}H_{23}N_7O_7$	LEUCOVORIN	ANTIDOTE	
473.20497	$C_{25}H_{31}NO_8$	ETHYLNARCEINE	ANTITUSSIVE	
473.27774	$C_{27}H_{39}NO_6$	PREDNISOLAMATE	CORTICOID	
473.36576	$C_{33}H_{47}NO$	MOCTAMIDE	ANTICHOLESTEREMIC	
473.91289	$C_{14}H_{16}O_5CL_6$	TOLOXYCHLORINOL	SEDATIVE	
474.04020	$C_{19}H_{18}N_2O_4BRF_3$	BROMOXAMIDE	ANTHELMINTIC	
474.08534	$C_{21}H_{25}O_5BRF_2$	HALOPREDONE	CORTICOID	
474.20022	$C_{24}H_{30}N_2O_8$	MITOPODAZIDE	CYTOSTATIC	
474.22537	$C_{26}H_{34}O_8$	METHYLPREDNISOLONE SUCCINATE	CORTICOID	
474.27815	$C_{28}H_{39}O_5F$	FLUOCORTOLONE HEXANOATE	CORTICOID	
474.29814	$C_{28}H_{42}O_6$	AMBRUTICIN	FUNGIST./ANTIMYC.	
475.19634	$C_{24}H_{33}N_3O_3S_2$	PIPOTIAZINE	NEUROLEPTIC	
475.24352	$C_{29}H_{31}N_3OF_2$	FLUSPIRILENE	NEUROLEPTIC	MS
475.29339	$C_{27}H_{41}NO_6$	HYDROCORTAMATE	CORTICOID	
475.30060	$C_{21}H_{41}N_5O_7$	NETILMICIN	ANTIBIOTIC	
476.09865	$C_{22}H_{21}N_2O_8CL$	MECLOCYCLINE	ANTIBIOTIC	
476.13657	$C_{21}H_{24}N_4O_7S$	ACEFURTIAMINE	VITAMINE	
476.15029	$C_{27}H_{25}N_2O_4CL$	FECLOBUZONE	ANTIRHEUMATIC	
476.22306	$C_{29}H_{33}N_2O_2CL$	LOPERAMIDE	ANTIDIARRHOEAL	
476.25742	$C_{27}H_{37}O_6F$	BETAMETHASONE VALERATE	CORTICOID	
477.24525	$C_{26}H_{29}N_7F_2$	ALMITRIN	STIMULANT	
477.31625	$C_{21}H_{43}N_5O_7$	GENTAMYCIN C1	ANTIBIOTIC	
478.09808	$C_{20}H_{22}N_4O_6S_2$	VANYLDISULFAMIDE	ANTIBIOTIC	
478.11430	$C_{22}H_{23}N_2O_8CL$	CHLORTETRACYCLINE	ANTIBIOTIC	
478.19223	$C_{26}H_{32}O_5CLF$	CLOBETASONE BUTYRATE	CORTICOID	
478.20030	$C_{25}H_{31}O_8F$	TRIAMCINOLONE DIACETATE	CORTICOID	
478.23554	$C_{29}H_{34}O_6$	TRIBENOSIDE	VASODILATOR	
478.27307	$C_{27}H_{39}O_6F$	FLUDROCORTISONE BUTYLACETATE	CORTICOID	
478.28316	$C_{29}H_{38}N_2O_4$	DEHYDROEMETINE	ANTIBIOTIC	
479.20564	$C_{26}H_{29}N_3O_6$	NICARDIPINE	VASODILATOR	
479.20901	$C_{23}H_{33}N_3O_6S$	TAMETICILLIN	ANTIBIOTIC	
480.04967	$C_{14}H_{14}O_6HG$	MERCUMATILIN	DIURETIC	
480.19955	$C_{24}H_{32}O_{10}$	ACEVALTRATE	SEDATIVE	
480.26559	$C_{28}H_{37}N_4OCL$	CLOCAPRAMINE	NEUROLEPTIC	
480.27768	$C_{32}H_{36}N_2O_2$	BUTOXYLATE	ANTIDIARRHOEAL	
480.29881	$C_{29}H_{40}N_2O_4$	EMETINE	EXPECTORANT	
481.13076	$C_{24}H_{23}N_3O_6S$	TALAMPICILLIN	ANTIBIOTIC	
482.12130	$C_{25}H_{22}O_{10}$	SILYMARINE	PROTEC.LIVER THER.	

MASS	FORMULA	NAME	CATEGORY	MS
482.25880	$C_{19}H_{38}N_4O_{10}$	BETAMICIN	ANTIBIOTIC	
	$C_{19}H_{38}N_4O_{10}$	GENTAMYCINE B + X	ANTIBIOTIC	
483.11575	$C_{24}H_{26}N_3O_3BR$	NICERGOLINE	SYMPATHOLYTIC	
483.25219	$C_{30}H_{33}N_3O_3$	ROPITOIN	ANTIARRHYTHMIC	
483.25404	$C_{18}H_{37}N_5O_{10}$	BEKANAMYCIN	ANTIBIOTIC	
483.96854	$C_9H_{15}N_2O_{15}P_3$	URIDINE TRIPHOSPHATE	ENDOG.BIOMOLECULE	
484.23806	$C_{18}H_{36}N_4O_{11}$	KANAMYCINE A + C	ANTIBIOTIC	
484.28249	$C_{29}H_{40}O_6$	CORTISONE CYCLOPENTANEPROPIONATE	CORTICOID	
484.29372	$C_{28}H_{40}N_2O_5$	GALLOPAMIL	CORONARY DILATOR	
484.35526	$C_{31}H_{48}O_4$	TESTOSTERONE OXODODECANOATE	ANDROGEN	
485.07622	$C_{13}H_{17}NO_6HG$	MERSALYL	DIURETIC	
485.20161	$C_{25}H_{32}N_5OCLS$	IMICLOPAZINE	NEUROLEPTIC	
485.27774	$C_{28}H_{39}NO_6$	PREDNYLIDENE DIETHYLAMINOACETATE	CORTICOID	
485.68345	$C_{10}OCL_{10}$	CHLORDECONE	INSECTICIDE	
485.91890	$C_{14}H_{16}O_3I_2$	MONOPHEN (TM)	DIAGNOSTIC AID	
486.10325	$C_{26}H_{25}N_2OCL_3$	HETOLIN (TM)	ANTHELMINTIC	
486.13761	$C_{24}H_{29}O_5CL_2F$	FLUCLOROLONE ACETONIDE	CORTICOID	
486.30937	$C_{28}H_{42}N_2O_5$	FENOXEDIL	VASODILATOR	
488.10734	$C_{14}H_{26}N_4O_{11}P_2$	CITICOLINE	VASODILATOR	
488.12851	$C_{23}H_{25}N_4O_4CLS$	GLIDANIL	ANTIDIABETIC	
488.13327	$C_{24}H_{28}O_4CL_2F_2$	TRALONIDE	CORTICOID	
488.20463	$C_{26}H_{32}O_9$	ESTRIOL BISHEMISUCCINIC ACID	ESTROGEN	
489.09792	$C_{27}H_{20}NO_6CL$	TALMETACINE	ANALGESIC	
489.14391	$C_{14}H_{25}NO_5HG$	MERCUROPHYLLINE	DIURETIC	
490.16748	$C_{26}H_{26}N_4O_4S$	BENTIAMINE	VITAMINE	
490.27307	$C_{28}H_{39}O_6F$	DEXAMETHASONE DIMETHYLBUTYRATE	CORTICOID	
491.03448	$C_{21}H_{17}NO_9S_2$	SULISATIN	LAXATIVE	
491.05540	$C_{21}H_{18}N_3O_7CLS$	CEFOXAZOL	ANTIBIOTIC	
491.22024	$C_{23}H_{33}N_5O_5S$	GLIAMILIDE	ANTIDIABETIC	
491.27482	$C_{30}H_{35}N_3OF_2$	LIDOFLAZINE	CORONARY DILATOR	
492.15958	$C_{25}H_{26}O_8F_2$	ACEFLURANOL	------------	
492.25253	$C_{31}H_{32}N_4O_2$	BEZITRAMIDE	NARCOTIC	
492.27232	$C_{27}H_{40}O_8$	CORTOLONE TRIACETATE	CORTICOID	
493.05484	$C_{19}H_{19}N_5O_5S_3$	CEFAPAROL	ANTIBIOTIC	
493.14382	$C_{23}H_{28}N_3O_5CLS$	GLIBENCLAMIDE	ANTIBIOTIC	
493.32258	$C_{28}H_{47}NO_4S$	TIAMULINE	ANTIBIOTIC	
493.43558	$C_{28}H_{55}N_5O_2$	IMPACARZINE	VIRUCIDE	
493.88760	$C_{15}H_{12}O_3I_2$	PHENIODOL	DIAGNOSTIC AID	
493.98925	$C_{10}H_{22}O_{14}S_4$	MANNOSULFANE	CYTOSTATIC	
494.15116	$C_{26}H_{26}N_2O_6S$	CARINDACILLIN	ANTIBIOTIC	
494.21161	$C_{26}H_{32}O_7F_2$	FLUOCINONIDE	CORTICOID	
494.22353	$C_{27}H_{36}O_5CLF$	CLOCORTOLONE PIVALATE	CORTICOID	
494.24800	$C_{27}H_{36}O_6F_2$	FLUMETHASONE PIVALATE	CORTICOID	
494.99055	$C_{18}H_{19}N_5O_2BR_2$	BRINDOXIME	ANTIMALARIAL	
495.17942	$C_{29}H_{25}N_3O_5$	NICOMORPHINE	ANALGESIC	
495.18890	$C_{28}H_{28}N_3OCLF_2$	CLOPIMOZIDE	NEUROLEPTIC	
496.22612	$C_{29}H_{33}O_6F$	AMCINAFIDE	CORTICOID	
	$C_{29}H_{33}O_6F$	BETAMETHASONE BENZOATE	CORTICOID	
496.22726	$C_{26}H_{34}O_7F_2$	FLUMOXONIDE	CORTICOID	
496.23085	$C_{25}H_{36}O_{10}$	GLAUCARUBIN	ANTIBIOTIC	
496.27445	$C_{20}H_{40}N_4O_{10}$	GENTAMYCIN B1	ANTIBIOTIC	
496.28249	$C_{30}H_{40}O_6$	ABSINTHIN	NATURAL SUBSTANCE	

MASS	FORMULA	NAME	CATEGORY	MS
496.28249	$C_{30}H_{40}O_6$	ANABSINTHIN	NATURAL SUBSTANCE	
496.35526	$C_{32}H_{48}O_4$	ESTRADIOL DIENANTHATE	ESTROGEN	
497.16858	$C_{26}H_{27}NO_9$	IDARUBICINE	CYTOSTATIC	
497.21084	$C_{20}H_{35}NO_{13}$	VALIDAMYCIN	FUNGIST./ANTIMYC.	
497.22137	$C_{28}H_{32}NO_6F$	DEXAMETHASONE ISONICOTINATE	CORTICOID	
498.08270	$C_{12}H_{16}N_4O_5HG$	REDIRALT (TM)	DIURETIC	
498.11938	$C_{25}H_{23}N_2O_7CL$	BINIFIBRATE	ANTICHOLESTEREMIC	
498.15760	$C_{25}H_{32}O_6CL_2$	CLOBENOSIDE	ANTIPHLOGISTIC	
498.26176	$C_{29}H_{38}O_7$	ACRIHELLIN	------------	
498.27299	$C_{28}H_{38}N_2O_6$	SIMETRIDE	ANALGESIC	
500.08032	$C_{20}H_{28}N_2O_4CL_4$	TECLOZAN	ANTIBIOTIC	
500.09532	$C_{19}H_{25}N_4O_6S_2P$	UREDOFOS	ANTHELMINTIC	
500.18936	$C_{25}H_{29}N_4O_4FS$	GLIFLUMIDE	ANTIDIABETIC	
500.21587	$C_{26}H_{32}N_2O_8$	TRITOQUALINE	ANTIHIST./-ALLERG.	
501.12559	$C_{22}H_{29}N_3O_4CL_2S$	CHLOROBUTIN PENICILLIN	ANTIBIOTIC	
502.23668	$C_{28}H_{35}O_7F$	AMCINONIDE	CORTICOID	
502.97317	$C_{22}H_{19}NO_3BR_2$	DECAMETHRINE	INSECTICIDE	
504.08452	$C_{30}H_{16}O_8$	HYPERICIN	SEDATIVE	
504.10372	$C_{24}H_{28}O_4CL_3F$	TRICLONIDE	CORTICOID	
504.16904	$C_{18}H_{32}O_{16}$	MALTOTRIOSE	SUGAR	
	$C_{18}H_{32}O_{16}$	MELEZITOSE	SUGAR	
	$C_{18}H_{32}O_{16}$	RAFFINOSE	SUGAR	
504.20320	$C_{22}H_{30}N_{10}CL_2$	CHLORHEXIDINE	DESINFICIENT	
504.25233	$C_{28}H_{37}O_7F$	BETAMETHAZONE ACIBUTATE	CORTICOID	
504.31725	$C_{24}H_{40}N_8O_4$	DIPYRIDAMOL	CORONARY DILATOR	
505.22129	$C_{28}H_{31}N_3O_6$	HEPRONICATE	VASODILATOR	
505.34034	$C_{29}H_{47}NO_6$	COUMINGINE	CARDIOTONIC	
506.14377	$C_{25}H_{22}N_4O_8$	RUFOCROMOMYCIN	ANTIBIOTIC	
	$C_{25}H_{22}N_4O_8$	STREPTONIGRIN	CYTOSTATIC	
506.24571	$C_{34}H_{34}O_4$	PROMETHESTROL DIBENZOATE	ESTROGEN	
506.29179	$C_{28}H_{41}NO_6F$	DEXAMETHASONE DIETHYLAMINOACETATE	CORTICOID	
506.33961	$C_{33}H_{46}O_4$	NANDROLONE HEXYLOXYPHENYLPROPIONATE	ANABOLIC	
506.99575	$C_{10}H_{16}N_5O_{13}P_3$	ADENOSINE TRIPHOSPHATE	CORONARY DILATOR	
507.21673	$C_{26}H_{32}N_3O_2F_3S$	OXAFLUMAZINE	NEUROLEPTIC	
508.12486	$C_{23}H_{25}N_2O_9CL$	CLOMOCYCLINE	ANTIBIOTIC	
508.19917	$C_{23}H_{32}N_4O_7S$	LIBECILLIDE	ANTIBIOTIC	
508.22726	$C_{27}H_{34}O_7F_2$	DIFLUPREDNATE	CORTICOID	
	$C_{27}H_{34}O_7F_2$	PROCINONIDE	CORTICOID	
508.46894	$C_{26}H_{56}N_{10}$	ALEXIDINE	ANTIBIOTIC	
509.29887	$C_{27}H_{43}NO_8$	GERMINE	ANTIHYPERTENSIVE	
510.16854	$C_{24}H_{26}N_6O_5S$	PIRBENCILLIN	ANTIBIOTIC	
511.05148	$C_{16}H_{17}N_9O_5S_3$	CEFMENOXIME	ANTIBIOTIC	
511.18959	$C_{33}H_{25}N_3O_3$	NORBORMIDE	RODENTICIDE	
513.16350	$C_{26}H_{27}NO_{10}$	CARUBICINE	CYTOSTATIC	
515.29168	$C_{26}H_{45}NO_7S$	CHOLOTAURIC ACID	CHOLERETIC	
515.97949	$C_{21}H_{17}N_2O_5S_2AS$	THIOCARBAMIZINE	ANTIBIOTIC	
516.12678	$C_{25}H_{24}O_{12}$	CYNARINE	CHOLERETIC	
516.30957	$C_{31}H_{48}O_2S_2$	PROBUCOL	ANTICHOLESTEREMIC	
516.34509	$C_{31}H_{48}O_6$	FUSIDIC ACID	ANTIBIOTIC	
517.16312	$C_{23}H_{27}N_5O_7S$	PIPERACILLIN	ANTIBIOTIC	
517.88760	$C_{17}H_{12}O_3I_2$	BENZIODARONE	CORONARY DILATOR	
518.19407	$C_{30}H_{30}O_8$	GOSSYPOL	ANTIOXIDANT	

MASS	FORMULA	NAME	CATEGORY	MS
519.08018	$C_{22}H_{22}N_5O_4CLS_2$	SULPROCLONE	------------	
519.09948	$C_{20}H_{21}N_7O_6S_2$	CEFORANIDE	ANTIBIOTIC	
519.13443	$C_{23}H_{32}NO_6CL_2P$	ESTRAMUSTINE PHOSPHATE	CYTOSTATIC	
520.10125	$C_{20}H_{20}N_6O_9S$	LATAMOXEF	ANTIBIOTIC	
520.22278	$C_{28}H_{37}O_7CL$	BECLOMETHASONE DIPROPIONATE	CORTICOID	
520.35526	$C_{34}H_{48}O_4$	ESTRADIOL DICYPROPIONATE	ESTROGEN	
521.15869	$C_{30}H_{23}N_3O_6$	NICEVERINE	CORONARY DILATOR	
521.19507	$C_{31}H_{27}N_3O_5$	NALORPHINE DINICOTINATE	ANTIDOTE	
521.23146	$C_{32}H_{31}N_3O_4$	DIFENOXIMIDE	ANTIDIARRHOEAL	
522.09337	$C_{20}H_{20}N_8O_5CL_2$	DICHLOROMETHOTREXATE	CYTOSTATIC	
523.11244	$C_{20}H_{27}N_3O_9CL_2$	CHLORAMPHENICOL PANTOTHENATE	ANTIBIOTIC	
523.17013	$C_{28}H_{27}NOCLF_5$	PENFLURIDOL	NEUROLEPTIC	MS
524.05411	$C_{11}H_{18}N_2O_7SHG$	DIURGIN	DIURETIC	
524.45933	$C_{36}H_{60}O_2$	VITAMIN A PALMITATE	VITAMINE	
525.10352	$C_{18}H_{23}N_9O_4S_3$	CEFOTIAM	ANTIBIOTIC	
525.19903	$C_{23}H_{32}N_5O_7CL$	XANTIFIBRATE	ANTICHOLESTEREMIC	
525.24750	$C_{28}H_{35}N_3O_7$	VIRGINIAMYCIN	ANTIBIOTIC	
526.07797	$C_{30}H_{23}O_4BR$	BROMADIOLONE	RODENTICIDE	
527.04908	$C_{20}H_{21}N_3O_8S_3$	SOLUPYRIDINE	ANTIBIOTIC	
527.17915	$C_{27}H_{29}NO_{10}$	DAUNORUBICINE	CYTOSTATIC	
	$C_{27}H_{29}NO_{10}$	PIROZADIL	VASODILATOR	
527.20901	$C_{27}H_{33}N_3O_6S$	GLIQUIDONE	ANTIDIABETIC	
527.22677	$C_{27}H_{33}N_3O_8$	ROLITETRACYCLINE	ANTIBIOTIC	
527.23264	$C_{20}H_{37}N_3O_{13}$	DESTOMYCIN A	ANTIBIOTIC	
	$C_{20}H_{37}N_3O_{13}$	HYGROMYCIN B	ANTHELMINTIC	
528.10312	$C_{17}H_{30}N_4O_7S_2P_2$	IMCARBAFOS	ANTHELMINTIC	
528.21416	$C_{24}H_{36}N_2O_9S$	CELESTICETIN	ANTIBIOTIC	
530.14876	$C_{26}H_{28}N_4O_4CL_2$	KETOCONAZOLE	FUNGIST./ANTIMYC.	
530.27807	$C_{32}H_{38}N_2O_5$	CORTIVAZOL	ANTIPHLOGISTIC	
530.28797	$C_{30}H_{42}O_8$	PROSCILLARIDIN	CARDIOTONIC	
530.29385	$C_{23}H_{46}O_{13}$	NEOMYCIN C	ANTIBIOTIC	
531.61791	C_2I_4	TETRAIODOETHYLENE	DESINFICIENT	
532.26724	$C_{29}H_{40}O_9$	CALOTROPIN	CARDIOTONIC	
532.28363	$C_{30}H_{41}O_7F$	TRIAMCINOLONE HEXACETONIDE	CORTICOID	
532.52193	$C_{36}H_{68}O_2$	OLEYL OLEATE	PHARMACEUTICAL AID	
533.20997	$C_{29}H_{37}NO_4CL_2$	TEFENPERATE	------------	
534.04918	$C_{18}H_{32}O_2I_2$	DIIODORICINOLIC ACID	------------	
535.25700	$C_{31}H_{37}NO_7$	NICOCORTONIDE	------------	
535.40254	$C_{35}H_{53}NO_3$	TOCOPHEROL NICOTINATE	VITAMINE	
536.29854	$C_{29}H_{44}O_9$	ACTODIGINE	CARDIOTONIC	
536.43820	$C_{40}H_{56}$	CAROTENE	VITAMINE	
537.90852	$C_{21}H_{16}O_5BR_2S$	BROMCRESOL PURPLE	CHEMICAL	
538.28316	$C_{34}H_{38}N_2O_4$	NAFIVERINE	PARASYMPATH.-LYTIC	
538.44312	$C_{26}H_{54}N_{10}O_2$	IPEXIDINE	------------	
539.11446	$C_{21}H_{25}N_5O_8S_2$	MEZLOCILLIN	ANTIBIOTIC	
539.28026	$C_{21}H_{41}N_5O_{11}$	APRAMYCIN	ANTIBIOTIC	
540.84388	$C_{15}H_{10}NO_3CLI_2$	CLIOXANIDE	ANTHELMINTIC	
541.24829	$C_{21}H_{39}N_3O_{13}$	DESTOMYCIN A	ANTHELMINTIC	
542.03483	$C_{18}H_{18}N_6O_8S_3$	CEFONICIDE	ANTIBIOTIC	
542.31446	$C_{34}H_{42}N_2O_4$	BELLADONNINE	ANTIPARKINSONIAN	
543.17406	$C_{27}H_{29}NO_{11}$	DOXORUBICIN	CYTOSTATIC	
544.00286	$C_{18}H_{16}N_4O_{10}S_3$	AZOSULFAMIDE	ANTIBIOTIC	

MASS	FORMULA	NAME	CATEGORY	MS
544.17671	$C_{28}H_{32}O_9S$	PREDNISOLONE SULFOBENZOATE	CORTICOID	
544.18479	$C_{23}H_{36}N_4O_5S_3$	OCTOTIAMINE	VITAMINE	
544.21044	$C_{30}H_{32}N_2O_2CLF_3$	FLUPERAMIDE	ANTIDIARRHOEAL	
544.27259	$C_{36}H_{36}N_2O_3$	FETOXILATE	ANTIDIARRHOEAL	
544.30362	$C_{31}H_{44}O_8$	MEPROSCILLARINE	CARDIOTONIC	
545.13874	$C_{26}H_{28}N_3O_6CLS$	FIBRACILLIN	ANTIBIOTIC	
546.96124	$C_{18}H_{15}N_5O_5CL_2S_3$	CEFAZEDONE	ANTIBIOTIC	
548.27338	$C_{28}H_{40}N_2O_9$	ANTIMYCIN A1	PESTICIDE	
548.29854	$C_{30}H_{44}O_9$	CYMARIN	CARDIOTONIC	
	$C_{30}H_{44}O_9$	PERUVOSIDE	CARDIOTONIC	
549.20459	$C_{28}H_{31}N_5O_5S$	ROTAMICILLIN	ANTIBIOTIC	
549.98658	$C_{20}H_{24}O_2I_2$	DIIODODITHYMOL	DESINFICIENT	
550.27780	$C_{29}H_{42}O_{10}$	ADONITOXIN	NATURAL SUBSTANCE	
	$C_{29}H_{42}O_{10}$	CONVALLOTOXIN	CARDIOTONIC	
550.98183	$C_{19}H_{23}NO_2I_2$	BUFENIODE	ANTIHYPERTENSIVE	
553.87800	$C_{14}H_{16}N_2O_8S_2AS_2$	SULFARSPHENAMINE	ANTIBIOTIC	
554.04606	$C_{18}H_{18}N_8O_7S_3$	CEFTRIAXONE	ANTIBIOTIC	
554.24441	$C_{22}H_{42}N_4O_8S_2$	PANTETHINE	------------	
554.30437	$C_{33}H_{43}O_6F$	BETAMETHASONE ADAMANTOATE	CORTICOID	
555.19606	$C_{26}H_{37}NO_8S_2$	TIAPAMIL	ANTIARRHYTHMIC	
555.27518	$C_{21}H_{41}N_5O_{12}$	BUTIROSIN	ANTIBIOTIC	
556.07563	$C_{21}H_{24}N_4O_8S_3$	ARISTOPLOMB (TM)	ANTIBIOTIC	
556.15942	$C_{29}H_{24}N_4O_8$	NICERITROL	VASODILATOR	
556.74820	$C_9H_6NO_3I_3$	ACETRIZOIC ACID	DIAGNOSTIC AID	
557.29083	$C_{21}H_{43}N_5O_{12}$	PROPIKACIN	ANTIBIOTIC	
557.76860	$C_{10}H_9O_3I_3$	PHENOBUTIODIL	DIAGNOSTIC AID	
558.26897	$C_{28}H_{38}N_4O_8$	PACTAMYCIN	CYTOSTATIC	
560.24199	$C_{27}H_{42}N_2O_6CL_2$	CHLORAMPHENICOL PALMITATE	ANTIBIOTIC	
560.35336	$C_{25}H_{48}N_6O_8$	DEFEROXAMINE	ANTIDOTE	
561.29512	$C_{31}H_{39}N_5O_5$	ERGOCORNINE	SYMPATHOLYTIC	
562.21445	$C_{24}H_{34}N_8O_4S_2$	ANEURINE DISULFIDE	VITAMINE	
563.12654	$C_{16}H_{27}NO_6SHG$	MERCAPTOMERINE	DIURETIC	
563.18252	$C_{27}H_{33}NO_{10}S$	THIOCOLCHICOSIDE	MUSCLE RELAXANT	
563.31077	$C_{31}H_{41}N_5O_5$	DIHYDROERGOCORNINE	VASODILATOR	
563.34716	$C_{32}H_{45}N_5O_4$	DESOCRIPTINE	------------	
564.09613	$C_{20}H_{38}O_2I_2$	IODETRYL	DIAGNOSTIC AID	
564.14791	$C_{26}H_{28}O_{14}$	APIIN	NATURAL SUBSTANCE	
564.39673	$C_{40}H_{52}O_2$	CANTHAXANTHINE	NATURAL SUBSTANCE	
566.04158	$C_{24}H_{28}N_2O_4BR_2$	BROVANEXIN	EXPECTORANT	
568.13695	$C_{32}H_{24}O_{10}$	THERMORUBIN A	ANTIBIOTIC	
568.22393	$C_{29}H_{38}O_8CLF$	FORMOCORTAL	CORTICOID	
568.30362	$C_{33}H_{44}O_8$	HELVOLIC ACID	ANTIBIOTIC	
568.78459	$C_{11}H_{10}NO_2I_3$	CINAMIODIL	DIAGNOSTIC AID	
569.11982	$C_{15}H_{21}N_5O_6HG$	ORADON	DIURETIC	
570.15329	$C_{25}H_{26}N_6O_8S$	FUZLOCILLIN	ANTIBIOTIC	
570.18228	$C_{24}H_{26}N_8O_9$	DIOPTERIN	CYTOSTATIC	
570.23008	$C_{32}H_{34}N_4O_4S$	DIATHYMOSULFONE	ANTIBIOTIC	
570.35566	$C_{34}H_{50}O_7$	CARBENOXOLONE	TO THERAPY ULCERS	
570.62881	C_4HI_4N	IODOL	DESINFICIENT	
570.80024	$C_{11}H_{12}NO_2I_3$	IOPANOIC ACID	DIAGNOSTIC AID	
571.30648	$C_{22}H_{45}N_5O_{12}$	BUTIKACIN	ANTIBIOTIC	
571.78425	$C_{11}H_{11}O_3I_3$	IOPHENOXIC ACID	DIAGNOSTIC AID	

MASS	FORMULA	NAME	CATEGORY	MS
572.10825	$C_{16}H_{22}N_2O_8HG$	MELUGINAN (TM) INGREDIENT	DIURETIC	
572.45933	$C_{40}H_{60}O_2$	KITOL	NATURAL SUBSTANCE	
574.22750	$C_{27}H_{34}N_4O_{10}$	RAZINODIL	CORONARY DILATOR	
575.00215	$C_{17}H_{17}N_7O_8S_4$	CEFOTETAN	ANTIBIOTIC	
575.31077	$C_{32}H_{41}N_5O_5$	ERGOCRYPTINE	SYMPATHOLYTIC	
576.12583	$C_{28}H_{28}N_6S_4$	BISBENDAZOL	ANTHELMINTIC	
576.32984	$C_{32}H_{48}O_9$	CERBERIN	CARDIOTONIC	
577.32642	$C_{32}H_{43}N_5O_5$	DIHYDROERGOCRYPTINE	VASODILATOR	
577.67646	$C_{12}H_7O_5BR_4P$	BROMOFENOFOS	INSECTICIDE	
578.16356	$C_{27}H_{30}O_{14}$	GLUCOFRANGULIN	LAXATIVE	
	$C_{27}H_{30}O_{14}$	LESPEDIN	DIURETIC	
578.26282	$C_{32}H_{38}N_2O_8$	DESERPIDINE	ANTIHYPERTENSIVE	
	$C_{32}H_{38}N_2O_8$	MEFESERPINE	ANTIHYPERTENSIVE	
578.29518	$C_{28}H_{42}N_4O_9$	DIFEBARBAMATE	SEDATIVE	
580.42803	$C_{41}H_{56}O_2$	VITAMIN K2(30)	VITAMINE	
581.26382	$C_{33}H_{35}N_5O_5$	ERGOTAMINE	SYMPATHOLYTIC	
581.26567	$C_{21}H_{39}N_7O_{12}$	STREPTOMYCIN	ANTIBIOTIC	
581.35638	$C_{31}H_{51}NO_9$	ROSARAMICIN	ANTIBIOTIC	
582.24784	$C_{33}H_{34}N_4O_6$	BILIVERDINE	ENDOG.BIOMOLECULE	
583.27947	$C_{33}H_{37}N_5O_5$	DIHYDROERGOTAMINE	SYMPATHOLYTIC	
583.28132	$C_{21}H_{41}N_7O_{12}$	DIHYDROSTREPTOMYCIN	ANTIBIOTIC	
583.86178	$C_{20}H_{10}O_5I_2$	DIIODOFLUORESCEIN	CHEMICAL	
584.02764	$C_{20}H_{20}N_6O_7S_4$	CEFODIZIM	ANTIBIOTIC	
584.26349	$C_{33}H_{36}N_4O_6$	BILIRUBIN	ENDOG.BIOMOLECULE	
584.28328	$C_{29}H_{44}O_{12}$	G-STROPHANTIN	CARDIOTONIC	
584.30977	$C_{32}H_{44}N_2O_8$	LAPPACONITINE	NATURAL SUBSTANCE	
584.42295	$C_{40}H_{56}O_3$	CAPSANTHIN	NATURAL SUBSTANCE	
	$C_{40}H_{56}O_3$	FLAVOXANTHIN	NATURAL SUBSTANCE	
585.23225	$C_{29}H_{35}N_3O_{10}$	PECOCYCLINE	ANTIBIOTIC	
585.24935	$C_{21}H_{39}N_5O_{14}$	BLUENSOMYCIN	ANTIBIOTIC	
585.28574	$C_{22}H_{43}N_5O_{13}$	AMIKACIN	ANTIBIOTIC	
585.38181	$C_{38}H_{51}NO_4$	MYROPHINE	ANALGESIC	
586.20210	$C_{29}H_{48}O_2BR_2$	ACEBROCHOL	SEDATIVE	
586.26388	$C_{29}H_{38}N_4O_9$	PIPACYCLINE	ANTIBIOTIC	
588.18430	$C_{29}H_{32}O_{13}$	ETOPOSIDE	CYTOSTATIC	
588.19599	$C_{30}H_{26}N_4O_2F_6$	ANTRAFENINE	ANALGESIC	
590.38187	$C_{34}H_{54}O_8$	LASALOCIDE	COCCIDIOSTATIC	
591.34073	$C_{32}H_{49}NO_9$	CEVADINE	INSECTICIDE	
592.29960	$C_{30}H_{44}N_2O_{10}$	HEXOBENDIN	CARDIOTONIC	
594.27299	$C_{36}H_{38}N_2O_6$	CURINE	NATURAL SUBSTANCE	
595.27947	$C_{34}H_{37}N_5O_5$	METERGOTAMINE	SYMPATHOLYTIC	
596.38656	$C_{40}H_{52}O_4$	LACTIMEX (TM)	ANDROGEN	
597.20642	$C_{31}H_{36}N_3O_5CLS$	METOFENAZATE	NEUROLEPTIC	
597.26863	$C_{31}H_{39}N_3O_9$	MIKAMYCIN A	ANTIBIOTIC	
597.81113	$C_{12}H_{13}N_2O_2I_3$	IOPODIC ACID	DIAGNOSTIC AID	
598.27914	$C_{34}H_{38}N_4O_6$	HEMATOPORPHYRIN	SYMPATHOMIMETIC	
598.29374	$C_{30}H_{42}N_6O_5S$	GLICARAMIDE	ANTIDIABETIC	
598.37889	$C_{37}H_{55}O_4CL$	TOCOFENOXATE	VITAMINE	
600.14925	$C_{30}H_{24}N_4O_{10}$	NICOFURANOSE	VASODILATOR	
600.30468	$C_{32}H_{44}N_2O_9$	STREPTOLYDIGIN	ANTIBIOTIC	
600.41786	$C_{40}H_{56}O_4$	VIOLAXANTHIN	NATURAL SUBSTANCE	
602.25880	$C_{29}H_{38}N_4O_{10}$	LYMECYCLINE	ANTIBIOTIC	

MASS	FORMULA	NAME	CATEGORY	MS
602.43351	$C_{40}H_{58}O_4$	ORYZANOL	NATURAL SUBSTANCE	
603.36186	$C_{30}H_{53}NO_{11}$	BENZONATATE	ANTITUSSIVE	
604.09942	$C_{17}H_{18}N_6O_6HG$	ESIDRON (TM)	DIURETIC	
604.29960	$C_{31}H_{44}N_2O_{10}$	DILAZEP	CORONARY DILATOR	
604.49678	$C_{40}H_{64}N_2O_2$	BOLAZIN	ANABOLIC	
606.29412	$C_{34}H_{42}N_2O_8$	ETHYSERPINE	ANTIHYPERTENSIVE	
608.17413	$C_{28}H_{32}O_{15}$	DIOSMIN	NATURAL SUBSTANCE	
608.27338	$C_{33}H_{40}N_2O_9$	METHOSERPINE	ANTIHYPERTENSIVE	
	$C_{33}H_{40}N_2O_9$	RESERPINE	ANTIHYPERTENSIVE	**MS**
608.27791	$C_{23}H_{36}N_{12}O_8$	VIOMYCIN	ANTIBIOTIC	
609.29512	$C_{35}H_{39}N_5O_5$	ERGOCRISTINE	SYMPATHOLYTIC	
610.15339	$C_{27}H_{30}O_{16}$	RUTOSIDE	VITAMINE	
610.18978	$C_{28}H_{34}O_{15}$	HESPERIDIN	VITAMINE	
611.31077	$C_{35}H_{41}N_5O_5$	DIHYDROERGOCRISTINE	SYMPATHOLYTIC	
612.12094	$C_{25}H_{24}N_8O_7S_2$	CEFPIRAMIDE	ANTIBIOTIC	
612.12563	$C_{16}H_{22}N_6O_7HG$	MERALLURIDE	DIURETIC	
612.22385	$C_{32}H_{37}N_2O_8CL$	CHLOROSERPIDINE	NEUROLEPTIC	
612.23191	$C_{31}H_{36}N_2O_{11}$	NOVOBIOCIN	ANTIBIOTIC	
612.29810	$C_{31}H_{50}O_8P_2$	PHYTONADIOLDIPHOSPHORIC ACID	HEMOSTATIC	
612.81080	$C_{13}H_{14}NO_3I_3$	IOPROCEMIC ACID	DIAGNOSTIC AID	
613.76966	$C_{11}H_9N_2O_4I_3$	AMIDOTRIAZOIC ACID	DIAGNOSTIC AID	
	$C_{11}H_9N_2O_4I_3$	IOTALAMINIC ACID	DIAGNOSTIC AID	
613.80605	$C_{12}H_{13}N_2O_3I_3$	IOCETAMINIC ACID	DIAGNOSTIC AID	
	$C_{12}H_{13}N_2O_3I_3$	IOMEGLAMINIC ACID	DIAGNOSTIC AID	
614.31229	$C_{23}H_{46}N_6O_{13}$	NEOMYCIN B	ANTIBIOTIC	
615.29631	$C_{23}H_{45}N_5O_{14}$	PAROMOMYCIN	ANTIBIOTIC	
616.41865	$C_{33}H_{60}O_{10}$	NONOXYNOL 9	SOLUBILIZER ETC.	
618.30133	$C_{29}H_{42}N_6O_9$	AMICETIN	ANTIBIOTIC	
620.28328	$C_{32}H_{44}O_{12}$	SCILLIROSIDE	RODENTICIDE	
621.76352	$C_{14}H_9O_4I_3$	TIRATRICOL	ANOREXIC	
622.00242	$C_{27}H_{28}O_5BR_2S$	BROMTHYMOL BLUE	CHEMICAL	
622.00771	$C_{23}H_{28}O_4I_2$	HINDERIN	THYREOSTATIC	
622.30429	$C_{38}H_{42}N_2O_6$	TETRANDRINE	ANALGESIC	
624.82055	$C_{19}H_{11}NO_3CL_2I_2$	RAFOXANIDE	ANTHELMINTIC	
626.28126	$C_{29}H_{38}N_8O_8$	GUAMECYCLINE	ANTIBIOTIC	
626.41019	$C_{39}H_{59}O_4CL$	TOCOFIBRATE	ANTICHOLESTEREMIC	
627.15297	$C_{22}H_{29}N_9O_9S_2$	CEFBUPERAZONE	ANTIBIOTIC	
627.78531	$C_{12}H_{11}N_2O_4I_3$	IODAMIDE	DIAGNOSTIC AID	
	$C_{12}H_{11}N_2O_4I_3$	METRIZOIC ACID	DIAGNOSTIC AID	
627.82170	$C_{13}H_{15}N_2O_3I_3$	IOSUMETIC ACID	DIAGNOSTIC AID	
627.98418	$C_{22}H_{26}N_2O_8SAS_2$	SPIROTRYPAN (TM)	ANTIBIOTIC	
628.33598	$C_{34}H_{48}N_2O_9$	AJACINE	PESTICIDE	
629.02326	$C_{26}H_{19}N_3O_{10}S_3$	ANAZOLENE	DIAGNOSTIC AID	
629.73125	$C_{20}H_{10}O_4BR_4$	TETRABROMOPHENOLPHTHALEIN	DIAGNOSTIC AID	
629.76209	$C_{17}H_{12}O_4CL_{10}$	KELEVANE	INSECTICIDE	
629.76458	$C_{11}H_9N_2O_5I_3$	IOXOTRIZOIC ACID	DIAGNOSTIC AID	
630.25371	$C_{30}H_{38}N_4O_{11}$	APICYCLINE	ANTIBIOTIC	
632.52808	$C_{42}H_{68}N_2O_2$	MEBOLAZINE	ANABOLIC	
634.13226	$C_{32}H_{26}O_{14}$	ACTINORHODINE	ANTIBIOTIC	
634.28903	$C_{35}H_{42}N_2O_9$	RESCINNAMINE	ANTIHYPERTENSIVE	
635.23264	$C_{29}H_{37}N_3O_{13}$	MEGLUCYCLINE	ANTIBIOTIC	
635.77917	$C_{15}H_{11}O_4I_3$	THYROPROPIC ACID	HORMONE	

MASS	FORMULA	NAME	CATEGORY	MS
638.13208	$C_{15}H_{32}O_{12}SHG$	DIGLUCOMETHOXANE	DIURETIC	
638.82645	$C_{15}H_{16}NO_3I_3$	BUNAMIODYL	DIAGNOSTIC AID	
639.83428	$C_{15}H_{17}NO_3I_3$	THYROPANOIC ACID	DIAGNOSTIC AID	
640.17921	$C_{32}H_{32}O_{14}$	CHARTREUSIN	ANTIBIOTIC	
640.21693	$C_{34}H_{32}N_4O_9$	NICOMOL	ANTICHOLESTEREMIC	
640.80572	$C_{14}H_{14}NO_4I_3$	PROPYL DOCETRIZOATE	DIAGNOSTIC AID	
640.84210	$C_{15}H_{18}NO_3I_3$	TYROPANOIC ACID	DIAGNOSTIC AID	
641.80096	$C_{13}H_{13}N_2O_4I_3$	DIPROTRIZOIC ACID	DIAGNOSTIC AID	
643.39228	$C_{39}H_{59}NO_2CL_2$	PHENESTERINE	CYTOSTATIC	
643.71052	$C_{20}H_8O_5BR_4$	TETRABROMOFLUORESCEIN (EOSINE)	DESINFICIENT	
643.78023	$C_{12}H_{11}N_2O_5I_3$	IOXITALAMIC ACID	DIAGNOSTIC AID	
645.02370	$C_{25}H_{29}NO_3I_2$	AMIODARONE	ANTIARRHYTHMIC	
645.14241	$C_{25}H_{27}N_9O_8S_2$	CEFOPERAZONE	ANTIBIOTIC	
645.23225	$C_{34}H_{35}N_3O_{10}$	ZORUBICINE	CYTOSTATIC	
645.24802	$C_{25}H_{43}NO_{18}$	ACARBOSE	ENZYME INHIBITOR	
645.26240	$C_{35}H_{45}NO_6CL_2$	PREDNIMUSTINE	CYTOSTATIC	
645.31491	$C_{34}H_{47}NO_{11}$	ACONITINE	ANALGESIC	
645.92070	$C_{24}H_{21}O_6CL_6P$	FALONE	HERBICIDE	
648.49063	$C_{46}H_{64}O_2$	VITAMIN K2(35)	VITAMINE	
650.79007	$C_{15}H_{12}NO_4I_3$	DETROTHYRONINE	HORMONE	
	$C_{15}H_{12}NO_4I_3$	LIOTHYRONINE	HORMONE	
	$C_{15}H_{12}NO_4I_3$	RATHYRONINE	HORMONE	
652.11988	$C_{32}H_{24}N_6O_6S_2$	CONGO RED	DIAGNOSTIC AID	
652.35174	$C_{25}H_{44}N_{14}O_7$	CAPREOMYCIN IB	TUBERCULOSTATIC	
653.22128	$C_{32}H_{40}N_5O_5BR$	BROMOCRIPTINE	GYNECOL./OBSTRECT.	
654.17961	$C_{29}H_{34}O_{17}$	MONOXERUTIN	DECR.CAPILL.FRAG.	
654.39792	$C_{35}H_{58}O_{11}$	FILIPIN III	FUNGIST./ANTIMYC.	
656.15637	$C_{32}H_{32}O_{13}S$	TENIPOSIDE	CYTOSTATIC	
659.86139	$C_6H_{18}O_{24}P_6$	FYTIC ACID	VITAMINE	
660.22604	$C_{42}H_{32}N_2O_6$	GUAIFENSINEBISPHENYLCHINOLINCARB.	EXPECTORANT	
661.80605	$C_{16}H_{13}N_2O_3I_3$	IOBENZAMIC ACID	DIAGNOSTIC AID	
661.85219	$C_{22}H_{14}N_2O_2CL_2I_2$	CLOSANTEL	ANTHELMINTIC	
663.10913	$C_{21}H_{27}N_7O_{14}P_2$	NADIDE	ANTIDOTE	
664.10880	$C_{26}H_{38}N_2O_6S_4P_2$	ZILANTEL	ANTHELMINTIC	
665.30474	$C_{33}H_{47}NO_{13}$	NATAMYCIN	ANTIBIOTIC	
665.69824	$C_{19}H_{10}O_5BR_4S$	BROMPHENOL BLUE	CHEMICAL	
666.27886	$C_{35}H_{42}N_2O_{11}$	SYROSINGOPINE	ANTIHYPERTENSIVE	
670.42922	$C_{36}H_{62}O_{11}$	MONENSIN	ANTIBIOTIC	
670.79113	$C_{13}H_{12}N_3O_5I_3$	IOGLICIC ACID	DIAGNOSTIC AID	
670.81628	$C_{15}H_{16}NO_5I_3$	IOBUTOIC ACID	DIAGNOSTIC AID	
672.25054	$C_{37}H_{40}N_2O_8S$	CORTISUZOL	CORTICOID	
672.83193	$C_{15}H_{18}NO_5I_3$	IOLIXAMIC ACID	DIAGNOSTIC AID	
	$C_{15}H_{18}NO_5I_3$	IOPRONIC ACID	DIAGNOSTIC AID	
673.23706	$C_{33}H_{39}NO_{14}$	DETORUBICINE	CYTOSTATIC	
680.17546	$C_{35}H_{28}N_4O_{11}$	NICOFURATE	ANTICHOLESTEREMIC	
684.46012	$C_{41}H_{64}O_8$	PREDNISOLONE STEAGLATE	CORTICOID	
685.32559	$C_{25}H_{43}N_{13}O_{10}$	ENVIOMYCIN	ANTIBIOTIC	
	$C_{25}H_{43}N_{13}O_{10}$	VIOMYCIN	ANTIBIOTIC	
685.46258	$C_{34}H_{63}N_5O_9$	PEPSTATIN	ENZYME INHIBITOR	
686.22694	$C_{34}H_{48}O_6S_2CL_2$	TIAFIBRATE	ANTICHOLESTEREMIC	
686.35136	$C_{34}H_{54}O_{14}$	NEUTRAMYCIN	ANTIBIOTIC	
687.41938	$C_{35}H_{61}NO_{12}$	OLEANDOMYCIN	ANTIBIOTIC	

MASS	FORMULA	NAME	CATEGORY	MS
691.28718	$C_{34}H_{46}N_3O_{10}CL$	MAITANSINE	CYTOSTATIC	
692.34080	$C_{36}H_{52}O_{13}$	SCILLAREN A	CARDIOTONIC	
693.37243	$C_{36}H_{55}NO_{12}$	DESATRINE	INSECTICIDE	
695.24254	$C_{32}H_{41}NO_{16}$	DIETHYLAMINOMETHYLRUTIN	DECR.CAPILL.FRAG.	
695.29418	$C_{37}H_{45}NO_{12}$	RIFAMYCIN S	ANTIBIOTIC	
696.40261	$C_{44}H_{56}O_7$	FLUORESCEIN DILAURATE	DIAGNOSTIC AID	
697.30983	$C_{37}H_{47}NO_{12}$	RIFAMYCIN SV	ANTIBIOTIC	
698.35136	$C_{35}H_{54}O_{14}$	UZARIN	ANTIDIARRHOEAL	
699.22487	$C_{29}H_{33}N_9O_{12}$	PTEROPTERIN	CYTOSTATIC	
699.80644	$C_{15}H_{15}N_2O_6I_3$	ETHYLCARTRIZOATE	DIAGNOSTIC AID	
700.18509	$C_{30}H_{36}O_{19}$	TRI(HYDROXYMETHYL)RUTIN	DECR.CAPILL.FRAG.	
700.31402	$C_{27}H_{44}N_{10}O_{12}$	STREPTONIAZIDE	TUBERCULOSTATIC	
702.29818	$C_{32}H_{46}N_8O_6S_2$	ARCALION	VITAMINE	
705.85504	$C_{20}H_{10}O_6BR_2HG$	MERBROMIN	DESINFICIENT	
707.30541	$C_{37}H_{45}N_3O_{11}$	RIFAMYCIN X	ANTIBIOTIC	
707.35169	$C_{36}H_{53}NO_{13}$	LUCIMYCIN	ANTIBIOTIC	
707.37818	$C_{39}H_{53}N_3O_9$	BIETASERPINE	ANTIHYPERTENSIVE	
710.30979	$C_{35}H_{46}N_6O_8S$	AMOGASTRIN	DIAGNOSTIC AID	
710.35136	$C_{36}H_{54}O_{14}$	K-STROPHANTIN BETA	CARDIOTONIC	
710.85881	$C_{17}H_{20}N_3O_4I_3$	IOMORIC ACID	DIAGNOSTIC AID	
712.36701	$C_{36}H_{56}O_{14}$	DIGITALIN	CARDIOTONIC	
717.46633	$C_{37}H_{67}NO_{12}$	BERYTHROMYCIN	ANTIBIOTIC	
718.35645	$C_{38}H_{54}O_{13}$	COLOCYNTHIN	LAXATIVE	
719.71076	$C_{13}H_{16}O_8CL_{12}$	PETRICHLORAL	HYPNOTIC	
720.36622	$C_{45}H_{52}O_8$	FENERITROL	ANTICHOLESTEREMIC	
720.44487	$C_{40}H_{64}O_{11}$	DERMOSTATIN A	FUNGIST./ANTIMYC.	
723.23745	$C_{33}H_{41}NO_{17}$	ETHOXAZORUTOSIDE	DECR.CAPILL.FRAG.	
724.33063	$C_{36}H_{52}O_{15}$	HELLEBRIN	CARDIOTONIC	
729.17745	$C_{32}H_{35}N_5O_{11}S_2$	PIRIDICILLIN	ANTIBIOTIC	
730.81226	$C_{15}H_{16}N_3O_7I_3$	IOSERIC ACID	DIAGNOSTIC AID	
733.46124	$C_{37}H_{67}NO_{13}$	ERYTHROMYCIN	ANTIBIOTIC	
734.46052	$C_{41}H_{66}O_{11}$	DERMOSTATIN B	FUNGIST./ANTIMYC.	
734.88397	$C_{21}H_{24}NO_4I_3$	TYROMEDAN	HORMONE	
736.11253	$C_{24}H_{36}N_2O_{18}S_3$	GLUCOSULFONE	ANTIBIOTIC	
736.43978	$C_{40}H_{64}O_{12}$	CAINCIN	DIURETIC	
742.23204	$C_{33}H_{42}O_{19}$	TROXERUTIN	DECR.CAPILL.FRAG.	
743.31850	$C_{27}H_{49}N_7O_{17}$	STREPTOMYCIN B	ANTIBIOTIC	
744.60566	$C_{50}H_{80}O_4$	DIETHYLSTILBESTROL DIPALMITATE	ESTROGEN	
752.27741	$C_{50}H_{40}O_7$	BENZQUERCIN	DECR.CAPILL.FRAG.	
752.29538	$C_{43}H_{48}N_2O_6S_2$	INDOCYANINE GREEN	DIAGNOSTIC AID	
753.29966	$C_{39}H_{47}NO_{14}$	RIFAMYCIN O	ANTIBIOTIC	
	$C_{39}H_{47}NO_{14}$	STREPTOVARICIN F	ANTIBIOTIC	
753.33604	$C_{40}H_{51}NO_{13}$	STREPTOVARICIN D	ANTIBIOTIC	
753.41015	$C_{43}H_{55}N_5O_7$	VINDESINE	CYTOSTATIC	
755.31531	$C_{39}H_{49}NO_{14}$	RIFAMYCIN B	ANTIBIOTIC	
761.35422	$C_{29}H_{55}N_5O_{18}$	LIVIDOMYCIN	ANTIBIOTIC	
762.86363	$C_{18}H_{24}NO_8I_3$	IOTRIZOIC ACID	DIAGNOSTIC AID	
764.43470	$C_{41}H_{64}O_{13}$	DIGITOXIN	CARDIOTONIC	
767.11522	$C_{21}H_{36}N_7O_{16}SP_3$	COENZYME A	ENDOG.BIOMOLECULE	
767.31531	$C_{40}H_{49}NO_{14}$	STREPTOVARICIN E	ANTIBIOTIC	
767.33125	$C_{37}H_{49}N_7O_9S$	PENTAGASTRIN	DIAGNOSTIC AID	
769.33096	$C_{40}H_{51}NO_{14}$	STREPTOVARICIN C	ANTIBIOTIC	

MASS	FORMULA	NAME	CATEGORY	MS
770.26688	$C_{38}H_{42}N_8O_6S_2$	BISBENTIAMINE	VITAMINE	
774.65261	$C_{52}H_{86}O_4$	PROMETHESTROL DIPALMITATE	ESTROGEN	
776.55258	$C_{48}H_{76}N_2O_4S$	CHAULMOSULFONE	ANTIBIOTIC	
776.68672	$C_{15}H_{11}NO_4I_4$	THYROXINE	HORMONE	
776.85412	$C_{17}H_{22}N_3O_8I_3$	IOPAMIDOL	DIAGNOSTIC AID	
780.42961	$C_{41}H_{64}O_{14}$	DIGOXIN	CARDIOTONIC	
	$C_{41}H_{64}O_{14}$	GITOXIN	CARDIOTONIC	
785.32587	$C_{40}H_{51}NO_{15}$	STREPTOVARICIN G	ANTIBIOTIC	
785.45616	$C_{40}H_{67}NO_{14}$	LEUCOMYCIN A	ANTIBIOTIC	
788.85412	$C_{18}H_{22}N_3O_8I_3$	METRIZAMIDE	DIAGNOSTIC AID	
790.86977	$C_{18}H_{24}N_3O_8I_3$	IOPROMIDE	DIAGNOSTIC AID	
792.67843	$C_{56}H_{88}O_2$	VITAMIN D1	VITAMINE	
793.42486	$C_{41}H_{63}NO_{14}$	PROTOVERATRINE A	ANTIHYPERTENSIVE	
794.44526	$C_{42}H_{66}O_{14}$	METILDIGOXIN	CARDIOTONIC	
796.22414	$C_{41}H_{32}N_8O_{10}$	RIBOFLAVINE TETRANICOTINATE	VITAMINE	
796.42452	$C_{41}H_{64}O_{15}$	DIGINATIN	CARDIOTONIC	
799.47181	$C_{41}H_{69}NO_{14}$	DIPROLEANDOMYCIN	FUNGIST./ANTIMYC.	
804.04572	$C_{30}H_{32}N_2O_{14}S_5$	SOLASULFONE	ANTIBIOTIC	
805.26290	$C_{39}H_{43}N_5O_{12}S$	PENIMOCYCLINE	ANTIBIOTIC	
806.44526	$C_{43}H_{66}O_{14}$	ACETYLDIGITOXIN	CARDIOTONIC	
806.86469	$C_{18}H_{24}N_3O_9I_3$	IOGLUCOL	DIAGNOSTIC AID	
	$C_{18}H_{24}N_3O_9I_3$	IOGLUMIDE	DIAGNOSTIC AID	
808.42452	$C_{42}H_{64}O_{15}$	GITALOXIN	CARDIOTONIC	
809.41977	$C_{41}H_{63}NO_{15}$	PROTOVERATRINE B	ANTIHYPERTENSIVE	
810.19217	$C_{42}H_{30}N_6O_{12}$	INOSITOL NICOTINATE	CORONARY DILATOR	
810.39389	$C_{43}H_{58}N_2O_{13}$	RIFAMIDE	ANTIBIOTIC	
810.42038	$C_{46}H_{58}N_4O_9$	VINBLASTINE	CYTOSTATIC	
811.34152	$C_{42}H_{53}NO_{15}$	STREPTOVARICIN B + J	ANTIBIOTIC	
813.35717	$C_{42}H_{55}NO_{15}$	ACLARUBICIN	ANTIBIOTIC	
813.45107	$C_{41}H_{67}NO_{15}$	MIDECAMYCIN	ANTIBIOTIC	
	$C_{41}H_{67}NO_{15}$	TROLEANDOMYCIN	ANTIBIOTIC	
818.73367	$C_{18}H_{17}NO_4I_4$	ETIROXATE	ANTICHOLESTEREMIC	
820.88034	$C_{19}H_{26}N_3O_9I_3$	IOHEXOL	DIAGNOSTIC AID	
821.67582	$C_{20}H_{10}O_4I_4$	IODOPHTHALEIN	DIAGNOSTIC AID	
822.38400	$C_{46}H_{54}N_4O_{10}$	VINFORMIDE	CYTOSTATIC	
822.40513	$C_{43}H_{58}N_4O_{12}$	RIFAMPICIN	ANTIBIOTIC	
822.44017	$C_{43}H_{66}O_{15}$	ACETYLDIGOXIN	CARDIOTONIC	
	$C_{43}H_{66}O_{15}$	ACETYLGITOXIN	CARDIOTONIC	
823.35409	$C_{43}H_{49}N_7O_{10}$	VIRGINIAMYCIN S	ANTIBIOTIC	
824.39965	$C_{46}H_{56}N_4O_{10}$	VINCRISTINE	CYTOSTATIC	
827.33644	$C_{42}H_{53}NO_{16}$	STREPTOVARICIN A	ANTIBIOTIC	
827.46672	$C_{42}H_{69}NO_{15}$	IOSAMYCIN	ANTIBIOTIC	
837.79431	$C_{19}H_{10}O_7I_2SHG$	MERALEIN	DESINFICIENT	
838.36499	$C_{43}H_{50}N_8O_{10}$	VERNAMYCIN B (DELTA)	ANTIBIOTIC	
838.43509	$C_{43}H_{66}O_{16}$	ACETYLDIGINATIN (ALPHA)	CARDIOTONIC	
841.44599	$C_{42}H_{67}NO_{16}$	CARBOMYCIN	ANTIBIOTIC	
842.51401	$C_{43}H_{74}N_2O_{14}$	SPIRAMYCIN I	ANTIBIOTIC	
843.39739	$C_{46}H_{58}N_5O_8CL$	PROGLUMETACIN	ANALGESIC	
852.38064	$C_{44}H_{52}N_8O_{10}$	VERNAMYCIN B (BETA + GAMMA)	ANTIBIOTIC	
853.46258	$C_{48}H_{63}N_5O_9$	VINGLYCINATE	CYTOSTATIC	
858.42492	$C_{42}H_{66}O_{18}$	THEVETIN B	CARDIOTONIC	
860.49221	$C_{47}H_{72}O_{14}$	IVERMECTIN II	PESTICIDE	

MASS	FORMULA	NAME	CATEGORY	MS
862.19565	$C_{42}H_{38}O_{20}$	SENNOSIDE A + B	LAXATIVE	
862.68391	$C_{59}H_{90}O_{4}$	UBIQUINONE	ENDOG.BIOMOLECULE	
866.39629	$C_{45}H_{54}N_{8}O_{10}$	MIKAMYCIN B	ANTIBIOTIC	
872.05464	$C_{34}H_{28}N_{6}O_{14}S_{4}$	EVAN'S BLUE	DIAGNOSTIC AID	
872.40418	$C_{42}H_{64}O_{19}$	K-STROPHANTIN (GAMMA)	CARDIOTONIC	
872.40418	$C_{42}H_{64}O_{19}$	THEVETIN A	CARDIOTONIC	
872.68939	$C_{57}H_{92}O_{6}$	PROPANETRIYL TRILINOLENATE	DERMATIC	
874.50786	$C_{48}H_{74}O_{14}$	IVERMECTIN I	PESTICIDE	
876.45208	$C_{47}H_{64}N_{4}O_{12}$	RIFAPENTIN	TUBERCULOSTATIC	
878.45381	$C_{44}H_{62}N_{8}O_{11}$	ETAMYCIN	ANTIBIOTIC	
878.73634	$C_{57}H_{98}O_{6}$	PROPANETRIYL TRILINOLEATE	DERMATIC	
880.57594	$C_{45}H_{84}O_{16}$	NONOXYNOL 15	SOLUBILIZER ETC.	
884.52457	$C_{45}H_{76}N_{2}O_{15}$	SPIRAMYCIN II	ANTIBIOTIC	
891.99033	$C_{32}H_{24}N_{6}O_{15}S_{5}$	TRYPAN RED	ANTIBIOTIC	
898.54022	$C_{46}H_{78}N_{2}O_{15}$	SPIRAMYCIN III	ANTIBIOTIC	
898.87565	$C_{20}H_{28}N_{3}O_{13}I_{3}$	IOGLUCOMIDE	DIAGNOSTIC AID	
902.35926	$C_{39}H_{54}N_{10}O_{13}S$	ALPHA-AMANITIN	NATURAL SUBSTANCE	
903.34327	$C_{39}H_{53}N_{9}O_{14}S$	BETA-AMANITIN	NATURAL SUBSTANCE	
911.49774	$C_{42}H_{65}N_{13}O_{10}$	SERALASIN	ANTIHYPERTENSIVE	
915.51915	$C_{46}H_{77}NO_{17}$	TYLOSIN	ANTIBIOTIC	
920.40418	$C_{46}H_{64}O_{19}$	GITOFORMATE	CARDIOTONIC	
923.48785	$C_{47}H_{73}NO_{17}$	AMPHOTERICIN B	FUNGIST./ANTIMYC.	
925.50350	$C_{47}H_{75}NO_{17}$	NYSTATIN	FUNGIST./ANTIMYC.	
927.83807	$C_{60}H_{111}O_{6}$	TRIETHANOLAMINE OLEATE	SOLUBILIZER ETC.	
942.48244	$C_{47}H_{74}O_{19}$	DESLANOSIDE	CARDIOTONIC	
956.80442	$C_{60}H_{108}O_{8}$	SORBITAN TRIOLEATE	SOLUBILIZER ETC.	
958.51373	$C_{48}H_{78}O_{19}$	ASIATICOSIDE	NATURAL SUBSTANCE	
962.85137	$C_{60}H_{114}O_{8}$	SORBITAN TRISTEARATE	SOLUBILIZER ETC.	
968.49809	$C_{49}H_{76}O_{19}$	LANATOSIDE A	CARDIOTONIC	
983.43889	$C_{49}H_{61}N_{9}O_{13}$	DESGLUGASTRIN	DIAGNOSTIC AID	
984.04270	$C_{33}H_{24}O_{6}S_{2}HG_{2}$	HYDRARGAPHEN	DESINFICIENT	
984.49300	$C_{49}H_{76}O_{20}$	LANATOSIDE B + C	CARDIOTONIC	
987.48479	$C_{45}H_{69}N_{11}O_{12}S$	CARBETOCIN	------------	
990.48244	$C_{51}H_{74}O_{19}$	PENGITOXIN	CARDIOTONIC	
991.42556	$C_{43}H_{65}N_{11}O_{12}S_{2}$	DEMOXYTOCIN	GYNECOL./OBSTRECT.	
1000.40658	$C_{50}H_{60}N_{6}O_{16}$	ETAMOCYCLINE	ANTIBIOTIC	
1000.48792	$C_{49}H_{76}O_{21}$	LANATOSIDE D	NATURAL SUBSTANCE	
1001.50830	$C_{48}H_{67}N_{13}O_{11}$	ARFALASIN	------------	
1006.43646	$C_{43}H_{66}N_{12}O_{12}S_{2}$	OCYTOCIN	GYNECOL./OBSTRECT.	
1030.53485	$C_{49}H_{70}N_{14}O_{11}$	ANGIOTENSINAMIDE	ANTIHYPOTENSIVE	
1039.43680	$C_{46}H_{65}N_{13}O_{11}S_{2}$	FELYPRESSIN	VASOCONSTRICTOR	
1041.41606	$C_{45}H_{63}N_{13}O_{12}S_{2}$	ORNIPRESSIN	VASOCONSTRICTOR	
1044.88736	$C_{72}H_{116}O_{4}$	XANTHOLYL PALMITATE	OPHTALMIC	
1049.45351	$C_{43}H_{67}N_{15}O_{12}S_{2}$	ARGIPRESTOCIN	GYNECOL./OBSTRECT.	
1050.52470	$C_{50}H_{82}O_{23}$	F-GITONIN	CARDIOTONIC	
1055.43171	$C_{46}H_{65}N_{13}O_{12}S_{2}$	LYPRESSIN	VASOCONSTRICTOR	
1059.56140	$C_{50}H_{73}N_{15}O_{11}$	BRADYKININ	VASODILATOR	
1068.42696	$C_{46}H_{64}N_{14}O_{12}S_{2}$	DESMOPRESSIN	VASOCONSTRICTOR	
1077.72875	$C_{55}H_{103}N_{3}O_{17}$	PRIMYCIN	FUNGIST./ANTIMYC.	
1083.43786	$C_{46}H_{65}N_{15}O_{12}S_{2}$	ARGIPRESSIN	VASOCONSTRICTOR	
1084.47266	$C_{52}H_{76}O_{24}$	MITHRAMYCIN	FUNGIST./ANTIMYC.	
1085.56531	$C_{68}H_{79}NO_{11}$	COFISATIN	LAXATIVE	

MASS	FORMULA	NAME	CATEGORY	MS
1100.42081	$C_{51}H_{64}N_{12}O_{12}S_2$	ECHINOMYCIN	ANTIBIOTIC	
1100.57672	$C_{53}H_{76}N_{14}O_{12}$	TEPROTIDE	ANTIHYPERTENSIVE	
1109.37534	$C_{55}H_{59}N_5O_{20}$	COUMAMYCIN	FUNGIST./ANTIMYC.	
1110.63116	$C_{54}H_{90}N_6O_{18}$	VALINOMYCIN	INSECTICIDE	
1127.47567	$C_{18}H_{10}N_2O_7I_6$	IOGLYCAMIC ACID	DIAGNOSTIC AID	
1129.68191	$C_{49}H_{91}N_{15}O_{15}$	POLYMYXIN D2	ANTIBIOTIC	
1139.51205	$C_{20}H_{14}N_2O_6I_6$	ADIPIODONE	DIAGNOSTIC AID	
1140.70594	$C_{60}H_{92}N_{12}O_{10}$	GRAMICIDIN S	ANTIBIOTIC	
1142.35075	$C_{49}H_{62}N_{10}O_{16}S_3$	SINCALIDE	DIAGNOSTIC AID	
1142.46776	$C_{54}H_{70}N_{12}O_{12}S_2$	TRIOSTIN C	ANTIBIOTIC	
1143.69756	$C_{50}H_{93}N_{15}O_{15}$	POLYMYXIN D1	ANTIBIOTIC	
1154.74993	$C_{52}H_{98}N_{16}O_{13}$	POLYMYXIN E2	ANTIBIOTIC	
1182.50944	$C_{57}H_{82}O_{26}$	CHROMOMYCIN A3	ANTIBIOTIC	
1187.65636	$C_{56}H_{85}N_{17}O_{12}$	KALLIDIN	VASODILATOR	
1188.73428	$C_{55}H_{96}N_{16}O_{13}$	POLYMYXIN B2	ANTIBIOTIC	
1196.52509	$C_{58}H_{84}O_{26}$	OLIVOMYCIN A	CYTOSTATIC	
1202.74993	$C_{56}H_{98}N_{16}O_{13}$	POLYMYXIN B1	ANTIBIOTIC	
1215.52810	$C_{22}H_{18}N_2O_9I_6$	IOTROXIC ACID	DIAGNOSTIC AID	
1226.49610	$C_{52}H_{74}N_{16}O_{15}S_2$	TRIGLYCILLYSINE VASOPRESSIN	VASOCONSTRICTOR	
1228.57244	$C_{56}H_{92}O_{29}$	DIGITONIN	NATURAL SUBSTANCE	
1238.65603	$C_{60}H_{86}N_{16}O_{13}$	BUSERELIN	DIAGNOSTIC AID	
1243.55940	$C_{24}H_{22}N_2O_9I_6$	IOTRANIC ACID	DIAGNOSTIC AID	
1253.55498	$C_{24}H_{20}N_4O_8I_6$	IOCARMIC ACID	DIAGNOSTIC AID	
1254.62848	$C_{62}H_{86}N_{12}O_{16}$	DACTINOMYCIN	CYTOSTATIC	
1264.59105	$C_{58}H_{84}N_{14}O_{16}S$	PHYSALAEMIN	VASODILATOR	
1268.56588	$C_{24}H_{21}N_5O_8I_6$	IOXAGLIC ACID	DIAGNOSTIC AID	
1282.65978	$C_{64}H_{90}N_{12}O_{16}$	ACTINOMYCIN C3	ANTIBIOTIC	
1287.58561	$C_{26}H_{26}N_2O_{10}I_6$	IODOXAMIC ACID	DIAGNOSTIC AID	
1289.65034	$C_{58}H_{91}N_{13}O_{20}$	AMPHOMYCIN	ANTIBIOTIC	
1296.04692	$C_{51}H_{40}N_6O_{23}S_6$	SURAMIN	ANTIBIOTIC	
1308.66553	$C_{68}H_{88}N_{14}O_{13}$	TYROCIDINE B	ANTIBIOTIC	
1309.61758	$C_{28}H_{28}N_4O_8I_6$	IOSEFAMIC ACID	DIAGNOSTIC AID	
1346.72815	$C_{63}H_{98}N_{18}O_{13}S$	SUBSTANCE P	ENDOG.BIOMOLECULE	
1347.67643	$C_{70}H_{89}N_{15}O_{13}$	TYROCIDINE C	ANTIBIOTIC	
1373.57948	$C_{28}H_{28}N_4O_{10}I_6S$	IOSULAMIDE	DIAGNOSTIC AID	
1421.74895	$C_{66}H_{103}N_{17}O_{16}S$	BACITRACIN	ANTIBIOTIC	
1540.96917	$C_{75}H_{144}O_{31}$	NONOXYNOL 30	SOLUBILIZER ETC.	
1636.71666	$C_{76}H_{104}N_{18}O_{19}S_2$	SOMATOSTATIN	TO THERAPY ULCERS	
1663.49236	$C_{72}H_{85}N_{19}O_{18}S_5$	THIOSTREPTON	ANTIBIOTIC	
1730.73523	$C_{68}H_{110}N_{22}O_{27}S_2$	TALISAMYCIN	CYTOSTATIC	
2118.16731	$C_{99}H_{155}N_{29}O_{21}S$	ALSACTIDE	------------	
2191.18369	$C_{101}H_{158}N_{30}O_{23}S$	CODACTIDE	HORMONE	
2352.93985	$C_{107}H_{138}N_{26}O_{31}CL_2$	ENDURACIDIN A	ANTIBIOTIC	
2366.95550	$C_{108}H_{140}N_{26}O_{31}CL_2$	ENDURACIDIN B	ANTIBIOTIC	
2844.75418	$C_{131}H_{229}N_{39}O_{31}$	MELITTIN	ANTIRHEUMATIC	
2931.58065	$C_{136}H_{210}N_{40}O_{31}S$	TETRACOSACTIDE	HORMONE	
3287.71385	$C_{150}H_{230}N_{44}O_{38}S$	TOSACTIDE	HORMONE	
6511.12032	$C_{284}H_{440}N_{86}O_{77}S_7$	APROTININ	ENZYME INHIBITOR	